Pest Management at the Crossroads

Pest Management at the Crossroads

by

Charles M. Benbrook, Ph.D.

with
Edward Groth III, Ph.D.
Jean M. Halloran
Michael K. Hansen, Ph.D.
Sandra Marquardt

Consumers Union
Yonkers, New York
1996

ISBN 0-89043-900-1

Consumers Union of United States Inc.
101 Truman Avenue
Yonkers, N.Y. 10703
914-378-2000

Pest Management at the Crossroads is a publication of Consumers Union, publisher of *Consumer Reports* magazine. Consumers Union is a nonprofit membership organization chartered in 1936 under the laws of the State of New York to provide consumers with information, education and counsel about goods, services, health, and personal finances; and to initiate and cooperate with individual and group efforts to maintain and enhance the quality of life for consumers. Consumers Union's income is derived solely from the sale of *Consumer Reports*, its other publications and from noncommercial contributions, grants and fees. In addition to reports on Consumers Union's own product testing, *Consumer Reports*, with more than 4 million paid circulation, regularly carries articles on health, product safety, marketplace economics and legislative, judicial and regulatory actions which affect consumer welfare. Consumers Union's publications carry no advertising and receive no commercial support.

When synthetic chemical pesticides came into widespread use after World War II, they were hailed as miracles of modern technology. They promised an era of abundant agricultural yields, the key to feeding a burgeoning global population, a potent weapon that would permit humans at last to conquer Nature, in field and forest, kitchen and garden.

It didn't take long to recognize that these miracle chemicals had costs and risks, as well as benefits. Acute poisonings of farm workers and children were the most obvious risks, but mounting scientific evidence gradually revealed a panoply of subtler hazards. Persistent pesticides accumulated in wildlife food chains, decimating populations of eagles, pelicans and other predators. Toxicological experiments showed that pesticides can cause cancer and birth defects, and damage or interfere with the nervous, endocrine, reproductive and immune systems in mammals.

Decades of research have only begun to unravel the many ways these chemicals affect human health. Yet, while the effects remain too little understood, we all are exposed to several pesticides in our food each day, and millions of Americans drink water tainted with pesticides. Pesticide use around the home, lawn and garden delivers occasionally larger doses. Science cannot say precisely how large the risks from these exposures are, for an individual. But a long-standing consensus holds that the collective risks to public health are substantial.

Health concerns aside, the promised conquest of nature by chemical pesticides has proved to be a tarnished miracle, at best. Genetic resistance to pesticides in pest populations and outbreaks of new pest problems when broad-spectrum insecticides remove natural checks and balances have led to escalating dependence on pesticide use, with no real decline in pest-induced crop losses. As pesticide use has expanded, so has the public cost of our reliance on chemical pest control. Beyond the largely unquantifiable costs of health risks, over a billion dollars is spent each year for the regulatory, surveillance, monitoring and enforcement programs we need to try to use pesticides safely.

The growth of regulatory bureaucracies in the U.S. EPA and in many states whose mission is managing pesticide risks rests on the assumptions that science can accurately define the risks pesticides will pose, and that regulators can ensure that risks never exceed benefits. We believe these premises are flawed. Nearly 25 years of Federal pesticide regulation have not notably reduced the aggregate public-health and ecological risks of pesticide use, and regulatory gridlock in the effort to control pesticides has spawned frustration and distrust of government on all sides.

There are better alternatives. For decades, researchers have sought to develop safer, ecologically sounder ways to manage pests. A variety of approaches, ranging from altering crop practices and using physical barriers to pest attack, to reinforcing and amplifying a pest's natural enemies, to disrupting a pest's life cycle, are in use today, and have come collectively to be known as Integrated Pest Management, or IPM. Pest management strategies that rely on interventions keyed to the biology of the pest—what we call biointensive IPM—can effectively minimize economic pest damage while avoiding both the health hazards and ecological disruptions associated with chemical pesticides. IPM still relies on some use of low risk pesticides, but generally only after other techniques have been used and steps are taken to minimize unwanted effects. Effective IPM strategies now exist for many pest problems, and most are economically competitive with conventional chemical controls.

Why, then, doesn't everybody use IPM? Many in agriculture and the home pest control business have begun to, and are at least mixing some IPM strategies with chemical-based controls. But chemical pesticides still dominate. One reason is that IPM strategies are specific to each pest, local soil, vegetation and climatic conditions, and other local factors. It requires multidisciplinary research, often years of it, to develop successful IPM methods, and unlike chemicals, once developed, IPM strategies can't be packaged and sold everywhere. In addition, many chemical pesticides cost comparatively little to use, in large part because the risks and social costs associated with their use are not included in their price.

Consumers Union has carried out research and advocacy on various pesticide problems for many years. In 1993, we determined that it was time to pull back and look at the big picture. Our environmental and public health experts concluded that the dominant national strategy of managing pesticide risks, one chemical at a time, has failed, and should be replaced by a strategy of lessening the need for pesticides by expanding reliance on biointensive IPM.

We set up a Pesticide Policy Reform Project, whose goal was to draw a roadmap for a long-term transition to make biologically based IPM the central focus of national pest management policy and investment patterns. We hired Chuck Benbrook, a pesticide policy expert who helped prepare two major reports on pesticide problems in the late 1980s at the National Academy of Sciences, to direct the project. He led a team of CU staff for more than two years, collecting and analyzing data, developing scenarios and recommendations.

In this report we summarize the origins of current policies and problems, and map out a transition to make biointensive IPM the predominant strategy by the year 2020. That transition will be driven primarily by market forces. It will come about more quickly and cost less if it is guided by far-sighted policies in both government and the private sector.

This report will be a valued resource for everyone involved in the effort to manage pests safely and reduce the individual and social costs of pesticides. But it's just a start. The changes we envision won't come about without a strong effort to inform policymakers and mobilize support for reform. We plan to engage in those efforts, and to continue our research and issue future reports on promoting IPM solutions for various pest problems.

Pest management is at a crossroads. We have the power to choose a better future, if we all seize the opportunity and commit our efforts to choosing the better path.

Edward Groth III, PhD
Consumers Union, Yonkers, NY, August 1996

Acknowledgements

Integrated Pest Management depends on people and many contributed their knowledge and experience over the course of the project. A special thanks to biointensive IPM practitioners and researchers who have contributed much to this book, including Pat Weddle, independent consultant in Placerville, California; Charles Mellinger, technical director of Glades Crop Care in Jupiter, Florida; Jennie Broome, California Department of Pesticide Regulation; Matt Liebman, University of Maine; James Cook, a plant pathologist with the Agricultural Research Service (ARS) in Pullman, Washington; Robert Goodman, plant pathologist at the University of Wisconsin—Madison, and Dennis Keeney, Director of the Leopold Center for Sustainable Agriculture at Iowa State University.

We have relied heavily on the pesticide use database compiled by Dr. Leonard Gianessi, analyst at the National Center for Food and Agricultural Policy in Washington, D.C. Thanks to Leonard for making the data publicly available. Merritt Padgitt, Economic Research Service analyst, provided key help in our work with the Cropping Practices and Chemical Use Surveys and other USDA electronic databases. We appreciate the cooperation of Maclay Burt and the Association of Natural Bio-control Producers in distributing the survey of companies rearing and selling beneficials. The assistance of the Wisconsin Potato and Vegetable Growers Association and members of the Randall Island Project team was essential in compiling information and materials in Chapter 1.

We appreciate the advice we received in conceptualizing and carrying out the project from Reggie James, Director of Consumers Union's Southwest Regional Office; Mark Silbergeld, Co-Director of the CU Washington Office; and Harry Snyder, Co-Director of the CU West Coast Regional Office.

A lot of numbers were crunched in the course of developing the report. John Evans used his extensive skills and learned a few new ones in carrying out most spreadsheet analyses. Latifa Satterlee also helped with the creation of the large database on pesticide use and toxicity levels and carried out several important analyses. Thanks to the many individuals in the Environmental Protection Agency who compiled and made available the electronic databases and other technical data we needed to undertake our analyses of risk levels and trends, and the impacts of regulation.

Thanks to the talented artists whose work lightens the reader's way through the book: Paul Buxman for the cover; several free-lance photographers, especially Richard Steven Street; John Kucharski, Agricultural Research Service photo editor, for his timely response to our many requests for ARS pictures; Ann Sorensen and Karen Lutz for the line drawings of beneficial insects. It has been a real pleasure working with Bill Buckley and his very professional staff at Complete Graphic Services, Inc. in Upper Marlboro, Maryland. We appreciate the good job done by our copy editor Ms. Deborah Eby. The designers at Complete Graphic Services (CGS) teamed up with Karen Lutz and did an excellent job in producing the web boxes throughout the book. Thanks to all the web masters who gave us permission to reproduce parts of their work in the web boxes.

A large number of external reviewers provided clear and insightful comments on the draft of the book, or parts of it. We owe a debt to Dale Bottrell, Jennie Broome, Theo Colborn, Sheila Daar, Polly Hoppin, Edwin Johnson, Tobi Jones, Dennis Keeney, Donald Kennedy, Lisa Lefferts, Pam Marone, Charles Mellinger, Eldon Ortman, Ann Sorensen and Pat Weddle. Several USDA and EPA experts also provided information, useful comments and technical assistance at several stages in the project. A special thanks to Larry Elworth for his assistance in providing information on the IPM Initiative and USDA program priorities.

Last, we thank our colleagues at Consumers Union for their valuable insight and unwavering support for the project. In particular, we are grateful to Rhoda Karpatkin, President of Consumers Union, and David Pittle, Vice President and Technical Director, for appreciating the potential of the project and providing us the support needed to undertake the effort.

Bug Identification

Assassin Bug
Hemiptera: Reduviidae
Executive Summary

Ladybird Beetle
Coleoptera: Coccinellidae
Chapter 1

Braconid Wasp
Hymenoptera: Braconidae
Chapter 2

Syrphid Fly
Diptera: Syrphidae
Chapter 3

Chalcid Wasp
Hymenoptera: Chalcidoidea
Chapter 4

Big-Headed Fly
Diptera: Pipunculidae
Chapter 5

Predatory Stink Bug
Hemiptera: Pentatomidae
Chapter 6

Big-Eyed Bug
Hemiptera: Lygaeidae: Geocorinae
Chapter 7

Brown Tachinid
Diptera: Tachinidae
Chapter 8

Green Lacewing
Neuroptera: Chrysopidae
Chapter 9

Beneficial Insect Drawings By:
Ann Sorensen, Chapters 1, 2, 3, 4, 5, 7 and 9
Karen Lutz, Executive Summary, Chapters 6 and 8

Table of Contents

Foreword i

Acknowledgements iii

Executive Summary: 1

    The Problem: Why Choose a New Road 1

    The Solution: Accelerated Progress Toward Biointensive IPM 4

    Getting There: Our Recommendations Provide a Roadmap 5

    Moving Ahead 10

Chapter 1: The Nature of IPM 11

    Many Ounces of Prevention 12

        Tampering with the Reproductive Process 12

        Unwelcome Intruders 17

        Many Little Hammers 18

        Relying on Natural Enemies and Other Beneficials 21

    New Tools Leverage Old Tricks 23

        Information Systems Help Shape Timely Field Responses 24

        Searching for Redundancy 27

    The IPM Continuum 27

        Four Zones Along the Continuum 28

Chapter 2: Pesticide Use and Reliance 31

    Reliance: A Key Concept 35

        Pesticides Can Create Problems and Heighten Reliance 36

    Indicators of Pesticide Use and Reliance 37

        Consumer Pesticide Use 39

        Pesticide Use in Agriculture 41

        Insecticide Use and Reliance 49

        Stable or Slowly Rising Reliance on Fungicides 52

    Reliance and Risk 53

Chapter 3: Pesticide Risks 57

    Environmental Risks from Pesticides 60

        Pesticide Toxicity to Beneficial Organisms 60

        Aquatic Toxicity 63

        Avian Toxicity 64

    Mammalian Toxicity and Human Health Risks 67

        Pesticides in the Body and the Environment 68

        Dietary Exposure 68

Exposure through Drinking Water 70

Other Routes of Exposure 71

Human Health Risks from Pesticide Exposure 73

The Increasing Complexity of Risk Assessments 75

Estimating Trends in Pesticide Risk 77

A Method to Track Average Risk Levels Over Time 78

Trends in Pesticide Toxicity and Risk Over Time 81

Pesticide Risk Assessment - An Insurmountable Challenge? 84

Chapter 4: Regulating Pesticides 89

The Early History of Pesticide Regulation: 1910 to the Early 1970s 91

FIFRA, Written in 1947, Retains Focus on Product Efficacy 91

The Mrak Commission Report: 1969 91

The 1970s: FIFRA Becomes an Environmental Law 92

The Goal of Regulation 93

Benefits Enter the Decision Process 93

A Recipe For Gridlock 94

1975 FIFRA Amendments Aim to Slow Down EPA 94

CEQ Tries to Shift Focus to Pest Management 97

Gridlock Takes Over: Regulation in the 1980s and 1990s 98

"FIFRA Lite" Passes in 1988 99

Another National Research Council Report Focuses on Policy 100

Alar Shifts the Focus of Public Debate 100

Unfinished Business 103

Setting Tolerances at Safe Levels: "Someday" Approaches 104

Setting Tolerances: An Abundance of Advice From the NAS/NRC 106

Setting Tolerances: Changes Made in the Food Quality Protection Act of 1996 108

Problems With the Reregistration Process 110

Regulating Competition Within the Pesticide Industry 111

Costs and Consequences of Pesticide Regulation 112

FIFRA Ensures Steady Growth in the Pesticide Toolkit 114

Regulation Wanes as a Factor Shaping Pesticide Use Patterns 115

Plenty of Choices for Growers 118

The Costs of Regulation and Pesticide Risk Management 119

Summary and Conclusions 122

Chapter 5: Government Adoption of IPM 125

The National Park Service 126

First Steps Toward IPM 127

The National Capital Area Demonstration Project 128

Going Nationwide 132

Training Activities 132

Record Keeping 133

General Services Administration 133

GSA Successes in the NCR - The "Termination of Extermination" 134

Promoting IPM through Contract Specifications - GSA Sets the Pace 135

Taking the NCR Program Nationwide 137

Department of Defense 137

The Department of Defense Plan 138

Meeting the Year 2000 Challenge 138

Matching Words and Actions - Challenges Persist for DOD 139

Success Stories 140

Base Conversion Trends 141

Chapter 6: Institutional Barriers 143

Eradication Programs 144

Medfly and Screwworm Programs 145

The Lower-Rio Grande BWEP 145

Policies that Shape Pest Management 148

Commodity Programs 149

Shaping the Market - Grading and Cosmetic Standards 153

Building and Sharing the Knowledge Base 154

USDA Pest Management Research 154

Trends in the Focus of University Research 157

Collecting and Sharing Information 160

Genetic Engineering and Biointensive IPM 165

Bt-Transgenic Plants 167

Herbicide Tolerant Plants 168

Overview of Biotech Priorities 169

How Biotechnology Can Support Biointensive IPM 170

Chapter 7: Biointensive IPM and the IPM Continuum 175

The Nature and Roots of Biointensive IPM 176

Definition of Biointensive IPM 178

Transitions and Adapting to Change 181

Soil Quality: The Foundation of Sustainable Agriculture 186

The IPM Continuum 188

Four Zones 189

The Pear Pest Management System Continuum in California: A Case Study 191

Measuring IPM Adoption: USDA and CU Definitions and Estimates Differ 196

ERS Estimates of IPM Adoption 198

Consumers Union's Estimates of IPM Adoption 199

Chapter 8: The Clinton Administration IPM Initiative 205

  Trouble from the Start 206

    No Yardstick Applicable to IPM 208

    EPA's "Pest SMART" Effort 208

  USDA Responds to the President's IPM Pledge 210

    New Funding Proves Elusive 211

  EPA's Reduced Risk Initiative 212

    A New Division Takes Over 212

    Focus on Registering Reduced Risk Biopesticides 216

    Special Caution Needed in Regulating Transgenic Plants 220

Chapter 9: Recommendations 225

  Mapping the Transition to Biointensive IPM 225

    The Appropriate Role of Government 225

    Goals for Progress Toward Biointensive IPM 226

    Reducing Pesticide Reliance, Use and Risks 228

  Rebuilding the Pest Management Infrastructure 229

    New Science and Technology 230

    Promoting Professionalism: Technology Transfer, Education and Certification ... 231

    Redesign Government Policies that Promote Pesticide Reliance 234

  Capturing the Power of Market Forces 235

    Broaden the Range of Consumer Choices 235

    Reward Biointensive IPM Innovators 240

    Use Government's Clout to Shape Markets for IPM 241

    Sharing the Costs of Progress Along the Continuum 241

    What Major Corporations Can Do 243

  Smarter, More Efficient Regulation 244

    Target High Risk Pesticides 245

    Don't Register New High Risk Products 247

    Speed Approval of Low Risk Biopesticides 248

    Reconsider the Role of Benefits 248

    Reduce and Share the Costs of Regulation 249

  Moving Forward 250

Appendix 1: 253

Bibliography: 255

List of Figures

1   Pesticide Expenditures in the U.S. By Sector: 1970 through 1995 I

2   Consumers Union's Goals for Progress Along the IPM
    Continuum in Agriculture Through the Year 2020 4

2.1 Pesticide Expenditures in the U.S. By Sector:
    1970 through 1995 33

2.2 Trends in Agricultural Pesticide Use by Type of Pesticide:
    Quantity Applied 1964 through 1992 44

3.1 The Toxicity and Selectivity of Widely Used Pesticides
    to Beneficial Arthropods (Natural Enemies) 62

3.2 Nine Herbicide Active Ingredients and
    Metabolites Found in a Sample of Drinking Water
    in Fort Wayne, Indiana, Spring 1995 71

3.3 Trends Over Time in Acute and
    Chronic Mammalian Toxicity of Pesticides
    Used in Agriculture 83

4.1 Size of the Pesticide Toolkit in Five Year Intervals 115

7.1 The Integrated Pest Management Continuum 190

7.2 Comparison of Synthetic Pesticide and Biopesticide
    Dose Equivalents Along the IPM Continuum:
    California Pear Producers 195

7.3 IPM Adoption by Major Pest Type Along the IPM Continuum:
    USDA Estimates for Vegetable Production 198

7.4 Distinguishing Characteristics of the Consumers Union and
    USDA Methods to Measure Adoption of IPM 201

7.5 Consumers Union's Estimate of IPM Adoption: Early 1990s Baseline 203

9.1 Consumers Union's Goals for Progress Along the IPM Continuum in
    Agriculture Through the Year 2020 228

9.2 Projected Expenditures on Conventional and Biopesticides Assuming
    Policy "Status Quo," 1996-2020 250

9.3 Projected Expenditures on Conventional and Biopesticides
    Assuming "Policy Change," 1996-2020 251

List of Tables

2.1 Indicators of Reliance on Herbicides for Weed Control Over
Four Decades, Major Crops 47

2.2 Insecticide Applications to Cotton by Chemical Family 51

2.3 Trends in Fungicide Use Since 1966 53

3.1 Relative Impacts of Pesticides on Beneficial Arthropods by Type of
Pesticide: Scale of 1 to 5 61

3.2 Agricultural Reliance on Pesticides Identified as Endocrine Disruptors:
Pounds of Active Ingredient Applied in 1992 75

3.3 Differences in the Acute Mammalian Toxicity of Pesticides Applied in 1992:
Top 10%, Median and Bottom 10% Use Groups 80

3.4 Differences in the Chronic Mammalian Toxicity (Mam Tox Score) of
Pesticides Applied in 1992: Top 10%, Median, and Bottom 10% Use Groups 81

4.1 Changes in the Pesticide Toolkit from 1971 to November, 1994 114

4.2 Number of EPA Regulatory Actions Involving Major Agricultural Use Pesticides
and Changes in Average Toxicity Levels 116

4.3 Private and Public Sector Expenditures on Pesticide Regulation and
the Management of Pesticide Risk: 1971 to 1995 120

4.4 Private and Public Sector Expenditures on Pesticide Regulation and
the Management of Pesticide Risk: 1996-2020 121

6.1 Entomology Research Priorities Evident in Research Article Citations 158

6.2 Plant Pathology Research Priorities Evident in Research Article Citations 159

6.3 Change Over Time in Weed Management Research Priorities, Agricola Citations,
1970-1971 through 1993-1994 163

6.4 Space Devoted to Pesticide Advertising Major Farm in Magazines 165

6.5 New Characteristics Associated with Genetically Engineered Crop
Varieties Planned for Introduction by 2000 170

7.1 California Pear IPM Scouting and Pesticide Application Criteria 193

7.2 California Pear Pesticide Use and Pest Management Cost Summary
Along the IPM Continuum 194

8.1 USDA IPM Initiative Funding Levels, FY 1994 through FY 1997
Budget Cycles 213

List of Web Pages

Gordon's Entomological Page 12

The Pherolist 16

Leopold Center for Sustainable Agriculture 20

Urban IPM - University of Florida 29

Tree of Life 30

American Crop Protection Association 32

AgraQuest 35

Interactive Identification of Adult Insects 40

Interactive Identification of Ants 41

Industry Task Force II on 2,4-D Research Data 43

University of Florida Book of Insect Records 52

Ag Answers - Ohio State University 55

Biological Control Virtual Information Center 61

Environmental Working Group - Water Quality 69

The EXtension TOXicology NETwork - EXTOXNET 73

Pesticide Action Network North America - PANNA 78

The Pesticide Properties Database (PPD) 87

TreeBASE - A Database of Phylogenetic Knowledge 98

THOMAS Information from Library of Congress 112

Department of Defense - Pest Management Information System 139

IPM Innovators CA Department of Pesticide Regulation 141

Animal and Plant Health Inspection Service (APHIS) 147

1996 Farm Bill 152

Environmental Working Group - Pesticides 154

National IPM Initiative FUNDING 1996 156

National IPM Initiative Implementation Program 157

National Alliance of Independent Crop Consultants 160

University of California Statewide IPM Project 161

University of Maine - Cooperative Extension Apple IPM Program 162

Biocontrol and IPM - Related Patents 171

Northeast Region Integrated Pest Management Page 177

California PestCast 188

The Entomology Department at Clemson University 192

Nematodes as Biological Control Agents of Insects 200

New York State Integrated Pest Management Program 202

USDA NRICGP Abstracts of Funded Research, FY 1995 209

USDA National Agricultural Statistics Service (NASS) 211

EPA (Press Releases) NTC EPA Awarded Grants 214

Cal-EPA and DPR News Releases 220

Agency for Toxic Substances and Disease Registry (ATSDR) 221

Information Systems for Biotechnology 223

Identification, Life-History, Damage, and Approaches to
Controlling the Gypsy Moth 232

National IPM Network National Server 239

Slow the Spread Gypsy Moth Pilot Project 247

Executive Summary

The way we manage pest problems is at a crossroads. For decades, we have relied primarily on chemical pesticides to control pest populations in agriculture, urban settings, homes and gardens. The evidence by now is clear that intensively chemical-dependent approaches often fail to manage pests effectively, and that the aggregate risks and costs they impose on our society are both unacceptably high, and getting higher.

For at least 20 years, an alternative approach called Integrated Pest Management (IPM), which relies primarily on biological and ecological interventions such as using pests' natural enemies, has been recognized by experts in the field as sounder and safer than chemical-dependent pest control. IPM methods have gradually been added to the pest management arsenal, but the transition to IPM has proceeded slowly.

This report calls for accelerating progress toward IPM. We believe achieving that goal is the surest and most cost-effective way to reduce the risks of chemical pesticides. Our recommendations outline a roadmap for a more rapid transition.

The Problem: Why Choose a New Road

In the decades since World War II, American agricultural, urban and household pest managers have wholeheartedly embraced an abundance of chemical pesticides. In 1995, U.S. pesticide sales totaled 1.25 billion pounds of active ingredients and $10.4 billion. Sales have increased steadily for the past 25 years, and even more steeply in 1994 and 1995 (see Figure 1). About three-fourths of total expenditures are for pesticides applied in the agricultural sector, but lawns and gardens, golf courses, parks, homes and public buildings and many other facilities where people live, work or play are also treated, often heavily, with pesticides.

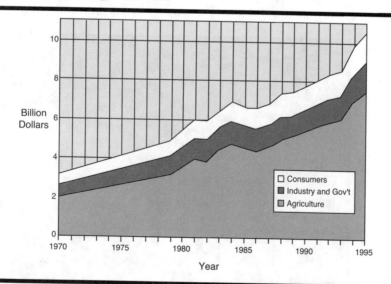

Figure 1 Pesticide Expenditures in the U.S. By Sector: 1970 through 1995

* Nominal dollars (i.e., not adjusted for inflation).
Source: 1970 to 1979 extrapolated from USDA data, 1979-1993 from (Aspelin, 1994); 1994-1995, from (Aspelin, 1996). See also Appendix 1 for details on data sources and projection methods.

Agricultural reliance on and use of pesticides have continued to increase in recent years. Compared to the early 1970s, pesticides are applied two to five times now to accomplish what one application used to do, and average rates of use per acre are still rising. While pesticide use has risen, crop losses to pests have not declined, and clear signs have emerged that chemical approaches to pest control do not work as well as they need to. More than 500 insect pests, 270 weed species and 150 plant diseases are now resistant to one or more pesticides, making them harder to control.

> In the last decade, the number of weed species known to be resistant to herbicides rose from 48 to 270, and the number of plant diseases resistant to fungicides grew from 100 to 150. Resistance to insecticides is so common—more than 500 pest species—that nobody is really keeping score.

When pesticide applications kill their natural enemies, species that normally cause economically insignificant damage can become major "secondary" pests; such pesticide-induced problems underlay the disastrous failure of attempts to eradicate the cotton boll weevil in Texas last year. Resistance and secondary pest outbreaks each year tend to increase reliance on pesticides, a vicious circle that experts call the "pesticide treadmill." Because of these pesticide failures, several major crops, especially cotton and potatoes, are facing pest management crises that threaten the livelihood of many growers.

Public concern with pesticides has focused on their human health hazards, which are substantial. Farm workers and other occupationally exposed groups bear the

greatest risk, but consumers are exposed to pesticides used in and around their homes and in public facilities. Some 110,000 pesticide poisonings are reported by Poison Control Centers each year, 23,000 people visit emergency rooms for the same reason, and about 20 people a year, mostly children, die from accidental pesticide poisoning.

Millions of people are exposed routinely around their homes and work to smaller pesticide doses that have no obvious ill effects, but these exposures can contribute significantly to possible long-term risk. We are all also exposed to pesticide residues in foods on a daily basis, and in some regions, especially the Midwestern "corn belt," herbicide-contaminated drinking water is an increasingly important exposure source.

As we demonstrate in Chapter 3, the kinds of risks pesticides pose to public health have shifted somewhat over the past 25 years, but the overall level of risk has not notably declined. Usage-weighted average toxicity of the insecticides, herbicides and fungicides in use today is as high as or higher than that of the pesticides used in the early 1970s, and total risk is rising as aggregate pesticide use increases.

Advances in toxicology and ecological risk assessment have also raised a wide array of new risk concerns. Where once the primary focus was on the possibility of

Farm workers are among those with the highest occupational exposures to pesticides. In 1994 EPA completed a decade-long effort to establish new farm-worker protection standards. The new rules may help reduce risks, but progress toward biointensive IPM will reduce them both more quickly and more significantly. Credit: California Farmer.

Protecting waterfowl from pesticides is a challenge in states like Wisconsin, Michigan, California and the Dakotas where agriculture, wetlands and wildlife share the same landscape. Credit: International Crane Foundation.

acute poisoning and the long-term risk of cancer, today risk assessors are aware that pesticides can affect the nervous, endocrine, immune and reproductive systems; that infants, young children, the unborn and other subpopulations are especially susceptible to many toxic effects; and that we are all exposed to combinations of toxic pollutants, whose effects may amplify each other. But science cannot currently tell precisely how large any of these risks are with respect to the use of a given pesticide.

Pesticides pose many risks beyond those to human health.

> EPA regulations took off the market one quarter of all insecticide pounds applied from 1971 to 1978, but only 2.6 percent from 1978 to 1986, and less than 1 percent since then.

Adverse effects on beneficial non-target organisms cause secondary pest outbreaks mentioned earlier, and can damage other life-supporting functions of ecosystems. Many of these risks are increasing as pesticide use grows.

Banning DDT and most other environmentally persistent chlorinated hydrocarbon insecticides in the 1970s helped restore populations of bald eagles and other once-endangered predatory birds. But the pesticides that replaced them, while less likely to persist and accumulate in food chains, are more acutely toxic and kill millions of fish and birds each year. Pesticides also damage soil microbial and invertebrate communities (earthworms and other organisms), and in the long run such impacts on soils' ability to sustain life may be far more costly to society than more visible wildlife kills.

Government regulation of pesticides has not succeeded at eliminating most of these problems. We would undoubtedly be far worse off without it, but the past 25 years of pesticide regulation have amounted to running hard just to stay in the same place. The Environmental Protection Agency (EPA) has banned some of the worst pesticides, but the agency approves about 10 new active ingredients for each one it takes off the market.

The impact of EPA decisions on pesticide use has also diminished with time. Agency rulings in the 1970s ended 25 percent of insecticide applications then in use, but EPA's actions since 1986 have reduced use by less than 1 percent. Regulating pesticides costs America well over $1 billion a year. As the risk-reducing impact of regulation has shrunk, the ratio of regulation's benefits to its costs has also declined substantially.

The inherent limitations of science and the requirement in law to balance the risks and benefits of pesticide use have made pesticide regulation an adversarial, difficult and costly process better known for its characteristic gridlock than for reducing the aggregate risks of pesticide use. In this era of shrinking budgets and diminished expectations of government, we cannot look to regulation to get us off the pesticide treadmill.

Instead, the surest, most cost effective way to promote sustainable agriculture and reduce pesticide risks in urban and household settings is to accelerate the pace of adoption of safer, ecologically sounder IPM methods. As more and more pest management tasks come to rely on IPM methods, reliance on pesticides and the associated risks will decline.

The Solution: Accelerated Progress Toward Biointensive IPM

Before we can map out a strategy for progress toward IPM, we need a clear vision of the goal. As we explain in Chapters 7 and 8, many different definitions of "IPM" have come into use. In this report, we use the term biointensive IPM (see box) to define the most advanced stage of IPM, the high level of ecologically based pest control that should be the ultimate goal of pest management in all settings. Chapters 1 and 7 give many examples of biointensive IPM systems now in use.

In reality, IPM systems fall along a continuum, which we have broken into four levels of adoption: No IPM (that is, pest management that is largely reliant on chemical controls); Low IPM; Medium IPM; and High, or biointensive IPM. The distinguishing characteristic of each level is the extent to which ecological and biological IPM methods are relied upon compared to reliance on chemical pesticides. The goal of policy, research and education should be to promote steady progress toward biointensive IPM from all starting points along the continuum.

Based on an analysis of the current extent of reliance on IPM methods relative to reliance on pesticides in agri-

Biointensive IPM

Biointensive IPM is a systems approach to pest management based on an understanding of pest ecology. It begins with steps to accurately diagnose the nature and source of pest problems, and then relies on a range of preventive tactics and biological controls to keep pest populations within acceptable limits. Reduced risk pesticides are used if other tactics have not been adequately effective, as a last resort and with care to minimize risks.

culture, we estimate in Chapter 7 that about 6 percent of crop acreage is currently managed with High (biointensive) IPM, and another 25 percent is now under Medium IPM. We propose as goals of national policy that acreage in biointensive IPM should double by the year 2000, that 75 percent should be in "High" and "Medium" by the year 2010, and that essentially 100 percent should be in "High" IPM by the year 2020 (see Figure 2).

For urban and household pest management, where people are more likely to be directly exposed to pesticides and pest problems tend to be easier to solve, we

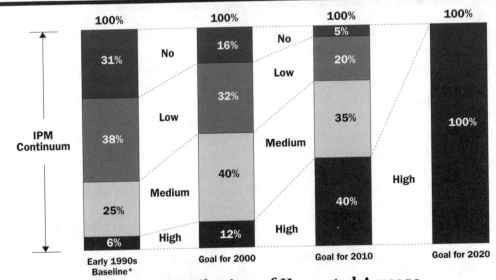

Figure 2 Consumers Union's Goals for Progress Along the IPM Continuum in Agriculture Through the Year 2020

Distribution of Harvested Acreage

* Based on Consumers Union's Best Estimates; see Chapter 7.

recommend that the transition to essentially 100 percent biointensive IPM be complete by the year 2010.

If these goals were largely achieved, we estimate that sales of conventional chemical pesticides would decline from about $10.4 billion a year today to about $5 billion in 2020. Sales of far safer biopesticides used in IPM systems would grow from less than 2 percent of the market now to about half of total sales in 2020. Under the same scenario, the total public health risk from pesticides would be reduced by at least 75 percent from today's levels. Ecological risks and the economic costs of regulation and other steps society must take to manage the risks of pesticides would be dramatically reduced as well.

Getting There: Our Recommendations Provide a Roadmap

What will it take to attain these goals? The essential first step is to make the transition to biointensive IPM the goal of national policy, and to set up realistic targets and timetables for progress. It is a goal of current federal policy to bring 75 percent of agricultural acreage into "IPM" by the year 2000. That target is based on an insufficiently rigorous definition of IPM and too modest a goal for progress; we urge that definitions and goals more like the ones we offer here be adopted instead. The federal government should take the lead in reviewing and reformulating national goals in this regard, promptly and with the participation of all affected interests.

Setting national goals and timetables and measuring progress are appropriate tasks for government. Government also has a role to play in setting an example, changing priorities and insuring a level playing field for IPM. But the transition to biointensive IPM will not occur by government decree, and regulation won't make it happen. It will be driven primarily by market forces, and will need to be crafted at the level of specific crops and problems, on local and regional scales, by people, businesses, researchers and others close to the problems.

In a "rational" market where all the costs and risks of pest management choices were reflected in prices, biointensive IPM would win over chemical pesticides, hands down. But the market is far from perfect. Many costs of chemical pest control are outside the price system, and many government policies and important institutions tend currently to promote or reinforce reliance on chemical controls. It will require conscious effort and intelligent, focused changes in public policy to remove those hurdles and accelerate progress. The transition to biointensive

In the 1930s, Dutch elm disease decimated the elm trees that graced the nation's streets and parks. Today, USDA scientists are working with the National Arboretum to develop new disease-resistant elm varieties. Credit: Scott Bauer, Agricultural Research Service

IPM will take time and commitment, talent, innovation, and investment by many different actors. Our recommendations define the major elements in the transition and roles for some key players.

1. Build the Infrastructure

Successful biointensive IPM depends very heavily on knowledge, and on the skills and expertise of farmers and other field practitioners. Expanding reliance on biointensive IPM requires building up the infrastructure of skills and knowledge, bringing new and improved biopesticides to market, and expanding access to and lowering the cost of IPM information and services. Some institutions and policies also are barriers to the use of biointensive IPM; they need to be removed or redirected.

Many farmers seek help from independent consultants as they strive to adopt IPM methods. Consultant Pat Weddle (left) and grape grower Fred Smeds are discussing canopy management needs in this grape trellis system. The painting on the cover of this report is a view of the Smeds' farm near Dinuba, California.
Credit: Charles Benbrook

Research priorities in both the public and private sectors are now skewed toward supporting and expanding reliance on chemical pesticides. Less than 13 percent of federal expenditures for research on pesticides or pest management last year supported work that contributes to biointensive IPM. In the private sector, research in biotechnology, which could potentially provide many innovations that would advance IPM, has instead focused on developing products that can exploit or expand reliance on chemical pesticides.

These priorities need to be reversed. The overall level of federal funding for pest management research (as opposed to research on pesticide use or problems associated with it) should be doubled over the next five fiscal years, and at least 75 percent of that research should support biointensive IPM directly. Private sector research priorities also need to put much more emphasis on supporting sustainable biointensive IPM techniques, not propping up failing chemical technologies. Much of the most promising work in this field is being pursued by small, innovative companies, and new public and private investment strategies are needed to help this effort grow.

Innovation and success in the practice of biointensive IPM by farmers, pest management advisors and others should be rewarded. One way to do that is to publicize innovations by awarding prizes. We urge government, environmental and consumer groups and others to set up awards programs, and to use them both to reward innovations and to raise the "profile" of biointensive IPM and its practitioners.

The number and expertise level of IPM practitioners in the field need expansion, to put advances in knowledge into wider practice where pests need managing. USDA and the cooperative extension system should emphasize training field-level pest managers in biointensive IPM, and expanding access to information on specific IPM solutions to particular pest problems. Opportunities should be created for farmers who have successfully applied biointensive IPM to share their knowledge with other farmers.

USDA, land grant universities and others should create new databases that support IPM adoption and make them available (as growing amounts of information are now) via the Internet. Continuing-education and certification programs should include expanded IPM training, such as new programs in urban and indoor biointensive IPM. The Federal Insecticide, Fungicide and Rodenticide Act should be amended to require proficiency in biointensive IPM for certification as a pesticide applicator or pest management advisor.

We strongly endorse the code of ethics being adopted by many pest management consultants who have pledged to accept fees only for providing information and expert advice, and to avoid depending for any income on the sale of pesticides or other products. We believe farmers and other consumers should seek advice only from such independent experts.

2. Redesign Government Programs To Promote IPM, Not Pesticide Use

Government-supported programs to eradicate certain insect pests, such as the cotton boll weevil, through intensive pesticide applications are costly and often cause more problems than they solve. Such pest-control programs need to be redirected to support biological controls and other safer, more effective IPM strategies.

Crop subsidy programs, which have created incentives for specialized farming and expansion of cropped acreage, have also promoted intensified reliance on pesticides. As the era of subsidies draws to a close, programs need redirection with a part of the support that is paid going to promote the practice of biointensive IPM.

USDA grading standards for fruits and vegetables should be revised so they no longer promote late-season pesticide applications to preserve cosmetic "perfection." The government, grower groups, and food processors and retailers should work together to develop market channels for less-than-perfect produce. USDA should grant selective exemptions from marketing orders to growers practicing biointensive IPM.

In administering national conservation and water-quality protection programs, USDA should offer cost-share incentives to help farmers accelerate their progress toward biointensive IPM. USDA crop insurance programs should be expanded to cover pest-induced crop losses, to eliminate "just-in-case" pesticide spraying. Such crop insurance coverage would also let the public share the risk of adopting innovative or unfamiliar biointensive IPM methods and increase the willingness of many growers to try IPM.

Tax-reform proposals in Congress are currently seeking to eliminate some forms of "corporate welfare" to more equitably share the burden of steps needed to balance the budget. Congress should aim its ax at the deductions pesticide manufacturers claim for the rebates,

bonuses to sales staff, and costs of respray programs they use to boost pesticide sales, all of which are currently fully deductible.

State and local governments should address their own policies related to pesticide use. For example, disclosure laws should require that consumers be informed by posted notices when public facilities have been treated with pesticides or with comparatively safer biointensive IPM techniques.

3. *Offer Consumers More Choices In the Marketplace*

More IPM products will come onto the market as farmers, building managers, homeowners, gardeners, lawn-care professionals and many other pest managers come to see IPM as an effective, safer and reasonably priced alternative to chemical pesticides. The process is under way, and in the next several years IPM systems need to build market presence and momentum as rapidly as advances in practical IPM methods can support.

Surveys of public opinion indicate a huge, largely untapped potential market for foods grown with "environmentally sustainable" pest management practices, but also show that most people do not recognize the term "IPM" or understand what environmentally sustainable pest management is. Public education is needed to help consumers recognize biointensive IPM, and know why they should choose products produced with it.

Consumers can use their buying power to support biointensive IPM both directly, when they control cockroaches in their kitchen or maintain their lawn, and

Broader choices and useful label and point-of-purchase information are needed in retail stores so those consumers wanting to buy "earth-friendly" food products will have more opportunities to do so. A growing number of stores offer organic produce and some are also selling "IPM-Grown" foods.
Credit: Food Marketing Institute

indirectly, by choosing fresh or processed foods, clothing and other products that were made using biointensive IPM. To harness the power of consumer choice, businesses offering these products and services need to commit themselves to adopt IPM in their production processes and to let their customers know they have done so.

Product labeling and certification are important means for communicating this information. More and better certification and labeling programs for IPM-grown foods and non-food products, from flowers to soybean inks and cotton-based fabrics, are needed.

Similar programs should be developed for IPM pest management products and services. EPA should permit and encourage sellers of pest management products that are fully compatible with biointensive IPM, such as many low risk biopesticides already on the market, to label them as such. Professional pest-management services should offer the same information to their customers that do-it-yourself consumers find on product labels.

Creating consensus criteria for certifying and labeling products and services as based on biointensive IPM will be a challenging task. A collective effort by the makers and sellers of products, IPM practitioners, citizen organizations and government agencies will be required to devise labeling and certification schemes that are clear, effective, accurate and fair. But these steps are vital to tap market forces to accelerate progress toward biointensive IPM.

Improvements are also needed in labeling and point-of-purchase information for conventional pesticide products. Consumers need to be better informed about the limited effectiveness and likely unwanted side effects of over-reliance on chemical controls. Labels on formulated pesticide products should fully disclose inert ingredients.

Additional information about the nature of pest problems, pest biology and ecology, and non-chemical pest management choices should be made available in retail stores, libraries and other places consumers seek advice when they have a pest problem. The information should come from independent sources (not from companies seeking to sell products) and should be accessible to ordinary consumers. Some such databases are beginning to appear now on the Internet; such vital information sources should be expanded, refined and made widely available.

4. Using the Market Clout of Government and Large Corporations

Agencies of federal, state and local governments, from the federal Department of Defense to local school boards, and large corporations, consume pest management products and services. Most also buy foods, clothing and other products that may be produced using biointensive IPM. We urge that this enormous collective purchasing

Robert Mondavi (left) is the owner of one of California's largest premium wineries. Brian Fitzpatrick (below, with daughter) owns the smaller Fitzpatrick Winery in El Dorado County. Both vintners offer wines made from organically grown grapes and in the process, are helping many grape growers advance biointensive IPM methods. Large and small companies alike can be innovators and leaders in the transition to IPM.
Credit: Richard Steven Street

power be consciously applied to build demand for biointensive IPM.

Government agencies and major corporations should adopt policies that make the use of biointensive IPM "standard operating procedure" for all pest management needs at the agency's or company's facilities. Plans and timetables for making the transition from current practices to 100 percent biointensive IPM should be established and publicized, so that these large economic entities can "lead by example."

Numerous successful existing programs, like the General Service Administration's indoor and urban IPM program or the Campbell Soup Company's program for minimizing pesticide use by growers with whom it contracts for raw materials, are models that should be emulated. Agencies and companies with expertise in biointensive IPM should expand their outreach efforts to assist others seeking to follow a similar path.

> **The acute toxicity to mammals of high risk insecticides is some 2,800 times as high as that of the least toxic insecticides. Pound for pound, the average chronic toxicity of high risk fungicides in use has tripled since 1971.**

Government and corporate procurement policies should also establish "buying IPM" as a goal. Imagine the impact on the market for IPM- or organically-grown cotton if the Pentagon were to accept no other cotton for military uniforms, or the effect on IPM practice in the potato industry if McDonald's announced that by the year 2000 all of its french fries would be "IPM-Grown."

Food processors and retailers can also help promote diversity of crop rotations—a fundamental IPM strategy for breaking pest and disease cycles—by working with grower groups to ensure that markets exist for rotational crops.

Some corporate policies that promote needless pesticide use should be revised in the interests of advancing biointensive IPM. For example, mortgage lending institutions should stop requiring homes to be treated for termites when there is no evidence of active infestation. And when termites are present, banks should offer homeowners assistance in finding exterminators certified in biointensive IPM termite treatment.

5. Smarter, More Efficient Regulation

While pesticide regulation has not eliminated pesticide problems and will not be the primary driving force behind the transition to biointensive IPM, regulation can be used consciously, intelligently and efficiently to "level

the playing field," accelerate progress and remove some obstacles in the road.

Pesticide regulation can and should make high risk chemical pesticides more difficult and more costly to use, by internalizing some of the current societal costs of their use. The Food Quality Protection Act, passed in July 1996, gives the EPA new mandates to lower the legal limits on pesticide residues in foods, to ensure "reasonable certainty of no harm" to infants and children and other vulnerable members of the public.

EPA should use that authority to drive down the aggregate risks of selected high risk pesticides. Our recommended target categories for priority action include the organophosphate and carbamate insecticides; endocrine disruptors; herbicides found frequently in drinking water; and the 10 most widely used fungicides. In administering this program, EPA may be able to create incentives for pesticide manufacturers and users to cooperate in achieving the legislation's goals, reversing the decades-long pattern of interminable delay and debate over agency decisions.

With the assent of Congress, which would need to grant the agency the authority to do so, we believe EPA should impose a system of registration fees, sufficient to cover the often substantial costs to government of pesticide risk and benefit assessments and other aspects of regulatory decision-making. Fees might be adjusted according to the degree of risk the pesticides in question posed, as another way to capture some of the social costs of using pesticides in their price.

We believe EPA should also adopt a more assertive posture toward new products that pose substantial health or ecological risks, and "just say no," early in the process. Such prompt denials would avoid draining agency resources on efforts to manage major new risks, like those posed by the herbicide acetochlor that EPA registered in 1994, or the approval in 1995 and 1996 of plant varieties genetically engineered to produce the endotoxin of *Bacillus thuringiensis (Bt)*. *Bt* is one of the safest and most valuable biopesticides now registered and is used as a foliar spray to control many damaging insects. Widespread planting of *Bt*-transgenic crops is likely to accelerate the emergence of resistance to *Bt*, forcing farmers to switch to more toxic insecticides. This will increase risks EPA has been stuggling to reduce.

No two pest management systems or spider webs are alike. For both to succeed, they must adapt to their environment and deal with what comes along each day.
Credit: Richard Steven Street

Instead, we believe EPA should refuse to register new transgenic *Bt* crop varieties and herbicide-resistant crop strains, and should revoke the registrations of any such products that involve pesticide active ingredients that have been credibly shown to trigger genetic resistance among target pest populations. EPA should also refuse to register new pesticides it believes are known or probable human carcinogens, such as acetochlor.

Finally, EPA needs to build on the recent success of its effort to speed approval of low risk biopesticides. These compounds, which include microorganisms, viruses, insect pheromones (chemicals insects use to communicate, for purposes like mating) and natural chemicals derived from plants, are essential components of biointensive IPM systems. Government not only should ensure a fast-track approval process for these products when their safety warrants it; it also should expand information available to the public describing these alternatives to chemical pest control weapons.

Moving Ahead

If most of these and other recommendations presented in Chapter 9 are adopted, we believe the pace of progress toward biointensive IPM would be markedly increased. This transition is essential, as the surest, safest and most cost effective way to reduce the excessive and still growing risks inherent in reliance on chemical pest control. The sooner, more rapidly and more widely it takes place, the better off the nation will be.

Moving ahead from today's crossroads will take the creative energy, vision and commitment of thousands of good people in agriculture, in corporations large and small, in government, in research and educational institutions, as well as the broad support of consumers and their choices in the marketplace. But the time is right, and we are optimistic that these elements are poised to come together and move the country more swiftly down the road to biointensive IPM.

The Nature of IPM

Understanding where pests come from and why is a key first step. IPM then seeks to undermine a pest's ability to be a pest.

No living thing is born a "pest." But populations of microorganisms, plants, insects, birds, and mammals from mice to elephants can balloon, overwhelming food supplies, degrading habitat and causing economic damage. In the process, such species become "pests."

Species are intrinsically inclined to grow and reproduce. Most fill the ecological niches accessible to them. A site on the World Wide Web, "Gordon's Entomological Home Page" (http://www.ex.ac.uk/~gjlramel/welcome.html), includes some fascinating details about how successful the insect can be in filling its niche. For example, in 1943 a British professor methodically surveyed the insects inhabiting an acre of British pasture land near Cambridge and found more than one billion arthropods, including 400 million insects and 666 million mites (Ramel, 1996). Entomologists have measured swarms of desert locusts in Africa with as many as 28 billion individuals. Although each locust weighs only about 2.5 grams, a swarm can total 70,000 tons!

Ants and termites are "social insects" that live in colonies and work together to build nests, seek out food and guarantee reproductive success. They can be incredibly effective in these basic tasks. One ant colony studied in Japan had more than one million queens, 300 million workers and 45,000 interconnected nests (Ramel, 1996). Homeowners frustrated with the battle against insect invasions may think the world would be a better place without ants and termites, but what a different world it would soon become. Scientists estimate that ants and termites together account for an incredible 20 percent of the total animal biomass on earth (Ramel, 1996). Ants and termites play critical roles in breaking down and recycling biomass and supplying the food chain that supports the animal kingdom. While considered pests in some places, ants and termites are essential to the world's ecosystems.

Before the arrival of man, the great events shaping evolution were weather and climate—the emergence of abundant plant life, the diversity of species and the cooling and warming of the earth. After humans settled in cities and developed agriculture to support growing numbers, the

> **Ants and termites account for an estimated 20 percent of the total animal biomass on earth! While these species are surely pests in some places, they are essential to life on earth.**

impact of this one species on the ecosystems it shared with others dramatically changed. Population and economic growth meant people needed more and more resources. Natural environments were disrupted to make room for agriculture, grazing, forestry and places to live, work, and play. Technology heightened our ability to do so.

Some 1.82 million species of plants and animals have been identified, about 60 percent of them insects (Gould, 1996). The number of unidentified insects and microorganisms could reach into the hundreds of millions. Of these, just a few thousand are considered pests, and then only in certain locations and at certain times. With so many species, why are so few considered pests?

Most species living where people settle find their environment dramatically altered. The majority adapt or move on and survive, but a handful actually thrive, particularly where man has most fundamentally altered natural habitats. Those that do often come to be seen as pests. For half a century, mankind has relied largely on pesticides to manage pests. The application of billions of pounds of pesticides since the 1950s over wide expanses of land, coupled with the way land is managed, have together undermined the biological and ecological forces and interactions that previously governed population dynamics among species. The results of the chemical era, while dramatic and positive in some places, have elsewhere produced mixed and often negative consequences.

Control failures and unacceptable environmental costs and health risks have led many people to look for new ways to manage pests. Instead of seeking stronger chemicals and applying them more aggressively, some pest managers are finding ways to reinforce nature's bag of tricks through a systems approach called biointensive Integrated Pest Management (IPM). As we show in subsequent chapters, well under than 10 percent of U.S. agriculture now employs biointensive IPM. We think our national goal should be 100 percent and set forth a roadmap to work toward that goal over the next 25 years.

The tip of the knife indicates the point where a codling moth worm borrowed into this pear. Once inside, the worm is almost impossible to control with pesticides, and as it matures and grows, the fruit is ruined (right photo). Credit: Richard Steven Street

A. Many Ounces of Prevention

The best way to deal with pests is to avoid them—not by moving to greener pastures or living in a bubble, but by denying pests a chance to get established and where they do, making it hard for them to thrive to the point where they pose public health threats, cause economic losses or interfere with people's activities indoors or out. Such preventive strategies are key components of all IPM systems. Biointensive IPM works best when multiple tactics are combined in a successful system that keeps pests under control so well people hardly notice—or care—that they are present.

1. Tampering with the Reproductive Process

Many insects use natural scents called pheromones to find members of the opposite sex with which to mate. In the pear and apple orchards of California's San Joaquin Valley; around Wenatchee, Washington; in the Hood River region in Oregon; and in many other places, a new biointensive IPM tactic called pheromone confusion is gaining acceptance. The idea behind the tactic, of which codling moth mating disruption (CMMD) is an example, surfaced half a century before the method became a commercial reality in the field (Kirsch, 1988). Hundreds of people in many different fields worked for more than 30

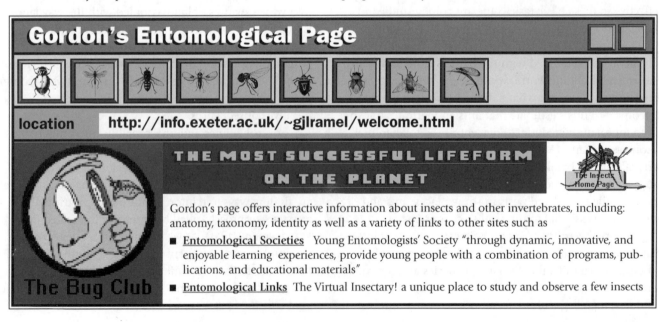

Gordon's Entomological Page

location http://info.exeter.ac.uk/~gjlramel/welcome.html

THE MOST SUCCESSFUL LIFEFORM ON THE PLANET

The Insects Home Page

Gordon's page offers interactive information about insects and other invertebrates, including: anatomy, taxonomy, identity as well as a variety of links to other sites such as

- **Entomological Societies** Young Entomologists' Society "through dynamic, innovative, and enjoyable learning experiences, provide young people with a combination of programs, publications, and educational materials"
- **Entomological Links** The Virtual Insectary! a unique place to study and observe a few insects

The Bug Club

years to make it possible for farmers in the 1990s to tap this new biologically based pest management tool (Howell, et al., 1992).

The pear farm run by Doug and Cathy Hemly near Cortland, California is part of the Randall Island Project, one of the nation's most successful farmer-driven participatory IPM research and demonstration projects. Success in reducing reliance on Guthion (azinphos-methyl), an organophosphate insecticide used to control codling moths, earned the Randall Island Project an "IPM Innovators" award in 1994 from California's Department of Pesticide Regulation. Several Randall Island Project team members, some involved since the early 1980s in refining biointensive IPM options, appear in the box on pages 14-15.

Elegant Simplicity

The codling moth is the most economically damaging insect species that plagues pear and apple growers around the world. The moth does its damage during its worm stage as it matures inside fruit (see photos on page 2). Codling moth mating disruption involves placing small twist-ties about 10 inches long up high in trees. The twist-ties are much like pipe-stem cleaners and are impregnated with a codling moth pheromone—a scent released by the female moths. It takes about 400 twist-ties per acre[1] to fill an orchard with enough scent to thoroughly confuse the male moths. Most exhaust themselves chasing the pheromone and do not find females. Females remain unmated and lay infertile eggs, and populations decline over time.

The system uses a tiny quantity of pheromone. Each twist-tie dispenser includes 0.0028 fluid ounces of pheromone, resulting in a maximum one-time application rate of 1.12 ounces per acre. On hot windy days, the twist-ties will give off more pheromone than on cooler, still days. But unlike conventional pesticides, the pheromone still is delivered gradually. In contrast, when an application of Guthion is made, 1.0 to 1.5 pounds of active ingredient per acre is sprayed into the orchard all at once.

Under most conditions, a pheromone application lasts 100 days, so on any single day, a few one-hundredths of an ounce at most is released into the orchard. Because these natural chemicals tend to be highly specific to just one species and are not toxic, pheromone confusion poses virtually no risk to farm workers or the environment. The tactic is an example of prevention-based technology that makes low-risk biointensive IPM systems feasible in places that may otherwise remain heavily reliant on pesticides.

Independent consultant Pat Weddle helped develop the CMMD system used on farms in the Randall Island Project. He is increasingly upbeat about the biointensive IPM "tools" he can draw upon in managing codling moth. But he and other IPM experts know from experience that mating disruption is not a panacea. On windy days, the pheromone can be blown out of the orchard, creating windows of opportunity for males to find females. If CMMD is not used on adjoining farms, moths can mate next door and move in to lay eggs.

Effectiveness

In recent years the Hemlys and other Randall Island growers have had to use one or two applications of Guthion or other insecticides to augment mating disruption, but this is much less than half the quantity of Guthion used in the late 1980s (Weddle, 1994). At our request, Pat Weddle carried out a study of pear pest management in California (see Chapter 7) which found that farmers using biointensive IPM generally are able to reduce reliance on synthetic pesticides from about 35 pounds of active ingredient per acre under conventional chemical-intensive systems to 13 pounds under biointensive IPM. Furthermore, the 13 pounds of pesticides applied in the biointensive IPM system is composed mostly of low-risk oils for mite control.

Guthion use generally is reduced from four or five applications per season to only one. In some years, Guthion is not even applied in some blocks (an area in

Randall Island Project Growers

Greene & Hemly, Inc.
 Doug Hemly, President/CEO
 Cathy Hemly, Special Projects Coordinator
 John Callis, Orchard Manager
 Duncan Smith, Assistant Orchard Manager
 Filomina Montano, Office Manager
 Jenny McClain, Grower Accounting

David Elliot and Sons, Inc.
Dave Elliot II, Principal
Dave Elliot III, Principal
Richard Elliot, Principal

Wurster Ranch
John Wurster, Principal,

Frieders Orchards
Chris Frieders
Darrell Frieders

Lincoln Chan Farms
Lincoln Chan
George Myers

Years of basic and applied research were required to bring codling moth mating disruption from the laboratory to the field. Many more years of effort and expanded research support will be needed to extend the mating disruption technique to other regions, pests and crops. The success of the Randall Island Project (RIP) depended upon public-private sector partnership in all phases and aspects of technology development, refinement and delivery to the field. Financing this novel extension of the infrastructure supporting biointensive IPM was also a team effort. Many individuals played a variety of important roles in supporting RIP growers, as noted below.

Steve Balling is the Director of Environmental Services for Del Monte Corp. and a founding director of the National Coalition for IPM. Through his leadership of the grower-supported Pear Pest Management Research Fund, Steve helped assure adequate funding for the RIP.

Francis Cave is Staff Research Associate in the laboratory of Dr. Steven Welter, College of Natural Resources, University of California-Berkeley. Dr. Welter (not shown), with assistance from Francis, directed and coordinated both research and implementation components of the RIP.

Jim Dahlberg and **Bob Castanho** are Pest Control Advisors (PCAs) with Harvey Lyman Co. and provided field services and sales support to many RIP growers.

Erryn Desmond is Technical Sales Representative of Trece, Inc., a manufacturer of the codling moth traps and lures used to help understand the population dynamics of the codling moth under mating disruption. Bill Lingren, President of Trece (not shown), donated most of the traps and lures used in the research portion of the RIP.

Phil Kirsch introduced CMMD technology to Sacramento River pear growers in the early 1990s while working for Pacific Biocontrol Ltd. and is currently President, IPM Technologies, Inc., a firm specializing in the production and marketing of pest monitoring systems.

Bud Moorhead is a retired University of California Cooperative Extension farm advisor. His early efforts with U.C. Extension colleagues R.S. Bethell and Bill Barnett (not shown) led to one of the first areawide IPM programs in California in the early 1970s.

Kris Mapes is Fieldman for the California Pear Growers Association and worked closely with growers, processors and PCAs in gathering and disseminating information.

an orchard, usually 10 to 40 acres in size). Under biointensive IPM, pear yields typically reach the 12 to 25 tons per acre range, depending on the density of trees and health of the orchard. This yield is well above the 10 to 15 ton average yields harvested per acre using conventional chemical-intensive management systems.

As with many biointensive IPM systems, cost is a concern and in some cases, a constraint (Kirsch, 1988; Weddle, 1994). The codling moth pheromone active ingredient is expensive to make and available from only one firm, Shin-Etsu Chemical Company Ltd. in Japan. Placing 400 twist-ties per acre into pear trees is far more labor intensive than driving through an orchard with a sprayer, a task which costs just a few dollars per acre. In addition, mating disruption, like most other biopesticide-based approaches, has to be carried out with skill and attention to detail.[2] Timing of interventions—biological or chemical—is one key to success in the field, and wise

Cheryl Norton, *formerly technical sales representative for Microflo Inc., was active in the sales and distribution of Isomate C+, the primary CMMD product used in the RIP. Cheryl is currently employed by Abbot Labs, Inc.*

Jean-Mari Peltier *is now Chief Deputy Director of California's Department of Pesticide Regulation. Previously she was Executive Director of the California Pear Growers Association and the California Pear Advisory Board. Bob McClain is the Assistant Director of the Pear advisory Board. Both organizations supported the development of biointensive IPM pear pest management strategies on behalf of the region's growers.*

Don Thompson *is President, Pacific Biocontol Ltd., and provided extensive technical support and product informa-*

tion on the use of Isomate C and Isomate C+ pheromone products. His work with both consultants and university personnel helped refine pheromone application methods and lower the cost of CMMD to growers.

Pat Weddle, *independent crop consultant based in Placerville, California, and consultant Don Miller (not shown), work with grower-clients accounting for a large portion of the RIP pear acreage. They were key contributors to the successful implementation of CMMD and provided much field level data used by researchers and companies to refine the technology delivery system.*

Thom Wiseman *is a PCA with John Taylor Fertilizers and a key participant in the RIP.*

Individuals contributing to the success of the Randall Island Project codling moth IPM program gathered in June, 1996 at the Greene and Hemly Ranch. Back row, left to right—John Callis, Duncan Smith, Dave Elliot III, Richard Elliot, Thom Wiseman, Dave Elliot II, Bob Castanho, Kris Mapes, Cheryl Norton. Middle row, left to right - Francis Cave, Erryn Desmond, Jenny McClain, Filomina Montano, John Wurster, Bob McClain, Jean-Mari Peltier. Front row, left to right - Patrick Weddle, Jim Dahlberg, Philip Kirsch, Steve Balling. Near chairs—Cathy Hemly (seated), Doug Hemly (standing). In shadows, left to right—Lincoln Chan, Bud Moorhead, Darrell Ferreira (almost invisible). Credit: Richard Steven Street.

decisions are possible only when accurate, up-to-date, site specific data are available and astutely interpreted (Howell et al., 1992). These steps require time, effort, experience and money.

Several technical refinements in the CMMD delivery system are under active exploration, including ways to lower the cost of gathering field data and more precisely metering out the pheromone as a function of pest pressure and weather conditions. Scientists and IPM experts in the Northwest are working with customized aerosol dispensers linked to weather stations and mini-computers. Together with field scouting data on population levels, such a system could make it possible to both reduce pheromone costs and increase efficacy.

A Long-Delayed Alternative

A new biopesticide is now available to Western tree fruit growers under an experimental use permit. The product is an insect growth regulator called Confirm, which contains the active ingredient tebufenozide. It works by triggering premature metamorphosis in most lepidopteran insects (butterflies and moths).

In the July 1967 issue of *Scientific American* magazine, Dr. Carroll M. Williams, a Harvard University biologist, published an article entitled "Third Generation Pesticides" outlining key scientific discoveries that make it "much more likely" that "…a harmful species of insect can be attacked with its own hormones… (especially) juvenile hormone that all insects secrete at certain stages in their lives" (Williams, 1967). The promise of such new technologies led, with considerable fanfare, to the formation of a number of new companies in the early 1970s,

including Zoecon, based in Silicon Valley.

Despite the discovery of several promising insect growth regulators and development of novel methods to extract and synthesize biopesticides, technical and economic hurdles arose. It proved more difficult than people expected to manufacture biopesticide products that were stable enough to work in the variety of conditions encountered across farms. Zoecon and most other startup companies were unable to move biopesticide products onto the market fast enough and gain market share sufficient to attract the investment capital needed to fund simultaneously the research, discovery, scale-up and marketing processes.

The effort needed to develop and commercialize the full potential of these biologically based solutions was postponed, in part because of technical hurdles, but also because of the steady stream of insecticides that came onto the market in the 1960s and 1970s. New chemicals and innovation in the manufacture, formulation and handling of pesticides reduced costs per acre treated. Specialized, large-scale equipment and aerial application techniques made it possible to cover large areas quickly. As described in Chapter 6, most farmers and scientists were impressed by the simplicity and effectiveness of insecticide-based systems. When an efficacy problem arose with one pesticide, a newer one was applied instead.

The focus of most pest managers shifted from pest management to pesticide selection and application. Interest in more complex biological solutions waned and the modest amount of public research funding supporting biological approaches all but disappeared (Robinson, 1996). Capital flowed into the pesticide industry, creating

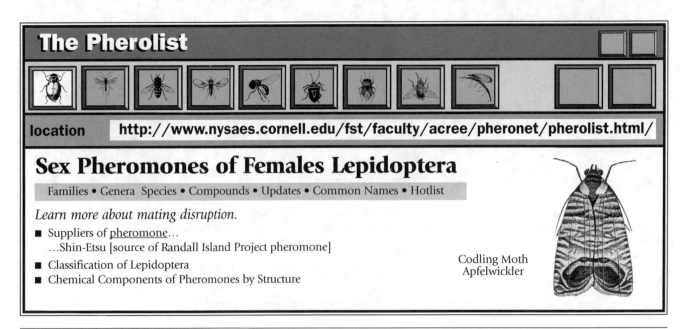

The Pherolist

location   http://www.nysaes.cornell.edu/fst/faculty/acree/pheronet/pherolist.html/

Sex Pheromones of Females Lepidoptera

Families • Genera Species • Compounds • Updates • Common Names • Hotlist

Learn more about mating disruption.

- Suppliers of pheromone…
  …Shin-Etsu [source of Randall Island Project pheromone]
- Classification of Lepidoptera
- Chemical Components of Pheromones by Structure

Codling Moth
Apfelwickler

Automated weather stations are used to track wind speed and temperature—both key factors governing the emergence and flight of codling moths. Scientists are working on linking such stations to computer-controlled aerosol canisters that would dispense pheromone into orchards on an "as needed" basis, lowering costs and improving efficacy. Credit: Richard Steven Street

the infrastructure that has come to make pesticide-based systems the pest management status quo.

2. Unwelcome Intruders

Most pet owners have had more than one encounter with fleas. Millions of dollars are spent each year attempting to control fleas. In the warm months of the year, a large portion of all visits to veterinarians involve illness and injury to cats and dogs either triggered or made worse by fleas. People who have learned to cope with fleas effectively have been practicing integrated pest management.

There are many methods to rid a pet of fleas. You can begin with a bath followed by regular use of a flea comb. But once a pet is free of fleas, the challenge for owners is to lessen the chances and severity of reinfestation. Many people succeed by taking a number of preventive steps. A thorough cleaning of areas where pets sleep and rest in the home is essential, and a dusting with silica aerogel may be necessary. One effective strategy is to create a space where pets spend most of their time and arrange it so that frequent and thorough cleaning is relatively easy.

Cleaning and vacuuming carpets, behind furniture and in other places fleas can hide is key to limiting reinfestation, and a beater-bar type vacuum cleaner is most effective. In one study, this type of machine removed 15 percent to 27 percent of flea larvae and 32 percent to 59 percent of eggs present in the carpet.[3]

Vacuuming also removes adult flea feces, the food source for developing larvae. As an additional precaution, many experts recommend that carpets be steam-cleaned.

Thorough cleaning in the home obviously will not control fleas outdoors. Especially during summer months, successful owners regularly bathe and comb pets, and use other preventive measures. In recent years, veterinarians have begun prescribing pills taken monthly that contain an insect growth regulator that enters the pet's bloodstream and disrupts the normal development of fleas.

Roaches and Other Uninvited Guests

Virtually every homeowner has dealt with ants and cockroaches. There are some 4,000 species of cockroaches, of which about 50 are considered pests, according to Agricultural Research Service (ARS) entomologist Dr. Richard Brenner (Kinzel, 1989). Cockroaches are among the many insects that reproduce very rapidly—one female can produce "up to tens of thousands of offspring a year…ARS scientists scoured apartments in Florida and turned up 20,000 cockroaches—in each apartment!" (Kinzel, 1989).

Americans spend $1.5 billion applying pesticides and hiring professional services to control cockroaches according to Brenner (Kinzel, 1989). The results are sometimes disappointing. Many populations are resistant to commonly applied products, and some pesticides work only in certain circumstances and miss part of the population in a given structure.

Many homeowners have had success reducing problems with cockroaches and other crawling insects by limiting their access to food and water. Open bags of food are stored in sealed containers. Thorough cleaning of countertops, around garbage cans and in trash storage areas is a must. Cracks and crevices used by crawling insects for access are sealed, and if infestations continue, treated with the relatively non-toxic boric acid or an appropriate insecticide. Just as in managing fleas, the key to success is a combination of tactics that focus on the simplest things people can do to make life difficult, if not impossible, for unwanted intruders. This process of drawing upon multiple tactics is homestyle IPM.

Agricultural Research Service entomologist Dr. Richard Brenner studies cockroach behavior in a specially built and equipped structure. Here, Dr. Brenner inspects a smokybrown cockroach using a filtered yellow light invisible to cockroaches. An estimated one-third of American households are home to this uninvited intruder.
Credit: Barry Fitzgerald, ARS

IPM in Schools

Growing concern about pesticide impacts on the young has led many parents and teachers to raise questions about pest management practices and pesticides applied in schools. Sometimes the answers are surprising and trigger more questions. In some communities, the information surfaced by concerned parents and teachers has helped stimulate public interest in and education about pest management and pesticide risks.

In Helena, Montana, Mary Ann Hayes started to ask questions about pesticides used in the area's schools after seeing a news program on the health problems experienced by many people following indoor exposure to the insecticide Dursban (chlorpyrifos). Hayes asked the principal of a local elementary school whether Dursban was used in the school's buildings. The principal did not

know the answer. Several more questions followed (Riley, 1996).

Mary Ann Hayes soon learned that Helena School District Number One had a contract with EcoLab Pest Elimination Service to apply Dursban every month in middle schools and high schools, including the one attended by her son, and every three months in the elementary schools. A series of newspaper articles appeared documenting the standard pest management practices in the district and the lack of knowledge of basic integrated pest management methods among school maintenance personnel. Hayes was able to find and share information on IPM successes achieved by other school systems, and sought allies like the National PTA (Parent Teachers Association) in making the case for change in Helena.

Her efforts led to a halt of Dursban spraying in Helena schools as of January, 1996. The district also established a subcommittee to assess available IPM practices and policies for schools. A new policy will be finalized before the 1996-1997 school year emphasizing pest prevention and least-toxic treatments (Riley, 1996). The episode has raised public understanding of the potential risks from pesticides applied in indoor settings and has encouraged others to ask questions of those making pest management decisions affecting the general public.

3. Many Little Hammers

Dick and Sharon Thompson run a diversified crop and livestock farm near Boone, Iowa. Through 20 years of onfarm experimentation, the Thompsons have elevated weed management to an art form. Instead of relying on herbicides, the Thompsons use "many little hammers"— a simple but descriptive phrase coined by two weed ecologists in a research review article describing multitactic integrated weed management systems (Liebman and Gallandt, 1996).

More is known about the Thompson farm—practices and systems, yields, costs and returns, production methods, weed counts, soil quality, environmental impacts—than any other farm of its type in America. The Thompsons have been carrying out onfarm research for about 15 years and publish an annual summary of results (Thompson et al., 1995). They have collaborated with dozens of scientists at Iowa State University (ISU), the Agricultural Research Service's Soil Tilth Center and the Leopold Center for Sustainable Agriculture at ISU. In any one season, there are about a dozen different trials underway on parts of the farm, along with detailed exploration of how the Thompson's diversified farming system affects the quality of the land, erosion and fertility levels, and the health and performance of animals on the farm. Dozens of reports and articles have been written on various aspects of the farm.

The Thompson operation was also one of 11 case study farms featured in the National Research Council report *Alternative Agriculture* (NRC, 1989a). The NRC case study describes the Thompson farm in detail and documents the way several practices are integrated to lower reliance on off-farm inputs including pesticides, fertilizers and animal drugs. The case study contrasts the farm's cost of producing corn and soybeans with nearby conventional farms—about $1.50 per bushel for corn and $3.90 for soybeans compared with $2.11 and $4.80 per bushel using conventional methods (Table 4, Thompson farm case study, NRC, 1989a).

The Thompsons are among the founding members of the Practical Farmers of Iowa (PFI), a successful farmer-led organization dedicated to discovering practical and sustainable farming systems. PFI cooperators carry out a series of production system trials across dozens of farms.

In most years, visitors ask Dick and Sharon Thompson and other PFI cooperators more questions about weed management than any other aspect of their operation. Weed management is one of the major challenges for Midwestern crop farms, along with the weather, prices and farm policy. Weed complexes evolve constantly to overcome the control measures used against them, so each year farmers must incorporate new combinations of practices and strategies into systems to effectively limit the buildup of weed populations (Ghersa et al., 1994; Liebman et al., 1996).

The "little hammers" used on the Thompson farm to control weeds in corn and soybean fields include crop rotations, cover crops and mechanical cultivation. By rotating crops, both during the growing season and in the fall when cover crops are sown, the Thompsons steadily change the microenvironment where weed seeds lie and weed plants grow.

In one year, foxtail seeds lying dormant in the soil for years might find the conditions just right and germinate strongly, requiring timely cultivation. In another year, with a different mix of crops, planting methods and timing of operations, a broadleaf weed like velvetleaf might do much better. In a diversified system like the Thompsons' no one species becomes dominant, and all species remain relatively easy to control through a combination of practices. Rotations and cover crops are probably the most important components of such inte-

grated weed management systems (Thompson et al., 1995; Wyse, 1992). But on the Thompson farm and in all other weed management systems, the *real* key to success in any given year, and over time, is good management based on information, timely actions and careful field operations.

The planting and cultivation systems used by the Thompsons have several other hammers built into them. The ridge-till planter, for example, leaves over half the soil surface undisturbed, which helps since tillage typically brings buried weed seeds to the surface and results in more weeds to manage. Right before and after the corn or soybeans germinate, the Thompsons run through the fields with a rotary hoe, a tillage tool that skims the surface of the soil, removing recently germinated weeds. The rotary hoe and cultivator are used for weed management between the rows until the crop grows large enough to "close canopy" and shade the soil surface, blocking the sunlight and warmth that signal weed seeds to germinate and then grow.

Another "Hammer"?

In the spring of 1995, the Thompsons were carrying out early season planting and cultivation in a field that had been treated with manure the previous fall—a practice that assures a strong flush of foxtail and other weeds because uncomposted manure from grazing livestock nearly always contains a large number of weed seeds. As expected, the field was almost totally green with newly germinated grass weeds about two inches tall. The Thompsons' ridge-till planter did a good job cleaning up the field. The ground went from green to nearly black after the planting operation but the Thompsons expected the weeds to return strong. They did not, despite high levels of seeds, fertile conditions and ample soil moisture.

At the 1996 annual meeting of the Weed Science Society of America, the Thompsons shared this story and asked for help from the scientists in the audience in understanding what might have caused the weeds to "just not bother" to grow.

Some ideas surfaced. Any plant—including weeds— is fair game for pathogens in the soil. Pathogens that attack the roots of weeds, but are less inclined or able to harm corn or soybean plant roots, might have played a roll in minimizing the Thompsons' weed management challenge. Indeed, a poster presentation at the same meeting by Dr. Robert Kremer, an Agricultural Research Service scientist from Missouri, described experiments in which he isolated several strains of microorganisms that thrive on the roots of green foxtail and which, under certain circumstances, were able to control foxtail growth

(Kremer, 1996). Likewise, scientists at Kansas State University have found soil bacteria that colonize the roots of tough-to-control winter annual grasses in wheat and were able to increase wheat yields in a field test involving a treatment with the bacterial isolates (Harris and Stahlman, 1996).

Others picked up on Kremer's finding and suggested an explanation for the absence of weeds observed by the Thompsons. The high levels of organic matter and available nutrients in the Thompsons' fields, coupled with the absence of any pesticides, which tend to depress microbial populations for several key weeks in the spring, could have resulted in a flush of microbes pathogenic to foxtail and possibly other weeds. These microbes killed off the weeds during the key few weeks after planting. It is also known that arthropods can team up with microbes in the soil, either directly consuming or degrading weed seed quality to the point where most seeds do not germinate or cannot thrive (Brust and House, 1988).

Understanding the role of these biological control mechanisms in integrated weed management on the Thompson farm will keep Dick and Sharon, and the researchers collaborating with them, busy for some time. Insights on biological weed management mechanisms are just beginning to emerge. They will need to be augmented by applied field research focusing on what farmers can do to affect microbial community diversity

> In 20 or 30 years, farmers may pay as much attention to the management of microorganisms pathogenic to weeds as they pay today to the selection and application of herbicides.

and population dynamics for weed management. Twenty or 30 years from now, farmers may pay as much attention to the management of microorganisms pathogenic to weed roots as they do now to the selection of herbicides and timing of their application.

It is also likely that in 10 to 20 years weed management systems based largely on microbial biocontrol, coupled with cultivation, will prove both more productive and profitable than today's herbicide-dependent systems, some of which can impair soil quality and lead to carryover injury (topics explored in Chapter 2). Larger and more diverse populations of soil microorganisms will do more than help farmers manage weeds. They make it possible to circulate higher levels of nitrogen and other essential nutrients in the soil, and also enhance the soil's ability to take in and hold water (Hudson, 1994; NRC, 1993b; Bezdicek and Granatstein, 1989; Drinkwater et al., 1995; Jawson et al., 1993).

The Thompsons are helping point the way to weed management systems that will produce higher yields profitably and without increasing agriculture's adverse impacts on the environment. In recognition of their contributions to the science of sustainable agriculture, the Thompsons were selected by the *Des Moines Register* as Iowa's 1996 "Farm Leaders of the Year," one of the state's most prestigious awards.[4]

Leopold Center for Sustainable Agriculture

location http://www.ag.iastate.edu/centers/leopold/Leopold.html

The Leopold Center is located at **Iowa State University**
- Our mission -- to reduce negative impacts of agriculture on resources and communities
- to develop profitable farming systems that conserve natural resources
- to work with ISU Extension and other groups to inform the public of new research findings

LEOPOLD CENTER

Research Programs
Interdisciplinary Research Issue Teams
- Weed Management
- Agroecology

4. Relying on Natural Enemies and Other Beneficials

The Russian wheat aphid first appeared in North America in Mexico around 1980. The insect probably traveled from its homeland in south central Russia by catching a ride in a grain shipment. By 1986 the aphid had reached Texas and by 1990 was well established in 16 western states and three Canadian provinces (U.S. Agricultural Plant Health and Inspection Service [APHIS], 1993c).

USDA scientists felt the Russian wheat aphid was a good candidate for classical biological control, the Department's preferred strategy for dealing with introduced pests, as set forth in the APHIS "Biological Control Philosophy." Adopted August 7, 1992, this policy statement reads in part, "Wherever possible, biological control should replace chemical control as the base strategy for IPM." The full statement is posted on the APHIS World Wide Web site (see page 147), an excellent source of information with links to many other sites addressing biological control and IPM, including urban and home pest management needs.

Consistent with its policy, APHIS began a worldwide search for the natural enemies of Russian wheat aphids. As this effort progressed, millions of pounds of insecticides were sprayed across America's wheat belt with

> As a result of the release of parasitoids and the Fillmore District's commitment to biointensive IPM, insecticides have been needed on only about one percent of the region's citrus acreage to control California red scale.

mixed results and poor economic returns, since wheat is a low-value crop. The aphid has been costly, reducing wheat income $221 million since 1987 and costing farmers some $21 million in insecticide applications (U.S. APHIS, 1993c).

Two new species of predacious ladybug beetles were found in Russia, and experiments started as soon as specimens could be brought through quarantine procedures. USDA scientists had to figure out whether the ladybugs would survive in U.S. wheat growing regions, and how farmers could increase the odds the ladybugs would reach population levels high enough to effectively control the aphids. Experience so far is encouraging but one lesson is clear to APHIS and other USDA scientists: "Widespread and repeated use of insecticides to control the Russian wheat aphid is the greatest hindrance to implementing biological control successfully. Most insecticides are more toxic to natural enemies than to aphids."[5]

Managing Citrus Red Scale

California citrus growers have spent decades fighting the insect red scale (*Aonidiella aurantii*), which causes scarring on the surface of citrus peels. A number of beneficial insects have been used to control red scale, with considerable success over the last 50 years. Organized efforts were initiated in 1922 by the Fillmore Citrus Protection District in Southern California. The first parasitoid released in Fillmore District citrus groves came from South Africa in 1937, and a second from India and Pakistan in the early 1960s (NRC, 1996). A parasitoid is an insect that lays its egg or eggs in or on another insect, and the larva uses the host's resources to develop. Upon emergence, most parasitoids kill their hosts.

Nearly 4.5 billion parasitoids have been released since 1961 in the District and until recently, most were reared in Fillmore's own insectaries. As a result of the release of parasitoids and the District's commitment to biointensive IPM, insecticides have been needed on only about one percent of the region's citrus acreage to control California red scale (NRC, 1996). Pest managers in the Fillmore District were aided by the favorable coastal climate where the District is located. Efforts to use mass-reared parasitoids in other California citrus growing regions have been less successful to date. University

Biological Control

In addition to classical biological control through importation of a predator or parasite, other steps can be taken to increase the diversity and populations of a pest's natural enemies.

Conservation techniques involve steps to avoid killing natural enemies—changes in tillage and farming practices, selection and more careful use of less broad-spectrum pesticides.

Augmentation is another tool, and entails the release of artificially reared populations of natural enemies. Biological control requires the weaving together of these techniques and is often the foundation of successful biointensive IPM systems.

Giving Nature a Helping Hand

When a new orchard or lawn is planted, or when people move into a new environment, it can take time for the biological processes central to biointensive IPM to regain solid footing. IPM systems can get out of balance for one reason or another, including when a new pest gets established or when there is unusual weather. Augmentive release of beneficial organisms is one tactic that can help bring pest populations back down below economic thresholds, especially if release is done early enough to give biological control organisms the time they need to work.

A new industry is emerging that rears and markets a growing range of beneficials. Begun in the 1970s in California, the industry has grown steadily. The first list of suppliers of beneficial organisms was compiled by two USDA scientists in 1977 and appeared in a book on the use of natural enemies (Ridgway and Vinson, 1977). California's pesticide regulatory program issued its first compilation of suppliers of beneficial organisms in 1979 (Hunter, 1979). Additional lists were released in 1981, 1982, 1985, 1989, 1992 and 1994. The list has grown from three pages listing 15 verified suppliers selling about 20 organisms in 1979 to 30 pages and almost 100 U.S. suppliers selling 120 organisms (Hunter, 1992 and 1994; Bezark, 1989; Bezark and Rey, 1982; Brunetti, 1981; Hunter, 1979). Organisms now available include more than 40 species of parasitic wasps, 15 mites and six species of predacious nematodes (Hunter, 1994).[6] Industry sales are now estimated at between $20 million and $50 million a year.[7]

To learn more about the industry, Consumers Union sponsored a survey in cooperation with the Association of Natural Bio-Control Producers (ANBP).[8] Our findings:

- the price per 1,000 predacious mites has declined from about $20.00 in 1980 to between $4.50 for large volume orders and $6.00 for most retail customers in 1995. The price of green lacewings has dropped by half;

- the price of all organisms has trended downward since 1980, with competition cited as the most important reason and increased volume the second most important;

- factors enhancing demand include increased use by consumers and the ornamental plants industry, and the need on many commercial farms to find less risky and less costly alternatives when pests become resistant to pesticides;

- field survivability of released organisms is a major concern in 30 to 50 percent of applications; and

- the average annual rate of growth in industry sales rose from 13 percent between 1986 and 1990, to 25.6 percent between 1991 and 1995.

New methods to raise, transport and release beneficial insects are emerging that will lower the cost of augmentive release as a pest management tactic. Scientific progress also is extending the scope of product lines to include a range of beneficial microorganisms that can play a role in microbial biocontrol of soil borne insects and associated plant pathogens.[9] Lessened reliance on broad-spectrum chemicals will improve the survival rate of beneficials released into fields or back yards, providing farmers and consumers a new and safe tactic to rely on.

researchers, consultants and the citrus industry are now working together to find ways to enhance natural enemy survival.

Statewide, parasitoids are released generally once a year on about one-third of California's 300,000 acres of citrus to control red scale. On each acre, from 10,000 to 120,000 parasitoids are released, costing between $40.00 and $96.00 per acre for the parasitoids and their release (Hoffman et al., 1996; Ridgway and Inscoe, 1996).

Growers relying on a pesticide based control system typically spray two to four times at a cost of about $40.00 to $80.00 per acre and achieve less consistent results (NRC, 1996). According to the NRC in its 1996 report on ecologically based IPM, the Fillmore District has "nearly perfected ecologically based management; as a result their pest management costs are the lowest of any district in California and their fruit quality and quantity among the highest." To extend such opportunities to others, a

The Colorado potato beetle is one of the world's worst insect pests. Only the Green peach aphid is resistant to more insecticides (Vasquez, 1996). Scientists and farmers developing biointensive IPM options find they need several tools to reliably manage this beetle. The fungus Beauveria bassiana (left) shows promise as a biopesticide when tank-mixed with Bt. A large team of scientists and farmer-collaborators in Maine has found that the predatory stinkbug (right) can also play an important role. Compared to conventional plots, the Maine team has dramatically reduced survival of overwintered adult Colorado potato beetles using both these tools in multitactic biological control systems (for details, see Chapter IV. in Alford et al., 1996). Credits: Dr. Matt Liebman, University of Maine

new industry is emerging to supply beneficial insects to farmers and homeowners and is described in the box "Giving Nature a Helping Hand."

B. New Tools Leverage Old Tricks

Information is a common denominator in all successful biointensive IPM systems. In general, the more pest managers rely on biology and prevention, the greater their need for information, coupled with timely and proper translation of that information into field-based action. Computers and telecommunications are lowering the cost of obtaining, analyzing and acting on information about pests, natural enemies, the weather and other factors affecting the performance of pest management systems.

Automated weather stations, electronic soil probes, new diagnostic techniques and advanced physiological models are among the new tools gaining wider use. Particularly encouraging progress has been made with grape IPM systems in California. A significant portion of the state's grape industry is successfully using biointensive IPM and a variety of companies, large and small, are working with farmer-led organizations to accelerate progress.

In partnership with the University of California Statewide IPM Program, growers in Napa, Sonoma and Kern counties have pioneered use of automated weather stations (see photo page 14) linked to computers and

"Over the years, researchers have developed insect models so that growers will know what stage the insect is in and when to spray. Diseases have been much more difficult. They respond to temperature and moisture, and while temperature is easy to measure we have had trouble measuring moisture. Now, there are several weather stations on the market that can measure leaf wetness, so we are looking to refine our disease prediction models."

Joyce Strand, *Coordinator U.C. Statewide IPM Program. Quote from "Weather Watchers," California Farmer (McMullin, 1996)*

"There is no way to maintain competitiveness in national and international markets if certain pesticides...are restricted or if pathogens become resistant to pesticide. Alternative control methods are needed. New, highly effective fungicides have been discovered, but methods for their judicious use to avoid development of resistance and to minimize risk to humans and the environment have not been developed yet...Emerging pathogens and reemerging diseases are increasingly important in plants, just as they are in humans and animals... [Plant] diseases should be recognized as facts of life, and efforts for recognizing and dealing with them should be rewarded, not penalized."

Dr. Sue Tolin, *Presidential Address 87th Annual Meeting of the American Phytopathological Society (Tolin, 1996)*

disease forecasting models developed over many years of effort by teams of U.C. researchers. The original group of 10 grower-collaborators has grown to 25 (McMullin, 1996).

The Statewide IPM Project is working to replicate such networks in all major fruit and vegetable producing regions. Large grants to help fund the effort have been made by the U.S. EPA and California's Department of Pesticide Regulation because of the potential to reduce reliance on and use of fungicides. Cambell Soup Company, a project collaborator in California, has made great strides in Mexico, California and Ohio in applying disease forecasting models in tomato, potato and other crops. Over 20,000 acres of produce under contract to Cambell Soup are managed using a combination of the TomCAST tomato model and the WISDOM potato disease forecasting model (described later in this chapter). Campbell Soup records show that across this acreage fungicide applications have been reduced over 50 percent—from around 10 applications per acre to about 4 (Bolkan and Reinert, 1994; Burnham, 1996).

1. Information Systems Help Shape Timely Field Responses

Potatoes always have been vulnerable to a range of diseases that can be passed on to new farms through infected seed stock. In 1913, scientists at the University of Wisconsin developed a method to produce "true-to-type" potato cultivars that were free of disease, resulting in the nation's first certified potato seed program (Johnson, 1993). This important step forward was the first in a long history of potato IPM innovations pioneered in Wisconsin.

Today, although growers like Steve Diercks take disease-free seed stock as a given, they still face plenty of challenges. Diercks grows 700 acres of potatoes along with rotational crops in Wisconsin's Central Sands region, near Coloma. The region is highly productive but its environment is also very sensitive. The Wisconsin Dells, the state's major water-based recreational area, is nearby as are the breeding grounds for a variety of wildlife, including the Sandhill Crane, the endangered Karner Blue butterfly and wild turkeys. The aquifer underlying most of the land is shallow. In the 1980s, the most acutely toxic pesticide used in America, the insecticide aldicarb (Temik), leached into a significant portion of the region's groundwater, triggering serious health concerns, a drop in real estate values and eventually a ban on aldicarb's use in potato production.[10]

In recent years, the toughest pest management problems facing potato growers worldwide have been caused by a series of hard-to-control strains of early and late blight—common foliar diseases that can devastate potato plants. In 1980, Steve Diercks and most other potato growers had to make about 12 applications of fungicide to control blight diseases, a degree of reliance that raised economic, environmental and food safety concerns. Working with the state's grower association and the University of Wisconsin, Diercks and other farmers were key parts of a team that developed and refined a computer program called WISDOM.

WISDOM contains four major modules:

- Disease Management
- Insect Management
- Irrigation Scheduling
- Weed Management

Developed with financial support from growers, the

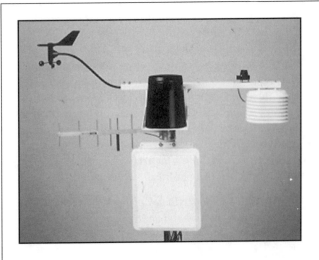

Automated weather stations (left) are increasingly relied upon to collect detailed information on temperature, humidity, wind speed and rainfall. Many such stations feed data back to a centrally located computer running disease forecasting models. Lee Hudson (right) is a grape grower in California's Napa Valley. The weather station in his vineyard transmits data to a base station at the University of California office in Napa. Credits: Left, Davis Instruments; Right, California Farmer

Wisconsin potato farmer Steve Diercks (right) uses the WISDOM computer program to help make a variety of pest management decisions. University of Wisconsin plant pathologist Dr. Walt Stevenson (left) helped develop WISDOM. "Twenty years ago, if a single Colorado potato beetle was spotted in one of our fields, the entire field was sprayed. Now we're able to calculate total degree growing days, and [spray] using WISDOM control guidelines," according to Diercks, who has cut insecticide applications from several per year to one in a typical year.
Credit: Wisconsin Potato and Vegetable Growers Association

state and the U.S. Department of Agriculture, WISDOM has helped make possible about a 40 percent reduction in the quantity of pesticides applied on Wisconsin potato crops between 1980 and 1994.[11]

The analysis of weather conditions and the prediction of the appearance of early blight and late blight has proven a particularly valuable part of WISDOM. Diercks uses WISDOM to determine when to make a first fungicide application and to stretch out the time between applications. It also is invaluable in determining irrigation and weed management practices. During the season, he enters a range of weather data—temperature, relative humidity and rainfall. The program then runs a variety of predictive models that include ways to determine when or whether economic thresholds are likely to be exceeded. Samples of WISDOM output appear on the next page.

Another Challenge

WISDOM is saving Wisconsin growers an estimated $110.00 per acre per year (Johnson, 1993).[12] The state's farmers grow potatoes on about 75,000 acres per year, so WISDOM could save as much as $9 million annually if adopted universally by all growers. Recognizing the importance of incremental development of WISDOM, the Wisconsin Potato and Vegetable Growers Association (WPVGA) currently provides about $400,000 per year for university research from industry check-off funds (personal communication, Dean Zuleger, WPVGA Executive Director).

Diercks and other growers have challenged the

University to extend WISDOM into the complex world of potato root systems and soil fertility. Other key research priorities identified by growers include development of cultivar-specific disease, insect and weed management predictive models, soil nutrient management, methods of enhancing plant health and soil quality through irrigation scheduling and alternative methods to meet the crop's nitrogen needs. It took the university several years to develop and calibrate the models now in the WISDOM program. Several more years will be needed to understand the dynamic interactions affecting healthy root growth and plant development across the variety of soil conditions found in the region. The economic savings could be great, however, as will the reduction in nutrients and pesticides lost to the environment.

The WISDOM system is helping potato farmers accurately predict when conditions are favorable—and unfavorable—for early and late blight disease. This screen from the program reports an actual example from a user's farm in the 1996 production season. Note that the model shows that the "severity value" threshold of 18 has been exceeded, indicating that the temperature and relative humidity has been conducive to blight growth. But since the P-Value threshold ("Physiological Days," a measure of the degree-days of growth of the potato plant) is not exceeded, the model recommends that the grower delay fungicide applications until the P-Day threshold is met. Credit: IPM Program, University of Wisconsin—Extension

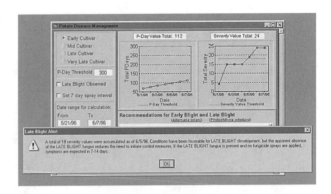

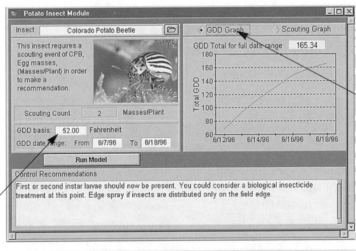

"Growing Degree Days" provide a way to predict insect phenology (the timing of life events and stages).

This is the temperature threshold when scouting should begin for the Colorado potato beetle.

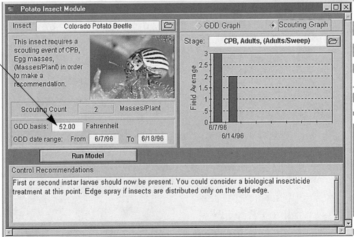

The WISDOM insect pest management module helps growers manage the Colorado potato beetle, a key insect pest wherever potatoes are grown. The control recommendation—"You should consider a biological insecticide"—is based on the combination of "Growing Degree Days" (GDD=165.34) plus the 6/14/96 scouting of the field which found on average 2 beetle egg masses per plant. Through the season, weather and scouting reports will be added into WISDOM weekly and pest population levels will be continuously projected as a way to optimally time pesticide applications and avoid unnecessary sprays. Credit: IPM Program, University of Wisconsin—Extension

2. Searching for Redundancy

Biointensive IPM is the sum of many parts. No one practice or method can be counted on to completely manage a pest problem in any given year, especially since weather conditions and other hard-to-predict factors can so dramatically, and in the case of plant diseases, so quickly cause major losses. Chemical-based systems depend on one or a few pesticides to keep pests below economic thresholds. Because most pesticides act quickly, it is relatively easy to monitor their effectiveness and judge whether and when an additional treatment is needed and economical.

Biopesticides and biointensive IPM often take longer to work. It is generally harder to predict pest population dynamics and natural enemy interactions and growers usually have fewer options to rescue a crop if biological interventions fail to keep up with pest pressure. For this reason, IPM systems that rely minimally on pesticides require a degree of redundancy in managing pests both on the farm and in urban settings.

Examples of combinations of practices and tactics that might provide redundancy include selecting resistant plant varieties, using rotations and different tillage systems to reduce weed and disease pressure, maintaining high levels of soil microbial activity coupled with attention to key microorganisms, encouraging overwintering of beneficials and when needed, release of beneficial organisms, and timely application of biopesticides.

C. The IPM Continuum

Integrated pest management systems range from largely dependent on pesticides to those that rarely, if ever, require chemical treatment. The diversity in IPM systems is driven by soils, climate, the nature of pest problems, the state of technology, the skill of pest managers and their commitment to biological approaches. IPM is often referred to as a *dynamic* systems approach to pest management because it must change with the seasons and rise to the challenge posed by pests that find ways to adapt and thrive.

IPM systems can be thought of as falling along a continuum. In the shift from chemical-intensive to biointensive IPM, reliance on treatment-oriented interventions with pesticides drops and reliance on prevention-based, biological practices increases. Hence, *reliance* is the distinguishing characteristic in placing pest management strategies and systems along the IPM continuum.

Evolution of the IPM Continuum

In a series of workshops on constraints to IPM adoption in 1993 sponsored by the National Foundation for Integrated Pest Management Education (Sorensen, 1994), Dr. Steve Balling, an IPM specialist with Del Monte Foods, was among the first to use the concept of an IPM continuum in helping growers think through steps needed to make incremental progress toward biointensive IPM (Balling, 1994). Balling's continuum ran from "Conventional" chemical-based pest management systems to "Systems Pest Management" reliant on information and biological controls.

Dr. Polly Hoppin and colleagues in the World Wildlife Fund's (WWF) pollution prevention program further developed the concept of an IPM continuum in 1994 and 1995, incorporating pollution prevention and source reduction concepts in the course of a project focusing on reducing pesticide use and risks in the Great Lakes Basin (Hoppin et al., 1996; Hoppin, 1996). In 1995, WWF sponsored a series of stakeholder meetings on IPM measurement issues, and carried out an empirical application to weed management in corn and soybean production in the Midwest (Benbrook, 1996).

In 1994, the USDA formalized and applied the continuum concept in quantifying IPM adoption, a project described in detail in Chapter 7 (Vandeman et al., 1994). The department divided pest management systems into five categories—"Not Classified," no IPM and three levels of IPM adoption, each characterized by progressively greater reliance on basic IPM and biologically based pre-

---

Biointensive IPM

Full discussion of the IPM continuum and what we mean by biointensive IPM appears in Chapter 7. Because the term "biointensive IPM" features so prominently throughout the report, we preview here our definition:

Biointensive IPM is a systems approach to pest management that is based on an understanding of pest ecology. It relies on resistant varieties and promoting plant health, crop rotation, disrupting pest reproduction, and the management of biological processes to diversify and build populations of beneficial organisms. Reduced risk pesticides, including biopesticides, are used only as a last resort and only in ways that minimize risks.

ventive practices. Analyses of the USDA measurement methodology carried out by CU and WWF in 1995 contributed to the evolution of the IPM continuum and measurement methods now used by both organizations.

1. Four Zones Along the Continuum

In analyzing stages of IPM adoption, goal setting and monitoring progress, we divide the IPM continuum into four zones or levels:

■ "No IPM" systems are largely dependent on pesticides and include few if any preventive practices. Scouting and other practices needed to use pesticides cost-effectively don't constitute "IPM." They must be accompanied by some preventive measures to move into the "Low IPM" zone.

■ "Low Level IPM" systems include scouting and application in accord with economic thresholds, proper timing and operation of spray equipment, and also some preventive practices. Such systems still remain reliant on pesticides to a significant degree.

■ "Medium Level IPM" systems incorporate multitactic preventive measures, coupled with efforts to enhance populations of beneficial organisms, especially by cutting back on use of broad-spectrum and persistent pesticides. Preventive measures assume a major portion of the pest management burden, markedly lessening reliance on pesticides.

■ "Biointensive IPM" systems (also called "High Level IPM") rely primarily on preventive practices that limit pest pressure, diversify and build populations of beneficial organisms, and enhance plant defenses and vigor. Pesticides are used only as a last resort and broad-spectrum, ecologically disruptive products are avoided at all times.

The IPM continuum is portrayed graphically in Figure 7.1 on page 190. As progress is made along the continuum, both the quantity and the nature of scouting and other information needed to make IPM work change.

Biointensive IPM is information and management intensive. It depends upon the management of habitats and biodiversity within buildings, in backyards and agroecosystems, both above and below the ground. Access to a steady supply of resistant plant and tree varieties has played a critical role in the past and will become even more vital in the future. Biointensive IPM weaves tools and tactics together in patterns suggested by timely observation and the principles of biology and ecology. Done with skill, it minimizes reliance on pesticides first by preventing pest problems and second by working with natural processes and interactions to limit pest damage.

In urban settings, indoors and in agriculture and forestry, pest problems are not going away nor are difficult pesticide choices. As we deal with both, incremental progress toward biointensive IPM will provide farmers, land managers and consumers better ways to manage pests and society less risky choices, and for these reasons it will be worth the effort and investment that is now needed to collectively accelerate progress along the IPM continuum.

[1] The precise number depends on tree size, openness of the canopy, weather and codling moth population numbers.

[2] In addition, growers that shift to biopesticides may experience, for a period of time, greater problems caused by secondary pests previously controlled by organophosphate and synthetic pyrethroid insecticides applied to deal with primary pests like the codling moth. Accordingly, dealing with such secondary pest species that emerge as primary pests is sometimes a part of the transition to biointensive IPM.

[3] Cited in "Reduced Chemical Management of Fleas," part of a consumer guide to indoor pest management on the Internet that is part of the "National IPM Network" (see several Web page boxes). Suggestions for non-chemical flea control are found on the University of Florida web site accessible at http://hammock.ifas.ufl.edu/tmp/reducefl.html.

[4] The article announcing the award provides an overview of the Thompson farm, the birth of the Practical Farmers of Iowa, and a review of several cooperative research projects that have been carried out on the farm. The article appeared in the February 11, 1996, *Des Moines Register*.

[5] "Biological Control of the Russian Wheat Aphid" (U.S. APHIS, 1993c) is one of several informative pamphlets available from APHIS. The APHIS World Wide Web site has an extensive list of IPM and biocontrol resources available to the public, most free of charge (see the box on page 147 for how to access the APHIS WWW page).

[6] The most recent list can be obtained by writing for "Suppliers of Beneficial Organisms" to the Department of Pesticide Regulation, 1020 N Street, Room 161, Sacramento, California 95814-5624.

[7] Estimate attributed to the California Department of Pesticide Regulation and reported in "The Booming Bug Eats Bug Industry," in *Business Magazine*, January/February, 1995.

[8] Survey results provided in a March 11, 1996, letter to Charles Benbrook from Maclay Burt, Executive Director of the ANBP. Respondents collectively account for more than 85 percent of industry sales.

[9] For a review of a wide range of emerging technologies, see "Biologically Based Pest Controls: Markets, Industries, and Products," a background paper by three USDA scientists prepared for the Congressional Office of Technology Assessment (Ridgway et al, 1994); and (Hoffman et al., 1996).

[10] EPA decided in 1995 to reinstate the potato use of aldicarb, a move opposed by the Wisconsin Potato and Vegetable Growers Association. The association and academic experts in the state are advising growers not to use aldicarb because of its excessive risks to wildlife, farmers and applicators, and water quality.

[11] For more on the development of WISDOM and its importance, see "Clean Water and Clear Profits" (Johnson, 1993).

[12] Data compiled by and available from Dr. Walt Stevenson, Department of Plant Pathology, University of Wisconsin-Madison.

Urban IPM - University of Florida

location http://hammock.ifas.ufl.edu/en.html

Urban Integrated Pest Management

IPM

"This manual on pests in and around the home, is a compilation of information on biology, identification, and pest management practices for urban pests. By learning about these specific pests it should be possible to reduce pesticide use in the home. The reduced pesticide use should improve the health and safety of our families and the Florida environment."

"University of Florida, Institute of Food and Agricultural Sciences"

- **Urban Pests and Pest Management**
  - Lawn Insect Pests
  - Structural Insect Pests
  - Biting and Stinging Insects
  - Fabric and Wood-Destroying Pests
  - Insects Around Food
  - Occasional Invaders
- **Using Pesticides Safely**
- **How To Buy Pest Control Services**
- **Insect Identification**
  - Identification Laboratory.

Tree of Life

location   http://ag.arizona.edu/ENTO/tree/phylogeny.html

The Tree of Life

A distributed Internet project containing information about phylogeny and biodiversity

Discussion of Phylogenetic Relationships
References

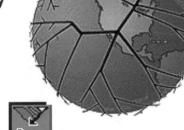

```
                        ===== Megaloptera (dobsonflies and fishflies)
                        |
              ===|==== Raphidioptera (snakeflies)
    ======|    |
          |    |   ===== Neuroptera (lacewings, antlions, etc.)
          |    ======= Coleoptera (beetles)
          |
          |         ?= Strepsiptera (twisted-wing parasites)
          |
  <<===|      ======= Hymenoptera (wasps, bees, ants)
          |    |
          |    |      == Trichoptera (caddisflies)
          |    |  ===|
          |    |   |  == Lepidoptera (moths and butterflies)
  Containing clade(s): Neoptera
```

Blister beetle (Eukaryotes, Coleoptera)
Photograph © 1995, David Maddison

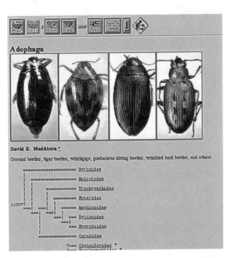

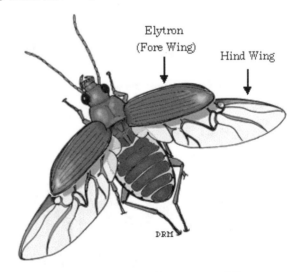

Elytron
(Fore Wing)

Hind Wing

DRM

Tree of Life design and icons copyright © 1996 David Maddison and Wayne Maddison.

Pesticide Use and Reliance

Searching for simple solutions to pest problems, many Americans have grown excessively reliant on pesticides. As a result, the effectiveness of pesticides is slipping and risks are rising.

Viable systems for controlling pests using far less pesticides exist for many crops and home pest problems. New biologically based pest management products, techniques and systems are emerging across the country that will make biointensive Integrated Pest Management (IPM) systems both more reliable and more affordable. Yet chemical pesticides remain the dominant method of pest control in the United States.

Just how dominant is the subject of this Chapter. Here we introduce the concept of reliance and the linkages between pest management systems, reliance and pesticide use. Some observers have noted declines in recent years in the pounds of pesticides applied—soybean herbicides, for example—and many assume that a reduction in the pounds applied translates into comparable reductions in reliance and pesticide risks. This is not necessarily the case. A common way to reduce pounds of pesticide applied is to switch to a more potent and persistent product that works at a lower rate. But as a result of doing so, other risks can be triggered— impacts on aquatic ecosystems or soil organisms, for example. This is why reducing reliance on all pesticides is a critical goal and why pesticide risks need to be evaluated holistically per acre or area treated, not simplistically as a function only of the pounds of pesticides applied.

In this chapter we describe and apply methods to measure pesticide use and reliance. We find that reliance on pesticides has been on the increase for twenty years. More applications are being made per acre of farmland and in and around the home, and on average, a greater number of different active ingredients are needed to manage pests effectively. Indeed, the quantity of pesticides applied in many settings is still rising.

Industry Structure

The pesticide manufacturing and formulation industry is dominated by corporate giants. The top six companies accounted for 67.4 percent of total industry sales in 1995

> **Reliance on pesticides has risen steadily for decades. The impacts of pesticides on beneficial organisms have triggered new pests and made old ones tougher to control. These new problems require more treatments and soon farmers find themselves on the pesticide treadmill.**

(American Crop Protection Association [ACPA], 1996). The top dozen account for more than 90 percent of total pesticide sales. Mergers, acquisitions and new partnerships have reduced the number of pesticide producers to about 16 and have brought much of the seed industry under the control of pesticide manufacturers (Gianessi, 1995). The most recent merger, between Sandoz and Ciba, created Novartis, the world's largest agrichemical company with combined sales of more than $4.4 billion in 1995—almost double those of its next largest competitor, Monsanto (Gianessi, 1995).

There are about 100 other major firms that produce active ingredients and formulate end-use products (formulation entails chemical processes that combine active ingredients with "inert" ingredients, producing either a granular, dust, liquid or other sort of end-use product). Another 2,200 companies purchase pesticide active ingredients from basic producers, then formulate the ingredients into end-use products ready for homes and industries. A third group of 7,300 companies manufactures specialized pesticide products, typically for niche markets and specific applications. About 17,200 distributors market the pesticides that are sold in thousands of retail outlets (Aspelin, 1994). Between 35,000 and 40,000 commercial pest management firms employ some 351,000 certified applicators and provide pesticide application services to the public, industry and government sectors. A growing portion of these firms are offering an array of services along with product sales and custom application, including record-keeping, scouting and assistance in use of precision farming techniques (Hoffman, 1993).

Some 1.3 million individuals are certified to apply restricted use pesticides in the U.S., nearly 1 million of them farmers (Aspelin, 1994). Gaining certification requires attending a training course and periodic continuing education activities. When EPA finds that a pesticide may pose unacceptable risks to applicators, the environ-

Pesticides are manufactured at large facilities often located near oil refineries and rivers or the ocean. Pollution near plants and exposure among plant workers are among the problems heightened by pesticide-dependent pest management systems. Credit: Colorado State University

pet shampoos, flea collars, powders and products to control mice and rats (Whitmore et al., 1992).

In agriculture, forestry, mosquito control and aquatic weed management, a surprising number of people routinely come into contact with pesticides on the job at least part of each year. Pesticides are applied annually on some 900,000 farms and ranches over most cultivated cropland and a portion of pasture land (Aspelin, 1994). Millions of acres of public and private forests, Christmas tree farms and other wooded areas are treated with herbicides as part of reforestation efforts or with insecticides to control the Spruce budworm, Gypsy moth or other pests. Several million farmers, custom applicators, farm workers, water district workers and government employees come into contact with pesticides during normal workdays during part of the year, and in some cases, during much of the year.

Expenditures

Pesticides are a major U.S. industry and sales are booming worldwide as well—up 11.9 percent in the last year to $29 billion.[1] According to preliminary EPA estimates, some 1.25 billion pounds of pesticide active ingredients were sold in 1995 in the U.S., costing users $10.42 billion. Seventy-six percent of sales were to the agricultural sector, 12 percent to other industries and government and 12 percent to homeowners and gardeners (Aspelin, 1996).[2] Pesticide manufacturers in the U.S. also exported $2.2 billion in products and imported $1.7 billion in pesticide products, according to the American Crop Protection Association, the industry's major trade association (ACPA, 1996).

ment or the public, the agency can classify the pesticide for "Restricted Use." These pesticides then may be applied lawfully only by certified applicators or those working directly under a certified applicator's supervision.

And last, but most important, there are tens of millions of consumers of pesticides. Some four billion times a year, consumers apply pesticides in and around their homes. The average American home contains an inventory of three or four pest control products out of a possible 20,000 available in the consumer market: aerosols for flying insects, sprays for ants, traps and poisons for rodents and other small mammals, kitchen and bathroom anti-mold sprays, lawn and garden products,

American Crop Protection Association

location http://www.acpa.org/

Information on the following topics is available:

The Delaney Clause

Endocrine Disruption

- Statement on Endocrine, Chemicals and the Environment
- Endocrine, Chemicals and the Environment: A Research Database
- Suspected causes of a purported decline in male fertility
- Carcinogens and Anticarcinogens in the Human Diet
- Hormonal Effects: Pesticide Testing
- Breast Cancer

What's New?

"July 24, 1996 - The American Crop Protection Association praises the comprehensive food safety action taken by the U.S. House of Representatives in passing the bi-partisan "Food Quality Protection Act of 1996", by a 417-0 vote."

The ACPA survey reports that 84.2 percent of total U.S. expenditures for pesticides was in the agricultural sector in 1995. "Home and Garden" sales make up the largest segment outside of agriculture—slightly less than $400 million in 1995 (ACPA, 1996). Total industry sales grew 10.6 percent between 1994 and 1995, with domestic sales rising 7.8 percent and export sales growing 21.7 percent.

Pesticide sales have increased steadily in most years despite a reduction in the total pounds of active ingredients applied. This is due to stable or rising costs per acre treated with low dose insecticides and herbicides that sell for much more per pound—or ounce—than the products they replace (Gianessi, 1995; Gianessi and Anderson, 1993; Mayerfeld et al., 1996). Today, some pesticide active ingredients are nearly worth their weight in gold, and a few are worth more.[3]

The 1995 ACPA industry survey includes interesting data on pesticide expenditure levels and recent trends:

- herbicides purchased by corn farmers made up almost 24 percent of total agricultural sales of all pesticides. Soybean herbicides accounted for another 21 percent.

> **Some pesticide active ingredients are nearly worth their weight in gold, and a few are worth more.**

- cotton farmers spent $550 million on insecticides— slightly less than 43 percent of total agricultural insecticide expenditures. Insecticide expenditures by cotton producers rose 43.1 percent from 1994 to 1995—evidence of serious problems with chemical-intensive cotton insect management systems in Texas, California and much of the South and ill-fated boll weevil eradication program efforts (see Chapter 6 for details).

- fungicide expenditures are the fastest growing segment of non-agricultural markets, growing 15.9 percent from 1994 to 1995.

- nursery and ornamental operations cut insecticide expenditures by 14.1 percent from 1994 to 1995, an accomplishment not matched by turf managers (expenditures up 4.2 percent), pest control operators (up 13 percent) or homeowners (up 1.4 percent).

Since 1979, total expenditures on pesticides have risen from $4.83 billion to $10.42 billion (according to EPA)—a 116 percent increase over 16 years, or about 5 percent

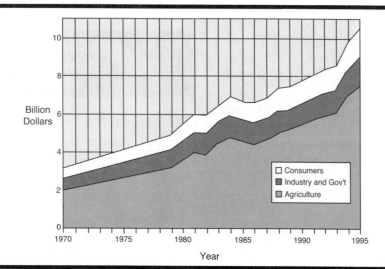

Figure 2.1 Pesticide Expenditures in the U.S. By Sector: 1970 through 1995

* Nominal dollars (i.e., not adjusted for inflation).
Source: 1970 to 1979 extrapolated from USDA data, 1979-1993 from (Aspelin, 1994); 1994-1995, from (Aspelin, 1996). See also Appendix 1 for details on data sources and projection methods.

Aerial application was an important innovation in pesticide delivery technology and lowered the cost and time required to apply pesticides. For the first time, tall crops like corn and sugarcane could be sprayed economically late in the season. Aerial application is a dangerous profession and can cause problems when pesticides drift onto surrounding crops, water bodies or into suburban areas.
Credit: Richard Steven Street

annually. Adjusted for inflation, pesticide expenditures have grown about 3 percent annually. Figure 2.1 presents total pesticide expenditures by major sector since 1970, drawing on USDA and EPA data (Aspelin, 1996).

Farmers and ranchers, in particular, are spending more on pesticides. Between 1983 and 1993, EPA data show that agricultural expenditures on pesticides rose almost 35 percent (Aspelin, 1994). In 1991, the $5.7 billion that farmers spent on pesticides was 3.9 percent of total production costs, a share which rose to 4.2 percent two years later (Aspelin, 1994).

Costs have risen the most in regions and crops where pest resistance to chemicals and secondary pest problems have drawn farmers onto the "pesticide treadmill," a phrase coined by Dr. Robert van den Bosch in the late 1970s to describe rising reliance on pesticides in several California crops (van den Bosch, 1978). Pesticide expenditures of several hundred dollars per acre remain common on farms producing fruits and vegetables and ornamental crops.

In most row crops (those generally planted in rows like corn, sorghum and cotton), pesticide expenditures typically fall between $20.00 and $50.00 per acre. Herbicides now account for about 17 percent of average variable corn production costs and 30 percent of average

variable soybean production costs nationwide (Swinton and King, 1994; Liebman et al., 1996). In addition, Iowa State University cost of production data show herbicide expenditures rising as a portion of total cash production expenditures, while net returns to corn and soybean production have fallen. A 1993 Iowa State University study estimated that corn producers using conventional farming systems spent an average $27.06 per acre on herbicides and insecticides (Bultena et al., 1993). The same study found that farmers who identified their production systems as sustainable spent an average $8.63 per acre on pesticides.

Herbicides account for 65 percent of farms' total pesticide expenditures—more than three times the share for insecticides. Consumers and homeowners, on the other hand, are far more likely to purchase and apply insecticide products, which account for almost 72 percent of 1993 sales to the home and garden market (Aspelin, 1994). Homeowner expenditures on lawn and garden products rose almost 44 percent between 1983 and 1993.

Biological Options: A Small But Growing Slice of the Market

Biological pest management options encompass reduced-risk biopesticides, beneficial organisms and other biologically based pest management products and services. Together, these pest management products, inputs and approaches make up a small but growing share of expenditures. Biopesticide and beneficial organisms sales reached about $188 million in 1991, or about 2.6 percent of total pesticide sales, according to USDA pest

Biopesticides and Biologically Based Pest Management Products and Inputs

"**B**iologically based materials ... are those of natural origin or that are nature-identical, and are divided into the following product groups: bacteria, viruses, fungi, nematodes, mass-reared arthropods [beneficial insects], microbially produced toxins [e.g. *Bt*], behavior-modifying chemicals [e.g. pheromones], botanical insecticides, and transgenic plants. However, it should be emphasized that these products represent only a portion of the tactics that might be considered as alternatives to conventional pesticides (Ridgway et al., 1994)."

Pesticides are also used to treat external insect parasites that can attack cattle, sheep and horses. These cattle are moving through a dipping vat containing the insecticide coumaphos to control ticks.
Credit: Agricultural Research Service

management specialists (Ridgway et al., 1994). The definition used by Ridgway and colleagues in the cited paper, "Biologically Based Pest Controls: Markets, Industries, and Products," appears on page 34.

A 1995 study by the Freedonia Group projects that biopesticide sales (not including beneficial organisms) will increase by more than 20 percent annually from 1995 to 2000 (*Chemical and Engineering News*, 1996). Some 45 microbial biopesticides are now registered, along with more than three dozen pheromones, about 30 low risk natural floral lures or repellents and five natural insect growth regulators (data from Poster Number 52 presented at Third Annual National IPM Forum, EPA, 1996e).

Steady growth is expected in the years ahead as the supply of biopesticides extends into key new agricultural and consumer markets. The rate of growth will be determined by the degree of changes in public and private sector pest management research priorities and whether a national commitment is made to help and reward pest managers moving along the IPM continuum (see Chapter 9 for projections through the year 2020 of pesticide and biopesticide sales under status quo and policy change scenarios).

A. Reliance: A Key Concept

The need to manage pests, and hence reliance on pest management practices and systems, is determined by several things including the pests present in an environment, the presence of ample habitat, food and moisture for them, whether their natural enemies are well established, and how people have managed pests in the past. Reliance can be defined broadly as "the need for pest management interventions." Reliance is often defined more narrowly—for example, reliance on pesticides, or

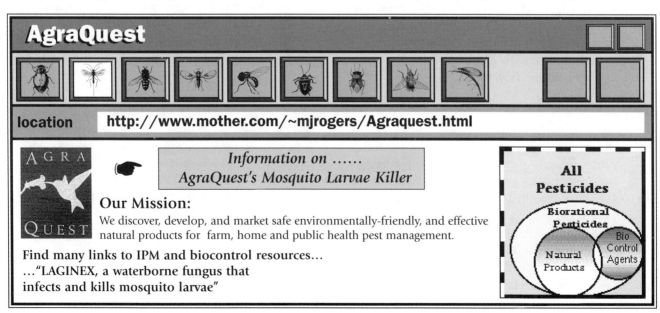

on mechanical cultivation to control weeds, or on periodic bathing of pets to treat fleas.

Pesticide *use,* measured in pounds, is not the same thing as pesticide *reliance.* A pest manager might use only a few ounces of a pesticide in a particular situation, but if nothing else is done to avoid or manage the target pest, reliance on pesticides would still be complete. Decisions pest managers make can have long term effects on reliance on pesticides—how near a wetland or river one chooses to live, what fruits and vegetables are grown in a backyard garden and whether pest-resistant varieties of trees, lawn grasses or shrubs are selected when undertaking landscaping projects.

1. Pesticides Can Create Problems and Heighten Reliance

Applying pesticides without care and knowledge of pest physiology can do more harm than good, and can lead to even greater reliance. Several of today's major pests started out as relatively innocuous and progressed to pest status only after pesticide use created an ecological vacuum in which they were able to thrive (Olkowski et al., 1991; NRC, 1986, 1996). Poorly timed and excessive insecticide use, in particular, has drawn many pest managers onto the pesticide treadmill (Metcalf, 1993). According to Dr. Robert Hall, an entomologist associated with the University of Guelph in the Canadian province of Ontario:

> "During the 1940s, 1950s and 1960s great reliance was placed on pesticides to control insects, mites and fungi. Pesticides were so effective, however, that growers relied on them to the exclusion of other pest control practices. This led to the overuse of pesticides and the emergence of several problems."[4]

In a policy paper on IPM, the World Bank is more blunt:

> "Since the 1940s, pest management technology has increasingly relied on chemical pesticides. Although in some cases this use has led to significant short term alleviation of pest problems, it has not led to long term sustainable solutions. In fact, it has often led to further pest problems, putting farmers in a vicious cycle of pests and pesticides, and increasing the burden on the environment."[5]

A recent assessment of pest management in Iowa explains why Midwestern farmers have become so reliant on pesticides, especially herbicides for weed management:

> "From about 1960 to 1980, pesticides offered farmers a way to reduce the risks of pest damage with little need for precise management. 'Cookbook' pest control was possible because of the availability of wide-spectrum, persistent pesticides that could be applied at high rates. Use of wide-spectrum pesticides meant that one or two products could control all the producer's pest problems; persistent products meant they could be applied at a convenient time for the farmer and did not have to be timed precisely to changing pest stages; and high rates meant that the recommended application was likely to be effective regardless of soil properties, pest conditions or weather." (Mayerfeld et al., 1996)

Reliance Is Still High

Since the 1960s the pesticide treadmill has remained a recurrent feature of pest management in America, with cotton production the most dramatic example in recent years.

Cotton farmers in Texas lost more than $150 million in 1995 because of poorly timed use of insecticides (see Chapter 6 for details). California cotton yields in 1995 dropped by more than 20 percent despite a doubling of the number of insecticide applications and a large increase in expenditures per acre (Rehman, 1996). Indeed, most major cotton growing regions in 1995 experienced serious losses despite unusually heavy pesticide use. An insect pest management crisis committee was formed in Louisiana to develop an action plan to save the industry and better manage resistance. As noted earlier, cotton insecticide expenditures nationwide jumped a remarkable 43.1 percent from 1994 to 1995 (ACPA, 1996).

Problems persist across much of the cotton belt in 1996. Recent increases in bollworm populations in sev-

> *"Most importantly, however, California farmers need to limit or reverse our dependence on synthetic pesticides for our own purposes (as opposed to limiting consumer health concerns). Management flexibility, cost of application, cost of product, pest resistance, preservation of beneficial insects, regulatory control, are each serious considerations and these alone should motivate our industry towards less pesticide dependence, particularly as to high risk products."*
>
> **Mr. William Thomas,** *Attorney representing agricultural industry clients*[7]

The pea leafminer has emerged as a major pest in California's Salinas Valley in large part because of insecticides applied for other pests. Here, Cooperative Extension entomologist Bill Chaney inspects a celery plant for leafminer damage. Credit: Burnham Media Services

eral states have led Monsanto Co., developer of cotton varieties manufacturing their own *Bacillus thuringiensis* (*Bt*), to advise growers to be ready to spray despite planting *Bt*-transgenic cotton (Kaiser, 1996). Monsanto has reported that 20,000 acres of *Bt* cotton had failed as of early July, with the most difficult period for insect pest management still to come in many regions. (See Chapters 6 and 8 for more discussion of *Bt* cotton).

Many vegetable producers also have fallen victim to the pesticide treadmill. In California's Salinas Valley, vegetable growers are dealing with a new pest, the pea leafminer (sometimes called the serpentine leafminer). Insecticide expenditures by lettuce growers rose from between $275 to $300 an acre in 1989 to roughly $600 last year, an increase attributed "almost entirely to the pea leafminer," according to University of California entomologist Dr. Bill Chaney. He offered the following warning in a story appearing in California's major farm magazine, *California Farmer*:[6]

> "Desperate growers continue to use pyrethroids, but these chemicals are simply not effective. They kill some adults, but not enough to do any good, and the good is outweighed by the predators (beneficial insects) that are killed."

B. Indicators of Pesticide Use and Reliance

Use of pesticides is generally measured by the quantity of active ingredient applied on a crop or in a given geographic region, such as in a state or even a backyard. Some pesticides are applied once a year, others are sprayed as often as every few days. Insecticides and fungicides are applied on average three to five times per growing season on fruit and vegetable crops, although fungicides are sometimes applied a dozen or more times to ward off aggressive fungal pathogens. Reliance on fungicides varies much more widely than on herbicides. Use is highest in humid regions where warmth and moisture can provide pathogens ideal conditions for rapid growth, and is typically modest in dry western regions where irrigation is used to just meet crop water needs.

Reliance and use are higher where most of an area needs to be sprayed, or where several applications must be made in most years to deal with a pest. Lower reliance and use occurs where only parts of an area, such as a forest, field or building, need to be treated (spot-spraying) or where a given class of pests create only occasional problems. Certain lawn or ornamental diseases, for example, occur only in dry areas and others only in wet years.

Multiple Measures Needed

A full understanding of reliance on and use of pesticides requires several different measurements. One set of indicators focuses on treatment-oriented measures of pesticide use—the quantity of pesticides applied on a given area and pounds applied per acre. Other measures relate to the frequency and intensity of use in a given area. Basic measures of use include:

■ *Pounds Applied*—the sum of pounds of an individual active ingredient, class of ingredients or all pesticides applied on a crop (or crops) in a given area.

■ *Rate of Application*—pounds active ingredient (a.i.) applied per square foot of lawn, acre of cropland or unit area treated (such as per tree in an orchard or per cubic foot in a storage facility).

■ *Percent Area Treated*—the percent of an area that is sprayed with a type of pesticide, or the portion of a structure that is treated.

■ *Area- or Acre-treatments*—the number of applications of a single pesticide or type of pesticide in a given area or on a given acre.

■ *Products Applied*—the number of distinct active ingredients needed to deal with pests at a given location.

Other Indicators

Additional measures are useful in assessing different circumstances and overall pest management system performance, including efficacy, cost and environmental impacts. These indicators or measures include:

■ *Treatment Frequency*—the time between applications of a given type of pesticide.

■ *Percent Expenditures*—expenditures on pesticides as a percent of total production expenses or as a percent of total pest management expenditures.

■ *Relative Toxicity and Persistence*—the relative toxicity and persistence of pesticides applied.

We refer to such measures in several places throughout this book and stress the need for better methods and data to calculate toxicity-adjusted measures of pesticide use and reliance.

Measuring Reliance

Reliance on pesticides is the sum of reliance on herbicides, insecticides, fungicides, and other pesticides such as algicides and rodenticides.[8]

Whether in the home, a school or on a farm, certain combinations of factors arise periodically—unusual weather or emergence of a new pest—that can cause pest populations to swell. During such periods, reliance on pest management interventions in general, and pesticides in particular, can increase for a period of time. Hence, reliance should be monitored over several years. When reliance on pest management interventions increases during several years in a decade but rarely declines much, it is a sign that changes in the ecology of a farming system, or in a backyard, have made it easier for pests to thrive.

Reliance on pesticides is complete, or nearly so, where little or no effort is made other than applying pesticides to deal with pest management challenges. As reliance on pesticides falls, reliance on other sorts of pest management interventions typically rises. Knowledge of pest biology and life cycles, habitat needs and food sources is essential in order to reduce reliance on pesticides.

The methods used and data needed to measure pesticide use and reliance change under different circumstances and as a function of the questions people are hoping to answer with the data collected. If a farmer is trying to reduce pest losses or pest management costs along the edges of an orchard, or just in certain parts of a field, he or she generally need only assess the factors contributing to problems managing pests in those locations.

But when analysts try to determine the most cost-effective way to reduce herbicide contamination in a specific watershed or aquifer, additional data on natural resource conditions and land use, and more policy and management options will warrant study. A different set of

In California's Central Coast region, the damaging insect Phylloxera *has invaded many vineyards, where it attacks grape root systems, cutting yields and eventually killing plants. Grape growers in many parts of the state have spent millions replanting vineyards where* Phylloxera *has become established because there is no effective chemical or biological treatment for this pest. But in the Central Coast region, some growers have discovered that by spoon-feeding water and nutrients to plants through drip irrigation systems, the loss in grape yields can be limited and the life of infected vineyards extended (Oltman, 1996). Drip irrigation also helps conserve water and electricity, and reduces costs.*
Credit: Richard Steven Street

Measures of reliance must take into account unusual circumstances that can heighten pest pressure from year to year. In the 1996 production cycle, pear growers in California struggled with fire blight, a bacterial disease that is a minor problem in most years. But a wet spring in 1996 provided ideal conditions for the bacterium and many pest managers had to intensify pesticide applications and non-chemical interventions to limit spread and damage. Here, workers on the Greene and Hemly Ranch (see Chapter 1) are trimming branches infected with fire blight, the only practical way to save trees once infection is established. The skill and care of trimming crews becomes a critical factor in catching all branches showing signs of infection and avoiding even worse problems in future years.
Credit: Richard Steven Street

data and measures will be needed to understand the links between changes in weed management systems and herbicide use, run-off patterns within the watershed, leaching potential and water quality. And then, as water quality program administrators in Washington and state capitals assess where to target funding appropriated to lower herbicide contamination of drinking water, they will need even more aggregated data and a different set of measures capturing interactions between farm markets and policy, weed management and reliance on herbicides, contamination levels and risks, at the state and regional levels.

1. Consumer Pesticide Use

Consumers spend a lot on pesticides and pest management—almost $400 million on products in 1995 (ACPA, 1996) and a few billion more for pest management services to control termites, treat lawns and cope with other pests. However, much less is known about pesticide use in and around the home than about pesticide use in agriculture. To fill this gap, the EPA commissioned a "National Home and Garden Pesticide Use Survey" in the late 1980s (Whitmore et al., 1992). The data collected provide the most detailed snapshot available of consumer pesticide use. This EPA-sponsored

report is the source of facts in this section unless otherwise noted.

Pesticides at Home

About 85 percent of U.S. households had one or more pesticide products in the home in the late 1980s. Most kept three to five pesticide products on hand. Single-family households stored about three times more products, on average, than households in multiple family dwellings.

Some people are careless in storing pesticides in and around the home. The home use survey explored access to pesticides by children, defining a product as "securely stored" if it is locked in a room, in a child-proof cabinet or stored more than four feet off the floor. Almost half of the households with children under five had at least one pesticide stored insecurely. This finding helps explain why poison control centers typically get more calls involving possible pesticide poisoning of children than any other category.

Most pesticides in the home are packaged in the form of ready-to-use containers or concentrates. The major form of disposal is throwing empty or partially used containers in the trash. But many consumers—six percent of households—do not dispose of pesticide products because people do not know how to do so safely.

The sting of a fire ant (left) is painful and sometimes triggers allergic reactions. Multiple bites can be fatal. This troublesome pest can also cause real problems for mowing equipment used in farm fields and pastures, since the mounds (right) can be over 12 inches in height. Credits: USDA

Some of these products contain pesticides that are now banned. In the late 1980s, an estimated one million households, for example, still stored products containing chlordane; 150,000 had products with DDT; 70,000 had heptachlor; and 85,000 stored the herbicide Silvex (a formulation of 2,4,5,-T that is known to contain dioxin as an impurity).

About 80 percent of American households have lawns. Approximately eight million households use a commercial lawn care service. When surveyed, half of consumers using lawn care services remembered receiving written notification stating when pesticides were applied in their yards and addressing the safety precautions that should be taken.

Another two million lawns are treated with pesticides by a non-household member (but not by a lawn care company), with products bought off the shelf at hardware stores or garden supply centers. Consumer lawn care products and the formulations applied by lawn care companies tend to be mixtures of fertilizer and herbicides, insecticides and sometimes fungicides. By selling a few common mixtures, the industry keeps costs down, but on the downside, many applications include one or more active ingredients not really needed on a particular lawn, or only marginally useful in many areas.

Almost one-fifth of all households (16.5 million) had homes commercially treated for indoor pests. Only 23.5 percent of these households got written notification

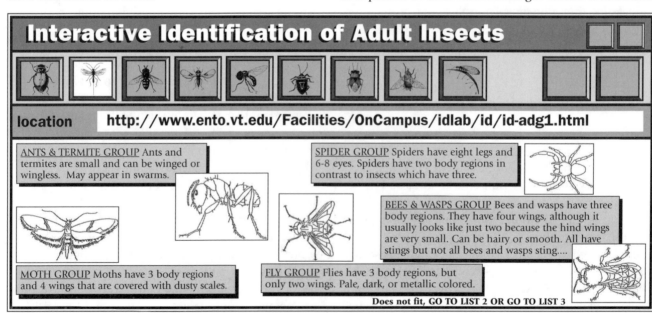

Interactive Identification of Adult Insects

location http://www.ento.vt.edu/Facilities/OnCampus/idlab/id/id-adg1.html

ANTS & TERMITE GROUP Ants and termites are small and can be winged or wingless. May appear in swarms.

SPIDER GROUP Spiders have eight legs and 6-8 eyes. Spiders have two body regions in contrast to insects which have three.

BEES & WASPS GROUP Bees and wasps have three body regions. They have four wings, although it usually looks like just two because the hind wings are very small. Can be hairy or smooth. All have stings but not all bees and wasps sting....

MOTH GROUP Moths have 3 body regions and 4 wings that are covered with dusty scales.

FLY GROUP Flies have 3 body regions, but only two wings. Pale, dark, or metallic colored.

Does not fit, GO TO LIST 2 OR GO TO LIST 3

> *"... a surprising 19 percent of the value of sales of pesticides represent retail sales to individual householders... Pesticides so applied may be especially hazardous, because they are dispersed in a locally concentrated way by untrained persons."*
>
> **Pest Control: An Assessment of Present and Alternative Technologies** *(NRC, 1975)*

from their service providers of pesticides used, and just 21 percent were given written safety precautions to follow after applications.

Human nature can heighten reliance on pesticides in and around the home. Many people are too busy to read or pay adequate attention to label directions and warnings. Some believe that "if a little bit works, more will work better." A few question the need for caution, either because they believe the government would not allow the use of unsafe products, or because they think society has gone "overboard" in trying to reduce risks from chemicals.

Illegal sale of repackaged pesticides for use in residential buildings is yet another wildcard that has recently gotten the attention of state regulators and the EPA, as

evidenced in the box "Black Markets for Pesticides Pose Major Risks for Unwary Consumers."

2. Pesticide Use in Agriculture

Farmers and ranchers applied some 966 million pounds of pesticide active ingredients in 1995, according to the EPA (Aspelin, 1996)—on average, about three pounds of active ingredient per acre on the approximately 300 million cultivated acres in American agriculture (Anderson, 1994). The range in application rates per acre and unit area is broad. Herbicide application rates per planted acre in 1992 ranged from 0.24 pounds active ingredient on wheat, to 5.6 pounds on rice and 7.1 in citrus groves, with even higher rates on parts of golf courses.[9]

The range of insecticide and fungicide applications per acre is broader—less than one-tenth pound per planted acre in many crops to more than 15 pounds or more in high value fruit and vegetable crops like apples, tomatoes, citrus and peanuts. Vegetables are sprayed with about 20 percent of all pesticides, yet account for less than two percent of harvested cropland (Anderson, 1994). Strawberry crops can receive an incredible 500 pounds of pesticides per acre—including 200 to 300 pounds of methyl bromide soil fumigant. This contrasts

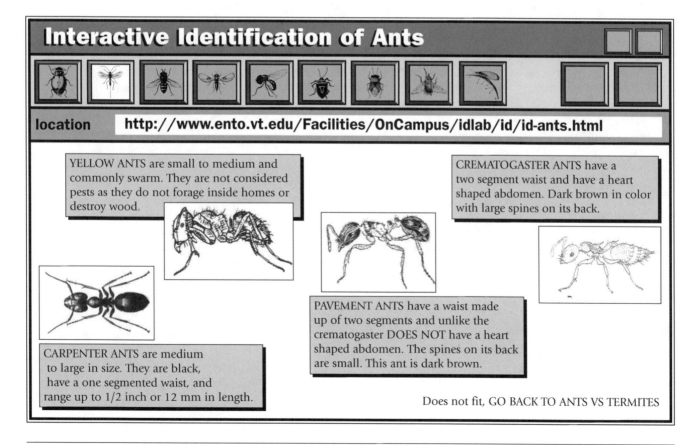

Black Markets for Pesticides
Pose Major Risks for Unwary Consumers

State regulatory officials and EPA have worried for years about "off-label" uses of pesticides—any application of a pesticide product not authorized on the label, or prohibited by the label. Probably the most common violation of labels is also one of the most potentially serious—less than full adherence to personal safety precautions, like wearing gloves when mixing pesticides or a long-sleeved shirt when applying them.

In recent years a new concern has surfaced—black markets for older, relatively inexpensive but highly toxic pesticides. The illegal use of the insecticide chlorpyrifos in grain bins where oats were stored led to a wave of adverse publicity and millions of dollars in losses for General Mills. Illegal application of the insecticide aldicarb to watermelons grown in California caused hundreds of confirmed illnesses and more than a thousand reported cases of illness.

Black market pesticide sales are also occurring in urban America. A series of contaminated residential sites have been found by the EPA in Ohio. A cleanup is underway and is expected to cost nearly $10 million, according to a July 11, 1995 statement mailed out to the states and EPA regions by the "State FIFRA Issues Research and Evaluation Group" (SFIREG, 1995). This group is composed of state regulators, EPA officials and pest management experts and meets periodically to advise EPA on pesticide regulatory issues. Its statement read in part:

> "Recent experiences in Michigan and Ohio with methyl parathion serve notice of possibly widespread diversion of agricultural insecticides, especially restricted use pesticides, to urban uses... diversion of restricted use pesticides to urban and non-agricultural...uses are alarming...and a very significant threat to human health. Several other states have identified similar problems...."
> "Our most recent investigation in Region V identified what appears to be an ongoing black market for restricted use pesticides. This underground market includes diversions, transport, repackaging, and commercial and private use of methyl parathion in residential buildings."

Many consumers have used the organophosphate insecticide malathion in and around the home and are aware this insecticide has been applied aerially over urban areas for control of the Medfly. Malathion is comparatively low in acute toxicity and has an oral LD-50 of 2,100 parts per million. But its chemical cousin, methyl parathion, is 150 times more toxic (oral LD-50 of 14 ppm, International Programme on Chemical Safety [IPCS], 1994). Methyl parathion poses severe acute and long-term hazards to any consumers who may mistakenly assume it is roughly as toxic as malathion and apply it with the same lack of safety precautions common when malathion is applied. A few drops of technical grade methyl parathion on an individual's skin can prove fatal.

with the average pesticide spraying rate for winter wheat—about 60 percent of cropland growing winter wheat is treated, nearly 40 percent is not. On the acres treated, the average rate of application is 0.40 pounds active ingredient per acre, the vast majority herbicides (USDA, 1995b).

Use by Type of Pesticide

Figure 2.2 shows trends in agricultural pesticide use from 1964 to 1992 based on USDA data (Anderson, 1994). There was steady growth in the pounds applied until the early 1980s when the switch to low dose herbicides and insecticides started to reduce overall pounds applied. A dramatic shift has occurred in the relative share of pounds applied from insecticides to herbicides. Insecticides accounted for 55 percent of pesticide quantity applied in 1964 and herbicides, some 24 percent, yet by 1982 herbicides accounted for 76 percent and insecticides only 14 percent. Fungicide use has been the most stable, accounting for about 9 percent of pounds applied in the 1960s and about 7 percent in the 1990s.

The "Other" category in Figure 2.2 includes fumigants used for soil-borne insects and associated plant pathogens and treatment of harvested foodstuffs, desiccants used to defoliate cotton or hasten the maturation process of other plants, rodenticides and a variety of other pesticides.

Pesticide Use Patterns

A pesticide use pattern is the combination of where, when and how a pesticide is applied to control a given pest, whether on farms, in or around the home, on forest and range land or elsewhere. Pesticide use patterns are determined by several factors. They are bounded by pesticide product label directions, which include maximum rates of application (both for a single application and for the sum of all applications in a season or year), pre-harvest and field re-entry intervals, safety precautions, requirements for protective clothing and other requirements regarding when, where and how a pesticide may be applied.

Use patterns also are determined by how difficult a given pest is to control and how prevalent it is. Scouting may reveal that a given pest is a problem in just some parts of a field or certain blocks in an orchard. Spot-spraying can then be targeted to where the pest is present above economic threshold levels. While a full label rate might be applied where the pest is present at damaging levels, the rate of application per acre over an entire field might be significantly lower.

A high risk use pattern is a crop-pest-pesticide combination in which applications of toxic pesticides are routinely required under circumstances that expose non-target organisms. Well known high risk use patterns include soil-borne insect and plant disease management on strawberry farms, boll weevil and other cotton insect pest control, apple scab management in humid production regions, organophosphate-based termite and fire ant control programs and plant disease control in potato production.

Herbicide Use in Agriculture

Weeds compete with crops for moisture, nutrients and sunlight and reduce yields if not controlled. Herbicides are the primary method used to manage weeds in American agriculture and account for the largest share of pesticide use—664 million pounds of active ingredients in 1995 (Aspelin, 1996). This represents about 53 percent of the 1.25 billion pounds of active ingredients used nationwide that year.[10] The amounts spent by farmers on

herbicides in 1995 accounted for 63.6 percent of total U.S. pesticide sales (ACPA, 1996). Two crops—corn and soybeans—accounted for 65 percent of total herbicide sales in 1995 (ACPA, 1996).

Herbicide use as measured by pounds applied grew 85 percent between 1971 and 1976, reaching 368 million pounds. A single new active ingredient—alachlor—accounted for about 45 percent of the growth (Gianessi and Puffer, 1991). Herbicide use has fluctuated over the

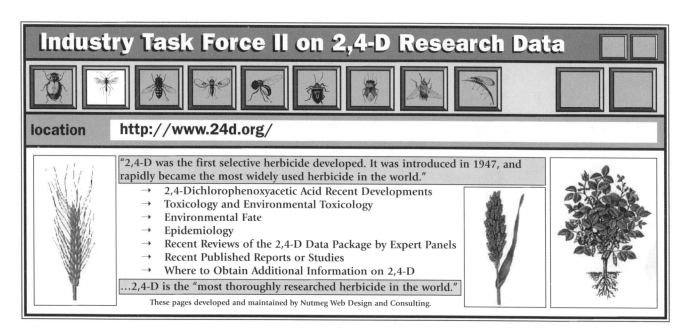

Industry Task Force II on 2,4-D Research Data

location http://www.24d.org/

"2,4-D was the first selective herbicide developed. It was introduced in 1947, and rapidly became the most widely used herbicide in the world."

→ 2,4-Dichlorophenoxyacetic Acid Recent Developments
→ Toxicology and Environmental Toxicology
→ Environmental Fate
→ Epidemiology
→ Recent Reviews of the 2,4-D Data Package by Expert Panels
→ Recent Published Reports or Studies
→ Where to Obtain Additional Information on 2,4-D

...2,4-D is the "most thoroughly researched herbicide in the world."

These pages developed and maintained by Nutmeg Web Design and Consulting.

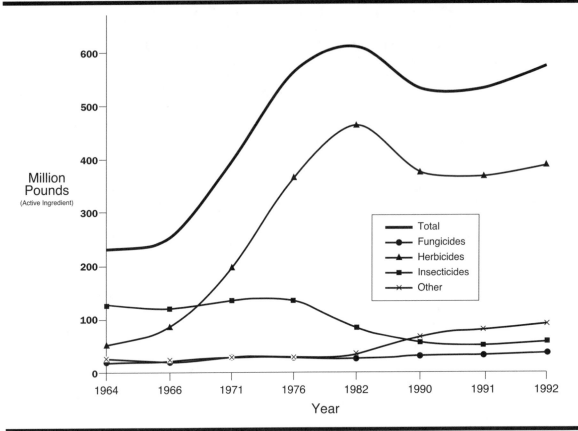

Figure 2.2 Trends in Agricultural Pesticide Use by Type of Pesticide: Quantity Applied 1964 through 1992

Million Pounds
(Active Ingredient)

Legend:
- Total
- Fungicides
- Herbicides
- Insecticides
- Other

Year

Source: USDA Agrichemical Use Surveys, 1994-1992. Data derived from Table 3.3.2, Agricultural Resources and Environmental Indicators, Agricultural Handbook No. 705, Economic Research Service, USDA (Anderson, 1994).

last decade as a function of several factors but farm programs have been the most variable. Farmers producing major program crops including corn and other feed grains, cotton, rice, soybeans and wheat were required to idle a portion of their cropland periodically to remain eligible for government income support payments. The use of land retirement to reduce surplus production and boost commodity prices resulted in some years in a major portion of cropland lying fallow. For example, EPA pesticide use data show agricultural herbicide use trending downward modestly from 1981 through 1983, but then rising 22 percent in 1984. This sharp increase was largely a result of the end of the USDA's "Payment-In-Kind" program, which idled an extra 45 million acres of cropland in 1983 (Aspelin, 1994; Anderson, 1994).

The growth rate in pounds applied was steepest between 1966 and 1971 when total use rose by more than 10 percent per year (Lin, et al., 1995). The average

rate of application during this period rose from 1.3 pounds of active ingredients (a.i.) per planted acre to 1.9. In the early 1980s, manufacturers began producing herbicides that are effective at much lower rates of application per acre. A dozen herbicides applied at less than 0.2 pounds per treated acre now command significant market share and some recently registered products are applied at a fraction of an ounce per acre (USDA, 1995b; Mayerfeld et al., 1996). In some cases, low dose herbicides may actually cause more problems, although different problems, than older products applied at much higher rates per acre. The reasons several low dose herbicides are effective—their potency and persistence—may also cause them to adversely impact nearby crops, rotational and cover crops, and aquatic vegetation (Ahrens and Fuerst, 1990; Loux et al., 1989). They may also reduce soil microbial diversity during a key part of the growing season, heightening the plant's vulnerability to

Farmers are able to cover 50 to 100 acres or more per day with large spray rigs pulled behind tractors. Rising sales of the corn herbicide alachlor (Lasso) accounted for a large portion of the rapid growth in herbicide use in the early 1970s. Alachlor use peaked in the early 1980s at over 85 million pounds of active ingredient and declined to about 50 million pounds in 1993. In 1994 a similar product called acetochlor was registered and aggressively marketed. In the last two years, alachlor use has fallen some 20 million pounds and acetochlor use has risen to well over 23 million (USDA, 1996c).
Credit: Agricultural Research Service

root pathogens and diseases and reducing the bioavailability of phosphorous (Liebman et al., 1996; Fletcher, et al., 1993; Forlani, et al., 1995).

Other problems affecting farmers and landowners arise from the fact that railroad shipping cars, trucks, onfarm storage tanks and application equipment are used to handle and apply many different fertilizer and pesticide mixtures. Even when tanks are thoroughly cleaned, minute traces of sulfonylurea herbicides may be left in such equipment where they can contaminate a subsequent load of liquid fertilizer or insecticide. If such loads are applied on sensitive crops like ornamentals, pears, cherries, and sugarbeets, problems can emerge. The extraordinary potency of sulfonylureas is highlighted in the excerpt in the box from a DuPont study in France carried out to determine a safe level of sulfonylurea emissions from a new manufacturing plant.

Sulfonylurea herbicide contamination from an improperly cleaned railroad car has been implicated as a possible cause of major crop losses in the southeast in the early 1990s following application of a formulation of the DuPont fungicide benomyl (Benlate). Ornamental growers—which account for just 5 percent of Benlate sales—were hardest hit (Gianessi, 1995). Over 220 lawsuits have been filed and many more settlements were reached outside of court. More than $500 million in compensation for damages has been paid to growers and many cases are not yet resolved. The cause of the problem, and the source of the contamination, if any, is still disputed by parties to the litigation. Regardless of the outcome of pending and future litigation, the impact of this episode on DuPont is significant given that total annual U.S. sales of Benomyl in the early 1990s were about $40 million and the company's total domestic pesticide sales were about $1 billion (Gianessi, 1995).

Several other low dose herbicides have also caused injury to crops and vegetation, both in farm fields and nearby. New concerns have also arisen in recent years about the impacts of these herbicides on soil health and plant physiology. In general, toxicity to plants, carryover and efficacy problems are more serious in years when moisture and temperature patterns deviate from the norm and alter the rate of breakdown of these materials or their uptake by weeds (Ahrens and Fuerst, 1990). Accelerated breakdown can lead to mid- and late-season weed control problems and delayed breakdown can

---

"Our studies have shown that small emissions of sulfonylureas from the Cernay Plant can adversely affect the vegetation surrounding the Plant. Accordingly, we have set a very tight emission standard of one gram per hectare per year of sulfonylurea. This provides a safety factor of a little less than 2x for the most sensitive vegetation surrounding the Plant and we will work diligently to maintain this standard."

Excerpt from: *"Final Report on the Response of Vegetation Near the Cernay (France) Plant to Sulfonylureas" (Barrier, 1988)*

The ability to cover large areas in a short time is one reason reliance on herbicides has risen so dramatically. In some areas, special trucks (left) are used as mobile landing pads for helicopters, to speed up the reloading of tanks. Herbicide mixed with fertilizer is often applied by airplanes (right) just after fields are planted. Credits: Left, Colorado State University; Right, Richard Steven Street

cause injury to fall planted crops or the next year's crop. These and possibly related herbicide carryover problems appear to be growing more common and serious in several Midwestern states in 1996, especially on fields treated with certain combinations of herbicides and insecticides.[11]

Reliance on Herbicides is Rising

Despite a downward trend since the early 1980s in pounds of herbicide a.i. applied, USDA statistical bulletins clearly show that from the 1960s to the 1990s, reliance on herbicides for weed management has risen steadily. Table 2.1 provides an overview of trends in herbicide reliance and use indicators—percent acres treated, pounds of active ingredient applied and application rates per acre. In the case of corn production:

■ percent of crop acres treated has risen from about 50 percent in the 1960s to more than 96 percent in the 1990s (Anderson, 1994; Mayerfeld et al., 1996).

■ the average number of active ingredients applied per acre has risen from one active ingredient on about half the planted acres to more than 2.5 active ingredients on almost all acres (data not reported in table). As a result, the number of distinct acre-treatments (an application of a single herbicide active ingredient on an acre) has gone up about four-fold.

> Over 12 percent of the herbicide applied in Iowa in 1994 was purchased through a respray program because of some form of product failure, both increasing use and hastening the emergence of resistant weeds.

■ pounds applied per acre is up from about 1.05 pounds a.i. per acre to nearly three pounds.

In Table 2.1, note the steady rise in corn and soybean acres treated since the mid-1960s, reaching 95 percent or more after 1982, compared with the relatively stable portion of wheat acres treated—a climb from 41 percent to only 51 percent since the early 1970s. Reliance on herbicides continues to rise in many places for several reasons, including the trend toward larger farms and equipment, adoption of no-till planting methods to reduce soil erosion, most farmers' desire to keep fields as weed-free as possible and difficulty in covering large areas with mechanical cultivation, particularly in years when weather conditions are unfavorable.

Only one indicator is falling for most crops—the pounds of herbicide active ingredients applied. This drop is due to the lower rates of application needed for many of the more potent herbicides now gaining market share (Gianessi and Anderson, 1993; Mayerfeld et al., 1996), not because of reduction in reliance on herbicides as a weed management tool. The percent of acres cultivated for weed control—a proven, affordable alternative to herbicide use—is falling in most Midwestern states (Buhler et al., 1992; Liebman et al., 1996; Benbrook, 1996; USDA, 1994b and 1995b). Farmers also made fewer banded applications of herbicides in 1994 than in 1993. "Banding" is another simple, effective way

Table 2.1 Indicators of Reliance on Herbicides for Weed Control Over Four Decades, Major Crops

	Mid 1960s	Early 1970s	1982	1992
Corn				
Area Surveyed (1000 Acres)	66,000	74,180	79,400	71,400
% Acres Treated	50	79	95	96
Quantity Applied (1000 lbs a.i.)	35,000	101,060	243,410	198,900
Application Rates*	1.05	1.73	3.23	2.90
Soybeans				
Area Surveyed (1000 Acres)	37,400	43,480	72,000	53,050
% Acres Treated	27	68	95	97
Quantity Applied (1000 lbs a.i.)	10,400	36,520	125,200	58,800
Application Rates*	1.03	1.23	1.83	1.14
Wheat				
Area Surveyed (1000 Acres)	54,500	53,820	79,800	55,890
% Acres Treated	26	41	42	51
Quantity Applied (1000 lbs a.i.)	8,600	11,620	18,068	12,400
Application Rates*	0.6	0.53	0.54	0.43
Rice+				
Area Planted (1000 Acres)	1,800	1,826	3,295	3,174
Quantity Applied (1000 lbs a.i.)	2,600	7,980	14,090	11,300
Application Rates*	1.4	4.37	4.28	5.57
Cotton+				
Area Surveyed (1000 Acres)	12,500	12,360	10,000	10,110
Quantity Applied (1000 lbs a.i.)	5,000	19,610	17,300	19,000
Application Rates*	1.1	1.9	1.8	2.1

*Average pounds active ingredient per treated acre included in surveys; rice data are pounds applied per planted acre.
Source: From Table 7 in Lin et al., 1995; rice data calculated from Appendix tables.
+Data on percent acres treated not reported.

to cut herbicide applications by as much as 60 percent (Mayerfeld et al., 1996).

There is additional evidence in Iowa that reliance on herbicides is rising. Farmers had made progress from the mid-1980s to 1993 in reducing herbicide use and reliance by adopting banding, cultivation and other cultural practices. But aggressive marketing of several new herbicides, coupled with respray guarantee programs, convinced many farmers to drop reduced-chemical weed management alternatives.[12] Respray programs entail offers to compensate farmers for the cost of an additional herbicide application if a previous application fails to achieve the advertised level of control.

Academic and industry weed management experts have acknowledged that respray agreements have raised farmers' weed control expectations unrealistically and have become marketing tools (Mayerfeld et al., 1996; Fawcett, 1995a). About 12.5 percent of the herbicide applied in Iowa in 1994 was purchased through a respray program, according to Dr. Michael Owen, a specialist in the economics of weed management at Iowa State University.[13]

A recent article in *Prairie Farmer*, a major farm magazine asks, "Time to Rethink Resprays?" The author traces

Herbicide Resistance—A Growing Problem

By the time farmers began to rely heavily on herbicides in the early 1960s, resistance to insecticides among many pest species was a common phenomenon. Scientists documented the first known case of resistance in a weed species (common groundsel) to a herbicide (the triazine, simazine) in 1968 in Washington State (Warwick, 1991). Resistance spread but more slowly than rising reliance on herbicides. Prior to 1980, most new occurrences of resistance involved the same family of herbicides—the triazines. In the 1980s, efficacy problems emerged with new chemical families (groups of active ingredients with similar chemical structures and properties), including the phenoxy herbicides (especially 2,4-D), the dinitroanalines (especially trifluralin) and paraquat.

In its 1986 report on pesticide resistance, the National Research Council (NRC) reported that 48 weed species were resistant to herbicides, citing data compiled in 1984 by Dr. Homer LeBaron (NRC, 1986). Since the mid-1980s, the number of resistant species, the scope of resistance and its significance to farmers have grown dramatically. EPA is now aware of 270 weed species resistant to herbicides, many of them resistant to several active ingredients—a 460 percent increase in the prevalence of herbicide resistant weed species over just a decade (U.S. EPA, 1996g).

According to Dr. Jodie Holt, Professor of Botany and Plant Sciences at the University of California–Riverside, "It is clear that although herbicide resistance was later to appear than pesticide resistance in insects and fungi, resistance in weeds is rapidly increasing at a rate equivalent to that of insecticide and fungicide resistance." (Holt, 1992)

The first case of resistance to the newly introduced low dose sulfonylurea herbicide chlorotoluron was reported in 1985 in blackgrass, otherwise known as slender foxtail. Many grassy weed species are now resistant to several low dose products. "Multiple-resistance" occurs when a species is resistant to active ingredients in two or more chemical families (like resistance to triazine and sulfonylurea herbicides, which work through different modes of action). "Cross-resistance" occurs when a weed species that is resistant to a herbicide in one chemical class, say the triazines, becomes resistant to another triazine never before used on it (resistance "crosses" from one triazine to the second). Multiple-resistance is regarded a more worrisome development than cross-resistance. In recent years, scientists have documented several cases of both cross-resistance and multiple-resistance in the same weed species (Gill, 1995; Hager, 1996).

One research project in Australia found that heavy herbicide use since 1968 in wheat production created a genotype of rigid ryegrass resistant to nine different classes of herbicides and 25 different active ingredients, making "this population difficult to control with herbicides" (Burnet et al., 1994). According to Dr. Holt, "The most important new development in herbicide resistance in weeds has been the recent discovery of multiple-resistance to chemically unrelated herbicides…Such an occurrence is commonplace with insecticides, and is attributed to a common degradation system for seemingly unrelated pesticides…This so far unpredictable multiple-resistance to herbicides poses a serious threat to crop production in situations where optional methods of weed management have not been developed." (Holt, 1992)

In a surprising and significant development, ryegrass in Australia has now developed resistance to another major herbicide—glyphosate (Roundup; a broad-spectrum product that controls almost all weed species).[14] This is the first documented case of resistance to glyphosate, the world's best-selling pesticide (Fahnestock, 1996).

Great effort has been invested over the last 10 years in developing genetically engineered glyphosate-resistant plant varieties so that growers of genetically engineered varieties of cotton, soybeans, canola, sugar beets, potatoes and wheat will be able to spray glyphosate directly over fields. Several such herbicide tolerant plant varieties have been approved for commercial use in the U.S. despite concerns raised by many scientists that such varieties would heighten reliance on herbicides in general and might accelerate emergence of glyphosate-resistant weeds. In light of the recent discovery of glyphosate-resistant ryegrass, scientists in Australia are reconsidering approval of plant varieties engineered to resist glyphosate. We return to these issues in Chapters 6 and 8.

resprays to the early 1980s, when Shell Chemical Co. guaranteed the performance of Bladex (cyanazine) in corn weed management (Stout, 1996). Other companies soon adopted the practice "to remain competitive," according to University of Illinois weed scientist Marshall McGlamery (quoted in Stout, 1996). An industry representative also quoted in the article states, "Resprays are likely to continue as long as there's no regulation on it and a major profit in herbicides."

> In 1994 the average acre of corn was sprayed with 2.5 different herbicide active ingredients, totalling nearly 3 pounds applied.

Iowa weed management expert Michael Owen notes that over the last decade most farmers have cultivated row crops at least once following application of herbicides, a combination that in most years and weather conditions produced reliable results. In some years the herbicide alone was able to keep weeds in check, but in other years cultivation was essential to fully mix the herbicide in the soil profile and catch weeds that survived the initial herbicide application. But Owen says there is still "incredibly high and inappropriate use of resprays" in Iowa (quoted in Stout, 1996):

> "The bottom line is that growers don't want to cultivate. The system allows them to get by without it. We need to bring back use of mechanical control in a timely fashion."

Resprays are also an important cost and sustainability concern since repeat applications of the same herbicide active ingredient can accelerate the emergence of resistant weed species (see the box, "Herbicide Resistance—A Growing Problem").

3. Insecticide Use and Reliance

The quantity of insecticides applied on major agricultural crops has fallen significantly between 1964 and 1993, dropping from 128 million pounds of active ingredient to 57.8 million pounds—a 70 million pound decrease, according to USDA chemical use survey data (Anderson, 1994). The precipitous drop in chlorinated hydrocarbon, organophosphate and carbamate use on cotton accounts for about two-thirds of this decline (see Table 2.2 for details). In 1976, over 64 million pounds of insecticides were applied to cotton fields but just six years later, total quantity applied had declined to 19.2 million. The causes of this sharp drop in pounds applied included the emergence of resistance, the adoption of IPM, cancellations of several insecticides, and the shift from insecticides applied at one to two pounds

per acre per application, to products applied at much lower rates (Gianessi and Anderson, 1993; Anderson, 1994).

USDA data show total insecticide use on major crops falling from 1971 through 1990 but remaining roughly stable since (Anderson, 1994). Use on a few crops has declined greatly—cotton, sorghum, soybeans. On others it has fluctuated up and down, changing no more than 25 percent from one decade to the next. But quantity of insecticide applied is a misleading indicator of reliance because:

■ Pound for pound applied, the average potency, and in many cases toxicity, of insecticides has gone up several-fold over the last two decades.

■ Insecticide treatments have gone up in most crops from one to three per acre on average in the 1960s to three to six in the 1990s, while the percent of acres treated and the number of active ingredients per acre have remained stable or risen, in most crops. For example, in the 1960s, the average cotton acre was treated about 1.3 times with one or two insecticide active ingredients, whereas in 1994, the average acre was treated 5.7 times with 3.5 different active ingredients (Anderson, 1994; USDA, 1995b).

A significant portion of the drop in quantity of insecticides applied on most crops was brought about by the shift away from routine calendar spraying. Resistance and serious secondary pest problems have led farmers to apply different and additional active ingredients per acre and to intensify spray schedules during periods of peak pest pressure and crop vulnerability. Resistance also has prompted farmers to increase the amount of cropland that is scouted and managed under IPM with the help of professional crop consultants.

Insecticide Reliance Now Rising

USDA cropping practices survey data show that the average rate of insecticide application on major field crops (corn, soybeans, cotton, wheat, and potatoes) has gone up from 1.05 pounds active ingredient per acre in 1991 to 1.33 pounds in 1995, and the average number of treatments with a distinct active ingredient per acre has almost doubled, from 1.8 in 1991 to 3.5 in 1995 (USDA, 1991, 1995b). These recent trends are evidence of rising reliance on insecticides, despite the longer-term drop in total pounds applied.

EPA data show that the quantity of insecticide active ingredient applied in agriculture, on all crops, rose from 210 million pounds in 1986 to 252 million in 1995—a 20 percent increase over the last decade despite the trend toward lower-dose products (Aspelin, 1994, 1996). EPA estimates of pesticide quantities applied differ from USDA's because EPA includes all crops, range, and pasture, and also includes some active ingredients not part of USDA's annual chemical use surveys. Across all sectors (agriculture, industry, and home and garden), EPA data show insecticide use rising from 295 million pounds in 1986 to 334 million pounds in 1995—a 13 percent increase in 10 years.

> **"Almost any way you find to kill an insect, it will find a way not to be killed." Dr. George Georghiou, University of California, Riverside**

Trends in Resistance

Resistance among insect species to insecticides is "a consequence of basic evolutionary processes"(NRC, 1986). A committee convened by the National Research Council in 1984 produced a comprehensive assessment of resistance in the United States:

"During the early 1950s, resistance was rare, while fully susceptible populations, of insects at least, have become rare in the 1980s... Resistance in insects and mites rose from seven species resistant to DDT in 1938 to 447 species resistant [to one or more insecticides] in 1984... Almost half of these species are able to resist compounds in more than one of [five major] classes of insecticides, and 17 species can resist compounds in all five classes."
A June 25, 1996 EPA briefing paper on resistance reports that there are more than 500 insect and mite species resistant to one or more pesticides and that resistance is increasing the average toxicity of insecticides applied and the frequency of applications (EPA, 1996g). According to Dr. George Georghiou, author of the overview chapter in the 1986 NRC resistance report: "Unquestionably the phenomenon of resistance poses a serious obstacle to efforts to increase agricultural production and to reduce or eliminate the threat of vector-borne diseases." (NRC, 1986). In a June 1996 article on resistance to cotton insecticides, Dr. Georghiou stated, "Almost any way you find to kill an insect, it will find a way not to be killed" (quote in Rehrman, 1996).

Resistance in common household insects like cockroaches and ants is also a growing concern. Many people are unaware that household insecticides, including those used by commercial pest management companies, may be slipping in effectiveness, requiring more frequent and heavier applications. A recent study concluded that most cockroaches "had intermediate or high-level chlorpyrifos and propoxur resistance (two widely used insecticides).

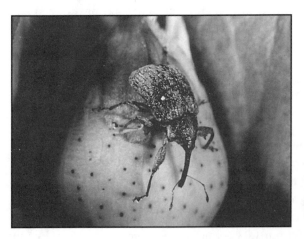 

The "mean old" boll weevil (left) remains a major cotton pest. More insecticide has been sprayed to control the boll weevil, and related secondary pests, than any other insect pest in America. The whitefly (right) is the toughest new cotton pest to emerge in recent years. Over a few days, population levels can explode, sucking the juice from cotton leaves and leaving a sticky, white gum behind. Pesticides work poorly in controlling the whitefly. Here, Agricultural Research Service scientist James Duffus wades through a Blythe, California cotton field heavily infested with whiteflies. Credits: Left, Rob Flynn, Agricultural Research Service; Right, Ed McCain, Agricultural Research Service

Chemical control programs are increasingly likely to fail unless strategies for insecticide use that do not rely entirely on these types of compounds are followed" (Hemingway et al., 1993).

Insecticide resistance has been especially devastating to the cotton industry (Metcalf, 1993; NRC, 1986; van den Bosch, 1978; NAS, 1975). Cotton is grown in many hot regions of the country with relatively long growing seasons—the same conditions that favor the emergence of dominant pests. Many cotton insects bore into the cotton boll where they are protected from most pesticides. Multiple applications are necessary to ensure adequate

control. New insecticides tend to get registered first for cotton and used more heavily there because it is not a food crop.[15]

Resistance forces farmers to switch chemicals. Producers who have gone through this cycle several times develop a keener interest in IPM along the way. Nationwide, 42 percent of cotton acreage was scouted by a commercial service in 1994, the highest percentage of any crop for which USDA has data (USDA, 1995b). The impacts of resistance on cotton insecticide use is reviewed more fully in the box "Resistance Drives the Search for New Cotton Insecticides."

Resistance Drives the Search for New Cotton Insecticides

Insects are extraordinarily adept at learning how to live with insecticides. Once an insect population develops resistance to one insecticide, the time required for cross-resistance to develop to another insecticide in the same chemical family is usually just a few seasons, or even months. As a result, pesticide manufacturers have to continuously commercialize new active ingredients within major chemical families, while also searching for pesticides that work through novel modes of action. But the number of insect species exhibiting both cross-resistance and multiple-resistance to insecticides is large and still growing.

Three major chemical families accounted for most insecticide use from the 1960s through 1980s—the organochlorine, or chlorinated hydrocarbons (DDT, aldrin/dieldrin, toxaphene, chlordane/heptachlor); the organophosphates (parathion, malathion, chlorpyrifos, terbufos) and carbamates (aldicarb, carbofuran, carbaryl). In the mid-1980s the synthetic pyrethroids came into use (permethrin, cypermethrin, esfenvalerate). Table 2.2 shows the evolution of reliance on different chemical families in cotton insect pest management.

As resistance and EPA cancellations drove down the use of organochlorines—particularly DDT, aldrin and toxaphene—from 1964 to 1982, the use of organophosphates (OPs) doubled. In the 1976-1982 period, resistance caught up with the OPs. The pyrethroids came into widespread use in the 1980s, sharing the control burden with OPs and sharply reducing pounds applied, since the average rate of application for synthetic pyrethroids is about one-tenth that for an OP.

Table 2.2 Insecticide Applications to Cotton by Chemical Family (Million Pounds a.i.)

	1964	1966	1971	1976	1982	1992
Organochlorines	54.6	45.4	33.0	18.6	1.2	1.2
Organophosphates	15.6	14.3	28.6	31.4	12.9	13.4
Carbamates	6.2	4.5	10.3	12.2	3.5	4.0
Pyrethroids	0.0	0.0	0.0	0.0	0.8	0.9
Other	1.6	0.7	1.5	2.0	1.0	0.3
Total*	78.0	64.9	73.4	64.1	19.2	19.9

* Totals may not add up as result of rounding.
Source: Calculated from USDA Chemical Use Surveys, multiple years.

4. Stable or Slowly Rising Reliance on Fungicides

Fungicide use was relatively stable from 1971 through 1990 but rose 15 percent in the next two years, according to USDA survey data (Anderson, 1994). EPA data show that a clear upward trend in fungicide use began in the 1990 season, when the pounds applied across all sectors totaled 116 million, reaching 164 million pounds in 1995—a 41 percent increase over five years (Aspelin, 1996). Compared to the 1980s, reliance on fungicides is rising in several crops—rice, cotton, potatoes, vegetables (other than potatoes)—and has fallen somewhat in a few crops—citrus and apples (Anderson, 1994).

Increased reliance, especially in potatoes, is caused by the emergence of new disease strains that are hard if not impossible to control with fungicides or other pesticides. Changes in water management, fertility and related agronomic practices have also increased reliance in some regions and crops. Relatively less emphasis has been placed on breeding disease resistance into plant varieties by many plant breeders and some seed companies (Robinson, 1996). Together these changes and factors have made plants in some regions more susceptible both to new and old plant pathogens. Table 2.3 summarizes trends between 1966 and 1992 in the use of fungicides in agriculture based on USDA data. USDA surveys do not include several crops and two widely used inorganic fungicides included in EPA's dataset (copper and sulfur), which explains most of the differences between the data cited above and in Table 2.3.

Three fungicides have dominated applications since the mid-1960s—captan, benomyl and the EBDC family

Agricultural Research Service (ARS) plant geneticist Dr. Doug Wilson Compares a normal cotton leaf to one deformed by cotton leaf crumple, a viral disease transmitted by whiteflies.
Credit: Jack Dykinga, ARS

(the ethylene bisdithiocarbamates, which include mancozeb, maneb, thiram, zineb, ziram and metiram). In 1966, these fungicides accounted for 63.7 percent of the total pounds applied, dropping to just below 40 percent in the early 1970s, rising again to between 51 percent and 53 percent from 1982 through 1992 (Gianessi, 1992; Gianessi and Anderson, 1995).

Fungicide application rates per acre remained relatively stable from the 1960s to the early 1980s in most crops but trends then diverged. For some crops, the number of acres treated has gone down but the number of

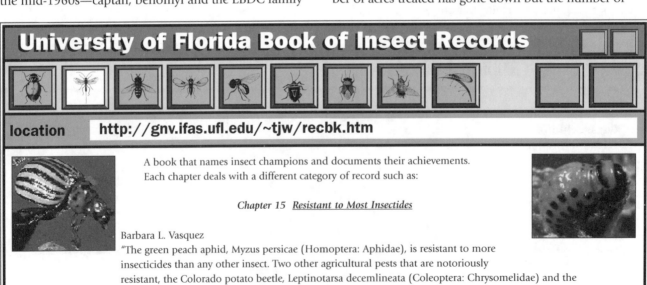

University of Florida Book of Insect Records

location http://gnv.ifas.ufl.edu/~tjw/recbk.htm

A book that names insect champions and documents their achievements. Each chapter deals with a different category of record such as:

*Chapter 15 **Resistant to Most Insecticides***

Barbara L. Vasquez
"The green peach aphid, Myzus persicae (Homoptera: Aphidae), is resistant to more insecticides than any other insect. Two other agricultural pests that are notoriously resistant, the Colorado potato beetle, Leptinotarsa decemlineata (Coleoptera: Chrysomelidae) and the diamondback moth, Plutella xylostella (Lepidoptera: Plutellidae), are strong runners-up."

Table 2.3 Trends in Fungicide Use Since 1966 (Thousand Pounds a.i.)

	1966	1971	1976	1982	1990	1992
Pounds Applied:						
All Fungicides* (1000 pounds a.i.)	21,660	30,906	29,546	27,519	31,641	37,358
Rates of Application+						
Apples	20.2	17.9	16.1	13.5	9.8	9.4
Citrus	4.6	7.8	4.9	4.3	3.6	4.2
Potatoes	2.4	2.9	3.0	3.1	2.0	2.7
Other Vegetables	1.2	1.8	1.6	3.1	4.6	4.9
Peanuts	0.7	2.9	4.4	3.6	4.0	4.0

*Excluding Sulfur and Copper.
+Pounds of all fungicide active ingredients applied to crop in a season.
Source: Pounds applied (Anderson, 1994); rates of application (Lin et al., 1995).

applications and pounds applied per acre treated has increased. In other crops, about the same percent of crop acres are treated, but the number of applications is down. Data elements needed to monitor fungicide reliance include the nature and number of different active ingredients applied, how many times each active ingredient is applied on an acre and the rate applied each time, and the portion of crop acres treated with each active ingredient.

Consumers traditionally have not relied heavily on fungicides and spent only $744,000 in 1995 in the "Home and Garden" market category—just $1.00 on fungicides for every $280 on insecticides (ACPA, 1996). But fungicide sales to homeowners rose 41.7 percent between 1994 and 1995, a trend that warrants monitoring.

> Fungicide use has risen 41 percent since the 1990 season. New tough to control strains of blight in potatoes has been the major reason why.

Trends in Resistance

Like herbicide resistance, the first instance of resistance to fungicides occurred in the late 1960s. Resistance in plant pathogens emerged more slowly because of two major factors: use of non-selective compounds with multiple modes of action, and the limited role plant detoxification mechanisms play in combating fungicides (Delp, 1988). The 1986 NRC report on resistance documented "at least 100 species of plant pathogens" resistant to fungicides, citing data from 1984. In its 1996 assessment of resistance, the EPA reports 150 resistant plant pathogens—

a 50 percent increase over the last decade (EPA, 1996g).

The increase would be greater if not for the EBDCs, a major class of fungicides that have never triggered resistance in any fungal pathogen because of their complex mode of action (Delp, 1988; EPA, 1996g). As more selective fungicides were introduced in the 1970s and 1980s, episodes of cross-resistance became more common, affecting whole classes of compounds. Multiple-resistance also is a growing concern in some regions heavily reliant on fungicides. Indeed, resistance to many newer fungicides introduced in the early 1980s emerged so quickly that a 1988 report issued by the American Phytopathological Society concluded that the capacity of pathogens to adapt to selective fungicides "makes it difficult to be optimistic that organic chemistry will be able to solve the fungicide resistance problem" (Delp, 1988).

C. Reliance and Risk

One goal of biointensive IPM is to reduce the quantity of pesticides applied and the number of acre-treatments, while also reducing the average toxicity of pesticides applied and the risks stemming from applications. The only reliable way to monitor the linkage between reducing pesticide use and reliance and reducing pesticide risks is to study a pest management system before and after changes are made. Changes must be noted in both pesticide acre-treatments and quantity applied, then weighted by the relative toxicity of the chemical applied, taking into account its environmental fate.

Low Dose Pesticides Do Not Change Reliance But Are Changing Risks

The switch in the late 1980s and 1990s to highly active low dose insecticides and herbicides has reduced some categories of risk, including applicator exposure and chronic health risks from herbicides in drinking water. But low dose pesticides have increased other agricultural, ecological and environmental risks, even when present at levels too low for the most sensitive equipment to detect (EPA, 1989).

> A 1988 report concluded that the capacity of plant pathogens to adapt to selective fungicides "makes it difficult to be optimistic that organic chemistry will be able to solve the fungicide resistance problem."

Many low dose pesticides work because they are persistent and have a specific physiological mode of action. These same properties, however, also may promote development of resistance in target pest populations (Burnet et al., 1994; Warwick, 1991; Wrubel and Gressel, 1994). Persistent pesticides are more likely to trigger resistance because they last longer in the environment—whether in a homeowner's basement or a farm field—and thus sustain selection pressure longer. This selection pressure occurs during the time when only resistant pests can survive a pesticide dose and go on to reproduce. Their genotype is selected for its ability to overcome or detoxify the pesticide. Only a few pests need survive to instill resistant genes in a population, a process that can occur within a season or two (NRC, 1986; Maxwell et al., 1990; Holt, 1992).

Attempting to lower pesticide risks by switching to low dose products can also disrupt ecosystems and food chains in unexpected ways, posing unanticipated risks. Some new (and old) pesticides reduce populations of mycorrhizae that play an essential role in making phosphorous available to plant root systems (Forlani et al., 1995; Huber and

McCay-Buis, 1993). Others can disrupt microbial communities that colonize plant roots or the surface of plant leaves, heightening the plants' vulnerability to damaging pathogens (Gilbert et al., 1994; NRC, 1989a; Whipps et al., 1993). Persistent insecticides that are highly toxic to target pests can reduce pest populations so effectively that beneficial organisms preying on pests also disappear, rendering the crop more vulnerable late in its production cycle.

Growing reliance on highly specific and persistent pesticides is clearly shifting the nature of risk, levels of risk, and who and what part of the environment bears different risks. It will take years for science to provide a comprehensive assessment of overall risks. For these reasons, it is best to assess reliance holistically and reduce it systematically.

Environmental problems and health risks from pesticide use can be reduced most quickly through progress along the IPM continuum, coupled with action by regulators to restrict or ban known high risk products. The next chapters set forth the reasons for such a dual strategy and its essential elements.

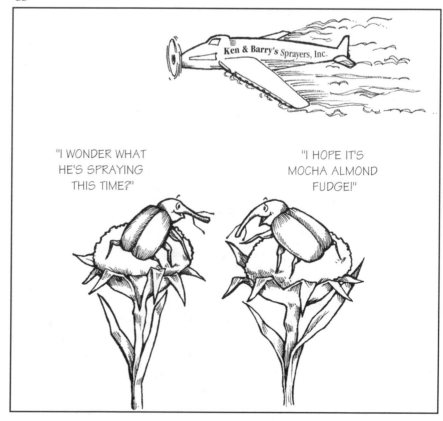

[1] Global sales growth estimate from *Agrow* March and April, 1996 issues.

[2] EPA and industry estimates of pesticide use and expenditures vary. The industry survey represents sales of the leading 20 to 25 companies. EPA estimates for the same years include sales by all firms in the industry. All EPA pesticide expenditure data are reported in nominal dollars (Aspelin, 1994, 1996).

[3] Gold has been trading recently for about $390.00 per ounce, according to the "Your Money" feature in the August, 1996 *Consumer Reports*. An ounce of codling moth pheromone from Shin-Etsu Chemical Company, Tokyo, Japan, would cost about $604.00. More than a dozen pheromones sell for $604.00 per ounce or more (1995 Shin-Etsu Chemical Co. product catalogue). The insecticide abamectin sells for about $330.00 per ounce (Gianessi, 1995).

[4] Quote from Chapter 1 (Reuveni, 1995).

[5] From the "Foreword," *Integrated Pest Management: Strategy and Policy Options for Promoting Effective Implementation*, World Bank, March 1996 (draft).

[6] Dr. Chaney quotes from Mid-March, 1996 *California Farmer*.

[7] Quote from remarks delivered in Sacramento, California on October 6, 1995 before the Pest Management Advisory Committee, California Department of Pesticide Regulation.

[8] Several other classes of pesticides play a role in insect pest management, either by impacting target pests or beneficials, such as nematicides (used to control nematodes), miticides (mites) and soil fumigants (insects, weeds and plant pathogens).

[9] "Wheat" pesticide use is sometimes reported as all wheat, and other times winter wheat, spring wheat or durum wheat, or combinations of these types. In addition, wheat pesticide use is sometimes reported per planted acre and sometimes per harvested acre, which can matter since 10 percent to 15 percent of planted acreage is generally not harvested (see for example, Appendix Table 3 in Lin et al., 1995). Hence, wheat pesticide use data can be easily misinterpreted because only about one-half of winter wheat acres are treated, but over 95 percent of other types of wheat are treated.

[10] EPA, USDA and National Center for Food and Agriculture Policy (Gianessi and Anderson, 1995) estimates of pesticide use vary modestly as a function of crops and regions included in estimates, statistical techniques, time frames and the active ingredients included.

[11] See the crop consultant and other pest management and precision farming discussion groups on @g Online for recent examples of the problems farmers are experiencing with low dose and other herbicides. The address for @g Online on the World Wide Web is http://www.agriculture.com

[12] These were among the points made by Dr. Michael Duffy and Dr. Michael Owen during their presentations at the "Weed Biology, Soil Management, and New Approaches to Weeds Workshop," June 26-28, 1995, at the Scheman Continuing Education Building, Ames, Iowa. The workshop was sponsored by the National Soil Tilth Center, ARS/USDA.

[13] Reported at the Workshop described in footnote 11.

[14] Information on the discovery of Roundup resistant ryegrass in Australia is from the July 8, 1996 PANUPS Internet posting (Pesticide Action Network North America Updates Service). The PANUPS bulletin draws upon several sources including *The Canberra Times*, *Financial Review* and *The Australian*.

[15] Cotton seeds are used as a source of oil, which plays several roles in food preparation. A byproduct of the crushing process, cotton-seed meal is feed to livestock. Before a new cotton insecticide is registered, tolerances must be established for residues in these byproducts of the cotton ginning process and in some cases, meat and dairy products.

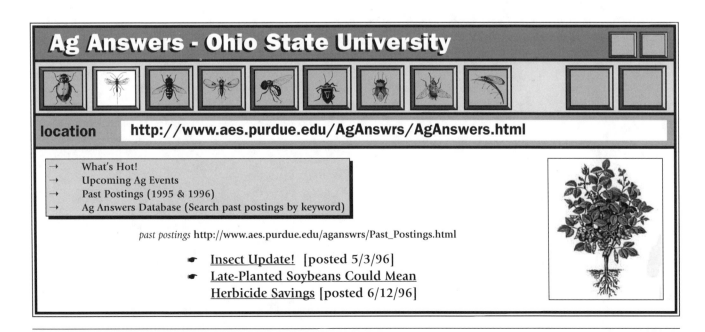

Pesticide Risks

Surprisingly little progress has been made since the 1960s in reducing overall pesticide risks. Widely used products still pose substantial risks to human health and to the ecological processes that sustain all life.

Since the 1960s, billions of dollars have been spent on pesticide health and safety studies, regulation and on research that has brought about 300 new pesticide active ingredients to market. Progress has been made in lowering some pesticide risks to human health and the environment, but on balance, today's chemical-intensive pest management systems pose as much risk, overall, as those in the 1960s and early 1970s, and in some circumstances pose more risk.

Managing pesticide risks and comparing risk levels over time is complicated because the nature of harm caused by pesticides has changed dramatically as different pesticides have come and gone. The distribution of risks among segments of the human population most likely to suffer adverse impacts—farm workers and consumers—also has changed, as have types of wildlife at greatest risk and parts of the environment most vulnerable to contamination. And there is no way retrospectively to gather the data and conduct the research needed to determine the scope and severity in the 1960s of human health and environmental risks stemming from the pesticides used in that era, making comparisons between then and now incomplete. Nevertheless, some clear trends and conclusions regarding the nature of risk emerge from the data reviewed in this chapter.

Overview

Since the 1960s—the "golden age of pesticides," in the words of two agricultural scientists (Ragsdale and Sisler, 1994)—the use of several highly toxic and environmentally damaging pesticides has been stopped, including:

- most uses of the chlorinated hydrocarbon insecticides (DDT, chlordane and heptachlor, endrin, aldrin and dieldrin, toxaphene and lindane) were banned.

- herbicides containing dioxin (especially 2,4,5-T, also called Silvex) either were banned or manufacturing processes were altered to lower dioxin content markedly.

- the fumigants DBCP (dibromochloropropane) and EDB (ethylene dibromide) were banned.

- high risk dust and liquid formulations, including several marketed to homeowners, of carbon tetrachloride, ben-

---

The following basic terms are used throughout this book

Risk is the probability of some adverse impact or effect caused by a pesticide. It is a function of exposure and toxicity. Exposure is a function of use, caution exercised by applicators, environmental fate and many other factors.

Toxicity is the capacity of a pesticide to cause a defined adverse impact on a living organism; it includes potency, a measure of the capacity of a pesticide to do harm per unit of exposure.

Hazard is a known set of potential adverse impacts, like acute poisoning or cancer. Potential hazard is comparable to the notion of risk as we use the term, and is also a function of exposure and toxicity.

---

zene, chlordecone and mirex, as well as several very acutely toxic insecticides, were phased out or banned.

- a variety of inorganic pesticides involving formulations of lead, arsenic, mercury, copper and zinc were banned for most uses.

As these highly hazardous ingredients were driven off the market, others gained wider use. Despite gaps in data and the need for more analysis, enough is known about major categories of risks associated with use of soil fumigants, insecticides, fungicides and herbicides to draw some conclusions about general trends in risk levels since the 1960s.

Agricultural use of **soil fumigants** has always been concentrated on relatively few acres in a few regions where high-value fruit, vegetable and ornamental crops are grown. Modern day soil fumigants like methyl bromide, 1,3-Dichloropropene (Telone) and metam-sodium (Vapam) are toxic, volatile and pose significant risks, including ozone layer depletion. In addition, these fumigants often must be applied at a higher rate to be as effective as those used in the 1960s and 1970s were. We cannot judge whether overall soil fumigant risks have gone up or down since the 1960s, but we are confident that changes in the nature and uses of soil fumigants have had little impact on total pesticide risk levels and trends.

Insecticides are used much more widely and frequently than fumigants in both agriculture and urban settings, and in the home. Insecticides contribute prominently to aggregate pesticide exposure and risks, especially among farm workers and applicators, and in terms of environmental pollution. Insecticides that replaced chlorinated hydrocarbons used in the 1960s generally pose different and more varied risks. Today's insecticides are markedly more acutely toxic to humans, mammals, aquatic organisms and many other life forms, including beneficial arthropods. On the positive side, current risk data indicate that long-term chronic exposure to contemporary insecticides may be somewhat less hazardous to mammals and humans than was true for insecticides of the past.

> Overall insecticide risks today seem at least as great as they were in the early 1970s. Where reliance has increased, both on the farm and in urban settings, risks are probably greater today, with the possible exception of cotton growing regions.

Most insecticides used today are applied at lower rates than the major products of the 1960s were. But the number of products being applied, number of applications, and the diversity and duration of uses all have risen or remained about the same, as shown in Chapter 2. Hence, many people today are exposed to insecticides more often, for longer periods and through more routes of exposure than in the past. In addition, reliance on insecticides in agriculture is rising. The average application rate on major field crops (corn, soybeans, cotton, wheat, and potatoes) has gone up from 1.05 pounds active ingredient per acre in 1991 to 1.33 pounds in 1995, and the average number of treatments with a distinct active ingredient per acre has almost doubled, from 1.8 in 1991 to 3.5 in 1995 (USDA Cropping Practices Surveys, 1991-1995).

Adverse impacts of insecticides on beneficial organisms and associated consequences for crops and environmental quality are also increasing. While several dozen relatively safe biopesticides, such as *Bt*, have been registered, these products still account for only a few percent of insecticide sales and treatments. Pest managers in many regions and situations remain firmly stuck on the "pesticide treadmill."

For these reasons, overall insecticide risks today seem at least as great as they were in the early 1970s. In regions where reliance has increased, risks stemming from insecticide use are probably greater today than in the 1970s, with the possible exception of cotton growing regions.

National agricultural reliance on and use of relatively high risk **fungicides** have remained comparatively stable since the 1960s, although usage has recently been rising. Fungal plant diseases are constantly evolving, and in the last few years, several tough-to-control new strains have plagued wheat and potato farmers in particular. Average fungicide application rates in major field crops have risen from 2.2 pounds active ingredient per acre in 1991 to 3.5 pounds in 1995, with potatoes accounting for much of the increase (USDA Cropping Practices Surveys, 1991-1995). Few new fungicides have gained registration since the 1970s. Most of those that have pose risks roughly comparable to the products they are displacing.

In addition, since the mid-1970s plant breeders of new crop and horticultural varieties have been focusing more on yields, processing traits, hardiness in shipping and aesthetic appeal than on improving resistance to

The line between backyard and vineyard is often narrow in California, creating another challenge for pest managers. The need to eliminate applications of many pesticides along the edges of housing developments, near roads, schools and parks has helped stir interest in biointensive IPM and organic farming techniques.
Credit: Richard Steven Street

plant diseases (Robinson, 1996). Farmers generally have become more specialized and less likely to use crop rotations to break disease cycles (Madden, 1992; NRC, 1989a, 1993b). As a result, plant pathogens and diseases are as damaging and difficult to control as ever, and most golf courses, ornamental growers, and fruit and vegetable farmers in humid regions remain heavily reliant on fungicides (e.g., see USDA, 1994b, 1996d; Gianessi and Anderson, 1995). The nature of risks from fungicides has changed relatively little in the last 30 years, but the overall level of risk from this category of pesticides is now probably rising as reliance on them increases.

Trends in **herbicide** risks are more complicated to evaluate because many variables have changed over the last three decades. It is clear that the risks posed by herbicides are growing both more diverse and more prevalent in urban, suburban and rural settings. Acres of lawns and crops treated and the number of products applied have risen dramatically; changes in toxicity have been mixed; and pounds applied have trended downward. Still, because of much wider use in urban areas and around the home and higher levels of reliance in agriculture, overall herbicide risks today clearly exceed those of the early 1970s.

Herbicide contamination of drinking water, now a common seasonal occurrence in many regions, is an important relatively new route of exposure for millions of Americans. Herbicide impacts on the health and stability of many aquatic ecosystems are on the increase, sharply so in some areas (Walker et al., 1995). The recently introduced low-dose agricultural herbicides pose greater hazards to crop plants, rotational crops and adjoining vegetation, as well as to aquatic ecosystems and soil microorganisms.

Overall Risks

The evidence reviewed in this chapter supports the conclusion that pesticide risks today are at least as serious as they were in the early 1970s. In addition, overall risk and some specific types of risks appear to be currently increasing. They are likely to continue rising until we manage as a nation to change the pest management status quo, moving away from reliance on pesticides through

> Pesticide risks today are at least as serious as they were in the early 1970s and are rising in some regions and circumstances. Significant overall reductions in risk will require changing the pest management status quo, moving away from such high levels of reliance on pesticides through incremental progress toward biointensive IPM.

incremental progress toward biointensive IPM.

Progress in developing safer pesticide products, coupled with adoption of Integrated Pest Management (IPM) systems and greater attention to the need for safety precautions, have lowered the per treatment risk for individual pesticide products in many, but not all circumstances. But the number and range of treatments are rising, and people are exposed more often and for longer periods by more routes to a wider variety of pesticides than in the past. Many pesticides widely used today are much more potent and biologically active than products used in the past, despite being less toxic in certain respects to some organisms, usually including mammals. The net results of changes in pesticide chemistry and modes of action include a diversification in the nature of risks and heightened uncertainty over the consequences of pesticide use, new exposure pathways, and more complex threats to environmental integrity and ecosystem function, including agroecosystems.

Further research on the levels of and trends in pesticide risks to human health and ecosystems is clearly needed. We hope the data presented here and our conclusions will motivate others to carry out more detailed analyses on individual crops, categories of pesticides, types of risk, as well as all risks together. Insights that emerge from such analyses will help both in setting IPM research and education priorities and in targeting regulations.

The capacity to monitor pesticide risk trends is also critical in judging when and where IPM and regulation have done their job and reduced pest management system risks comfortably below levels society is willing to accept. That day remains in the future. Still, it is time to begin formulating ways to tell when it draws close, or recedes, for example because of the emergence of new pests or slippage in the efficacy of pest management systems.

Information on trends is valuable to policy makers, but recognizing inflection points, that is, times when pesticide risks start either rising or falling sharply compared to the recent past, is even more critical. If policy makers miss or do not respond to such changes, problems are likely to grow more serious and persist longer than they might otherwise and cost more to overcome.

A. Environmental Risks from Pesticides

Most environmental risks and ecological damage from pesticide use result from toxic effects of pesticides on various living organisms. Ozone depletion and impacts on air quality are exceptions, although living things ultimately face consequences from these changes as well.

Impacts on non-target organisms, including humans, depend on how the pesticide degrades and moves through the hydrological cycle, the soil and food chains. Factors such as the prevalence of treatments in an area, the toxicity of a product to various organisms and its environmental fate—persistence, likelihood of leaching into groundwater or contaminating surface water via runoff—all affect exposure, and hence hazards, to non-target organisms.

Fish and bird kills caused by pesticides tend to occur where much of the land in a defined geographic area—a watershed or a golf course, for example—is treated with the same or similar pesticides. Adverse impacts on beneficial organisms tend to be greatest where several different pesticides, especially insecticides, are applied routinely.

Some classes of pesticides are toxic to almost all life forms. The organophosphate and carbamate insecticides fall into this category, as do many soil fumigants. Other pesticides are relatively safe for most life forms, including beneficial organisms, but are highly toxic to certain fish, birds or microorganisms. The fungicide benomyl, for example, is extremely toxic to earthworms and several aquatic organisms (Mayer and Ellersieck, 1986), but poses modest acute risk to mammals (International Programme on Chemical Safety, 1994). One class of insect growth regulators is toxic to shellfish and aquatic organisms dependent on chitin to form parts of their exo-skeletons or shells, but relatively non-toxic to most other non-target organisms.

> *"The chemical war is never won, and all life is caught in its violent crossfire."*
>
> **Rachel Carson,** *Silent Spring, 1962*

1. Pesticide Toxicity to Beneficial Organisms

Secondary pest problems result from the adverse impacts of pesticides on non-target beneficial organisms that have been helping control populations of target pests, often unbeknownst to pest managers. Most serious cotton insect pests in the last decade, for example, are secondary pests. Resistance to insecticides used to control the boll weevil or tobacco budworm—cotton's two most damaging pests—has led to an increase in the number, frequency and toxicity of insecticides applied. Intensified applications, in turn, have reduced the diversity and populations of surviving beneficials, permitting previously innocuous species to undergo rapid population growth and become damaging secondary pests.

To avoid this pesticide treadmill, scientists have sought pesticide active ingredients that are selective—ideally, chemicals that affect only the target pest. The selectivity of pesticides and their impacts on beneficial organisms have been comprehensively reviewed by Oregon State University entomologists Dr. Brian Croft and Karen Theiling (Croft, 1990; Theiling and Croft, 1988). They assessed the relative impacts of pesticides on target pests and on more than 600 species of beneficial arthropods, mostly parasitoids and predator species.

The analysts scored impacts of 400 pesticide active ingredients on beneficials, using a 5-point scale, where 1 represents no effect, 5 represents between 90 and 100 percent mortality, and intermediate values represent toxicity levels between those extremes. The authors calculated average scores for each pesticide's impact on beneficials, then divided pesticides into three general categories: "selective" materials with toxicity values less than 2.8; "moderately toxic" pesticides with values between 2.8 and 3.5; and "harmful" ones, with values of more than 3.5. Some results of their analysis are shown in Table 3.1.

In general, Croft and Theiling found that predators were less susceptible to pesticides than parasitoids, but that pesticide impacts on predators were more variable. Insecticides were the most toxic class of pesticides, followed by herbicides, acaricides (mite-killers) and fungicides. Among insecticides, the synthetic pyrethroids were the most toxic to beneficial arthropods, and products like *Bt* and IGRs (insect growth regulators) were least harmful to beneficials.

These results and other data in the Croft-Theiling database show that insecticides are "harmful" to both major types of beneficial arthropods, fungicides fall into the "selective" category for both types of beneficials, and herbicides are "moderately toxic" to predators and "harmful" to parasitoids.

Measuring Selectivity

The authors developed a useful measure of a pesticide's relative toxicity to target pests in contrast to beneficial arthropods—the selectivity ratio. This variable is the dose required to kill 50 percent of the target pest divided by the dose needed to kill 50 percent of affected beneficial species. Selectivity ratios for different pesticide active ingredients varied from 0.0001 to greater than 3,000. Using a log transformation, the authors compressed this wide range down to a scale from 1 to 9 to reduce the impact of outliers. Any pesticide with a selectivity ratio (log transformed) index value of 5 was neutral— i.e., the dose required to kill 50 percent of the target pest equaled the dose required to kill 50 percent of beneficials. The average transformed selectivity ratio value was 4.6, indicating that pesticides are, on average, slightly less damaging to beneficial arthropods than they are to target pests (Theiling and Croft, 1988).

Figure 3.1 presents some of the study's major findings on toxic effects (scale of 1 to 5) and selectivity (scale of 1 to 9), focusing on pesticides widely used today. Based on their findings, Croft and Theiling conclude that:

Table 3.1 Relative Impacts of Pesticides on Beneficial Arthropods by Type of Pesticide: Scale of 1 to 5

(1=No Impact; 5=90% to 100% Mortality)

Pesticide Class	Predators	Parasitoids	All Beneficials
Insecticides	3.61	3.74	3.65
Fungicides	2.59	2.58	2.59
Herbicides	2.83	3.10	2.95
All Pesticides	3.43	3.57	3.47

Source: Adapted from Table 2 (Theiling and Croft, 1988).

"Increasing toxicity to non-target arthropods has prevailed since the development of DDT, and has persisted through the synthetic pyrethroids ... the most commonly used pesticides tend to be moderately to highly toxic to natural enemies, while the selective compounds are less commonly used and tested."

Impacts on Other Organisms

Despite widespread interest in their work, Croft and Theiling were unable to secure funding to continue

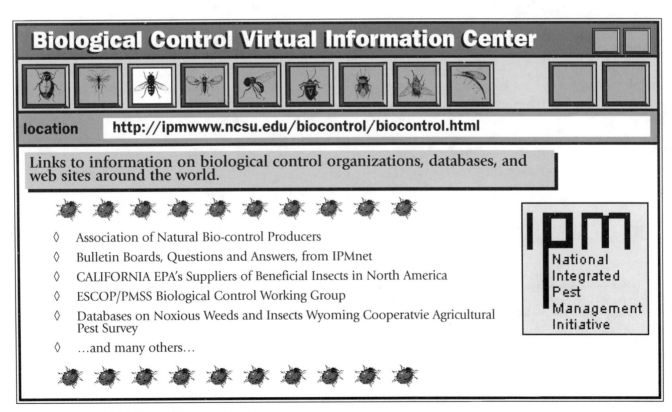

Biological Control Virtual Information Center

location http://ipmwww.ncsu.edu/biocontrol/biocontrol.html

Links to information on biological control organizations, databases, and web sites around the world.

◊   Association of Natural Bio-control Producers
◊   Bulletin Boards, Questions and Answers, from IPMnet
◊   CALIFORNIA EPA's Suppliers of Beneficial Insects in North America
◊   ESCOP/PMSS Biological Control Working Group
◊   Databases on Noxious Weeds and Insects Wyoming Cooperatvie Agricultural Pest Survey
◊   ...and many others...

ipm
National Integrated Pest Management Initiative

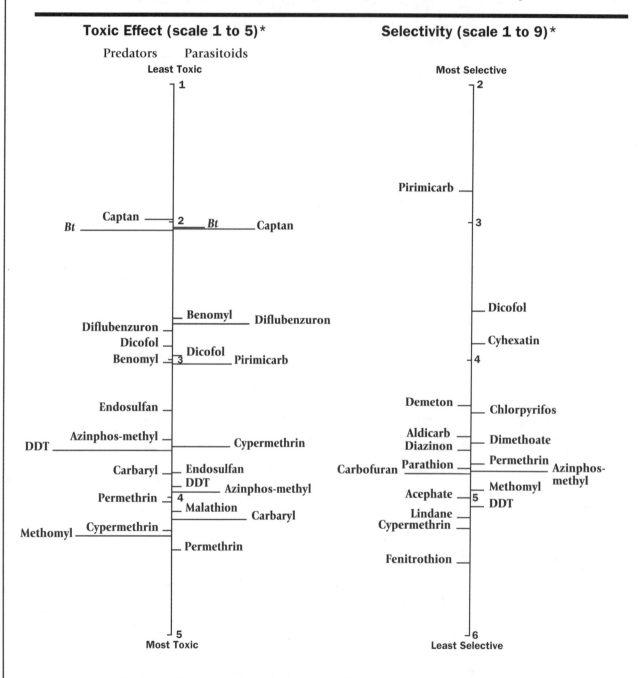

Figure 3.1 The Toxicity and Selectivity of Widely Used Pesticides to Beneficial Arthropods (Natural Enemies)

*Toxic Effect Scale: 1=0% mortality; 2=<10% mortality; 3=10-30%; 4=30-90%; and, 5=90-100% mortality. Selectivity Ratio Scale: 5=neutral impact; values less than 5 are progressively more selective; values grater than 5 are progressively damaging to beneficial arthropods. No values fall below 2 or above 6 so just the range 2 through 6 is shown.

Source: Adapted from Theiling and Croft, 1988, Tables 4 and 7.

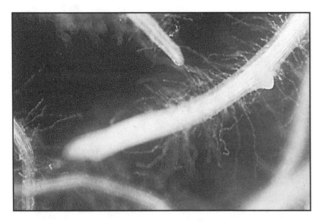 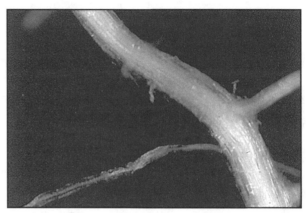

The wheat root pathogen Pythium attackes the tiny hair-like feeder roots evident on the normal root (left). The diseased root (right) will be less efficient in extracting moisture and nutrients from the soil and will lead to higher nutrient losses in surface water runoff. Credit: Dr. James Cook, ARS

building their database. No comparable database exists on pesticide impacts on microorganisms, even though there is much evidence that pesticides adversely affect soil microbial communities, weakening root systems, heightening plant susceptibility to diseases and reducing the availability of key nutrients, especially nitrogen and phosphorous (Cook and Veseth, 1991; Huber and Watson, 1974; Huber and McCay-Buis, 1993; Hudson, 1994; Daane et al., 1995; Gilbert et al., 1994; Jawson et al., 1993; Liebman and Epstein, 1992, 1995; NRC, 1993b; Werner and Dindal, 1990).

2. Aquatic Toxicity

Pesticides pose risks to fish and other aquatic organisms, which in turn play roles in aquatic food chains. While most pesticides are not applied to water bodies intentionally, drift from applications nearby, atmospheric deposition and runoff from treated fields, application error and illegal use can still pose risks to sensitive organisms. In general, pesticides are much more toxic to young fish, shrimp and other aquatic animals than to adults (Mayer, 1986; Mayer and Ellersieck, 1986). Water temperature also can heighten pesticide toxicity, since at

Coaxing Mother Nature Back on the Team

Where reliance on synthetic pesticides is high, a first step toward more biologically based pest management often involves reducing use of broadly toxic products so that beneficial organisms have a chance to become reestablished. This process takes time—sometimes just a few months, in other cases many years—before complex food chains and soil quality can be restored (NRC, 1993b).

In the Midwest it takes about five years for a healthy population of earthworms to become established on row crop land once a farmer cuts back on tillage and use of pesticides toxic to worms. But the dividends can include a faster and more thorough breakdown of organic material, greater infiltration of water and water holding capacity, and healthier root development. According to Ohio State University entomologist Dr. Clive Edwards, "What comes out the back end of a worm is up to 10 times more useful that what goes in the front."[1]

Much more research is needed on the impacts of pesticides on beneficial arthropods, soil microorganisms and worms, and other beneficial organisms—a need we return to in our Recommendations. Despite gaps in knowledge, much information is available on beneficial arthropods and other organisms that can help keep pests under control and improve the health of the soil and ecosystems. Some locations on the World Wide Web offering such information are noted in Web page boxes.

higher temperatures, animal metabolic rates tend to be higher. Fortunately, pesticides often break down quickly in water in hot and humid regions.

Fast breakdown of pesticides in warm water was not enough to avoid major problems in the bayous of Louisiana in recent years. A string of major fish kills since 1990 have been caused by aerial applications of Guthion (azinphos-methyl) to control the sugarcane stalk borer. Conservative estimates place the 1991 loss at one million fish—largemouth bass, yellow bass, striped bass, bluegill, perch "... the 1991 poisonings were among the worst in U.S. history," according to a review of several Guthion poisoning incidents. At least 15 fish kill incidents were confirmed by the state in 1991.[2]

Comparable incidents have occurred in many other regions. Levels of endosulfan and methyl parathion in a 16 mile stretch of Big Nance Creek, a tributary of the Tennessee River, reached toxic concentrations for a variety of fish.[3] State agency personnel estimated the kill at 240,000 fish, made worse by a flush of rains that washed recently applied pesticides off cotton fields.[4]

The most complete published compilation of aquatic toxicity data on pesticides was released in 1986 by the U.S. Fish and Wildlife Service (FWS). The report covers some 5,000 studies of impacts of 410 chemicals on 66 aquatic species; many studies include several life stages and exposure intervals (Mayer and Ellersieck, 1986). Among the major conclusions:

- Water fleas such as *Daphnia* are generally the most sensitive species, followed by other crustaceans like shrimp and crayfish. Amphibians are least sensitive.

- Rainbow trout are the most sensitive fish species tested, second only to water fleas among all species tested.

- Temperature increases the toxicity of organophosphates—on average, 5.1 fold for each 10 degree centigrade increase in water temperature.

- Sensitivity to pesticides is much greater in young organisms.

- Many pesticide active ingredients are toxic to aquatic organisms and fish even in the low parts per billion range.

Immune System Key Target

Just as in humans, one of the mechanisms through which pesticides adversely impact fish is the immune system (see the review by Dunier and Siwicki, 1993). Several chlorinated hydrocarbon and organophosphate insecticides are known to adversely impact fish immune systems. Trout and salmon species are particularly sensi-

tive to some pesticides, apparently because they affect the neuroendocrine system in ways that can markedly depress immune response. A report by the Northwest Coalition for Alternatives to Pesticides documented several adverse pesticide impacts on the Coho salmon (Grier et al., 1994), some of which reflect the immuno-toxicity of pesticides used in Washington state agriculture and forestry.

3. Avian Toxicity

Rachel Carson's documentation of the impacts of DDT and other chlorinated hydrocarbon insecticides on birds in *Silent Spring* struck a chord with the public because many people had noticed greater than normal seasonal decreases in local bird populations, and had wondered why. The adverse impacts of many pesticides on birds are now well documented. For example, EPA has carried out an extensive assessment of the avian risks posed by the highly toxic granular soil insecticide carbofuran (Furadan).

The EPA estimates that this single carbamate insecticide causes one to two million bird deaths a year. The U.S. Fish and Wildlife Service has documented more than 150 incidents of bird kills caused by carbofuran, some involving more than 2,000 birds (U.S. FWS, 1993). In Virginia, carbofuran use by corn farmers has been implicated in dozens of bald eagle deaths, triggering years of controversy involving the State's Fish and Wildlife Service, agriculture department, farmers and the pesticide's manufacturer.

In many states farmers and ranchers have to exercise great caution in managing pests and conserving soil in order to not adversely impact water quality and native fish populations. Because of their efforts, Idaho's Falls River remains a high quality trout stream enjoyed by many fly fisherman, including Michael Benbrook.
Credit: Charles Benbrook

The EPA has been working toward banning a number of granular formulations of carbofuran and other soil insecticides because birds sometimes mistake the insecticide grains for seeds (Best and Fischer, 1992). Rice is now the only major crop on which granular carbofuran applications may still be made. Manufacturers began formulating granular insecticides in response to EPA concerns that the liquid formulations were exposing mixer-applicators to unacceptable risks. In this and many other cases, human risks were reduced but avian risks rose as a result.

A frequent cause of poisoning in eagles and other birds that feed on carrion is consuming the carcasses of sheep or other animals that have been baited with pesticides—often illegally—to kill coyotes. At least two eagles were killed in southeastern Idaho in March or April 1995 after feeding on a sheep carcass laced with aldicarb, according to the January 15, 1996 report from the pesticides section of U.S. EPA Region 10.[5]

Recent Fish and Wildlife Service data on avian poisoning incidents show that two families of insecticides—organophosphates and carbamates—were the most frequent cause of pesticide-related bird kills in 1994 and 1995, including episodes involving Canada geese, many species of ducks, pheasants, common grackles, robins and blue jays (U.S. FWS, 1996). These episodes are hardly a surprise since both the U.S. FWS and the EPA are aware that several insecticides will in some locations be lethal to birds even when used in accord with the label (U.S. FWS, 1993).

Immune System Again a Major Concern

As with fish, the immune system of birds may be a particularly sensitive target of pesticide toxicity. Since birds have to contend with a number of parasites and pathogens, anything that suppresses immune response may also impair a bird's ability to deal with otherwise benign threats.

In one of the first studies of its kind, scientists at Kansas State University found that when bobwhite quail were exposed to carbaryl, a common carbamate insecticide, at levels that commonly remain in a field after

> *"Carbofuran is very toxic to terrestrial and aquatic fauna ...Eleven field studies and several monitoring programs corroborate that proper use of carbofuran consistently causes wildlife losses."*
>
> **U.S. Fish and Wildlife Service,** *1993*

Crimson clover is one of the most popular cover crops in vineyards and orchards in California because of its hardiness and ability to attract beneficial insects. Credit: Richard Steven Street

> *"...diazinon use on golf courses and sod farms causes an unreasonable risk to birds commonly and with considerable frequency. Moreover, the record (of EPA's special review of diazinon) fails to show that regulatory alternatives short of cancellation would reduce risk to reasonable levels."*
>
> **EPA Administrator Remand Decision Upholding Diazinon Cancellation on Sod Farms and Golf Courses** *(EPA, 1990c)*

normal agricultural use, the quail were much more susceptible to a disease transmitted by the protozoan parasite *Histomonas meleagridis* (Zeakes et al., 1981). At the higher of two doses tested, the insecticide led to the death of more than 60 percent of the birds, far more than in the control group.

Trends in Bird and Fish Toxicity

In the 1960s and 1970s, the ecological impacts of pesticide use were magnified due to relatively high per-acre applications of chemicals that were both persistent and prone to concentrate as they moved up food chains. Use of insecticides, the most toxic category of pesticides to most non-target organisms, peaked in the early 1970s. Cotton accounted for almost half of all pounds applied, so wherever cotton was a common crop, ecological impacts were significant. But these general trends and data often mask significant regional, local—or even backyard—impacts of pesticide use on wildlife andthe environment.

Pest resistance to chlorinated hydrocarbon insecticides like DDT, chlordane, aldrin/dieldrin and toxaphene, coupled with EPA regulations, promoted a switch during the 1960s and 1970s to organophosphates (OPs) and carbamates. These chemicals are much less persistent and less likely to concentrate in food chains, but are more acutely toxic to many non-target organisms. Pesticide risks to wildlife diversified in the 1970s and worsened in many regions (Colborn et al., 1993; Facemire, 1991). A significant number of persistent, older insecticides remained in food, water and soil at gradually declining levels even as wildlife and non-target organisms were exposed to new hazards.

Excerpts from the Erice Workshop Consensus Statement on Environmental Endocrine-Disrupting Chemicals November 5-10, 1995

"We are certain of the following":

"Endocrine-disrupting chemicals can undermine neurological and behavioral development and subsequent potential of individuals exposed in the womb or fish, amphibians, reptiles, and birds, the egg. This loss of potential in humans and wildlife is expressed as behavioral and physical abnormalities."

"Because the endocrine system is sensitive to perturbation, it is a likely target for disturbance…Man-made endocrine-disrupting chemicals range across all continents and oceans."

"Gestational exposure to persistent man-made chemicals reflects the lifetime of exposure of females before they become pregnant. Hence, the transfer of contaminants to the developing embryo and fetus during pregnancy and to the newborn during lactation is not simply a function of recent maternal exposure."

"The developing brain exhibits specific and often narrow windows during which exposure to endocrine disruptors can produce permanent changes in its structure and function."

"Sexual development of the brain is under the influence of estrogenic (female) and androgenic (male) hormones. Not all endocrine disruptors are estrogenic or anti-estrogenic. For example, new data reveal that DDE, a breakdown product of DDT, found in almost all living tissue, is an anti-androgen in mammals."

"We estimate with confidence that":

"Every pregnant woman in the world has endocrine disruptors in her body that are transferred to the fetus. She also has measurable concentrations of endocrine disruptors in her milk that are transferred to the infant."

"Because certain PCBs and dioxins are known to impair thyroid function, we suspect they contribute to learning disabilities, including attention deficit hyperactivity disorder and perhaps other neurological abnormalities. In addition, many pesticides affect thyroid function and, therefore, may have similar consequences."

"Our judgment is that":

"The benefits of reduced health care costs could be substantial if exposure to endocrine-disrupting chemicals were reduced."

"The message that endocrine disruptors are present in the environment and have the potential to affect many people over a lifespan has not effectively reached the general public, the scientific community, regulators, or policy makers. Although this message is difficult to reduce to simple statements without over- or understating the problem, the potential risks to human health are so widespread and far-reaching that any policy based on continued ignorance of the facts would be unconscionable."

Statement signed by 18 scientists from around the world (International School of Ethology, 1995)

Research on bird nesting and feeding behavior is essential in understanding which pesticides pose threats to breeding populations. Here, a University of Wisconsin researcher is returning a banded swan to a lake surrounded by some of Wisconsin's productive cropland.
Credit: Wolfgang Hoffman

average mammalian pesticide toxicity levels and decrease certain risks faced by people and other mammals. But some of these chemicals also appear to be having unexpected impacts on non-target organisms and interactions among organisms. New pesticides also may affect animal immune, endocrine or neurological systems in subtle but important ways. The need for more data, new test methods and field research is pervasive.

B. Mammalian Toxicity and Human Health Risks

The first step in assessing pesticide risks to human health is estimating exposure. Pesticide exposure assessment requires summing doses derived from residues stored in the body from past exposures and new doses ingested in food and water, inhaled in air, or absorbed through the skin. For people who work with pesticides or where they are frequently applied, occupational exposure often dwarfs all other sources combined (Moses et al., 1993).

Among the public at large, people who live in homes where pesticides have been applied frequently or who work in treated buildings sometimes receive greater exposure in these settings than through all other routes combined (U.S. EPA, 1990a; Grossman, 1995; Whitmore et al., 1992). In most cases, people are unaware when they are exposed to pesticides since posting of notices is rarely required and infrequently used. For example, a 1995 survey of 47 golf courses in Arizona found that only half notified golfers when pesticides would be or had been used.[6]

Everyone has pesticide residues in his or her body from past exposure. People also are exposed to pesticides through their diet nearly daily, but typically at very low levels. As much as a quarter of the American population may be exposed to detectable levels of pesticides in drinking water for periods ranging from a few weeks

Regulators focused more attention in the 1980s on ecological risks and requested more studies on aquatic, avian and other forms of ecotoxicity. Several products were canceled, suspended or dropped by manufacturers largely or solely because of ecological risks. While several pesticides highly toxic to wildlife are no longer used or are applied less widely, new wildlife risks are emerging. Several recently released herbicides, for example, can cause adverse impacts on microbial communities in the soil and on vegetation in aquatic ecosystems (Forlani et al., 1995; Fletcher, et al., 1993). Such impacts can in turn alter food chains and the competitive balance among organisms and species.

The trend toward more specific pesticides that work through a distinct mode of action has helped lower

> **Insecticides pose by far the greatest risk to most small mammals, birds and aquatic oganisms. Insecticide pounds applied nationwide have fallen since the early 1970s but reductions in cotton growing areas account for almost half of the drop. In addition, the average ecotoxicity of insecticides per pound applied has clearly risen since the early 1970s.**

to a substantial part of the year, and several million people are exposed by this route year-round (Goolsby et al., 1993; Nelson and Jones, 1994; U.S. EPA, 1990b). Recent research has shown that pesticide metabolites and breakdown products often are present in drinking water at higher concentrations than parent compounds (Kolpin et al., 1996).

In western states, most major rivers flow through high-valve, productive cropland. This Idaho alfalfa field is also home to deer, nesting birds and small mammals. Credit: Charles Benbrook

1. Pesticides in the Body and the Environment

Humans store residues of certain pesticides in body fat, and residues are released into the bloodstream when the body converts fat to calories. There is good news—average levels of DDT and the related metabolite DDE in serum (blood samples) and human milk declined from the 1960s through the early 1980s (Colborn et al., 1996). The bad news is that average pesticide residue levels in blood, breast milk, soil, fish and sediment stopped declining in the 1980s despite the end of most uses of organochlorine pesticides 20 years ago. DDT and DDE, as well as dioxins and PCBs, remain among the most commonly detected residues in fish and root crops like carrots, sugar beets and potatoes.

In addition, there is evidence that concentrations of these old and persistent chemicals are rising again in some places. Large quantities of old pesticides are bound to soil particles and sediment in the bottom of rivers, lakes and estuaries. Floods, dredging and storm conditions can stir up sediment containing pesticide residues. Normal microbial activity then decomposes sediment and in the process, can release once-bound pesticide residues into the environment where they can enter the food chain.

Concentrations of banned pesticides in U.S. soil and water can increase through another mechanism— atmospheric deposition and transport. DDT, chlordane, heptachlor and other persistent chemicals still are widely used in Asia, South America and other places. A 1995 arti-

cle in *Science* documented the global distribution of 22 organochlorine compounds, most of them pesticides (Simonich and Hites, 1995). Low levels of pesticide residues were found all over the world, even thousands of miles from where the products had been used. According to the article: "Even though DDT has been banned in the United States since 1973, its degradation products are very persistent in the environment; high concentrations of *p,p′*-DDE were still found in parts of the Midwest and Southwest." (Simonich and Hites, 1995).

2. Dietary Exposure

Most people consume from five to eight different foods each day in appreciable quantity, plus two to four beverages. The odds are good that one to three of the foods and one or two of the beverages will contain low levels of pesticide residues. At least a few of the foods will contain residues of more than one pesticide (USDA, 1995f, 1996b). During an average day, most of us consume trace amounts of three to five pesticides through our diet (NRC, 1993a; Wiles and Campbell, 1993b; Wargo, 1996; USDA, 1995f, 1996b).

The Food and Drug Administration (FDA) conducts an annual "Total Diet Study," to assess pesticide residues in common baskets of food selected in grocery stores around the country (Jones, 1996). FDA residue monitoring and comparable tests run by USDA, states and private laboratories consistently show that pesticide residue levels are generally well below existing tolerance levels—the legal limits governing pesticide residues in foods (Wargo, 1996; NAS, 1993a).

There were 9,341 pesticide tolerances in place as of April 1994 (Aspelin, 1994). The majority of tolerances covering high risk pesticides were set before 1970 and are based on the residue levels thought to remain after normal use of the pesticide according to label instructions. These "unavoidable" residue levels were estimated and tolerances were set by expert panels convened in the 1950s and 1960s by the Food and Drug Administration (NRC, 1987). There was little or no health and safety data at the time on which potential health risks to consumers could be assessed. In Chapter 4, we explain in more detail why consumers should not rest assured that residues far below tolerances are always "safe."

> Some 39 percent of 7,328 samples tested for residues in 1993 by USDA's Agricultural Marketing Service had two or more residues. One apple sample contained nine different pesticides.

Since the mid 1970s, tolerances have been set more carefully and with fuller consideration of available health and safety data. Still, the legal limits are based on residues remaining after pesticide applications made in accord with pesticide product labels. The health standards that should apply in setting and adjusting tolerances, and whether tolerances should be health-based or set using risk-benefit assessment, have been lively topics of debate for 15 years. By passing major food safety and pesticide regulatory reform legislation in July, 1996, Congress has finally settled many key aspects of the debate for now, although EPA faces difficult technical challenges in implementing the new health-based standard in H.R. 1627, the "Food Quality Protection Act of 1996" (see Chapter 4).

Complex Mixtures

Annual surveys by the USDA's Agricultural Marketing Service (AMS) provide clear evidence that consumers are exposed to mixtures of pesticide residues in their diets (USDA, 1995f, 1996b). AMS data in recent years show that residues of multiple active ingredients are nearly the norm and are surely not exceptional. In 1993, AMS examined 7,328 food samples and found residues of 58 different pesticides. Almost all were insecticides and fungicides applied on fruit and vegetable crops. Of these samples, 2,879 (39 percent) contained two or more residues. Diets composed of a variety of foods inevitably contain multiple residues.

Only a few studies have assessed the impact of complex mixtures of pesticides. A study done in Italy was set up to reflect both the levels of exposure commonly found in foods and the distribution of residue levels (Lodovic et al., 1994). The authors examined effects of mixtures of 15 pesticides most commonly found in the Italian diet and observed a number of indicators that the pesticide mixtures impaired rat liver function and induced free-radical damage of DNA.[7]

This damage occurred at relatively low doses that were comparable to actual exposure levels in the human diet. The authors also concluded that the impact of the residues "was abolished at higher levels of administration" through a mechanism discussed later in this chapter.

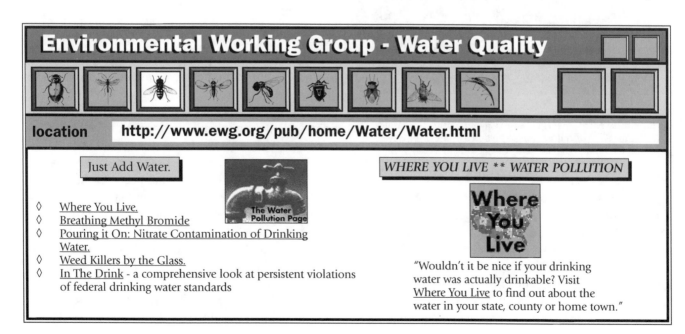

Environmental Working Group - Water Quality

location http://www.ewg.org/pub/home/Water/Water.html

Just Add Water.

◊ Where You Live.
◊ Breathing Methyl Bromide
◊ Pouring it On: Nitrate Contamination of Drinking Water.
◊ Weed Killers by the Glass.
◊ In The Drink - a comprehensive look at persistent violations of federal drinking water standards

The Water Pollution Page

WHERE YOU LIVE ** WATER POLLUTION

Where You Live

"Wouldn't it be nice if your drinking water was actually drinkable? Visit Where You Live to find out about the water in your state, county or home town."

3. *Exposure through Drinking Water*

Since water makes up a large portion of a person's total diet by weight, pesticide residues in water—even in the parts per billion range—can account for a significant share of total exposure. This is especially true among people not occupationally exposed and those who do not eat fish or other foods with high residue levels. While insecticide and fungicide residues are by far the most prevalent pesticides in foods, herbicides are most common in drinking water.

Herbicides in drinking water can account for a significant share of people's total exposure to pesticides in regions where row crops (e.g. corn, cotton, and sorghum) dominate the landscape (Goolsby et al., 1993; Mayerfeld et al., 1996; Hoppin et al., 1996). Some 24 million people are exposed to herbicides in drinking water in the Midwest and Great Lakes regions, according to a study released in 1994 by the Environmental Working Group (EWG) (Wiles et al., 1994). Allowable levels of many herbicides in drinking water exceed standards applicable to foods by a factor of 10 or more, despite the potential for much greater exposure from water.

Pesticide runoff into irrigation canals, streams and rivers can pose significant risks. This sign is posted in California's Imperial Valley and is intended to discourage people from swimming, fishing or drinking from this polluted river. Credit: Richard Steven Street

In most farming systems and soils, about 2 to 3 percent of applied herbicides are lost to surface water runoff (NRC, 1993b; Thurman, et al., 1991). Pesticide leaching into groundwater varies according to soil type, tillage and planting systems, irrigation methods and patterns of rainfall (Pease et al., 1993). Municipal drinking water utilities (and of course, their customers) spend millions of dollars annually testing for pesticides in drinking water, filtering

pesticides from contaminated water and seeking alternative water supplies (Carlin, 1990).

The EWG's first report on pesticides in drinking water—*Tap Water Blues*—found that about 95 percent of the people drinking from surface water sources in Missouri are exposed to two or more active ingredients (Wiles, et al., 1994). Herbicide contamination in the Great Lakes Basin also is widespread—100 percent of the samples studied by the U.S. Geological Survey in 1991 and 1992 contained atrazine. Most also contained either alachlor or metolachlor (Goolsby et al., 1991, 1993). In a second report released in August 1995, the EWG reported results of extensive surface water quality monitoring carried out in 29 cities throughout the Midwest in the spring and early summer of 1995. Results confirmed the earlier study's basic findings. Many contaminant levels exceeded MCLs (see Figure 3.2), and samples with four or more herbicide active ingredients were found in 21 of 29 cities.

4. *Other Routes of Exposure*

Beyond diet and drinking water routes of exposure, people encounter pesticides in numerous ways. Most of these routes of exposure have not been adequately studied and cannot be quantified as fully as residues ingested in food and water. Nevertheless, the available evidence is sufficient to suggest that non-dietary sources account for much higher exposure and risks to some people, during certain periods, than routine residue levels in food and water.

Many people are exposed to pesticides in the workplace. Those most highly exposed include workers in food storage and transportation jobs who fumigate truckloads or containers filled with produce or grain and those who open such containers, inspect or unload and clean them. Inspectors at border crossings and customs officials also can be at high risk when they must enter trucks or containers en-route to inspect for exotic pests, search for drugs or assure compliance with various record-keeping requirements. Several deaths occur annually around the world when railroad and ocean shipping workers are unaware that a given shipment has been treated with a highly volatile and toxic fumigant and fail to take appropriate precautions when unloading fumigated shipments.

A much larger number of applicators and farm workers are also exposed occupationally, especially those who load, mix, or spray pesticides, or work in fields frequently treated, and workers performing certain tasks within pesticide manufacturing plants. In 1977, 35 workers in a pesticide plant in Occidental, California were found to be

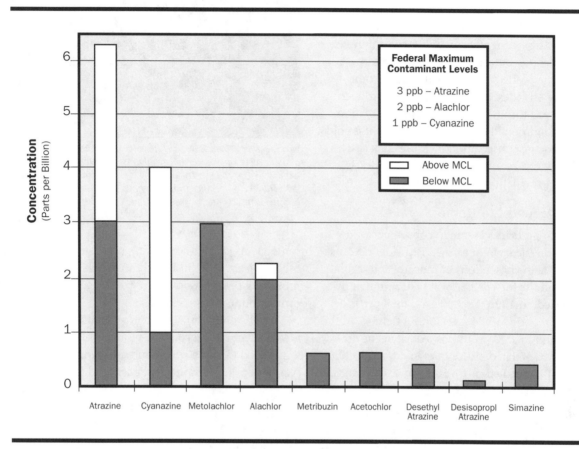

Figure 3.2 Nine Herbicide Active Ingredients and Metabolites Found in a Sample of Drinking Water in Fort Wayne, Indiana, Spring 1995

Federal Maximum Contaminant Levels

3 ppb – Atrazine
2 ppb – Alachlor
1 ppb – Cyanazine

☐ Above MCL
▨ Below MCL

Concentration (Parts per Billion)

Atrazine Cyanazine Metolachlor Alachlor Metribuzin Acetochlor Desethyl Atrazine Desisopropl Atrazine Simazine

Source: Herbicide and metabolite data from *Weed Killers By the Glass* (Cohen et al., 1995).

sterile due to exposure to the pesticide DBCP. At least 2,000 more workers who applied the pesticide on banana plantations in Central America were also sterilized (Thrupp, 1989). This and other episodes helped trigger cancellation of this pesticide and stricter controls in manufacturing facilities.

U.S. factory workers are protected by Occupational Safety and Health Administration regulations, but OSHA's current health protection standards in regulations have been criticized for being too lenient and often inadequately enforced.

Farm workers are not protected by OSHA standards. In the early 1990s, the U.S. EPA developed a Worker Protection Standard which would have established new requirements for the training of farm workers, notification of pesticide use, protective clothing and other safeguards.

However, the standard became highly controversial. When finally issued, it was so weakened that its original proponents regard it as likely to have little effect (Moses, 1996).

There are no national statistics compiled on farm worker pesticide poisonings. California keeps the best records of pesticide-related illnesses, and about half the illnesses reported in the state are associated with agricultural work. About 1,000 cases of agricultural pesticide poisonings are reported to the state annually (Pease et al., 1993). However, this figure is believed to seriously undercount actual poisoning episodes—with one analyst estimating that up to 80 percent of all incidents may go unreported (Wilkinson, 1990). Most reports come from medical providers. Agricultural workers, especially undocumented workers, frequently lack access to or do not seek medical treatment when suffering symptoms of poisoning (Mines and Kearney, 1982). Even for those that do have access, pesticide poisoning is easy to misdiagnose (Pease et al., 1993). Finally, many physicians are unaware of reporting requirements (Pesticide Safety Center Advisory Panel, 1992).

Office workers can also be exposed to pesticides on the job. Office buildings, schools, storage facilities and other structures are frequently sprayed to control insects, molds, and other pests. Risks are greatest in circumstances where the pesticides are volatile and become airborne. Such pesticides, or their breakdown products, can then be spread throughout a building's ventilation system. In air-conditioned buildings and where it is cold in the winter, energy conservation measures that seal buildings tightly can exacerbate exposure episodes as a result of limited circulation of fresh air.

Use In and Around the Home

A wide variety of pesticides is sold to consumers for use in the home, and on the lawn or garden. Pesticides do cause problems, despite the best efforts of industry and regulators to offer products for sale that will pose minimal risks if used as directed. In 1990, 110,000 accidental pesticide exposures were reported to Poison Control Centers. In the same year, around 23,000 people visited emergency rooms for pesticide-related health care. And from 1980 to 1990 about 20 people died each year from acute pesticide poisoning episodes (Blondell, 1992).

Insecticides are most commonly used indoors. Although the most widely marketed household bug-killers generally contain active ingredients of comparatively low mammalian toxicity, such as the synthetic pyrethroids, many household products do contain more toxic ingredients, and the ways in which consumers use the products may contribute to substantial levels of exposure.

Some products, such as pet flea collars and the now-banned "no-pest strips," work by constantly emitting insecticide vapors, which are readily inhaled by people living in the same space (as well as by their pets). Insect "bombs" can fill a room with insecticide residues that can remain for some time after treatment in rugs, on floors and in drapes and on furniture. Spraying baseboards and crevices for roaches can leave residues on floors. Infants and toddlers playing on floors or carpets

Farm worker exposure and risk from pesticide use in orchards remains a major focus of growers and regulators. Biointensive IPM helps by reducing reliance on pesticides. Cover crops eliminate the need for herbicides between rows in this orchard and also provide habitat for beneficial insects and microorganisms. Credit Richard Steven Street

can pick up insecticide residues on their hands, toys, and other objects, and through thumb-sucking and other mouthing behavior normal for their age, ingest significant amounts of pesticides.

An enormous array of lawn and garden pesticides is sold to individual consumers, and additional quantities are applied to urban and suburban lawns and ornamental plantings by professional gardeners and lawn-care companies. Most of the more toxic families of pesticides, including the organophosphate and carbamate insecticides and most of the principal fungicides used in agriculture, are also sold to homeowners, albeit often in more dilute formulations than those on sale to certified pest managers. In terms of the intensity of applications per unit of area, lawns and gardens are often far more heavily treated with pesticides than are most agricultural crops (Hansen, 1993).

The ordinary consumer is not trained in pesticide application techniques, and probably is not accustomed to following all the precautions called for on product labels, such as protective clothing and the like. Many people no doubt assume that "more is better," and may exceed recommended application rates or frequencies, ignore recommended intervals before re-entering treated areas, or in other ways increase their likelihood of significant exposure. The fact that pesticide products are sold

> **Many people are exposed to pesticides at work. Those who fumigate, load and unload shipments of food treated with pesticides, and farm workers, pesticide mixers, loaders and applicators often face risky situations that demand skills, information, properly fitted safety equipment and caution to avoid harm.**

off-the-shelf in grocery stores, drug stores and hardware stores may create a presumption on the part of consumers that these products must be safe. Unfortunately, that assumption is not always warranted.

People can also be exposed to pesticides in public places including parks, schools, museums, libraries and golf courses. Pest problems can occur in any building, and unless the manager is trained in IPM, the first impulse may well be to apply pesticides. Highly manicured outdoor areas like golf courses, where there is a premium on eliminating weeds, also tend to be aggressively sprayed, especially in heavily traveled areas (i.e., the middle of fairways and putting greens).

From this evidence it seems probable that, for at least a significant subset of the general population, pesticide use in and around the home accounts for the

> **Many people assume that "more is better" and exceed recommended pesticide application rates. Unfortunately, this assumption can lead to complacency and carelessness, turning relatively safe products into hazardous ones.**

greatest part of exposure and risk. While it may be common to think of pesticide exposure as what we consume in our foods and water, there are in fact concentric circles of exposure: at the center, the farm workers and other occupational groups with the highest exposures; next, people for whom use of pesticides in their homes and on their lawns and gardens elevates their exposure to well above average; and, at the end of a declining gradient, the large portion of the population for whom dietary exposure and occasional home pesticide use account for most of their risk.

5. Human Health Risks from Pesticide Exposure

Human health risks from pesticides are determined by many factors beyond the dose and toxicity of each chemical. The risk associated with a given exposure level varies greatly across the population as a function of age, health status and individual susceptibility to a given toxic effect. Regulators and toxicologists are working to protect individuals of all ages and exposure profiles, while also minimizing across-the-population risks from routine daily chronic, low-level exposures. These are distinctly different scientific and regulatory challenges.

People face widely divergent exposure levels and patterns. Occupational pesticide use and contaminated drinking water can produce especially high exposures. Socioeconomic factors also seem to affect exposure levels across the American population (Moses et al., 1993). Some pesticides can cross the placental barrier from the mother to the growing fetus (NRC, 1993a). Levels of chlorinated hydrocarbon insecticides detected in stillborn fetuses were significantly higher than levels found in normal babies.[8]

Cancer Risk

Many pesticides raise concerns because of their cancer-causing potential. More than 70 active ingredients cause

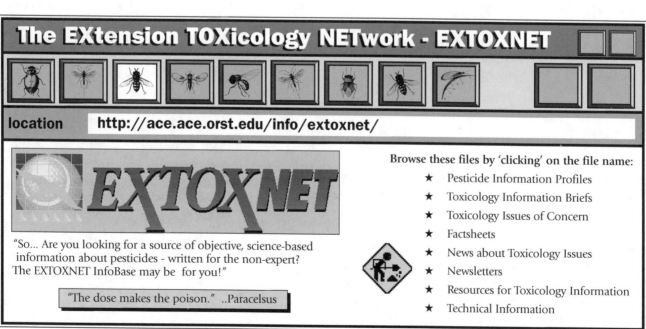

The EXtension TOXicology NETwork - EXTOXNET

location   http://ace.ace.orst.edu/info/extoxnet/

EXTOXNET

"So... Are you looking for a source of objective, science-based information about pesticides - written for the non-expert? The EXTOXNET InfoBase may be for you!"

"The dose makes the poison." ..Paracelsus

Browse these files by 'clicking' on the file name:

★ Pesticide Information Profiles
★ Toxicology Information Briefs
★ Toxicology Issues of Concern
★ Factsheets
★ News about Toxicology Issues
★ Newsletters
★ Resources for Toxicology Information
★ Technical Information

cancer in animal tests, and cancer risks have been the most common reason cited by EPA in pesticide cancellation and suspension actions (U.S. EPA, 1994).

In the years ahead, fewer regulatory actions are likely to be triggered solely or largely by a pesticide's potential to cause cancer. EPA already has carried out detailed risk-benefit assessments of nearly all known cancer-causing pesticides. It has canceled or severely limited the use of about three dozen, and left about two dozen more on the market after imposing various restrictions and adding safety precautions on labels (see Chapter 4 for more details). Pesticide manufacturers also have more carefully screened new active ingredients for cancer-causing potential in recent years, and with few exceptions, do not try to commercialize chemicals that demonstrate significant risk in this regard. One of those exceptions, however, is the corn herbicide acetochlor, a high risk oncogen first registered in 1994.

Endocrine-Disrupting Pesticide Effects

In coming years, other health concerns are likely to drive regulation, including the cluster of adverse health and reproductive effects associated with endocrine-disrupting pesticides. A 1993 article in *Environmental Health Perspectives* (Colborn et al., 1993) identified pesticides known at the time to be potentially disruptive to the endocrine system. Two dozen known endocrine disrupting pesticides are still in use today, including several of the most widely used active ingredients, both on the farm and in the home:

Endocrine-Disrupting Pesticides Currently in Use

Herbicides (5)	Insecticides (11)		Fungicides (8)
Alachlor	Lindane	Carbaryl	Mancozeb
Atrazine	Methomyl	Dicofol	Maneb
Trifluralin	Permethrin		Thiram
Metribuzin	Cypermethrin		Metiram
2,4-D	Aldicarb		Zineb
	Ethyl Parathion		Ziram
	Methyl Parathion		Benomyl
	Endosulfan		Vinclozolin[9]
	Methoxychlor		

A recent article in *Science* showed that combinations of two pesticides—endosulfan in conjunction with chlordane or DDT for example—were 160 to 1,600 times more estrogenic than either pesticide alone (Arnold et al., 1996). This and other recent findings lend credence to many scientists' concern that in certain circumstances, pesticide residues in food, water or the body might interact synergistically. Active ingredients are not the only culprits. Nonylphenol,

another endocrine disruptor, is an inert ingredient used in some product formulations (White et al., 1994). Pesticides also may interact with other known endocrine disruptors that everyone is exposed to through air, water and food, including dioxins and PCBs (Arnold et al., 1996; Colborn et al., 1996). Table 3.2 shows that 40 percent of total pounds of active ingredients used in agriculture in 1992 was known endocrine disruptors.

Developmental Neurotoxicity

Another significant current focus in pesticide toxicology is the apparent vulnerability of the developing central nervous system (CNS). The human brain is not fully formed until about age 12. Scientists now recognize that the CNS and brain are particularly vulnerable to damage by organophosphate (OP) and carbamate insecticides (Rodier, 1995). These pesticide families include 18 of 20 most widely used agricultural insecticides, occur as residues in nearly everyone's daily diet, are used widely to control termites, cockroaches, mosquitoes and fire ants in urban and suburban areas, and are common in consumer lawn and garden insect-control products (USDA, 1994d, 1995f; NRC, 1993a; Wargo, 1996; Whitmore et al., 1992; Grossman, 1995; Olkowski et al., 1991; Hansen, 1993). Children will inevitably be exposed to these chemicals, and since they all have a similar mechanism of neurotoxicity (they block the action of cholinesterase enzymes involved in the transmission of signals between nerve cells), the effects of multiple residues are quite likely to be additive (NRC, 1993a).

Scientists at the University of Wisconsin-Madison have carried out a series of important studies on how complex mixtures, including pesticides, affect human health. A 1993 report explored how drinking water residues commonly found in Wisconsin's Central Sands vegetable growing region affect the rat immune system (Porter et al., 1993). Rats treated with a single herbicide—metribuzin—displayed abnormal thyroid function. The effect was enhanced significantly in rats treated with a mixture of commonly found pesticide residues (aldicarb, methomyl and metribuzin).

> *"(Our) findings support the concept of the interconnectedness of the nervous, endocrine, and immune systems and raise the likelihood of impacts on all three systems if one is shown to be affected...These results strongly suggest the need to reassess currently allowed 'safe' levels of chemicals based on adult dosages that are accepted in groundwater and in our food supplies."*
>
> **Dr. Warren Porter** *and Colleagues, University of Wisconsin-Madison*

6. The Increasing Complexity of Risk Assessments

The fact that pesticides can affect multiple physiological processes and developmental stages, both directly and indirectly, complicates research and risk assessment. Sometimes pesticide active ingredients are quickly metabolized (broken down or otherwise detoxified) when ingested by humans or test animals. In other cases, primary or secondary metabolites may be as toxic as or even more toxic than the parent compound. The toxicity of metabolites is a major concern in the Midwest, since herbicide metabolites and breakdown products are found more frequently in drinking water wells, and often at higher levels, than parent compounds (Kaplin et al., 1996).

A few examples illustrate the complex challenges risk assessors face. Thiram, a member of the EBDC family of fungicides, can potentiate (magnify, possibly to dangerous levels) the effects of two common medicines given to children—diphenhydramine (Benadryl) and dimenhydrinate (Dramamine). Thiram and related fungicides also may potentiate the effects of methylphenidate (Ritalin), a widely prescribed drug used to treat hyperactive children, by blocking the action of an enzyme system that normally metabolizes Ritalin.[10]

A significant increase in rat mortality was observed in a study combining exposure to three substances encountered by troops serving in the Gulf War—permethrin and DEET (N,N-Diethyl-m-toluamide), two insect control products, and the anti-nerve gas pill pyridostigmine bromide (PB), which was taken by a majority of service members in the theater of operations.[11] Several scientists continue to explore the possibility that the so-called Gulf War Syndrome was caused by the synergistic impacts of pesticides, medicine and pollutants to which soldiers were exposed. The possibility that heat, stress and fatigue impaired the soldiers' immune systems, increasing vulnerability to chemical agents, is also being assessed.

The EBI (ergosterol-biosynthesis-inhibiting) fungicides prochloraz, propiconazole and penconazole increase the toxicity of organophosphate insecticides by hastening their enzymatic conversion to more biologically active forms.[12] The EBI fungicides also synergistically enhance the toxicity of synthetic pyrethroids to honeybees.[13] Scientists studying the impact of multiple pesticide exposures on fish have documented interconnected and multiple effects from exposure to one or more pesticides, with the central

> "Although it is extremely difficult to assess neurodevelopmental effects, the CNS (central nervous system) may be peculiarly vulnerable during a prolonged period of development, even if exposure is at a level known to be safe for adults."
>
> **Pesticides in the Diets of Infants and Children**
> (NRC, 1993a).

Table 3.2 Agricultural Reliance on Pesticides Identified as Endocrine Disruptors*: Pounds of Active Ingredient Applied in 1992

Type of Pesticide	Total Pounds Applied	Pounds Applied		Endocrine Disruptor as % of Total
		Not Endocrine Disruptor	Endocrine Disruptor	
Fungicides	38,110,140	21,373,222	16,736,918	44%
Herbicides	453,878,500	257,925,307	195,953,193	43%
Insecticides	97,913,661	73,650,696	24,262,965	25%
All Pesticides	589,902,301	352,949,225	236,953,076	40%

* Note—This table reflects 1992 use data on the 32 pesticide active ingredients listed in the 1993 *Environmental Health Perspectives* article; it does not include vinclozolin or any additional suspect active ingredients. Pounds applied data calculated from Gianessi and Anderson, 1995.

nervous system and brain being the "first target of pollutants" (Dunier and Siwicki, 1993).

Part of the complexity of risk assessment is the difficulty of establishing cause-effect relationships between pesticide exposure and health effects, even when individual pieces of the causal process are well documented. Some people exposed to pesticides and other chemicals suffer ill effects hours, days, weeks and even months or years after exposure. Exposure to one chemical may slow down the normal detoxification of another, which in turn hastens the conversion of other chemicals or pathogens into more active or virulent forms. Still other chemicals may depress immune response or render a particular organ system temporarily vulnerable. Such combinations of causal, potentiating and mitigating factors are the norm in the real world and may help explain why only a small portion of the population suffers adverse health consequences from pesticide exposures tolerated by most people.

> **Multiple exposures are the norm in the real world. Risks are greatest among those who are both exposed more heavily than usual and who are also, at a particular time, more vulnerable to the adverse toxicological impacts pesticides can trigger.**

Recent research indicates that certain impacts of some toxic chemicals and drugs may be observed only at very low levels of exposure, while at higher dose levels, such as those used in most animal tests, the effects change or disappear (Lodovic et al., 1994). This provocative hypothesis suggests that for some effects of some chemicals, there may be an "inverse dose-response curve;" that is, very low doses are potentially hazardous while higher doses may be less so. One theoretical explanation for such unexpected results is that in some circumstances, with certain chemicals, higher doses can trigger normal metabolic detoxification mechanisms, whereas at very low doses, the detoxification process is not triggered and exposure lingers long enough to cause problems (Lodovic et al., 1994). If further research

> "... weaknesses in the present law cause real world problems for everyone involved in producing and distributing our food, and for, most of all, the people who consume it—especially our children. According to the National Academy of Sciences, infants and young people are especially vulnerable to pesticides—chemicals can go a long way in a small body."
>
> **Remarks by the President,** "Food Quality Protection Act" Bill Signing, August 3, 1996 (White House, 1996a)

confirms the validity of this counterintuitive relationship between dose and risk, a whole new layer of complexity will be added to risk assessment.

Inert Ingredients Pose Risks Too

Concerns linger over pesticide inert ingredients and their impact on acute and chronic toxicity. Inerts often are present in formulated end-use products (ready to apply or mix) at concentrations far higher than active ingredients. One category of surfactants and inert ingredients is made from or contains alkylphenols, a class of chemicals known to disrupt endocrine functions.[14] But knowledge of inert ingredient toxicity and environmental fate is generally limited. Additional studies on both individual inert ingredients and on formulated products are needed, to assess risks of endocrine disruption, neurological impacts, allergic reactions and other potential adverse health and environmental effects.

New EPA regulations require that product labels approved in the future must disclose the presence of so-called Category One inerts (specific listed ingredients known to pose significant toxic risks), but not their concentration in formulated products. If inerts are not on the Category One list, federal law allows companies to claim that the identity of other inert ingredients is "confidential business information," and most manufacturers do. This lack of disclosure has slowed scientific efforts to better understand the risks posed by inert ingredients and remains a contentious public policy issue.

Individual Susceptibility Varies

Many factors—age, general health status, diet, genetic predisposition—affect how an individual's body deals with pesticide exposure. Understanding why some people are harmed and others are not, and protecting the vulnerable, remains a difficult task.

Our bodies are blessed with the ability to overcome pathogens, injury and toxic chemicals through more than one mechanism, so that even when one system is impaired, the body is usually protected. But scientists are worried that multiple exposures to chemicals that can impair immune response, often through different modes of action, may together erode the body's defenses. Subtle effects of chemicals may make people more vulnerable to viruses, pathogens, abnormal cell growths and bacteria that, while always present, generally do not trigger or progress to disease. (For a thorough review of global literature, see Repetto and Baliga, *Pesticides and the Immune System,* 1996.)

Pesticide regulatory policy may provide ample protection for healthy adults who are not exposed at work or through unexpected incidents. The same cannot be said for pregnant women, the unborn, infants and children, the elderly, the chronically ill, chemically-sensitive individuals and those with compromised immune systems or rare genetic vulnerabilities (NRC, 1993a). These more vulnerable people may collectively account for up to a third of the U.S. population.

Assessment of *population risk* from exposures to pesticides must take into account highly variable real-world exposure patterns to multiple residues, as well as differences in individual susceptibility. Population risk is regrettably not part of the contemporary science base for pesticide regulation, which protects healthy adults from exposure to each pesticide, one at a time, based largely on pesticides' effects on adult rodents in laboratory studies.

Safety factors considered when establishing each active ingredient's Reference Dose are designed to account for individuals' varying susceptibility, but these calculations are crude and inadequate. (For a thorough explanation of why this is particularly true during pregnancy and infancy, see NRC, 1993a; Colborn et al., 1996).

C. Estimating Trends in Pesticide Risk

Reducing human health risks has been a primary goal driving pesticide regulation and research on safer pesticides and ways to use pesticides. Clearly, how successful past efforts to lower pesticide risks have been is key information for setting future policy priorities. Here, we assess levels and trends in average mammalian toxicity of pesticides as an indicator of trends in risk to humans.

In a perfect world, we would assess pesticide risk levels and trends by drawing on accurate toxicity and exposure data for all pesticide ingredients and all kinds of individuals within the exposed populations. But the data to measure exposure, toxicity or risks with such precision do not exist. As a surrogate measure, we used routine risk assessment methods and data compiled by the World Health Organization and the U.S. EPA to estimate the average acute and chronic mammalian toxicity of pesticide active ingredients. We calculated average toxicity levels for categories of pesticides weighted by pounds of active ingredients actually applied in agriculture. We

assessed trends by comparing these calculated aggregate risks for three years roughly a decade apart, 1971, 1982 and 1992.

Changes in the toxicity of pesticides in use over time clearly affect risk levels and trends, but using only pesticide toxicity and pounds applied as measures of risk leaves important factors out of the equation. Pesticide persistence and environmental fate, formulations, application methods, weather, the intensity of use within a region or around the home or workplace and how closely safety precautions and product label instructions are followed, all can affect exposure and thus health risk. Changes in the age distribution, health status, genetic characteristics, stress and diet and exposure to other natural and synthetic chemicals of the exposed population can affect susceptibility to toxic effects. Unfortunately, comprehensive, reliable data on most of these factors are not readily available, nor are there obvious or agreed-upon ways to model the effects of all these variables on the total public health risk from pesticides. We are satisfied that our approach, while limited to calculations of the average toxicity of pesticides in use over time, is nevertheless a revealing analysis, and a useful starting point for examining this issue.

There is no single "right way" to estimate average toxicity values or rank pesticides according to risk. Several different formulas and methods should be explored (Landy, 1995), and several are noted in the box "Methods to Rank Pesticide Risks and Impacts." In this analysis, we sought a method to roughly quantify average pesticide mammalian toxicity and risk levels over time and across different regions, crops and pesticide types. Insights gained were used to answer two key questions—have pesticide risk levels gone up or down in response to regulatory policies over the last three decades? And are risks currently increasing or decreasing?

Ongoing efforts are developing better test methods and ranking systems for specific impacts and applications. Pest management specialists are focusing on ways to compare relative impacts of pesticides on beneficial organisms and agroecosystems. Biological scientists and health specialists are working toward ways to quantify the toxicity of chemicals to the endocrine, immune and reproductive systems (Colborn et al., 1993 and 1996; Naiman et al., 1995; U.S. EPA, 1996a; Repetto and Baliga, 1996). Risk estimation and ranking methods developed to date lack information needed to fully capture the benefits stemming from improvements in pesticide manufacturing processes, formulations, packaging, handling, application and mixing/loading procedures. And both regulators and pest managers face an enormous challenge in trying to accurately measure and manage relative risks from pesticides as they are actually applied in the field.

1. A Method to Track Average Risk Levels over Time

The pesticide industry, government research agencies and regulators have worked for 30 years to reduce pesticide toxicity and risks. Billions of dollars have been invested in efforts to understand, manage and reduce pesticide risks (see Chapter 4). Yet until now no one has attempted to draw upon available data to estimate overall trends in pesticide toxicity and risks. And for this reason, no one has been able to speak with much authority in answering the key question whether overall pesticide toxicity and human health risks have gone up or down since the early 1970s.

This question is central to any assessment of the impacts of regulation, pesticide product innovation and IPM adoption. In support of our effort to answer it, the U.S. EPA provided us with access to recently compiled computer datasets not previously available to analysts outside the agency. We combined these data on the mammalian toxicity of pesticide active ingredients with comprehensive pesticide use databases available electronically from the National Center for Food and Agricultural Policy, an independent group of researchers that is part of Resources for the Future in Washington, D.C. (Gianessi and Anderson, 1995) and the USDA (USDA, 1983, 1974).[17] Together, these data made it possible for us to estimate overall mammalian toxicity of pesticides and related human health risk trends. To our knowledge, this is the first analysis of its kind.

For herbicides, insecticides and fungicides, and all three categories of pesticides together, we have estimated national average pesticide mammalian toxicity levels for three years: 1971, 1982 and 1992. Reasonably complete and consistent pesticide use data are available for these three years. Usage data (in pounds applied) combined with toxicity scores provide a weighted index of risk. In all years studied, a dozen or fewer active ingredients within each class of pesticides accounted for three-quarters or more of the total pounds of pesticides applied within that class.

Our focus is on standard and available indices of acute and chronic mammalian toxicity; consequently, our analysis encompasses just those risks assessed with the health and safety data routinely submitted to EPA on most pesticides. Neither available data, EPA risk assessments nor the method we present here comprehensively cover all areas of human health risk, as noted elsewhere in this chapter. As more complete data on effects like developmental neurotoxicity become available and can be incorporated into risk comparisons, both the estimated levels of risk and relative rankings of individual compounds and classes of pesticides may change.

Similar analyses need to be conducted using data on aquatic and avian toxicity, and on impacts on beneficial organisms. We have not attempted these here, but encourage others to do so. We are also mindful of the limitations inherent in this analysis and hope other investigators will carry the analysis forward.

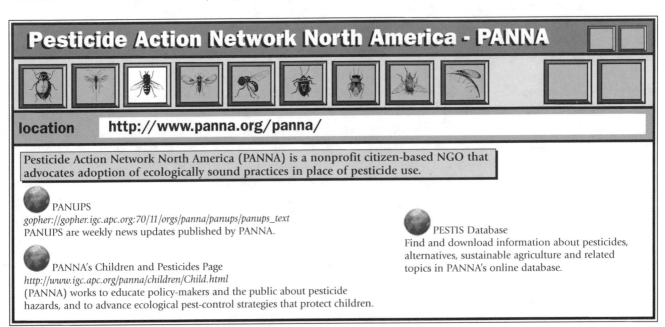

How We Assessed Pesticide Toxicity Levels and Trends

Here's how we carried out our analysis: We first listed all pesticide active ingredients used in a given year, and assigned each a code to indicate type of pesticide: fungicide, herbicide or insecticide. Then, we incorporated data on pounds applied in each of three years studied, and added in acute and chronic toxicity data for each pesticide. As an index of acute mammalian toxicity, we used oral LD-50 data expressed in milligrams per kilogram in the test animal's diet (or, parts per million [ppm]). The data came from the World Health Organization's classification of pesticides (International Programme on Chemical Safety, 1994) or Farm Chemicals Handbook (Sine, 1996) when an LD-50 from WHO was not available. The LD-50 is the dose that kills half the exposed group of test animals; the higher the acute LD-50 value, the less acutely toxic the pesticide.

For our index of chronic toxicity, we developed a composite variable, Mammalian Toxicity Score ("Mam Tox Score"), for each pesticide active ingredient. The components of Mam Tox Score are: Reference Dose (RfD); cancer potency factor, or Q*, and the EPA cancer classification; and capacity to disrupt the endocrine system.

For pesticides that are not oncogenic (tumor-producing) and are not known to disrupt the endocrine system, Mam Tox Score is simply 0.1 divided by the Reference Dose. (The smaller the RfD, the more toxic the pesticide; the values of Mam Tox Score increase as RfDs decline. We used 0.1 in the numerator to make the numeric values of Mam Tox Score easier to read by reducing the number of zeroes). For active ingredients that are oncogens, the formula adjusts the value as a function of cancer potency factors and EPA classification codes. Higher Q* values lead to higher Mam Tox Score values; a pesticide classified as a Class A (human carcinogen) or Class B (probable human carcinogen) is scored higher than a pesticide in Class C (possible human carcinogen). If a pesticide is known to disrupt the endocrine system, we made an additional modest upward adjustment in the value of Mam Tox Score. For pesticides that are oncogens and endocrine disruptors, these factors account for about one-third of the value of Mam Tox Score, and the RfD component of the formula accounts for about two-thirds.

We experimented with over 20 different ways to combine these factors into a composite measure of chronic mammalian toxicity. Different formulas shifted all values up or down roughly proportionally and caused a few active ingredients to rise or fall somewhat in relative rankings. But the different formulas produced essentially the same trends and basic insights when we compared average toxicity levels across types of pesticides or over time.

Once each active ingredient's acute and chronic toxicity score had been computed, we next ranked pesticide active ingredients in order of relative toxicity. Rankings were constructed for each of three major types of pesticide, and then, for all pesticides combined, for each of the three years—a total of 24 rankings.

Distributions of Risk

We were interested in several characteristics of the distribution of ranked risk values. Consider, for example, the rankings of herbicides used in 1992 by acute toxicity. The ingredients are listed from most toxic (smallest LD-50) to least toxic (largest LD-50). To gain a sense of the distribution of toxicity levels, we then calculated the use-weighted average LD-50 for the group of herbicides at the top of the list that collectively accounted for 10 percent of the total pounds applied in 1992. We call this the "Most Toxic Group" in the tables and text that follow; it represents the most toxic decile. The same calculation is made at the bottom end of the acute toxicity ranking, to find the use-weighted average toxicity of the "Least Toxic Group." The Median Toxicity value is the LD-50 of the herbicide that falls at the 50th percentile of cumulative pounds applied.

Last, average toxicity values in the "Most Toxic" and "Least Toxic" groups are then used to calculate the "Toxic Differential"—the lower of the two use group values divided into the higher one. This ratio indicates how much more toxic, pound for pound applied, the most hazardous group of pesticides within a category are when compared with the least toxic group of pesticides in that category and year.

In many cases, the answer is **lots** more toxic, as is evident in the "Toxic Differential" column in Tables 3.3 and 3.4.

Table 3.3 Differences in the Acute Mammalian Toxicity of Pesticides Applied in 1992: Top 10%, Median and Bottom 10% Use Groups*

Type of Pesticide	Most Toxic Group*	Median Toxicity*	Least Toxic Group*	Toxic Differential+
	(Acute Toxicity measured as LD-50 in parts per million) *Lower numbers = More Toxic*			
Fungicides	1,072.0	7,375.0	10,000.0	9.3
Herbicides	320.0	1,866.0	8,859.0	27.7
Insecticides	1.8	66.0	4,951.0	2,829.0
All Pesticides	43.1	1,626.0	9,557.0	222.0

* Pesticide active ingredients were ranked in descending order of acute toxicity within each group (fungicides, herbicides, insecticides), and the pounds of each active ingredient applied were entered in the dataset. The Most Toxic Group is those active ingredients at the top of the toxicity ranking that collectively account for 10 percent of total pounds applied. The reported toxicity value is the weighted average LD-50 value within the group. The Least Toxic Group accounts for 10 percent of pounds applied at the bottom of the toxicity rankings. Median Toxicity is the LD-50 for the ingredient at the 50th percentile of cumulative pounds applied in each category.

+ Toxic Differential equals the 1992 use-weighted toxicity value for the Least Toxic 10% use group divided by the toxicity value of the Most Toxic 10% use group.

Results of our analysis are presented in Tables 3.3 and 3.4 and in Figure 3.3. The tables show use-weighted average pesticide toxicity data for 1992. We also calculated, but have not presented here, average toxicity values for 1982 and 1971, and for individual crops and regions. "Toxic Differential" values for a type of pesticide used on a specific crop, or in a given region, are often much higher than the national averages, which tend to mask differences across crops and regions.

Several important insights emerge from these tables. In the case of acute toxicity (Table 3.3):

■ There is less than a 10-fold difference between the most toxic and least toxic fungicide use groups; hence there is little to be gained from regulators focusing on the acute toxicity of this group, short of restricting all products. But the differences in the "Toxic Differentials" of fungicides and insecticides is huge—about 595-fold. This is why insecticides account for so many more farm worker poisonings than fungicides, despite the much more elaborate safety precautions and restrictions accompanying insecticide use.

■ The Toxic Differential between the most and least acutely toxic insecticides is enormous—2,829. Note

also that half the pounds of insecticides applied had LD-50 values lower than 66 ppm (the median toxicity group value). So, the insecticide with "median" acute toxicity is almost five times as toxic as the most toxic herbicides.

■ The use of several of the most toxic insecticides would have to be restricted or banned in order to substantially lower both the Most Toxic levels and reduce the toxic differential. But also note there are alternatives that are far less acutely toxic. There were eight active ingredients in the Least Toxic group in 1992 and today there would be three dozen or more because of the registration since 1992 of over 50 low risk biopesticides.

Comparable insights are evident on chronic mammalian toxicity in Table 3.4:

■ Again, insecticides are by far the most toxic type of pesticide, although the Toxic Differential is much lower than the case with acute risks.

■ The most toxic fungicides are only one-tenth as toxic as the most toxic insecticides.

Table 3.4 Differences in the Chronic Mammalian Toxicity (Mam Tox Score) of Pesticides Applied in 1992: Top 10%, Median, and Bottom 10% Use Groups*

Type of Pesticide	Most Toxic Group*	Median Toxicity*	Least Toxic Group*	Toxic Differential+
	Larger numbers = More Toxic			
Fungicides	257.4	11.3	1.93	133.4
Herbicides	154.7	31.7	1.72	90
Insecticides	2,508	51.2	5.9	425
All Pesticides	955	30	1.7	562

* Pesticide active ingredients were ranked in descending order of chronic toxicity within each group (fungicides, herbicides, insecticides), and the pounds of each active ingredient applied were entered in the dataset. The Most Toxic Group is those active ingredients at the top of the toxicity ranking that collectively account for 10 percent of total pounds applied. The reported toxicity value is the weighted average Mam Tox Score within the group. The Least Toxic Group accounts for 10 percent of pounds applied at the bottom of the toxicity rankings. Median Toxicity is the Mam Tox Score foe the ingredient at the 50th percentile of cumulative pounds applied in each category.

+ Toxic Differential equals the use-weighted Mam Tox Score value for the Most Toxic 10% use group divided by the toxicity value of the Least Toxic 10% use group

2. Trends in Pesticide Toxicity and Risk Over Time

How have average acute and chronic mammalian toxicity levels changed among pesticides applied in agriculture in the 1970s, 1980s and 1990s? Trends in average pesticide active ingredient toxicity levels are an indicator of the overall combined impact of regulation, the discovery of new pesticides and changes in pest management systems and the choices pest managers make.

We calculated average use-weighted toxicity levels for each class of pesticides in each of the three years 1971, 1982 and 1992. To calculate the average chronic toxicity of herbicides applied in 1992, for example, we multiplied the Mam Tox Score value of each herbicide active ingredient (see box, page 79) by the pounds applied that year, added all the products together (e.g., atrazine pounds applied times atrazine Mam Tox Score, plus alachlor pounds applied times its Mam Tox Score, and so on), then divided the sum by the total pounds of herbicides applied, to get the use-weighted chronic toxicity average value. Acute toxicity averages were calculated the same way using an index based on each active ingredient's LD-50.

The four panels within Figure 3.3 present values and trends in acute and chronic mammalian toxicity for

fungicides, herbicides and insecticides for the three years. Actual numerical scores appear in the figures. The top two panels show the average acute and chronic toxicity of "High Risk" pesticides, which we define here as the most toxic chemicals in each class that account for 10 percent of pounds applied (labeled "Top 10% Acute/Chronic Toxicity"). This top 10 percent of applications accounts for from 40 to 80 percent of total acute or chronic use-weighted toxicity in the various categories in a given year.

The bottom two panels in Figure 3.3 show trends in aggregate average acute and chronic toxicity index levels for all insecticides, herbicides and fungicides. Note that we inverted the vertical scale in the acute toxicity panels so that an upward trend line corresponds to rising average acute toxicity, as is the case with Mam Tox Score values and trend lines. (Because of the wide range of values, the vertical scale is logarithmic in all four panels, and each interval represents an order of magnitude change in toxicity.)

What Figure 3.3 shows rather dramatically is that there has been little overall reduction in the aggregate acute and chronic toxicity of agricultural pesticides from 1971 to the present time.

Over the 21-year period shown, the acute toxicity of the average pound of insecticide applied increased. For

Methods to Rank Pesticide Risks

Several research teams have developed multiattribute risk classification or ranking schemes for comparing pesticide risks and to guide the selection of pesticides likely to pose the least risk in a given situation.

The "Environmental Impact Quotient" was developed by a team at Cornell University (Kovach et al., 1992). It strives to provide a tool for growers to balance the ecological, environmental and toxicological impacts of alternative pest management systems reliant on different combinations of pesticides.

The system developed by Dr. William Pease[15] and colleagues at the University of California-Berkeley School of Public Health contains both "Human Health Impacts" and "Natural Resources Impacts." The Berkeley team compiled a large database and used it to rank major pesticides used in California according to a number of different criteria and concerns. Health parameters include acute and chronic toxicity measures and data on farm worker poisoning incidents and the frequency of other illnesses caused by pesticide exposure (Liebman and Pease, 1995; Landy, 1995). Natural resource parameters include frequency of contamination of California groundwater, hazards to aquatic life and to terrestrial ecosystems. The series of reports published during the project demonstrate the need for several different functional forms and statistical techniques in carrying out ranking and classification exercises (Pease et al., 1993a, 1993b; Landy, 1995; Liebman and Pease, 1995; Walker et al., 1995).

The "Environmental Yardstick" was developed in the Netherlands and is now being applied to Midwestern pesticide risk concerns (Reus et al., 1994). It focuses on the potential for pesticides to leach into groundwater and harm non-target organisms key to biointensive IPM.

The system supporting the Stemilt Growers "Responsible Choice" program in the Pacific Northwest is one of the most sophisticated used anywhere in the world (Reed, 1995). It assigns points to various pesticides and pest management practices, both during the production season and post-harvest, as a function of pesticide toxicity, worker risks and ecotoxicity. Based on an annual review by grower-cooperators and regional IPM experts, Stemilt Growers chooses a total number of maximum points allowed in the next season. Growers who stay within the maximum allowed are able to sell their fruit through the "Responsible Choice" program. A similar system has been developed by Australian scientists working with apple growers (Penrose et al., 1994).

The USDA Natural Resources Conservation Service's "National Agricultural Pesticide Risk Analysis" (NAPRA) system reflects years of work by dozens of research teams. It is used at the field level as a planning tool to help growers evaluate pesticide runoff and risk potential, based on a known set of soil parameters, cropping patterns and tillage and planting methods (Bagdon et al., 1994; Senus et al., 1995). It is now being used and refined in several watersheds across the country.

Several "Red/Yellow/Green" pesticide classification schemes are used to guide pesticide selection in "Integrated Fruit Management" (IFM) programs in dozens of countries[16] around the world (Organization for Economic Cooperation and Development, 1991; Ministry of Environment, Lands and Parks, 1994) and a contingent valuation scheme has been developed by researchers at Iowa State University (Higley and Wintersteen, 1992).

These systems divide all pesticides registered for use on a crop—apples for example—into three categories: "Red" list pesticides are prohibited, with some narrow exceptions in certain programs; "Yellow" list products may be used with caution as long as all other preventive measures are in place and the products are applied in ways that lessen worker risks and adverse impacts on beneficials; and, "Green" list products are generally permitted. The classifications are a function of mammalian toxicity, impacts on non-target beneficial organisms and ecological risks. Several European countries have implemented detailed IFM programs in major producing regions and a sizable portion of acreage is now enrolled. Enrollment in and compliance with IFM program guidelines are emerging as key criteria in both government farm and environmental subsidy programs and in marketing efforts. They may also play a role in international trade in the years ahead.

Figure 3.3 Trends Over Time in Acute and Chronic Mammalian Toxicity* of Pesticides Used in Agriculture

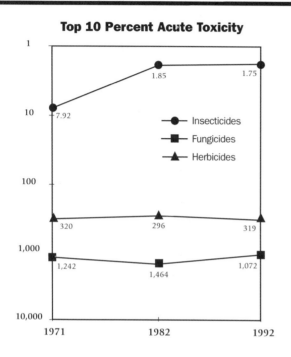

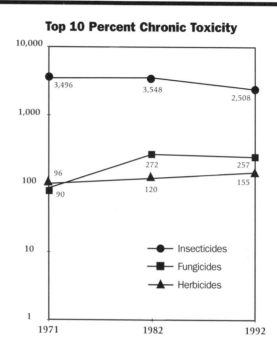

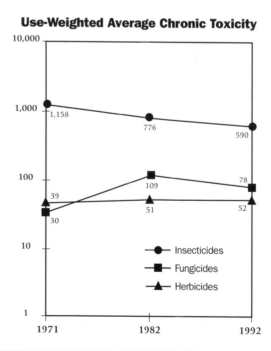

*Acute Toxicity is measured by use-weighted oral LD-50 values; the scale in the left panels is LD-50 values in parts per million in the test diet. The measure of chronic toxicity (right panels) is use-weighted Mam Tox Score values (see the box "How We Assessed Pesticide Toxicity Levels and Trends"). Both vertical scales are logarithmic; each interval represents an order of magnitude change in toxicity. Upward sloping lines correspond to increasing use-weighted toxicity; downward sloping, decreasing toxicity.

all insecticides, the use-weighted LD-50 index value rose from 18.9 to 6.9; that is, the average pound of insecticide applied in 1992 was 2.7 times as acutely toxic as the average pound of insecticide applied in 1971. In the high risk group of insecticides, the average pound applied in 1992 was 4.5 times as toxic as the average pound applied in 1971. In contrast to acute toxicity, the chronic toxicity of insecticides has declined. The average use-weighted toxicity of all insecticides applied in 1992 was 51 percent of the average pound applied in 1971. For high risk insecticides, the 1992 score was 71 percent of the 1971 value.

Among herbicides it is notable how little toxicity has changed in the two decades shown. For the average pound of all herbicides applied, there has been a modest decline in acute toxicity and a modest increase in chronic toxicity. Average toxicity has changed little since 1982 because the same dozen active ingredients dominated total pounds applied in both 1982 and 1992.

The trends for fungicides are consistent in the high risk group and the overall use-weighted average. Chronic risks have trended upward, with average scores more than doubling between 1971 and 1992, while acute risks have remained stable and low.

The overall lesson to be drawn from Figure 3.3 is that, pound for pound, the pesticides in use today are on average about as hazardous to health (at least, as indicated by mammalian toxicity) as the ones in use in the early 1980s and early 1970s. Despite 25 years of pesticide regulation, there has been no real decline in overall risk. Average use-weighted toxicity of most categories has held steady or increased slightly, while among insecticides there has been a moderate decline in chronic toxicity but a relatively large increase in acute toxicity.

Figure 3.3 tells only part of the story. It does not reflect changes in routes and levels of exposure, which we discuss at the beginning of this chapter. It also does not reflect changes in the total pounds applied. Agricultural pesticide use peaked in the early 1980s, and then trended slightly downward until the early 1990s, not because reliance declined, but because of the shift to more potent low dose products. According to EPA's most recent data on total pounds applied in agriculture, total pesticide use has risen 20 percent from 1990 to 1995, with growth in fungicide use accounting for over half the increase (Aspelin, 1996). By the 1994 season, pounds applied in agriculture were at all-time highs, and have risen 13 percent above total pounds applied at the peak in the early 1980s. As reliance on pesticides has intensified, total use and risks have increased accordingly.

3. Pesticide Risk Assessment— An Insurmountable Challenge?

As the analysis we have presented here and in Chapter 2 has demonstrated, patterns of pesticide usage and reliance have changed over the past 25 years, and so have the nature and patterns of risks associated with chemical-based pest control strategies. Today, the potential risk to public health from herbicide applications is far higher than it was in the early 1970s. Risks from fungicides have been fairly stable for more than a decade but are likely to be rising now because use is rising. The most toxic insecticides in use today are, on average, about four times as acutely hazardous as the most toxic compounds used 25 years ago, while their chronic hazards have declined somewhat. The adverse impacts of insecticides on beneficial organisms have risen steadily and a wide array of secondary insect pests are gaining primary pest status.

Much more work is needed to develop and refine relative risk ranking schemes that can integrate different categories of risk and quantify changes in pesticide risk over time. We have taken a few important steps in that direction in this chapter, focusing on readily available measures of pesticide mammalian toxicity, and weighting toxicity according to usage to produce a rough index of the overall health risks of exposure. While this chapter presents an incomplete characterization of pesticide toxicity, exposure and risk, the trends indicated by our analysis are not reassuring.

Our Conclusion

Evidence presented here supports the conclusion that aggregate public health hazards from pesticide use have remained about the same since 1970. Risks have failed to decrease notably despite three decades of regulation, research and product development. And the risks associated with current patterns of pesticide use have probably been rising in the last few years as reliance on pesticides has increased and new exposure routes have become important.

There is another sense in which the risks of pesticide use are growing. Back in the 1960s and '70s, scientific concern about pesticides was focused primarily on acute

> *"The scientist can afford to be skeptical much longer than the person concerned with protecting public health."*
>
> **Dr. Keith Baverstock,** *Co-Coordinator of the World Health Organization's International Thyroid Project*[18]

toxicity (and occupational exposure) and on cancer as the dominant hazard to the wider public's health. As decades have passed, knowledge of the ways that pesticides can injure health has expanded and evolved. Today, pesticides need to be assessed not only for acute toxicity and carcinogenicity, but for the ability to cause birth defects, to interfere with reproduction, to damage the nervous, immune and endocrine systems, to affect development and behavior. The effects of pesticides on human health remain paramount, but effects on wildlife species, on other beneficial organisms, and on the stability of ecological relationships are also important, both as a puzzle scientists must assemble and because these effects can have substantial economic consequences.

The trend toward very potent, low-dose-per-treated-area pesticides is aggravating already serious pesticide resistance and secondary pest problems. This trend also imposes economic losses on farmers since when unusual soil temperature and moisture conditions occur, highly potent products can damage crops and nearby vegetation, or adversely impair soil microbial communities. On Midwestern corn and soybean farms, such risks stemming from use of low dose herbicides are clearly rising.

Science has also expanded the menu of things we want to know about pesticide hazards. It is clear we must go beyond assessing the effects of individual active ingredients, one at a time, and assess the risks associated with exposure to mixtures of pesticides—with and without other toxic environmental contaminants. And attention has shifted from measuring and managing the risks faced by an average healthy adult, to identifying necessary steps to protect more vulnerable subpopulations, such as infants and pregnant women, the unborn and elderly, and the immunocompromised.

We see the need for many changes in pest management and pesticide regulatory public policy. One of the most critical is a reevaluation of what we expect from science and how we use science in making judgments regarding acceptable levels of pesticide risk. It is the nature of science to continuously identify the next set of questions and the next generation of experiments. It is also the nature of policy makers and regulators to postpone difficult decisions until more convincing information is available. Together, these two tendencies can delay action even when there are good reasons—and sound science—supporting the need to act.

Knowing, in a scientifically convincing way, how a single pesticide compound present widely in food, water and consumer products is affecting the human nervous, immune, and endocrine systems, reproduction and devel-

opment remains well beyond the grasp of current methods. Knowing this for the effects of all the possible combinations of hundreds of active ingredients on thousands of species seems beyond even the imaginable reach of science. Long before we will understand the adverse impacts of the contemporary generation of pesticides, most will become obsolete and society will face the need to answer another set of questions. The rate of change in pest management systems, pesticide properties and use patterns, farming systems, pollution and the diet makes it almost impossible to sort out the contribution of a single factor—pesticide toxicity, for example—to public health outcomes and trends.

Over three or four decades, multiple billions of dollars have been spent testing and assessing and studying the toxic effects of pesticides, yet there is virtually no single active ingredient for which good answers exist to all the risk questions we now know to ask. If we knew how to get the answers, we still could not afford to do so in any but a small fraction of cases.

That, then, is the dilemma. Science has done a fine job of learning more of the right questions to ask. Unfortunately, most of them are still too difficult to answer with certainty, yet that is in effect what the law requires before regulators can act. Like it or not, our state of knowledge about possible adverse effects of current pesticide use patterns on health and the environment is limited and superficial, and it will remain so for a long time.

Some equate ignorance with safety. But that's wishful thinking, not science. We know more than enough to conclude that pesticides *can* be harmful in myriad ways, but less than is needed to *prove* that harm is occurring, or to link specific harm to a specific chemical and use.

Given the way the pesticide laws were written and have been interpreted by the EPA and the courts, harm essentially must be proven, or a pesticide's presumed benefits justify its continued use. But proving harm and causality in the ever-changing and chaotic real world is very difficult, just as proving safety is never possible with absolute certainty.

There are fundamental flaws and fallacies in the way we are now trying to manage pesticide risks; perhaps the biggest fallacy of all is our belief that we know enough to do this job well. Many attempts have been made to overcome the most obvious flaws in current law and policy, but most seem to just reinforce gridlock, delay incremental action and fuel controversy.

We believe this state of affairs is unacceptable. Outside the halls of EPA and Congress, and away from the businesses that make and use pesticides and depend on them for a livelihood, a great many ordinary citizens find our inability to answer basic scientific questions about pesticide risks quite risky in and of itself. This common-sense recognition of the limits of science and law, coupled with evidence reviewed here indicating that pesticide risks have not been significantly reduced over the last two decades, points to the essential failure of current approaches and the need to be open to alternative strategies to reduce pesticide risks.

New approaches are needed on several fronts. The food safety and pesticide regulatory reforms passed by Congress in July 1996, reviewed in Chapter 4, are one important step, which EPA now must implement.

Congress needs to provide increased funding for IPM research and education, as sought since 1994 by the USDA. Other critical steps are needed and discussed throughout this book. In particular, prudent steps should be taken without delay to begin widening safety margins in the uses of high risk pesticides to limit the consequences if we are underestimating and hence mismanaging pesticide risks. Encouraging and rewarding progress along the IPM continuum offer the greatest hope for significant and sustained progress in lowering pesticide reliance, use and risks, and making this an integral component of national policy and private initiative deserves the highest priority.

[1] Earthworm facts and Dr. Edward's quote from "Soil Boosters: Thriving Earthworm Populations Lead to a Good Crop Stand," *Ag Consultant Magazine*, March, 1996.

[2] "Hard News on 'Soft' Pesticides," T. Williams, *Audubon Magazine*, March-April 1993.

[3] This is also one of the reasons it is often difficult to prove that pesticide runoff causes fish and bird kills in such regions.

[4] Press Release, August 24, 1995, Alabama Department of Environmental Management; "Endosulfan Responsible for Alabama Fish Kill," from Pesticide Action Network North America Updates Service, February 23, 1996.

[5] Periodic reports on wildlife poisonings can be found on the EPA World Wide Web page. The "Pesticide Monitoring and Risk Management in the Northwest" report is posted under documents from Region 10, at [http://www.epa.gov/r10earth/-offices/ecocomm/pest0115.html?pesticides].

[6] The survey was done by P.B. Baker and results reported at the 1995 annual meeting of the Entomological Society of America (Grossman, 1996).

[7] Free radicals are chemicals that play a role in cellular aging, tissue degeneration and possibly cancer. Anything that induces greater free radical damage to DNA increases the risk or severity of a variety of ailments.

[8] "A Comparison of Organochlorine Insecticide Contents in Specimens of Maternal Blood, Placenta, and Umbilical-cord Blood from Stillborn and Live-born Cases," M.C. Saxena, M.K.J. Siddiqui and V. Agarwal, *Journal of Toxicology and Environmental*

Health, Vol. 11 (1983), pages 71-79. Study cited in (Moses et al., 1993).

[9] Vinclozolin was discovered to be an anti-androgen by an EPA research team in 1994 (see Kelce et al., 1995).

[10] For more discussion of these and other examples, see page 348 of the report *Pesticides in the Diets of Infants and Children*, NRC, 1993a.

[11] Results in a poster presented by Wilfred McCain at the Society of Toxicology meeting, March 10-14, 1996, Study No. 87-48-2665-95.

[12] "Interactive Effects Between EBI Fungicides and OP Insecticides in the Hybrid Red-Legged Partridge," Johnston, G., Walker, C.H., and Dawson, A. *Environmental Toxicology and Chemistry*, Vol. 13, No. 4 (1994), pages 615-620.

[13] "Evidence of Pesticide Synergism in the Honeybee," Pilling, E.D. in *Aspects of Applied Biology*, Vol. 31 (1992), pages 43-47.

[14] The key reference is "Environmentally Persistent Alkylphenolic Compounds Are Estrogenic," R. White, S. Jobling, S.A. Hoare, J.P. Sumpter, and M.G. Parker, Imperial Cancer Research Institute, Laboratory of Molecular Endocrinology, London, England, published in *Endocrinology*, Vol. 135 (1994), pages 175-182.

[15] In early 1996, Dr. Pease joined the staff of the Environmental Defense Fund in San Francisco, California.

[16] A special issue of *ACTA Horticulturae* (Volume 347: 1993) surveyed Integrated Fruit Management systems in South

Tyrol, Italy, Poland, the Netherlands and most other European countries. The paper by E. Dickler and S. Schafermeyer focuses on progress across Europe and seven major producing regions in which 40 percent or more of the fruit producing acreage is managed under Integrated Fruit Production guidelines consistent with those put forth in 1991 by the OECD (see OECD, 1991). In the U.S., fruit growers in the Pacific Northwest are farthest along in developing a similar program. The Hood River Grower-Shipper Association in Oregon has developed a comprehensive program that is in the process of being implemented. It is described in a February 3, 1995 document, "Mid-Columbia Integrated Fruit Production Program."

[17] USDA was unable to provide us a computer file with the 1971 pesticide use data contained in the report issued in 1974, based on the 1971 survey (USDA, 1974). We therefore entered this data manually into a spreadsheet database comparable to those we used in assessing use and toxicity levels in 1982 and 1992. In addition, the 1982 USDA dataset was augmented with fungicide use data from Leonard Gianessi (Gianessi, 1992).

[18] Quote from "Children Become the First Victims of Fallout," an article in the April 19, 1996 issue of *Science* on the marked jump in thyroid cancer among children exposed to radiation following the Chernobyl disaster in the former Soviet Union. Dr. Braverstock was discussing the recent WHO decision, controversial in some quarters, to recommend that all children in Europe have immediate access to iodine supplements for use in the wake of a nuclear disaster. Iodine deficiency increases the risk of a child developing thyroid tumors following exposure to radiation.

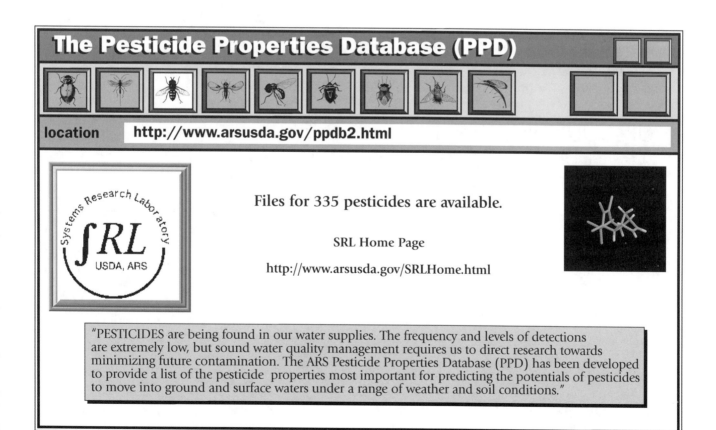

"OF COURSE ALL OF THESE PESTICIDES ARE SAFE.
AFTER ALL, THEY'RE REGISTERED WITH THE EPA."

Regulating Pesticides

Pesticide regulation has proved to be a difficult, costly, and controversial task. While it has achieved some major milestones, we have been running hard just to stay in one place.

Most scholars trace the modern era of pesticide regulation to the 1962 publication of Rachel Carson's famous book, *Silent Spring*. Carson raised public awareness of the adverse effects that can accompany pesticide use—especially bird and fish kills, and environmental degradation—setting the stage for government action to protect against those hazards. *Silent Spring* stirred public debate and triggered new research on pesticide properties and risks. Many voices urged caution and called for limits on pesticide use. But as impassioned as the early warnings may have been, they were based on incomplete understanding of pesticides' fate in the environment and adverse effects, and were no match for the enthusiastic embrace of pesticides by the farming and pest management communities. Pesticides seemed too good to be true, and well worth whatever imperfectly-defined risks they might pose.

> **Like farmers, regulators are also stuck on a sort of treadmill. When new risk concerns surface, registrants question the relevance or quality of data supporting risk findings and ask for time to do more studies. New regulations and testing requirements both slow and complicate the decision process. By the time regulators have the evidence needed to restrict pesticides, their useful life is often waning and attention must shift to new products gaining wider use.**

As use and reliance on chemical pesticides rose, clear adverse effects became evident in some areas, triggering new controversies. Environmental groups went to court, pursuing several high-stakes cases in the late 1960s and 1970s. The resulting publicity helped focus the nation's attention on the need to manage pesticide risks. Lost in the shuffle, however, was the underlying cause of pesticide problems—changes in farming systems and pest management strategies.

Overview

For some three decades, federal and state regulatory agencies acting under a variety of laws have overseen pesticide use, seeking to promote beneficial uses of pesticides while protecting public health and the environment from "unreasonable" adverse effects. Regulating pesticides has proved to be a difficult, costly and controversial task that faces obstacles deeply rooted in science, economics and adversarial politics. While regulation has achieved some milestones—many of the most hazardous pesticides used in the 1960s and 1970s have been taken off the market, for example—decades of regulation have not notably reduced the overall risks from pesticide use, as we have shown in Chapter 3. In truth, the fact that risks have not increased more dramatically is evidence that regulation has had important beneficial effects. But we have been running hard just to stay in place.

Much as farmers may find themselves stuck on the "pesticide treadmill," where pesticide use results in growing dependence on pesticides, our nation is stuck on a "pesticide regulation treadmill." The goals of regulation do not include reducing pesticide use or reliance. Instead, regulators are charged with implementing a law which calls for balancing pesticide risks and benefits. EPA decisions perpetuate, and indirectly promote, pesticide use by granting registrations, or leaving existing ones in place, on the basis that the products are economically beneficial and acceptably safe.

As more pesticides and uses are registered, and as pesticide toxicology advances, the list of pesticide-related risks that regulators need to be concerned about expands as well. Collectively, these processes in turn increase the need for regulation and the demands placed on the regulatory process.

The main focus of this chapter is on U.S. Federal pesticide regulatory policy, and on the evolution of philosophies and legal approaches over the years. For all the insight, effort and skill applied to the mission by several generations of legislators, regulators and other parties with a stake in the outcomes, two inescapable facts seem evident: First, pesticide regulation is mired in an adversarial process through which it has been exceptionally difficult to achieve agreement on the proper balance between risks and benefits. The result has been endless controversy and regulatory gridlock. Furthermore, since the 1988 law calling for accelerated reregistration of all pesticides, an enormous backlog of studies in need of review has built up, making the regulatory process inordinately slow and costly. Over the years, many reforms have been proposed by numerous blue-ribbon advisory committees. Some have been enacted, while others have been ignored. But for all the reforms and innovations, inefficiency and delay are still the logical outcomes of the contradictions in the laws Congress has enacted.

Second, the costs of the regulatory process have been enormous, both in monetary terms and in less tangible opportunity costs. The costs to the national economy of coping with pesticide risks currently exceed a billion dollars a year, and are projected to rise, with the private sector and the states likely to absorb a growing share of the costs. The marginal costs of regulating pesticides are increasing as well. In the 1970s, the EPA banned or severely restricted the use of the most environmentally damaging pesticides, and the agency's regulatory priorities since then have focused on reducing the use of selected high-risk ingredients. Today, with those goals largely accomplished, the agency has few "big-bang-for-the-buck" options left, and fewer easy choices. Risk assessments often cannot reliably predict which among 20 pesticides registered for a given use are more hazardous than the others; and the potential risk reduction attainable with a quantum of regulatory effort is shrinking.

Given this declining marginal benefit of regulation, the most effective way to reduce pesticide risks is to reduce pesticide use and reliance across the board. But neither the EPA nor any other agency has yet been given that mandate or the tools and resources to achieve it. While the nation has spent billions dealing with pesticide risks, we have invested just a few millions in developing and promoting IPM. These priorities must shift. It has been clear for many years that biologically based IPM can substantially reduce dependence on chemical pesticides over time and eliminate many risks associated with their use. What is needed now is a strategy for shifting gears, for placing appropriately increased emphasis on safely managing pest problems, so that we can reduce the emphasis on, and the costs of, *managing pesticide use.*

As long as pest management strategies continue to rely on chemical controls, which will go on to some extent even within an IPM framework, there will be a need to regulate pesticides. This chapter shows how current pesticide regulatory approaches came into being, and outlines some still-needed reforms that should be on the public agenda. But we also need to get beyond that—to acknowledge that even "reformed" pesticide regulation is not taking us far enough in the direction we want to go: that is, toward reduced reliance on and lower overall risk from pesticides. To make significant progress, we need to get off the "pesticide regulatory treadmill." We need policies and investment strategies, both in government and in the private sector, that put much more emphasis on developing biologically rational alternative strategies for managing pest problems, and on avoiding the risks of pesticides in the first place, rather than managing them after the fact.

> **A strategy is needed that places increased emphasis on safely managing pest problems, so that we can shift gears and reduce the emphasis on, and the costs of, managing pesticide use.**

The famous book Silent Spring *by Rachel Carson (above) raised public awareness of pesticide impacts on birds, fish and the environment (Carson, 1962). It also triggered scientific and policy debates which have continued to the present day.* Credit: Rachel Carson Trust

A. The Early History of Pesticide Regulation: 1910 to the Early 1970s

The nation's first pesticide law, passed in 1910, focused on protecting farmers from salesmen offering untested, sometimes unsafe, products for controlling insects, plant diseases and other afflictions. It was one of several consumer protection statutes passed in that era and was basically a "truth in labeling" law. Fraudulent claims on pesticide labels and misbranded products were subject to post-sale, post-use enforcement action by the USDA, if farmers or other pesticide users filed a complaint. The statute was essentially silent on the health or environmental consequences of pesticide use.

1. FIFRA, Written in 1947, Retains Focus on Product Efficacy

The 1940s ushered in the chemical era in American agriculture. The number of new pesticide products rose, spurring greater use but also revealing new problems. Congress recognized shortcomings in the 1910 law, and in 1947 passed the Federal Insecticide, Fungicide and Rodenticide Act (FIFRA). Like the 1910 Act, the new law was designed to protect farmers and the general public from ineffective, low-concentration or dangerous products, and gave USDA the enforcement responsibility. FIFRA lacked any mechanism to control pesticide use, but required registration of pesticide labels with the USDA before products could be sold. FIFRA gave USDA a mandate to recall unsafe pesticides, but the department did not set up procedures for review and recall of dangerous products until 1969.

Reliance on pesticides rose rapidly during the late 1950s and 1960s, outpacing knowledge about pesticide properties and toxicity. Poisoning incidents, crop losses and ecological damage stirred anger and controversy. Public institutions, including the courts, USDA, the Food and Drug Administration (FDA), Congress and state legislatures and land grant colleges were pushed and pulled by industry, environmentalists, farmers and other constituencies. The growing tumult over pesticide technology led to the first major national study on pest management and pesticide risks, commissioned in the late 1960s.

> **A law passed in 1947 gave the USDA a mandate to recall unsafe pesticides, an authority it did not exercise for more than 20 years.**

2. The Mrak Commission Report: 1969

The U.S. Department of Health, Education and Welfare established a commission to carry out the federal government's first in-depth assessment of pesticide risks. The "Commission on Pesticides and Their Relationship to Environmental Health" was chaired by Dr. Emil Mrak, Chancellor Emeritus of the University of California-Davis (and thus is also known as the Mrak Commission).

The Commission's final report, dated December 5, 1969 (U.S. Department of Health, Education, and Welfare [HEW], 1969), stated:

"... there is adequate evidence concerning potential hazards to our environment and to man's health to require corrective action. Our Nation cannot afford to wait until the last piece of evidence has been submitted on the many issues related to pesticide usage."

Three central conclusions summarized by Chairman Mrak in the report's cover letter set the stage for the government to conduct chemical-by-chemical safety assessments, the basic approach still in use 25 years later:

"1. Chemicals, including pesticides used to increase food production, are of such importance in modern life that we must learn to live with them.

2. In looking at their relative merits and hazards we must make individual judgments upon the value of each chemical, including the alternatives presented by the non-use of these chemicals. We must continue to accumulate scientific data about the effects of these chemicals on the total ecology.

3. The final decision regarding the usage of these chemicals must be made by the responsible government agencies..." (HEW, 1969).

Many of the Mrak Commission's major recommendations are still relevant today. Some were implemented, while others fell by the wayside. For example, the Commission urged "closer cooperation among the Departments of Health, Education, and Welfare, Agriculture, and Interior on pesticide problems through establishment of a new interagency agreement." Steps were taken in 1970 toward an interagency agreement but ended in 1971 with the formation of the EPA, by President Nixon's executive order. Responsibilities were shuffled dramatically, affecting the USDA, the EPA and the FDA. Bureaucratic tensions grew worse, not better, following the transfer of pesticide registration responsibilities from USDA to the newly formed agency. EPA and USDA subsequently have struggled for years over turf, budget and policy issues.

The cost-benefit standard Congress would embrace in the 1972 FIFRA rewrite can be traced to the Commission's suggestion that HEW consider the "adequacy of the evidence of hazard" as well as "possible consequences on human welfare that flow from the imposition of restrictions on human exposure." Although the Commission said government agencies should judge pesticides' relative merits, "…including the alternatives presented by the non-use of these chemicals," no federal agency assumed or was assigned responsibility to act on this recommendation. Weighing alternatives was largely outside the scope of EPA's mission, and most responsible policy makers in USDA and leaders in the farm community did not see a need for alternatives to pesticides.

> DDT use peaked in 1961 at about 150 million pounds of active ingredient—roughly one pound for every man, woman and child then living in the United States.

The Mrak Commission called for targeted action on high risk pesticides, specifically recommending cancellation of most DDT uses within two years and restricting the use of certain other pesticides. In the report's words, the government should "… restrict usage of certain persistent pesticides in the U.S. to specific essential uses which create no known hazard to human health or the quality of the environment." The EPA published a final cancellation order ending most uses of DDT in July 1972, and canceled registrations of eight other persistent organochlorine compounds in the 1970s. A few minor uses of some of these chemicals lasted into the 1990s. Two chlorinated hydrocarbon insecticides known to disrupt the endocrine system—endosulfan and methoxychlor—remained registered and are still used on some key food crops.[1]

Several Mrak Commission recommendations addressed the need to reduce risks incrementally. In particular, the Commission foresaw the need to establish limits for exposure to pesticide residues in foods and water and to be able to revise those limits as advancing research offered new insights into possible public-health consequences of pesticide exposure. In one especially prophetic passage, the Commission recommended that Congress should modify the Delaney Clause to allow the Secretary of HEW to exercise judgment regarding "when evidence of carcinogenesis justifies restrictive action." The report goes on to state (HEW, 1969):

"Indiscriminate imposition of zero tolerances may well have disastrous consequences upon the supply of essential food and threaten the welfare of the entire Nation. *Stepwise lowering of pesticide tolerances may in some cases be an effective and flexible instrument with which to execute policy."* (Emphasis added)

EPA has revoked many tolerances over the years following suspension/cancellation actions, but has rarely if ever tried to lower tolerances incrementally toward safer levels. This common-sense approach to lessening dietary pesticide exposure has surfaced in a number of legislative hearings, proposed bills and scientific reports, but it has never been a major EPA strategy to progressively lower tolerances to make it harder to use riskier pesticides. (With the passage of significant new food safety and FIFRA amendments this summer, discussed later in this chapter, this strategy may move to center stage.)

B. The 1970s: FIFRA Becomes an Environmental Law

EPA's maiden pesticide regulatory actions in 1972-1978—chiefly, the cancellation of chlorinated hydrocarbon insecticides—were fought by industry and farm organizations. Some people argue to this day that the bans were politically motivated and that the benefits of DDT always far outweighed its risks. This and other controversies simmered, again convincing Congress that changes were needed in the nation's pesticide law.

In 1972, Congress transformed FIFRA into one of the nation's first environmental statutes by grafting new authorities, decision rules, evidentiary processes and registrants' rights onto the law's basic labeling and product efficacy requirements. Major amendments in 1972 established the basic risk-benefit standard governing EPA pesticide decision-making. EPA was required to promulgate testing requirements needed to evaluate the health and safety, and environmental consequences of pesticide use, and was given authority to require registrants to submit such data as a condition of registration or reregistration. The agency was empowered to register pesticides as either "general use" or "restricted use". The 1972 amendments also addressed pesticide applicator training, farm worker safety provisions, the role of states, access to data and many other matters.

1. The Goal of Regulation

Congress's goal in the 1972 FIFRA rewrite was to give EPA tools and a mandate to remove high risk products from the market while ensuring an ample supply of effective pesticides. To accomplish that, Congress required EPA to balance pesticide risks and benefits—the basic regulatory decision rule that still guides the agency's actions. Congress defined the target as ensuring that pesticide products would not cause "unreasonable adverse effects on man or the environment." Given that almost all pesticides are toxic, weighing benefits was seen as necessary to determine what risks are "unreasonable." To discourage EPA from acting too aggressively, Congress imposed several hurdles along the path to suspending or cancelling a pesticide. Most important, it placed the burden of proof that a pesticide poses "unreasonable adverse effects" on the EPA, rather than requiring registrants to prove their products safe, and provided many procedural opportunities for manufacturers to challenge EPA's findings.

> New pesticides are guilty until proven innocent, with applicants bearing the burden of proof. Old pesticides are innocent until proven guilty, with EPA bearing the burden of proof.

The 1972 FIFRA amendments "grandfathered" all pesticides sold commercially before EPA was formed in 1970; that is, such products were granted fully registered status. EPA was required to review scientific data and reach a finding that risks exceeded benefits before it could cancel the use of a pesticide already on the market. But for a product not yet registered, the registrant bore the burden of proving that risks were minimal before EPA would permit it to be marketed. This placement of the burden of proof is crucial, since when data gaps existed—the norm, in pesticide risk assessments—products already on the market would remain in use until risk questions could be resolved.

2. Benefits Enter the Decision Process

In requiring EPA to balance the risks and benefits of pesticide use, FIFRA created a demand for both risk assessments and benefits assessments. The need for risk assessment is shared by many regulatory agencies, and the scientific community has devoted its attention for several decades to the task of developing sound and reliable methods for estimating the risks to health and the environment of chemical pollutants, including pesticides. Despite the quantity and quality of intellectual effort applied to this task, risk assessments for pesticides remain hotly disputed, especially when debated within contested regulatory proceedings. Compared to risk assessments, benefits assessment methodology for pesticides has been developed through less intense, less openly participatory processes, and has received less attention (and less acrimonious debate) in the regulatory process. But benefits assessment is a structurally flawed and weak leg on the regulatory stool.

The law requires EPA to base its benefits assessments

DDT used to be applied in large volumes with a minimum of safety precautions. These sprayers were typical of those used in the 1950s. Credit: USDA Archives, provided by Michael Weaver, Virginia Cooperative Extension

on data submitted by registrants, the USDA and land grant universities. A benefits assessment is generally carried out only when a pesticide is in regulatory trouble, and can serve as a registrant's last line of defense.

The foundation of most benefits assessments is comparative field efficacy studies, designed or directed by registrants and typically carried out by contractors or universities. The studies compare yields, crop quality and pesticide costs between a farming system using the pesticide under consideration and the "next best" registered alternative. The "bottom line" is the change in net crop income following the switch from pesticide X to next best pesticide Y.

The protocols allow little or no other changes in cropping or pest management systems and presume that the value of the pesticide under review is simply a function of the cost and efficacy of another pesticide. Non-chemical preventive practices or biointensive IPM options are generally not seriously considered; EPA does not require such data, and registrants understandably pass up the chance to be so thorough. Lacking this information, EPA has no basis on which to reach a judgment that non-chemical alternatives are effective and therefore has no basis to lower the estimate of benefits associated with use of a pesticide.

Registrants and others defending the use of a pesticide under EPA review have often predicted major crop and economic losses if products were banned, frequently citing benefits assessment studies. In fact, we don't know of a single documented case in which such high losses actually materialized. Not one. On one hand, this is fortunate and a testament to the innovative abilities of the American farmer. On the other hand, it is not exactly a ringing endorsement of the accuracy of benefits assessments. The benefits assessment process is routinely biased in favor of chemical solutions and against biological and management-based pest management systems.

Paradoxically, while high projected benefits have helped preserve high risk pesticide registrations, assessments showing low or negative benefits have rarely hastened cancellation of a pesticide. The theory is that the marketplace will take care of products that don't work as well as alternatives. But experience suggests otherwise. Many cases have been documented in which people apply pesticides that are not needed or do not work on the target pest. In public housing projects, building authorities

have sometimes stuck with ineffective indoor insecticides and rodenticides years after resistance began undermining product efficacy. Millions of dollars were spent in 1995 on fungicides to treat late blight in potatoes in one region of the country despite clear evidence that the product was ineffective against this particular strain of blight.[2] Pesticide ads and other marketing techniques can promote unnecessary use. Some lawn care companies, golf course managers and landscapers apply pesticides without knowing much about the need for treatment or its likely effectiveness.

3. A Recipe For Gridlock

Despite the intention of both Congress and EPA to expedite reviews of high risk active ingredients, the "Special Review" process for pesticides on the market has dragged on for as long as five to 10 years in many cases. While the review is in progress, sales and earnings continue to flow, providing strong economic incentives for manufacturers to drag out risks and benefits assessments. Profit margins earned by major manufacturers of older products typically fall between 20 and 30 percent of gross sales. Annual sales exceeded $100 million for 16 pesticide active ingredients in 1994 (Gianessi, 1995). No wonder some companies spend millions of dollars generating new data and mounting legal challenges against adverse EPA decisions.

If the law had instead required products to be phased off the market over three to five years starting at the initiation of a special review, and made it more difficult for a registrant to challenge EPA's judgment that such a step was warranted, many registrants would quite likely choose not to contest the EPA's decision. There would be less incentive to generate large volumes of data that EPA would have to review and act upon. Instead of investing millions of its own money and requiring EPA to spend millions of tax dollars to assess high risk but profitable old chemicals, industry and government could then invest resources more constructively in discovering safer new biopesticides and pest management systems.

4. 1975 FIFRA Amendments Aim to Slow Down EPA

In response to EPA's aggressive actions banning hazardous pesticides in the early 1970s, some affected parties complained to Congress, and some in Congress seemed

> In nearly every contested regulatory action, registrants have predicted huge economic losses if a pesticide use was banned. Those losses have never materialized. Not once.

to agree, that the new agency was over-zealous and inclined to act prematurely based on inadequate or erroneous scientific evidence. Legislators took several steps to change EPA's procedures, to change the terms of scientific debate, or when all else failed, to cut the agency's budget or give it explicit instructions on what it could and could not do with appropriated funds.

In this era, both EPA and Congress also sought advice repeatedly from the National Academy of Sciences/National Research Council and other expert authorities. In 1974, Congressman Jamie Whitten, then chair of the House Agriculture Committee, persuaded his colleagues to appropriate $6 million for an NAS study of how EPA used scientific information in decision-making. Part of that money supported studies on pesticide decision-making (NRC, 1978). In all, from 1972 to 1980 the NAS/NRC produced more than 10 volumes of reports assessing pest management and pesticide regulatory issues (see box, "No Shortage of Advice").

> **Lack of understanding of the ways pesticides adversely affect beneficial organisms is one reason many pest managers stick with chemical-based systems despite declining pesticide efficacy.**

In reauthorizing FIFRA in 1975, Congress imposed new procedural hurdles on EPA that further contributed to gridlock. Amendments required EPA to seek USDA review of all actions, and established a Scientific Advisory Panel drawn from the outside expert community, including some from industry, that had to endorse the agency's scientific conclusions before EPA could cancel a pesticide's registration. Another provision granted states more control over the training and testing of individuals for their certified applicator licenses. This licensing process comes into play when EPA labels high risk pesticides for "restricted use only," a step that usually includes limiting a product to use by certified operators in certain locations for environmental reasons, such as banning use within 200 feet of surface water or not allowing use of a certain termiticide (a pesticide designed to control termites) in specific types of basements.

As EPA began to classify certain major farm chemicals as "restricted use" pesticides in order to limit their risks, manufacturers and farmers worried about a shortage of certified applicators. State departments of agriculture, farm groups and the pesticide industry lobbied Congress heavily and FIFRA was amended to require states to make certification tests relatively easy to pass. This provision has since been rewritten to allow states to require applicators to pass a written test covering proficiency in reading and understanding of pesticide labels and application methods. In some states the test is "open book;" in others the test is closed book and quite rigorous.

The 1975 FIFRA amendments contained explicit language permitting EPA to make information about IPM techniques available to individuals on request, but *prohibiting* the states from requiring knowledge of or proficiency in IPM methods as a condition for being certified as a pesticide applicator. Congress took this step because

The grape skeletonizer (left) can do great damage in vineyards and has to be carefully managed. University of California entomologist Dr. Vernon Stern (right) developed a virus-based biopesticide for control of the skeletonizer. Credit: Richard Steven Street

No Shortage of Advice

Controversies over pesticide policy in the 1960s and 1970s led to a plethora of major studies by the National Academy of Sciences/National Research Council (NAS/NRC) and others, aimed at defining sound scientific and policy-making strategies for the nation and its regulatory agencies to follow in trying to manage pesticide risks. The list includes:

■ *Scientific Aspects of Pest Control,* (Steering Committee Chaired by C.E. Palm) (NRC, 1966).

■ *Pest Control: Strategies for the Future,* Agriculture Board, (Organizing Committee Chaired by Robert Metcalf) (NRC, 1972).

■ *Productive Agriculture & A Quality Environment,* Committee on Agriculture and the Environment, Division of Biology and Agriculture, (Chaired by Martin Alexander) (NRC, 1974).

■ *Pest Control: An Assessment of Present and Alternative Technologies,* Study on Problems of Pest Control, Environmental Studies Board, (Executive and Planning Committees Chaired by Donald Kennedy) (NRC, 1975).

■ *Pesticide Decision Making,* Committee on Pesticide Decision Making, Commission on Natural Resources, (Chaired by William Eden) (NRC, 1978).

■ *Regulating Pesticides,* Committee on Prototype Explicit Analyses for Pesticides, Environmental Studies Board, (Chaired by Robert Dorfman) (NRC, 1980a).

■ *Urban Pest Management,* Committee on Urban Pest Management, Environmental Studies Board (NRC, 1980b).

Perhaps the most comprehensive and far-sighted of these was the five-volume report, *Pest Control: An Assessment of Present and Alternative Technologies* (NRC, 1975). The study was chaired by Stanford University biologist (and later FDA Commissioner) Donald Kennedy. Several consultative panels and study teams produced volumes on pest management in cotton, corn and soybeans, forestry, and public health.

This was the first major national report to call attention to the serious threat posed by resistance to pesticides, predicting that "… The induction of genetic resistance in pest species and the disruption of natural control mechanisms constitute rising threats to the continued success of our current control technologies." The volume on cotton pest management states: "The immense value of natural biological control was not fully appreciated by entomologists or cotton producers until after the introduction of synthetic organic insecticides. When the effectiveness of the approximately 600 species of predators and parasites found in cotton is disrupted, often by a single insecticide application, many secondary pests do considerable damage to the crop" (NRC, 1975 at Volume 1, page 415). The report also highlighted emerging scientific concerns about synergistic effects of different pesticides, the need for more and better data on environmental fate and broad ecosystem impacts, and the importance of refining animal test models and methods for translating animal data to human risk estimates.

> *"The very success of pesticide chemicals has led to heavy reliance on them; yet their efficacy—indeed, their continued use—is challenged by several developments."*
>
> **Pest Control: An Assessment of Present and Alternative Technologies**. *Report of the Executive Committee (NRC, 1975)*
>
> In summing up its assessment of the prospects for chemical control, the committee projected that:
>
> *"The task of pest control over the next 10 years will almost certainly become larger rather than smaller. Contemporary chemical control of insects (though not of weeds and diseases) is decreasing rather than increasing in effectiveness…"* (NRC, 1975).

many argued there was a lack of proven IPM techniques for a particular crop grown in a state, other than traditional cultural practices and biological control.

Congress passed another important pesticide regulatory policy reform bill in 1978. This one gave EPA authority to grant conditional registrations as a way to speed up the registration process. Several new procedural hurdles were imposed, benefits were given more visibility and weight in regulatory decisions on high risk pesticides, and limits were placed on the types of data and evidence EPA could cite or draw upon in making risk estimates.

As the 1970s drew to a close, problems associated with pesticide use had begun to come into clearer focus, and society was struggling to find acceptable ways to balance the risks and benefits of these chemicals. Resistance to pesticides had emerged as a visible challenge. Resistance was spreading, not just among insect pests, but also in plant pathogens and weeds. Secondary pest problems and a growing appreciation of pest species' ability to adapt to chemical control strategies had lessened confidence that chemical pesticides would ever be the simple and affordable "silver bullet" so many pest managers sought. Tension was growing over pesticide risks, and regulation seemed to offer few solutions to the underlying problems. In response to these trends, the Council on Environmental Quality (CEQ), then a part of the Executive Office of the President, undertook a study on pesticides and pest management issues.

5. CEQ Tries to Shift Focus to Pest Management

The CEQ review of pesticide and pest management issues began in 1976 and picked up where the Kennedy report (NRC, 1975) had left off. CEQ's study focused on federal agency activities, with the specific goal of recommending changes in research priorities and institutional policies that would promote IPM adoption. The report, published in December 1979, was titled *Integrated Pest Management* (Bottrell, 1979).

The CEQ report focused on research needs to promote IPM in agriculture, forestry, the urban environment, public health programs and wildlife protection. The report suggests 24 "Policy Initiatives" in its closing chapter. The first recommendation—requiring federal agency implementation of IPM—called for an Executive Order directing each agency to adopt IPM on the lands and facilities it manages and develop a plan "to utilize all fiscal, budgetary, programmatic, and regulatory mechanisms within the scope of its responsibility to encourage the

development and utilization of integrated pest management in all sectors."

Another recommendation called for improving interagency coordination—as much a problem at the end of the 1970s as it was at the end of the 1960s. The most troublesome areas were USDA-EPA conflicts over the assessment of pesticide benefits and viable alternatives, and EPA-FDA disagreements over tolerance setting policy. CEQ recommended a variety of strategies to accelerate the discovery and commercialization of safer pest management systems and inputs, and highlighted the need for an "early warning system" to identify present or anticipated problems of pesticide resistance. At least two attempts have been made to address the latter need in farm legislation, but such a system has yet to be developed or funded. Other CEQ recommendations called for more research on the environmental effects of pesticides and effects on pest/beneficial-organism interactions.

The CEQ study recognized growing reliance on trained consultants in making information-intensive IPM systems work, which it considered a positive development. To encourage this trend, CEQ called on USDA and EPA to develop a model IPM certification and training program for private consultants. The report also called for prohibiting "any certified person or firm from engaging in the sale of any pesticide or receiving any compensation, reimbursement, or commission for any sale or application of any pesticide resulting from the person's or firm's pest control recommendations," an effort to break the commercial link that commonly exists between field advisors who help farmers and others design pest-management programs and specific pesticide manufacturers.

This suggestion has been restated in several other reports, but has not been enacted. It has been recognized in the National Alliance of Independent Crop Consultants' (NAICC) code of ethics and membership guidelines, which emphasize the need for independence from income based on pesticide sales.

The CEQ report called for relaxing certain grading and cosmetic standards for fresh produce, such as those that limit pest damage on fruit and vegetables and insect parts in harvested foodstuffs, to reduce pesticide use and residue levels. The report also highlights the need to analyze how marketing orders impact pesticide use. In 1996, first steps are being taken in this direction in California, where the USDA has ordered that less then perfect peaches, plums and nectarines can be sold in supermarkets as "utility grade" as long as they are clearly labeled (Hall, 1996).

Financial barriers to IPM adoption were also addres-

A New Method for Sharing Risk

On October 16, 1995, Agriculture Secretary Dan Glickman announced "… a new crop insurance option on a pilot program basis intended to help apple growers in Vermont and New Hampshire adopt new IPM strategies and technologies to combat apple scab."[3] The Secretary's announcement explains that insurance coverage will be offered only to apple farmers cooperating in a regional IPM research project. An important program goal is collecting data and experience to determine the feasibility of extending coverage to other apple growing regions.

The Ranking Minority Member of the Senate Committee on Agriculture, Nutrition and Forestry, Senator Patrick Leahy (a Democrat representing Vermont) has encouraged the Federal Crop Insurance Program to apply the concept to other pest and nutrient management challenges where unusual weather can cause substantial crop losses on farms using IPM, or other "Best Management Practices" designed to lessen agriculture's contribution to water quality degradation.

sed by CEQ in 1979. The report calls for improved mechanisms to allow society to share with farmers the increased risk of crop yield or quality losses during a transition to IPM. The report flagged the role of agricultural lenders in requiring pesticide-based systems as a condition for loans. CEQ also called for a pilot program offering crop and pest specific crop insurance for producers following recommended IPM strategies, an idea whose time may finally have come, as evident in the box "A New Method for Sharing Risk."

In the year that passed between the publication of the CEQ report and the end of the Carter Presidency, the Administration took steps to develop the Executive Order called for in Recommendation 1, and several interagency memoranda were finalized. But these efforts were ended by the new Reagan Administration in 1981.

CEQ's budget and staff were cut to about 25 percent of what they were in the Carter years, and the council's role in the policy process was virtually eliminated. A few agencies continued to develop and pursue IPM plans and policy reforms (see Chapter 5), but the sense of direction and urgency associated with a presidential initiative was soon gone.

C. Gridlock Takes Over: Regulation in the 1980s and 1990s

Congressional efforts to redesign pesticide management policy were relatively few in the 1980s, but there was no shortage of controversy in the pesticide regulatory arena. Some high profile pesticides were canceled, including the

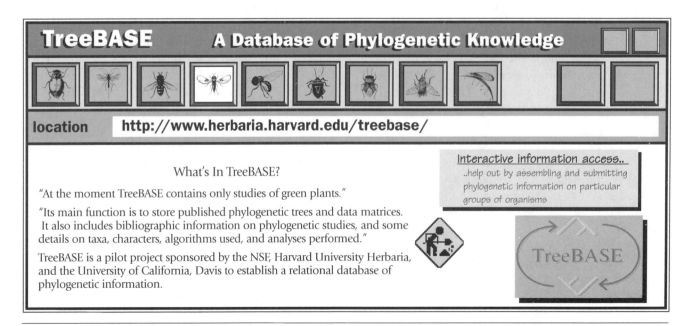

TreeBASE A Database of Phylogenetic Knowledge

location http://www.herbaria.harvard.edu/treebase/

What's In TreeBASE?

"At the moment TreeBASE contains only studies of green plants."

"Its main function is to store published phylogenetic trees and data matrices. It also includes bibliographic information on phylogenetic studies, and some details on taxa, characters, algorithms used, and analyses performed."

TreeBASE is a pilot project sponsored by the NSF, Harvard University Herbaria, and the University of California, Davis to establish a relational database of phylogenetic information.

Interactive information access..
..help out by assembling and submitting phylogenetic information on particular groups of organisms

TreeBASE

soil fumigants EDB (ethylene dibromide) and DBCP (dibromochloropropane), the herbicides 2,4,5-T and nitrofen (TOK), several insecticides, including monocrotophos and endrin, and the plant growth regulator daminozide, better known as Alar. Policy debates involving cancer risk assessment methods, acceptable levels of risk and data requirements received prominent attention. Scandals over the quality of the data submitted to EPA and the thoroughness of EPA reviews simmered and periodically erupted when the agency or others uncovered fraudulent practices or questionable risk assessment methods and findings.

Congressional oversight hearings in 1982 and 1983 placed another key issue on the table—one also raised by the Mrak Commission in 1969—the impact of the Delaney Clause on pesticide tolerance setting. We return to this issue when discussing tolerance issues in section D, "Unfinished Business."

> **Congressional efforts to redesign pesticide management policy were relatively few in the 1980s, but there was still no shortage of controversy. High profile pesticides were canceled, including EDB, DBCP, 2,4,5-T and Alar. Policy debates focused on cancer risk assessment, the Delaney Clause and acceptable levels of risk. Scandals over the quality of the data submitted to EPA and the thoroughness of EPA reviews simmered and periodically erupted.**

1. "FIFRA Lite" Passes in 1988

Several attempts were made in the 1980s to reform and reauthorize FIFRA. The chemical industry sought legislation to resolve disputes over data compensation policy, access to health and safety data, and other provisions governing patents and intellectual property (see section D). Environmentalists pushed for legislation to facilitate access to health and safety data. The role of states in either granting registrations not approved by EPA or setting their own, stricter tolerances when they judged federal limits inadequate emerged as a major source of controversy. And the reregistration of "old" pesticides, initiated in the 1972 FIFRA rewrite and still largely unachieved, became thoroughly bogged down.

Congress had granted registration to chemicals then on the market in 1972, and instructed EPA to review the risks and benefits of each old chemical and make reregistration or cancellation decisions by 1976. But it quickly became clear that EPA lacked the resources and procedures to get the job done in a reasonable period of time, especially given the major economic incentives registrants had to delay the process by offering to carry out and submit large volumes of new data. At its best, the process

was time consuming and resource intensive, and EPA lacked adequate tools and political clout to keep the process moving toward final decisions and enforceable changes in product labels that would expand margins of safety and avoid high risk situations.

Late in the 1980s, an unusual collaborative effort between industry and environmental leaders almost succeeded in gaining adoption of a comprehensive set of reforms. When the effort collapsed in 1988, Congress sought to salvage agreements reached on several major issues, especially reregistration, and passed a stripped-down bill ("FIFRA Lite"). These 1988 amendments gave EPA new authority to charge significant reregistration fees; to set priorities for reregistrations (including creating an "A" list for major food use chemicals); and postponed the date by which all reregistration actions were to have been completed to 1995 (which may have seemed realistic in 1988, but the target has recently slipped again, to sometime after 2010).

By 1990, EPA had made significant strides using its new authority. Priority lists and a detailed description of a "streamlined" reregistration process were published. Registrants (the manufacturers of pesticide products, generally) were sent letters asking them whether they wished to defend existing registrations. Those who did wish to were required to send EPA a check for up to $100,000 per active ingredient, to help cover costs of reregistration. Those who did not could request voluntary cancellations or expect EPA to cancel their registrations. EPA also sent letters to registrants of "A" list pesticides, requiring them to submit data to fill any remaining gaps in the base of information for risk and benefit assessment.

These EPA actions led registrants to abandon about 25,000 registered products by the end of 1991—more than half the 45,000 on the EPA's books in 1988 when "FIFRA Lite" was passed (EPA, 1994a). More than 400 active ingredients disappeared from the market completely. While the number of pesticides in need of reregistration fell by about half, the task remained enormous. More than 10,000 new studies were required to meet existing EPA testing guidelines just for the 350 active ingredients on List A (EPA, 1996b, 1995d).

2. Another National Research Council Report Focuses on Policy

Pest management and regulatory policy issues featured prominently in yet another major report from the National Research Council, *Alternative Agriculture*, published in 1989 (NRC, 1989a). This report included eleven case studies, seven of which dealt prominently with biological approaches to pest management.

The Committee's basic conclusions regarding the benefits of more biologically based agricultural production systems were viewed at the time as provocative (NRC, 1989a):

"Well-managed alternative farming systems nearly always use less synthetic chemical pesticides, fertilizers, and antibiotics per unit of production than comparable conventional farms. Reduced use of these inputs lowers production costs and lessens agriculture's potential for adverse environmental and health effects without necessarily decreasing—and in some cases increasing—per acre yields and the productivity of livestock management systems."

But the Committee also cautioned that, "Alternative farming practices typically require more information, trained labor, and management skills per unit of production than conventional farming," and stressed that, because of the lack of research emphasizing integrating existing knowledge into practical onfarm strategies, it was not yet possible to define precisely where and how alternative pest-management practices could be most usefully applied.

Calling for greater investment in research on the "development and use of biological and genetic resources to reduce the use of chemicals," the Committee bluntly stated that:

"Research on, and implementation of, biological control lags far behind total support for other pest control methods, even though several important pests remain difficult or costly to control by current methods."

The Committee noted the lack of information on economic and ecological thresholds for pest levels, and urged that such data be developed and widely shared with farmers. The report reviewed the impacts of federal farm policy, concluding that "Fertilizers and pesticides are often applied at rates that cannot be justified economically without consideration of present or future farm program payments." To level the playing the field when comparing farming and pest management systems, the Committee suggests that, "Regulatory policy may play a

role, particularly in raising the cost of conventional practices to reflect more closely their full social and environmental costs."

The Committee's major conclusions about pesticide regulatory policy focused on the bias against new products, inherent in FIFRA, and on the quality of benefits assessments. The report stated:

"Current federal pesticide regulatory policy applies a stricter standard to new pesticides and pest control technologies than to currently used older pesticides approved before 1972...(and) inhibits the marketing of biologically based or genetically engineered products and safer pesticides that may enhance opportunities for alternative agricultural production systems."

"A set of guidelines for assessing the benefits of pesticides under regulatory review should be developed. This procedure must include a definition of beneficiaries as well as an assessment of the costs and benefits of other available pest control alternatives. Benefits of control methods must be assessed as they accrue to growers, consumers, taxpayers, the public health, and the environment."

3. Alar Shifts the Focus of Public Debate

In the winter and spring of 1989 the CBS news program "60 Minutes" ran two hard-hitting segments focusing on pesticide regulatory issues, using the EPA's inability to deal with potential cancer risks to children posed by daminozide (Alar) as a prominent example. The first broadcast, in February, featured a new policy report by the Natural Resources Defense Council, which made a strong argument that EPA's gridlocked regulatory process was unable to get potentially hazardous pesticides off the market in a timely manner (NRDC, 1989). NRDC also argued forcefully that EPA's tolerance-setting procedures did not adequately take into account risks uniquely faced by children—an issue that was then a subject of great interest and discussion within the scientific community, but had not yet surfaced as a topic of public and Congressional debate.

Alar, or daminozide, is a plant growth regulator that was used to keep ripening apples on the tree, which helped growers save labor (picking) costs and improved the cosmetic appearance and keeping quality of red apples. Evidence had been accumulating since the 1970s that a breakdown product of daminozide called UDMH induced cancer in animal tests. This unavoidable metabo-

lite of Alar was formed when apples containing daminozide residues were heat-processed to make juice or applesauce. EPA twice proposed to ban daminozide during the early and mid-1980s, based on risk assessments showing that UDMH was a fairly potent carcinogen and that residues present in processed apple products were high enough to pose significant risks to the public. In its report, NRDC stressed that the risks to children were especially high, because children consume far more apple products per pound of body weight than adults do.

EPA's efforts to ban Alar had been frustrated by the determined resistance of the manufacturer (Uniroyal Chemical Co.) and by the failure of the agency's Scientific Advisory Panel to support EPA's judgment that its risk assessment was conclusive. EPA officials, interviewed in both "60 Minutes" segments, tried to explain why they had not acted to remove Alar from the market despite clear evidence of a significant risk. Assistant Administrator for Pesticides and Toxic Substances, Dr. John Moore, said his inability to cancel Alar revealed "the paradox of the statute." That is, as Moore explained, the law required EPA to prove that chemicals already on the market posed substantial risks before they could be cancelled, while a new chemical with risks

Mechanical cultivation (top left) is used at the Buena Vista vineyard in California to control weeds in the rows of grape plants, eliminating use of herbicides. The cover crops established between the rows are mowed periodically and help conserve moisture, provide habitat for beneficial organisms and improve soil quality. The rapidly spinning tines of the "Weed Badger" (top right) do a good job eliminating weeds in the rows, but the machine must be operated with care. Even the most skilled operator will occasionally come too close to the vines. The sheared vine (lower) will cost about $500.00 to replace, plus lost production. Progress along the IPM continuum and reducing pesticide use takes time and requires many new skills among all workers on a farm. Covering these costs during transitions can be a difficult challenge. Credit: Richard Steven Street.

comparable to Alar's would be denied registration.

The first "60 Minutes" broadcast, and a publicity campaign NRDC carried out to promote its report, provoked strong media interest and intense public reactions. The main message of both the "60 Minutes" show and the NRDC campaign was that pesticide regulation needed serious reform, and the public responded with predictable outrage to the spectacle of EPA's impotence to get an acknowledged problem chemical off the market. The media were less interested in complex regulatory policy debates, and played up the "human" elements of the story: the risk to children, parents' fears, the threat to health hidden in the very epitome of a healthful food, an apple. Predictably, some members of the public overreacted. A mother in Oregon was alleged to have chased down a school bus to remove an apple from her child's lunch box. School boards in several large cities ordered apples removed from school lunch menus, and apple sales slumped for a few weeks—despite clear statements by all authorities that it was UDMH in processed products, not daminozide in fresh apples, that posed the main risk. The media coverage fed on itself, and the story became a major national event.

During the early peak of publicity over Alar, the EPA, USDA and FDA issued a joint statement aimed at calming public anxiety. The government asserted that the risks daminozide might pose to individuals were very small and no reason to panic (true),

Government and industry's initial response to publicity about Alar was to reassure the public that no Alar had been sprayed on the recent apple crop. When independent testing showed those reassurances to be false, public anger, distrust, and concern about the safety of apples exploded. Editorial cartoonists had a field day with the Alar controversy. Credit: Jim Morin, Reprinted with special permission of King Features Syndicate

and that in any case the chemical had scarcely been used on the previous year's harvest. The three agencies cited a voluntary "boycott" of daminozide use that many apple growers had pledged to follow in 1986, in the wake of publicity about EPA's second failed attempt to cancel the registration, and estimated that no more than 5 percent of the apples then on the market had been sprayed with the chemical. At roughly the same time, an apple-processors' trade association released results of a study it said found daminozide residues in only 8 of 4,623 samples of apple juice.

Unfortunately, neither the government nor the apple processors had reliable data on the then-current levels of daminozide use by growers or residues in foods. Others, including Consumers Union and CBS (in its second "60 Minutes" segment) quickly published residue data based on recent surveys and state-of-the-art test methods, which showed that, growers' statements notwithstanding, Alar had been used on between 30 and 40 percent of the red

apples then on sale, and that about two-thirds of apple juices contained at least some traces of the chemical. The government's attempt to reassure the public backfired; when the reassurance was convincingly shown to be based on misinformation, public anger, distrust and cynicism about the government's ability to manage pesticide risks, and concern about the safety of apples, erupted again. At the request of the apple growers, Uniroyal asked EPA to cancel all food uses of daminozide, bringing that particular regulatory deadlock to an end.

The Alar events were a painful experience for all involved—federal officials, consumer and environmental leaders, apple growers and food processors, the media, and of course Uniroyal. Everyone taking part in the then-emerging discipline of "risk communication" during this period made mistakes, and most, we hope, learned from them.

After the dust had settled, it became clear that the outburst over Alar had had several beneficial outcomes. First, Alar was removed from the market. The EPA asserted, about two years later, after receiving the final results of additional animal carcinogenicity tests Uniroyal had conducted, that the evidence was conclusive that UDMH was a carcinogen, and the agency would have proceeded to cancel daminozide's registration had it not been voluntarily cancelled.

Apple growers and processors vowed not to get caught again with inadequate data about the safety of their products, and upgraded their pesticide monitoring programs. The apple industry, which had been seriously overcommitted to a single variety, Red Delicious, and which actually absorbed far greater economic losses in 1989 because of an oversupply of red apples that year than because of any impacts of the Alar debate (Roberts, 1994), is today more diversified and economically resilient. Growers in general are also much better prepared to discuss their pest management needs and practices with the public than they were before Alar, and there is probably better communication between growers and environmental organizations than existed before 1989.

After Alar, the media grew more cautious in reporting on risks, and while there has been an inevitable overreaction in the opposite direction (i.e., many stories asserting that nothing is as risky as it seems), a better balance seems to have been struck.

Most important, perhaps, the Alar debate persuaded the Bush Administration and leaders in Congress that pesticide policy and food safety reform were issues the public cared very much about. President Bush instructed William Reilly, his EPA Administrator, to make further streamlining of the reregistration process a high priority. And, although no major bill reforming tolerance-setting and risk-assessment procedures was passed by the Congress in the immediate wake of the Alar dispute, those events, coupled with another major report from the NAS/NRC in 1993 (this one on pesticides in the diets of infants and children; see later section), helped lay the groundwork for the reform legislation that finally passed this year.

> The Alar events were a painful experience for all involved but triggered many positive, and in some cases long overdue actions. Everyone taking part in the then-emerging discipline of "risk communication" during this period made mistakes, and most seemed to have learned from them.

Although most results of the Alar episode have proven positive for consumers and farmers, it may be hard to recognize that fact today. One unfortunate consequence of the intense uproar over Alar was that it offered conservative activists and others who believe our nation has gone too far in trying to control the risks of chemicals an issue they could use to rally the public to their cause. In the years since 1989, extensive and repeated propaganda from conservative authors and organizations like the American Council on Science and Health (ACSH, 1990, 1992, 1994) has retold the Alar story again and again, distorting events and omitting facts to transform the story into a morality tale about the dangers of "junk science," environmental advocacy, government overregulation of trivial risks, and media irresponsibility.

According to these advocates, Alar was a beneficial and safe chemical that was forced off the market by a deliberate scare campaign, mounted by NRDC and CBS. These "liberal" organizations, the story goes, set out to frighten the public, despite a lack of scientific data supporting their views, in order to enhance their own power and extend government interference with private industry's right to market the benefits of chemical technology. According to ACSH and others, this scare campaign

cost innocent apple growers more than $100 million in lost sales.

Like most political morality tales, this one is largely apocryphal, as the factual account of the Alar events just given demonstrates. But it has been told and retold so many times, and has been picked up and repeated uncritically by many pundits and journalists, most unaware of its ideologically driven distortions, that many people—even some who witnessed the events of 1989—have now come to accept it as largely true. In fact, it is a good example of the power of propaganda to revise history. The success of this revisionist campaign also illustrates that, as the 1990s dawned, the resurgence of conservative political philosophy on a national scale had introduced important and influential new perspectives into long-standing debates over how to improve pesticide risk management policy.

D. Unfinished Business

FIFRA has been rewritten and "reformed" numerous times, with many amendments that have improved the pesticide regulatory process, and many others that have merely added procedural hurdles, complicated the process, and contributed to gridlock. Here, we examine some of the major remaining needs and outline an agenda for further reforms.

Priority needs in reforming pesticide regulatory policy are very much in the eye of the beholder and reflect one's views of the goals of pesticide regulation. Perceptions of the role of regulation in the current political and economic environment have undergone some reanalysis in recent years. In our view, the regulatory tools available to EPA and the states need to be used intelligently and efficiently, both complementing market forces and compensating for the market's failures, to *gradually lower the overall risks of pesticide use*. To reduce overall risks—not just human health risks, but also environmental risks and impacts on ecosystems and important beneficial organisms—regulation needs to promote a gradual reduction in reliance on and use of most chemical pesticides. That can be accomplished in a variety of ways, but it is more likely to be accomplished if it is an explicit goal of policy.

Several regulatory tools can help attain this goal. The reregistration process needs to sharpen its focus on eliminating high risk broad-spectrum pesticides, and to achieve tangible and significant risk reductions if it is to justify the billions of dollars already invested in the process. The tolerance-setting process needs to emphasize downward revisions of tolerances in cases where existing limits are higher than current science suggests is truly safe. By cranking down tolerances in this manner, EPA can make it more costly and difficult to use some of the cheaper but riskier pesticides that have long been on the market, internalizing some of their true costs and leveling the economic playing field for safer, newer chemicals and biopesticides.

Priorities should also focus on chemicals whose efficacy against pests is declining because of resistance (hence lowering benefits). EPA needs to expand its benefits assessment process to take into account safer alternatives, including non-chemical IPM approaches, which would shift the risk-benefit balance against many uses of the riskier insecticides triggering secondary pest problems, in particular. Overall, these regulatory mechanisms need to be operated in concert with complementary efforts to develop and apply biointensive IPM methods, in a coordinated strategy aimed at transforming pest management practices, away from reliance on chemical controls and toward reliance on IPM.

1. Setting Tolerances at Safe Levels: "Someday" Approaches

Tolerances are the legal limits for pesticide residues in foods. Tolerances need to be set whenever a pesticide is to be used on a food crop; more than 9,000 tolerances specifying allowable residues of individual pesticides in individual foods (e.g., carbaryl in carrots) now exist. EPA sets tolerances in response to petitions from pesticide manufacturers; when a company wants to register a product for a food use, it must request that a tolerance be set. The petitions identify the crops for which registrations are being sought and propose the levels that need to be set. Tolerances are set high enough to ensure that in nearly all circumstances, residues that remain following applications of the pesticide in accord with label directions will be permitted (i.e. lower than the corresponding tolerance). See the box, "How Tolerances Are Set," for details.

While the tolerance-setting procedure described in the box is based on public-health principles that have long been followed by authorities setting environmental safety standards, some particular attributes of pesticide residues raise obvious concerns as to whether the limits

EPA sets adequately protect public health. Many pesticides are widely used; tolerances may exist for dozens of different foods. And many foods can be treated with dozens of pesticide active ingredients. A few years ago, more than 100 pesticides were registered for use on apples, for example. Thus, each tolerance covering residues in or on a given food represents only a small part of the risk posed by a particular pesticide, or from all pesticide residues on an individual food.

More fundamentally, most pesticides applied on growing fruit, vegetable and grain crops leave residues in foods or harvested forage and residues (which can then find their way into milk or animal products) at certain irreducible levels. When health considerations demand a lower tolerance than currently set, EPA typically does not take action, since it can only lower tolerances or cancel uses after conducting a thorough assessment of pesticide risks and benefits, a process which takes years. Thus, many tolerances continue for years to permit residue levels well above those an assessment based on health alone would define as "safe." EPA defends its slow pace in lowering such tolerances by pointing out that the residues found in the food supply rarely approach the admittedly unsafe published tolerance levels.

Exactly how wide is the gap between existing tolerances and "safe" levels? In 1992 the Senate Committee on Labor and Human Resources asked EPA this question. The agency provided data on the reference doses (RfDs) for pesticides, which define daily intake levels that are generally presumed to be safe, for non-cancer effects. EPA also provided estimates of the dietary intakes for dozens of food-use pesticides sanctioned (i.e., made legal) by current tolerances. The standard way EPA used at the time to estimate such exposure was to calculate the Theoretical Maximum Residue Contribution, or TMRC. This is a "worst case" estimate that represents the dose of a particular pesticide that could be present in a diet if all foods for which a tolerance exists for that pesticide contained a residue at the tolerance

> *"Logic argues that the EPA should focus its energies on reducing risk from the most worrisome pesticides on the most-consumed crops, and compelling reasons support such a strategy."*
>
> **Pesticide Residues in Food: The Delaney Paradox,** *(NRC, 1987)*

How Tolerances Are Set

Pesticide registrants propose a tolerance level for each food crop use, or ask EPA to grant an exemption from the requirement that a tolerance be set. There are two types of tolerances. "Raw agricultural" tolerances are set under Section 408 of the Food, Drug and Cosmetic Act (FDCA), and cover residues in or on fresh agricultural commodities at the time the food leaves the farm. "Processed food" tolerances are set under Section 409 of the FDCA and cover residues in processed foods. Section 409 tolerances are needed only when residues in processed food concentrate to a level higher than that found in raw agricultural commodities—for example, removal of water from tomatoes during heat processing usually results in concentration of residues in tomato paste.

The distinction between these two types of tolerances until recently was sometimes of major regulatory consequence, because historically the Delaney Clause applied when setting tolerances under Section 409, but not under Section 408. However, the Food Quality Protection Act of 1996 has eliminated this distinction, and residues in both types of foods will henceforth be treated in the same manner and tolerances will be set under the same health-based standard.

Before approval of a proposed Section 408 or Section 409 tolerance, EPA has to determine whether there is an analytical method available to detect residues in food at the tolerance level. Such a method is needed to enforce compliance with the tolerance level in the field. Almost all petitions are accompanied by documentation of an analytical method that EPA judges to be acceptable. The cost and difficulty of the method are sometimes a concern, but tolerances are rarely denied for lack of an analytical method.

Pesticide manufacturers base their proposed tolerance levels on analysis of data from field trials and food processing concentration studies. In the case of a tolerance on lettuce, for example, the registrant would spray the pesticide on a lettuce field at several rates both below and well above what is allowed on the product label and determine the resulting residues on the lettuce. For processed food tolerances, raw agricultural commodities destined for processing are spiked with residues below, at and above the proposed tolerance, the food is washed and processed and then residue levels are checked in the finished product. Using such studies, the registrant determines the level that residues in raw or processed foods are not likely to exceed under any conceivable circumstances. That is the tolerance level sought.

In reviewing a tolerance petition, EPA reviews product chemistry and field study data and toxicological health and safety data, and determines whether the level of exposure associated with the tolerance requested, plus any other tolerances sought or in existence for the same pesticide, poses an acceptable level of risk.

To answer this key question, EPA reviews all submitted toxicology data to identify the study with the toxic effect that occurs at the lowest level of exposure. It then establishes a "Reference Dose" (RfD) for the pesticide active ingredient; the RfD is based on the most sensitive effect, seen at the lowest level of exposure in animal tests, and incorporates a safety margin. Finally, EPA determines whether probable exposures resulting from establishment of the tolerances sought, plus any already in place, would leave adequate margins of safety; that is, EPA tries to estimate whether the residues allowed by the tolerances would cause any consumers to exceed the RfD for intake of that pesticide.

If total dietary exposure uses up just a portion of the RfD, approval of the tolerance petition is nearly certain. As estimated exposures from existing tolerances rise closer to RfDs, EPA becomes progressively more reluctant to establish new tolerances. The agency rarely establishes new tolerances for pesticides which already exceed their RfD.

level. Since those conditions are unlikely ever to be met, TMRCs substantially overstate actual dietary exposure to pesticides.

Nevertheless, the EPA's analysis was not reassuring. TMRCs for 60 pesticides exceeded their RfDs by a factor of 40 or more, and 19 other TMRCs exceeded their RfDs by a factor of 10. When EPA looked at exposures of infants, it found eight pesticides whose TMRCs exceeded the RfDs by more than 100-fold, and 37 more that exceeded the RfD by a factor of 10 or more. When EPA adjusted the TMRCs to reflect the percentage of crops that actually were treated with the pesticides (instead of assuming 100 percent treatment), estimates of exposure to some compounds dropped below the RfD, but two (of 10 examined) pesticides still exceeded the RfD by more than a factor of two.

When public officials, the media and others present information to the general public about pesticide residues in foods, the point is usually stressed that [whatever levels are under discussion] are "well within the legal limits." That assurance, however, can be misleading if it is taken to imply that the residues pose no risks. Tolerance-setting must strike a balance between risks and benefits, and some tolerances may be much higher than "safe" levels. EPA has testified that to reach "safe" levels, many pesticide tolerances would need to be lowered by factors of 10 to 100 or more. "Someday"—once that has happened—legally permitted levels could be more legitimately equated with safe levels.

2. Setting Tolerances: An Abundance of Advice From the NAS/NRC

Many of the recommendations of the expert committees that have advised the EPA and the Congress on pesticide policy matters over the years have focused on improving tolerance-setting. For instance, the 1969 Mrak Commission recommended progressively lowering tolerances to enhance safety and reduce use of the highest-risk pesticides. And two more in the unending series of NAS/NRC reports on pesticide regulation have addressed problems of tolerance-setting. *Regulating Pesticides in Food: The Delaney Paradox* (NRC, 1987), addressed problems related to tolerance-setting for carcinogenic pesticides, and the impact of the Delaney Clause. The 1993 NRC report *Pesticides in the Diets of Infants and Children* addressed the need for tolerances to take into account dietary differences and the greater susceptibility to toxic effects exhibited by those specific populations (NRC, 1993a).

The Food Quality Protection Act of 1996 has directly addressed the recommendations of both of these NRC reports. We will first outline what the problems are, or were, and then comment on how the new law has attempted to solve them.

The Delaney Paradox

The Delaney Clause is a provision in Section 409 of the Food, Drug and Cosmetic Act that prohibits government approval of a food additive "known to cause cancer in animals or man." Traditionally, food safety lawyers and toxicologists have equated oncogenicity (capacity to cause malignant or benign tumors in labora-

tory animal studies) with carcinogenicity. More than 70 pesticide active ingredients are carcinogens, using current classification criteria. Although it was initially enacted in 1958 to prohibit the use of known carcinogens as deliberate food additives, the Delaney Clause came to be a factor in pesticide tolerance setting beginning in the 1960s. As explained earlier, it applied to pesticide residues that tend to concentrate in processed foods (Section 409 tolerances) but not to those in raw agricultural commodities (Section 408 tolerances).

During the 1980s, EPA denied several tolerance petitions that sought approval to use oncogenic pesticides, because of evidence that residues would concentrate in processed foods. Some cases involved new pesticides posing much lower environmental or cancer risks than pesticides currently in widespread use on the same crops for the same pests (NRC, 1987). But the agency had never invoked the Delaney Clause in canceling the use of pesticides registered prior to the early 1970s. In order to cancel previously registered products under FIFRA, the EPA had to demonstrate that a pesticide's risks exceeded its benefits, a difficult task. Several high risk oncogenic pesticides were left on the market in the 1980s because of the lack of viable alternatives (NRC, 1987).

The NRC *Delaney Paradox* report estimated the level and distribution of "worst case" cancer risk in the diet stemming from some 2,500 tolerances covering food uses of 53 pesticides shown to cause cancer in laboratory experiments. "Worst case" cancer risks were estimated at almost 6,000 times the "negligible risk" level for carcinogens embodied in most federal law and regulation. (A cancer risk of one-in-one-million is considered "negligible.") The 1987 NRC committee recommended eliminating the Delaney Clause from pesticide law and consistently applying a "negligible risk" standard to all residues. The committee estimated that if all tolerances were lowered to "negligible risk" levels, the estimated total theoretically allowed cancer risk would shrink from 5,840 additional cases per one million people to 53 additional cases. The report also urged EPA to prioritize risks and target its efforts to eliminate the biggest risks from residues on the most widely-consumed crops first.

Infants and Children

In 1988 (before the Alar debate brought the issue to the public's attention), EPA asked the NRC to study the unique risks and issues involved in protecting pregnant women, the unborn, infants and children from pesticide exposure. That assessment took some five years to complete, and the report *Pesticides in the Diets of Infants*

Infants consume a less varied diet than adults and also need more food per pound of body weight to support the growth process—two reasons why tolerances set to protect adults may not be low enough to ensure ample margins of safety for children.
Credit: Charles Benbrook

land Children (NRC, 1993a) appeared in June 1993. A few days before the report was released, the Clinton Administration pledged to adopt the report's recommendations and made a commitment to promote adoption of IPM on 75 percent of the nation's harvested acreage by the year 2000, a pledge discussed in detail in Chapter 8.

The 1993 report recommended many fundamental changes in EPA's exposure and risk assessment methods, as well as in polices governing the setting of tolerances. The report's key conclusion was that "… determinations of safe levels of exposure should take into consideration the physiological factors than can place infants and children at greater risk of harm than adults" (NRC, 1993a).

The practical significance of this recommendation is enormous. Since government started setting tolerances in the 1950s, risk assessment methods and safety evaluations have been based largely on potential risks to healthy adults, as inferred from toxicity testing on adult animals. Infants and children can face relatively higher risks at the same level of exposure as adults, because of their inherent physiological susceptibilities (such as the rapid growth and development of the central nervous system). In addition, infants and children eat more food relative to their body weight, so their actual exposure levels are often higher than those that adults experience.

In determining tolerance levels, regulators apply a *safety* factor, now referred to as an *uncertainty* factor, in calculating exposure levels in humans not likely to pose any appreciable risk, based upon adverse effects observed in laboratory animal tests. Traditionally in the case of adverse health effects other than cancer and cholinesterase inhibition, EPA has determined a pesticide's "acceptable daily intake" (ADI), now called the "Reference Dose" (RfD), by applying a 100-fold safety factor. But the NRC committee concluded that "… an uncertainty factor of 100 may not be sufficient to account for the potential increased sensitivity of infants and children," and recommended adding a further 10-fold uncertainty factor for that specific purpose (NRC, 1993a).

The committee's report includes additional recommendations regarding how the EPA should set and adjust tolerances. The recommendations include considering all sources of exposure to pesticides, dietary and nondietary (including water and all liquids consumed, and exposures inside the home and outdoors), when evaluating risks and determining total exposure. The vast majority of current tolerances still reflect risk assessments taking into account only the exposure through food and beverages other than drinking water. In recent years EPA has also included exposure through drinking water in risk assessments, but very few food tolerances have been adjusted downward as a result. The NRC committee recommended that EPA not only consider exposure through water onsumed directly, but also consider residues that could be present in foods cooked or processed in water that contained pesticides.

The committee went even further in advising that regulators take into account *all* exposures that might contribute to a given adverse health outcome. Not only should EPA take into account all routes of exposure for a particular pesticide, it should also evaluate exposure to all pesticides, and other environmental pollutants as well, known to cause an adverse health impact through a common mode of action, such as cholinesterase inhibition. Since many pesticide active ingredients are closely related to other registered compounds, and have Reference Doses

"To properly evaluate the potential risk from exposure to multiple pesticides with common mechanisms for action, it is necessary to develop measures of total exposure to pesticides within the same class that reflect the overall toxicity of all pesticides combined."

Pesticides in the Diets of Infants and Children,
(NRC, 1993a).

based on the same toxic effect, this recommendation, which is now law, will require EPA to carry out several cumulative exposure and risk assessments, and adjust tolerances for groups of pesticides accordingly.

The tolerance-setting process involves several steps where assumptions must be made because reliable data are typically not available. EPA can generally estimate the residues left on crops sprayed with pesticides, based on field studies. But to evaluate risks and determine tolerances, two other critical variables also matter: the percent of crop acres actually treated with a pesticide, and the actual residue levels in foods as eaten by consumers. In the past, EPA and risk assessors have based pesticide dietary risk assessments on two "worst case" assumptions: that 100 percent of crop acreage will be treated with each pesticide registered for use on it; and that pesticide residues will be present at the applicable tolerance level in all foods when consumed. Clearly, both assumptions overstate risk and have triggered debate over just how EPA should estimate actual exposure for the purposes of risk assessment.

> The Food Quality Protection Act of 1996 defines "safe" as a "reasonable certainty that no harm will result from aggregate exposure to the pesticide chemical residue, including all anticipated dietary exposures and all other exposures for which there is reliable information."

On the second issue, extensive USDA and FDA monitoring data for pesticides in the diet show that residues typically occur at 1 to 10 percent of most tolerance levels, or even lower. Occasional samples may have much higher values (though violations of tolerances are rare), but average levels—which in general are more important from a health perspective—usually are far below the legal limits. Nevertheless, most environmental health specialists tend to agree with the 1987 and 1993 NRC committees, that tolerances should ideally reflect "negligible risk" levels, and that the definition of "negligible" should encompass sensitive groups like infants and children.

Assuming tolerances are set at such levels, as appears to be required by the legislation passed in July, 1996, actual residues found in food in the future would, on average, be considerably closer to tolerance levels. The frequency of relatively high residue levels, and mean levels, will decline, appreciably in some cases. But despite such progress, it is also likely that the frequency of over-tolerance residues will also rise, at least for a few years, as farmers adjust their pest management systems and food processors develop new methods to ensure that newly adjusted tolerances are not exceeded. The frequency of over-tolerance residues

will rise, despite lower average residue levels, because of significantly lower tolerances.

The issue of adjusting exposure estimates to account for the actual percent of crop acreage treated is trickier to resolve. The 1993 NRC committee studied extensive pesticide use and food residue data sets that showed that certain pesticides are sprayed multiple times on a large percent of the acreage of fruit and vegetable crops. Rates over 50 percent are common and rates close to 100 percent occur periodically in several crops in some states. The committee also noted that most fruits and vegetables are sprayed with several pesticides, sometimes with two or more that have comparable modes of action, and that many foods commonly consumed by infants and children contain multiple residues. For these reasons, even the "worst case" assumption that a pesticide is applied on 100 percent of a given crop could sometimes understate probable exposure levels. Taking into account both factors that tend to overstate and those that tend to understate likely exposure and risk, the committee advised regulators to proceed cautiously, and declined to recommend routine use of adjustments for the percent of a crop treated in estimating dietary exposure.

Finally, based on all its findings and conclusions, the committee's basic tolerance-setting policy recommendation (NRC, 1993a) says:

> "…EPA (should) modify its decision-making process for setting tolerances so that it is based more on health considerations than on agricultural practices… Children should be able to eat a healthful diet containing legal residues without encroaching on safety margins. This goal should be kept clear."

3. Setting Tolerances: Changes Made in the Food Quality Protection Act of 1996

After nearly 15 years of sporadic efforts to unravel the Delaney paradox and modernize food safety law and pesticide tolerance setting, the 104th Congress moved unexpectedly and expeditiously in 1996 to pass comprehensive reforms. Congress overcame partisan and interest-group deadlocks and found acceptable compromises on amendments to FIFRA and the Food, Drug and

Cosmetic Act, which were quickly and unanimously passed by both the House and the Senate. Many of the provisions of this new law address specific concerns about tolerance-setting discussed in the previous sections.

One major goal of the amendments is to eliminate the distinction between raw agricultural and processed food tolerances, as recommended by the 1987 NRC report on the Delaney Paradox. EPA will henceforth apply a uniform standard in setting all tolerances in food, under which the Administrator must determine that tolerance levels are safe, which is defined as finding that there is a "reasonable certainty that no harm will result from aggregate exposure to the pesticide chemical residue, including all anticipated dietary exposures and all other exposures for which there is reliable information."

With respect to cancer risk, "reasonable certainty of no harm" is essentially the same as "negligible risk;" that is, an estimated risk of one additional cancer per million people exposed for a lifetime. For non-cancer effects, a finding that predicted total exposure for all population groups, including infants and pregnant women, does not exceed an active ingredient's reference dose (RfD) would meet the "reasonable certainty of no harm" standard (assuming no other chemically-related pesticide active ingredients cause the same adverse effect through a common mode of action).

The bill permits the Administrator to set tolerances at a two-in-one million risk level for pesticides that cause non-threshold effects (i.e. cancer), but only under narrowly defined conditions. The Administrator may exercise this discretion in order to preserve benefits arising from continued use of a pesticide, when such use either "...protects consumers from adverse effects on health that would pose a greater risk than the dietary risk from the residue" or "use of the pesticide chemical...is necessary to avoid significant disruption in domestic production of an adequate, wholesome, and economical food supply."

For most pesticides, the significance of these exceptions is very limited. Under "worst case" exposure assumptions, high risk carcinogenic pesticides pose theoretical cancer risks on the order of 100 per million, a few even higher. Invoking the Administrator's discretion to avoid losing benefits would mean those risks would be reduced 98 percent, rather than 99 percent—not a big difference. Any tolerance set at the higher level because of a benefits finding expires in five years but can be extended if the Administrator determines that, based on a review of the current facts, the conditions in the benefits provision are still met.

The new legislation also directs EPA in setting tolerances to assess pesticide risks "taking into account

available information on" (food) consumption patterns among infants and children, and the "...special susceptibility of infants and children...including neurological differences between infants and children and adults, and effects of in utero exposure to pesticide chemicals." The bill also instructs EPA to consider the cumulative effects of residues that have a common mechanism of toxicity, and to incorporate an additional tenfold margin of safety so that tolerances will protect infants and children. The new law restricts EPA's authority to make adjustments for percent of crop treated, allowing this step only in the case of evaluating chronic exposure and risk, and only then if the Administrator has accurate data on pesticide use and "finds that the exposure estimate does not understate exposure for any significant population group."

The bill includes a "Consumer Right to Know" provision that requires EPA to publish and distribute for display in food stores a discussion of pesticide residues in foods, with details on those chemicals that pose a lifetime risk above one-in-one million (and up to two-per-million), along with recommendations for ways consumers can reduce their exposure to pesticide residues while maintaining a healthy diet.

The bill echoes a recommendation of the Mrak Commission by requiring EPA to review and adjust tolerances as needed to meet the bill's basic safety standards and requirements. It calls for a review of all tolerances within a 10-year period (one-third within three years; two-thirds within six years), and directs the Administrator to "give priority to the review of the tolerances or exemptions that appear to pose the greatest risk to public health."

In short, the Food Quality Protection Act of 1996 enacts important reforms of the tolerance-setting process proposed by several public-health minded expert committees over the years. These amendments promise to make tolerance-setting a more effective tool in driving changes in how pesticides can be used on food crops and should also help internalize some of the costs of using high-risk pesticides. But it is not clear yet how easily these new mandates can be carried out by EPA. The resource implications of the additional risk assessments

> *"...multiple residues; (can) interact synergistically to increase the total toxic potential. For example, synergistic effects between the (oranophosphates) malathion and EPN have been noted since 1957. Nevertheless, 33 of the 35 crops with tolerances for EPN also have tolerances for malathion."*
>
> **Pesticides in the Diets of Infants and Children,**
> *(NRC, 1993a).*

and other work required have not yet been determined. And the basic structure of FIFRA is unchanged, leaving open the prospect of protracted debate and litigation over EPA's assumptions, models, and judgments in every individual case where a new approach is applied and leads to substantial new restrictions on product use. Unless the community of interested parties shows an unusual new spirit of cooperative commitment to risk reduction as an overriding goal, there is no guarantee that the latest reforms will be any more immune to gridlock than past reforms have been.

4. Problems With the Reregistration Process

FIFRA amendments passed in 1988 set up an "accelerated" reregistration process and gave EPA seven (more) years to complete reregistration of most widely used pesticides. Major data gaps had to be filled, as a first step. Since the beginning of the accelerated process, EPA has received over 21,000 studies from registrants. Because of resource constraints, EPA cannot promptly review all such data submissions; the recent backlog of unreviewed studies amounted to almost 40 percent, or 7,800 studies (EPA, 1995b and 1996b).

As discussed earlier, one notable outcome of Congress's decision to allow EPA to charge substantial fees for reregistration was that about 25,000 little-used or obsolete products were abandoned between 1989 and 1991, about 54 percent of all those then registered (EPA, 1994a). Most of these products had modest market shares, or none at all.

Despite these and previous efforts to streamline it, the reregistration process is now far behind any schedule that was deemed reasonable when FIFRA amendments were passed. In 1972, Congress gave EPA until 1976 to reregister all old pesticides. By 1988, with the work for the most part still undone, Congress gave EPA until 1995 to finish it. More recently, the target was put off another 15 years, to 2010.

Aside from how long it takes, there are other problems with reregistration. Even when the process is completed, changes in pesticide use to reduce risks can take years to implement.

After completing its review of risk-benefit data and assessing its regulatory options, EPA issues a

Reregistration Eligibility Decision (RED), which is the agency's evaluation of a group of related active ingredients that sets forth the agency's findings. The RED generally requires changes in pesticide product labels prior to completing the reregistration. Label changes are the main mechanism to change the way the pesticide is used—for example, to reduce application rates to meet lower tolerances. New restrictions called for in REDs become enforceable only after they appear on pesticide product labels.

Product labels can contain detailed restrictions on when, where and how pesticides can be applied, to ensure that risks do not exceed benefits. For example, the label could ban application in fields with sandy soils, or prohibit use near wildlife breeding grounds or aerial application in rice-growing areas. To revise labels covering all uses of a major active ingredient, EPA must deal with several registrants, dozens to hundreds of end-use product labels, and a myriad of details.

> A RED has no regulatory status. It outlines risk reduction measures required for products containing a given active ingredient. Nothing changes in the real world until pesticide product labels are changed—a process which poses another round of challenges, as EPA is learning from experience.

For this process to run smoothly, EPA needs the cooperation of end-use registrants. If one or a few registrants in a group decide to contest changes, EPA can punish the recalcitrant registrants by cancelling those uses—a time- and resource-intensive process. If EPA chooses not to pursue cancellation, certain registrants may be able to keep old-label products on the market for another few years and gain competitive advantages as a result. Responsible registrants who work with EPA to quickly translate REDs into revised and enforceable labels may thus be penalized for willingness to cooperate. EPA's need to keep all registrants "on board" as label changes are crafted gives registrants leverage in negotiating changes more to their liking.

Through the end of Fiscal Year 1995, EPA had completed the label revision process for about 2,200 end-use products. EPA had suspended 300 of those products, meaning that roughly one in seven products (or their registrants) were found not in compliance with the conditions of reregistration. Another 750 products were reregistered and 1,175 were cancelled voluntarily at the request of registrants (EPA, 1995d).

By early 1995, EPA had issued 81 REDs covering 120 active ingredients, more than 3,500 products, and 500 tolerances. But according to the Office of Pesticide Programs' 1994 Annual Report, these REDs covered less than 10 percent of the herbicides and insecticides (by volume) applied that year in agriculture, only 4 percent of the herbicides and 10 to 15 percent of the insecticides applied by homeowners, and less than half the fungicides applied by both farmers and homeowners. The impact of the completed REDs may be modest, since many of the products covered are not used widely or pose little risk. These include the natural products boric acid, blood meal, *Heliothis zea* NPV (nucleopolyhedrosis virus) and *Bacillus thuringiensis (Bt)*. EPA began issuing REDs on major food use pesticides in 1994, but it is too early to assess impacts since for many the label revision process was still underway in mid-1996.

Progress in issuing REDs picked up in FY 1995. Forty were completed, bringing the total to 121 (EPA, 1995d). But more than 260 remain, and only 750 end-use pesticide products out of 4,633 covered by the completed REDs have actually completed reregistration. Once a reregistration is complete, it typically takes EPA one to three years to complete the label revisions, after which up to a year may pass before labels appear on commercial products in the market-place—the step that actually starts reducing excessively risky pesticide uses. While EPA may streamline the process somewhat, it appears reasonable to expect in most cases a two to three year lag between issuance of an RED and changes in pesticide use patterns.

Risk reduction actions proposed in REDs issued in FY 1995 are modest. Only two of 40 active ingredients—cyanazine and fenitrothion—are headed off the market voluntarily over the next several years. The fate of cyanazine is uncertain, however, since one registrant has pledged to aggressively seek reregistration. This move would, in effect, end the voluntary agreement and could force EPA to pursue cancellation. Five pesticides have been reclassified as restricted use and 14 have had some uses, mostly for low-volume crops, deleted. Personal protective clothing was required in 27 cases, and restrictions limiting worker access to treated areas were imposed or tightened in 21 cases.

All will have revised labels with up-to-date safety precautions and label directions, about half of which will include reductions in the maximum allowed application rate, frequency or total pounds that can be applied in a season. But in most cases, reduction in the maximum application rates will only bring labeled rates closer to

those that occur during actual use. The new labels will have modest impacts on actual use and reliance.

These problems illustrate yet again the difficulty EPA faces in reducing pesticide risks. Pesticide users and manufacturers can negotiate with or fight the agency at every step of the process, and even when agreements are reached they take much time and effort to implement.

During reregistration, new data submitted to EPA sometimes raise risk concerns that lead EPA to shift the pesticide into Special Review. Special Review is in theory a more intense process designed to resolve risk questions rapidly, so that pesticide uses suspected of posing unreasonable risks can either be cancelled or restricted to reduce risks. As in reregistration, pesticides remain on the market while undergoing Special Review, subject only to those restrictions that registrants are willing to accept in revised product labels.

Historically, Special Review has not worked as intended. Reviews have been stretched out for years by registrants intent on prolonging the process. One tactic is to keep developing and submitting more data to EPA. FIFRA requires EPA to take into account all evidence presented to it by registrants or anyone else during a Special Review, even if that means it must delay decisions in order to update and refine risk-benefit assessments. Since its formation, EPA has initiated about 115 Special Reviews. About 15 remain in progress, 45 have been completed, 16 reviews were ended after just a preliminary assessment of available data, and another 38 resulted in cancellations (including six cases prior to the beginning of the formal process) (EPA, 1994a).

> EPA may develop ways to streamline the process of completing label revisions, but it appears likely that there will be a two to three year lag between reregistration and enforceable label changes on products in the field.

5. Regulating Competition Within the Pesticide Industry

Regulatory programs can affect industry profits by controlling access to markets. In general, the more pesticide products that get through the registration process, the more competition, pushing prices down.

There are three major tiers in the conventional pesticide industry: basic manufacturers, typically large, multinational chemical, drug and energy companies that invest heavily in R&D; mid-scale regional formulators who manufacture some active ingredients and formulate others into finished products, but do little research; and specialty companies that formulate products from active ingredients bought from others and that serve niche markets in agriculture, urban America and other sectors.

Throughout the 1980s many attempts were made to resolve controversy over an issue of competition that had deeply divided the industry. The issue is when and under what conditions one company can cite pesticide health and safety data that were generated and paid for by another firm. Two provisions in FIFRA address these concerns. The law grants an "exclusive use" right to the company that generates the data, for specific time periods. FIFRA also provides for "data compensation"—if Company A wants to cite data that Company B has already submitted to EPA, concerning effects of an ingredient of both companies' products, Company A has to pay Company B for use of the data. FIFRA set up a mandatory data compensation mechanism to promote competition, encourage registrants to seek labels for minor crop uses (crops grown on relatively few acres), avoid duplicative testing costs, and limit animal suffering. Data compensation can also speed up EPA's decision process if the agency already has reviewed the data.[4]

Implementing this mechanism has proven to be a headache for EPA, consuming a sizable portion of staff and legal resources. Today, EPA has to keep track of which companies submitted which studies, when periods of "exclusive use" expire and who has offered to pay

whom for which data. This task is even more complex and resource-intensive than it might seem, since some studies had multiple sponsors, and the pesticide industry has been rapidly consolidating since the late 1970s. In addition, some companies fought with EPA during the 1980s over what constituted "fair compensation" for a given study. Costly administrative hearings and court cases were required to sort things out. EPA periodically found itself caught in the cross-fire between competing companies or segments of the industry. These provisions of FIFRA drain agency resources—and political capital—in mediating disputes, tracking legal proceedings and assuring that changes in FIFRA do not further complicate data compensation administration. In recent years, a new generation of issues has emerged involving how FIFRA impacts marketing decisions, competition and the price paid for pesticides, as described in the box "Price Gouging or Product Stewardship?"

E. Costs and Consequences of Pesticide Regulation

After a strong start in the 1970s, when several agency decisions substantially reduced the risks from chlorinated hydrocarbon insecticides, the impact of EPA regulation on pesticide use and risks has declined. Regulators tried

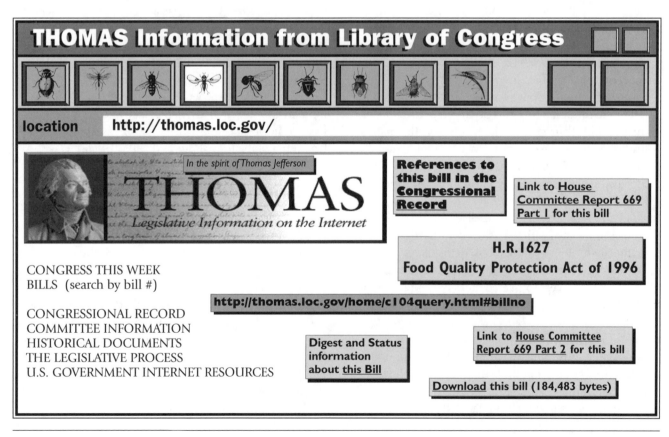

in the 1980s to target high risk pesticides and uses, and had some success imposing measures to expand margins of safety, especially for farm workers and applicators. But regulation has had surprisingly modest impact on the average toxicity levels across products in widespread use, as shown in Chapter 3. Use and reliance have held steady or risen. The number and diversity of pesticides available to farmers has risen steadily since the 1950s, although it dropped sharply for few years following passage of "FIFRA Lite" and the imposition of stiff reregistration fees. The number of pesticide active ingredients registered is rising again and is close to record-high levels.

Price Gouging or Product Stewardship?

Farmers are pursuing a class action lawsuit in North Dakota over alleged price gouging by BASF, manufacturer of the herbicide Poast (sethoxydim). The active ingredient makes up 18 percent of Poast brand herbicide products. Poast is registered for a wide range of crops, including several minor use crops—sunflowers, sugar beets, flax, potatoes and canola—grown on about 5 million total acres in North Dakota.

In order to compete more effectively in large-acreage crops like soybeans, alfalfa and cotton, BASF introduced "Poast Plus" in 1994, a formulation that contained 13 percent sethoxydim plus an adjuvant (an inert ingredient). Poast Plus was priced at about $8.00 per acre treated; Poast at $12.00. The manufacturer sought and received registration for Poast Plus on all the same crops as Poast, but decided to place only the four large acreage crops on the Poast Plus label, making use on sunflowers and other minor use crops a violation of the label (Tonneson, 1996). Several farmers applied the less expensive Poast Plus to minor use crops, but a complaint was filed (some contend by a BASF sales representative). The North Dakota Department of Agriculture investigated the incidents and levied several fines against farmers in 1994-1995, which caught the attention of the state Commissioner of Agriculture, Sarah Vogel.

An investigation was carried out, leading Commissioner Vogel to allege, "What BASF is doing is clearly a rip-off" (Tonneson, 1996). Commissioner Vogel's department made an unsuccessful attempt to resolve the issues with BASF by asking the company to add minor use crops to the Poast Plus label. In June 1995, the department granted a sunflower seed company a third-party label for Poast Plus covering the state's minor use crops under a provision that allows states to seek additional labels on federally registered pesticides to meet "special local needs." These needs usually arise from unexpected pest pressure, but the Poast Plus label in North Dakota was sought to avoid regulatory chaos. The new label also saved North Dakota farmers an estimated $2 million in 1995.

The state also asked EPA to investigate the legality of using FIFRA to restrict market access to an already reviewed and approved (and less expensive) pesticide. The EPA's review is ongoing, and a class action lawsuit is moving toward trial. BASF has asked EPA not to approve the "Special Local Need" label for 1996 in North Dakota or any other state, and has since released a new product similar to Poast Plus in content and price that is labeled for minor use crops.

The North Dakota case is just one of several identified in a recent state farm magazine article entitled "Pesticide Battle Brews: North Dakota's Agriculture Commissioner Charges BASF with Price Gouging" (Tonneson, 1996). Other examples are discussed in which manufacturers drop one label and replace it with two new products—one priced lower but labeled only for large acreage crops, another priced higher and labeled for minor crop markets where competition is less severe. To keep farmers from using the lower priced products, some companies apparently are including low concentrations of herbicide active ingredients that would damage minor use crops.

According to North Dakota farmer Todd Thompkins, BASF is not the only pesticide manufacturer to "pull these shenanigans." The way BASF utilized the labels for Poast and Poast Plus to leverage added profit was "…just another way for BASF to make a buck off farmers" (Tonneson, 1996).

Table 4.1 Changes in the Pesticide Toolkit from 1971 to November, 1994

		Fungicides	Herbicides	Insecticides	Total
1971-1974	**1971 Base # a.i.'s***	30	48	54	132
	New a.i.'s Registered	16	18	20	54
	Canceled/Suspended	0	0	5	5
	1975 New Base # a.i.'s	46	66	69	181
1975-1979	**1975 Base # a.i.'s**	46	66	69	181
	New a.i.'s Registered	12	22	21	55
	Canceled/Suspended	0	0	9	9
	1980 New Base # a.i.'s	58	88	81	227
1980-1984	**1980 Base # a.i.'s**	58	88	81	227
	New a.i.'s Registered	9	21	19	49
	Canceled/Suspended	2	1	1	4
	1985 New Base # a.i.'s	65	108	99	272
1985-1989	**1985 Base # a.i.'s**	65	108	99	272
	New a.i.'s Registered	2	29	24	55
	Canceled/Suspended	0	1	1	2
	1990 New Base # a.i.'s	67	136	122	325
1990-11/1/94	**1990 Base # a.i.'s**	67	136	122	325
	New a.i.'s Registered	5	4	15[+]	24
	Canceled/Suspended**	2	2	3	7
	11/1/94 New Base # a.i.'s	70	138	134	342

* Base number is an estimate from USDA 1971 survey of pesticide active ingredients used on major crops. The actual number of registered active ingredients is somewhat higher.

+ Includes 9 pheromones and 1 virus.

** Active ingredients canceled or suspended by EPA actions; does not include pesticide active ingredients voluntarily canceled as a result of the reregistration program.

Source: "Chemicals Registered for the First Time As Pesticidal Active Ingredients Under FIFRA" (EPA, 1994c).

1. FIFRA Ensures Steady Growth in the Pesticide Toolkit

There were 32 pesticide products registered with the USDA in 1932 (Moses et al., 1993). When responsibility for regulating pesticides was transferred from USDA to the newly formed EPA in 1971, the pesticide toolkit was still modest in size. About 54 insecticide active ingredients, 48 herbicides and 30 fungicides—a total of 132 active ingredients—accounted for most pesticide use in agriculture (USDA, 1973).

By the end of 1974, the number of pesticides available had risen to 181—54 new active ingredients had been registered, and EPA had removed only about 5 from the market (with several other actions underway). In each of the next five-year periods, the EPA registered five to 10 times as many new active ingredients as were removed by regulation (EPA, 1994c). The number of products that were voluntarily dropped by registrants was modest until 1990, when the prospect of large reregistration fees led to cancellation of some 54 percent of products then eligible

Figure 4.1 Size of the Pesticide Toolkit in Five Year Intervals

Legend:
- Insecticide
- Herbicide
- Fungicide

Year	Fungicide	Herbicide	Insecticide	Total
1975	46	66	69	181
1980	58	88	81	227
1985	65	108	99	272
1990	67	136	122	325
November 1, 1994	70	138	134	342

Source: "Chemicals Registered for the First Time As Pesticidal Active Ingredients Under FIFRA" (EPA, 1994c).

to be reregistered. Many of these active ingredients were obsolete and not used and, in many cases, are not reflected in the above table.

In 1990, there were about 325 active ingredients from which farmers could choose. As a result of reregistration, all or most of the dozens of little-used active ingredients dropped off the market. But by the fall of 1995, the pesticide toolkit was approaching its largest size ever, as a result of a record 41 new active ingredients registered in fiscal year 1995. In fiscal year 1996 another 30 to 40 new active ingredients are likely to be registered for the first time, bringing the total of new active ingredients registered since 1971 to about 300. Changes in the pesticide toolkit are presented in Table 4.1 and in Figure 4.1, based on an EPA report "Chemicals Registered for the First Time As Pesticidal Active Ingredients Under FIFRA" (EPA, 1994c).

2. Regulation Wanes as a Factor Shaping Pesticide Use Patterns

EPA got off to a fast start in the 1970s, initiating 22 special reviews or cancellation actions between 1971 and the end of 1977. The agency eventually canceled or severely restricted almost all those pesticides. EPA initiated another 20 such actions between 1978 and 1985, but has launched only 11 between 1986 and the present. The impact of final EPA regulatory actions during these three time periods is summarized in Table 4.2.

Table 4.2 requires some explanation. First, we reviewed the EPA records (EPA, 1994a), and developed a list of all regulatory actions initiated in three periods: 1971-1977, 1978-1985 and 1986-1994. We then reviewed the final outcomes of these actions and divided the cases into "Heavily Impacted" and "Not Heavily Impacted." A "Heavily Impacted" pesticide was one that had an estimated 80 percent or more of pounds applied eliminated as a result of regulation. Most were cancelled outright, ending 100 percent of use. The majority of "Not Heavily Impacted" cases experienced less than a 20 percent change in pounds applied after the completion of regulatory actions, although in most cases, the products were classified as "restricted use" and additional safety precautions were imposed.

The first row of numbers in Table 4.2 is the total number of cases; the second, the number of "Heavily Impacted" active ingredients; and the third, the number of "Not Heavily Impacted" active ingredients. The next

Table 4.2 Number of EPA Regulatory Actions Involving Major Agricultural Use Pesticides and Changes in Average Toxicity Levels

	1971-1977	1978-1985	1986-1994
Number of Cases	22	20	11
a.i.'s Heavily Impacted	15	8	6
a.i.'s Not Heavily Impacted	7	12	5
Average Acute Toxicity			
(LD-50 values*; Lower Numbers=More Toxic)			
a.i.'s Heavily Impacted	897	2,842	2,520
a.i.'s Not Heavily Impacted	4,402	4,098	5,035
Average Chronic Toxicity			
(Mam Tox Score* values; Higher Numbers=More Toxic)			
a.i.'s Heavily Impacted	4,376	1,452	89
a.i.'s Not Heavily Impacted	82	318	538

* Acute toxicity values are oral LD-50 values in mg/kg from (International Programme on Chemical Safety, 1994); "Mam Tox Score" is a composite measure of chronic mammalian toxicity (see Chapter 3). Source: Compiled from (EPA, 1994a, 1995c).

rows show the average acute and chronic mammalian toxicity of the active ingredients that were "Heavily" and "Not Heavily" impacted in each period. Rows four and five present average acute toxicity values, and rows six and seven, average chronic toxicity values. (For background on how these toxicity scores were calculated, see Chapter 3, and the box on page 79.)

The data in Table 4.2 demonstrate two key points: First, the EPA effectively targeted the pesticides with the greatest chronic toxicity to mammals in the 1970s, canceling most of their uses. The average chronic toxicity score in our scheme of the 15 heavily impacted active ingredients was 4,376, about five times the average chronic toxicity score of the active ingredients not heavily impacted. Second, the average chronic toxicity of pesticides subject to significant regulatory restrictions has declined markedly over time—from 4,376 during the period 1971-1977 to 89 from 1986-1994. In other words, the pesticides EPA has acted on

> There has been nearly a 50-fold decline in the average chronic toxicity of pesticides subject to significant regulatory restrictions in the early 1970s in contrast to the last decade.

since 1986 have only about one-fiftieth the chronic mammalian toxicity of those the agency targeted for action in the early 1970s.

Of course, chronic mammalian toxicity is only one aspect of pesticide risks, and EPA's more recent actions may have been triggered in some cases by other concerns, such as hazards to wildlife. Nevertheless, if mammalian toxicity is taken as a reasonable index of the benefits of EPA's actions in protecting against human health hazards of pesticides, it is clear that recent regulatory decisions have had far less "bang-for-the-buck" than did the agency's earlier actions.

In actions started in 1971-1977, EPA canceled essentially all uses of 10 major insecticides and the era's two most widely used fumigants—DBCP (dibromochloropropane) and EDB (ethylene dibromide). The insecticide cancellations resulted in the revocation of 480 tolerances and food use registrations. The two fumigants were used on 43 (DBCP) and 33 (EDB) crops. Hence, more than

550 food uses of these high risk pesticides were canceled, an average of 46 uses per active ingredient heavily impacted. Between 1978 and 1985, slightly less than 110 tolerances and food uses were canceled involving eight heavily impacted active ingredients, or about 14 uses per active ingredient.

About 100 food uses have been canceled since 1986 as a result of EPA action. Almost three-quarters of these are accounted for by the cancellation of the herbicide dinoseb. Several dozen more food uses have been dropped voluntarily by registrants, but most were dropped because of minimal or falling market share. In other cases, safety precautions have been required, with little or no impact on the volume of use. Further insight on the impact of regulation over time is presented in the box, "Impacts of Regulation on Insecticides."

EPA has calculated reference doses (RfDs) for the six active ingredients subject to in depth regulatory review since 1986 but largely left on the market. Their average RfD is 0.0014 mg/kg (the smaller the number, the more toxic the chemical). In 1992, there were 179

> **The acetochlor conditional registration granted in 1994 commits EPA to years of resource intensive reviews and risk assessments. All this on a product that is nearly identical to two other major herbicides already on the market. This action makes farmers no less reliant on herbicides and has done little to reduce risks associated with chemical-dependent weed management systems in the Midwest.**

herbicides, insecticides and fungicides in the Gianessi/Anderson national pesticide use database (excluding copper, sulfur, oils and botanicals). The average use-weighted RfD of the 29 most toxic of these 179 active ingredients, ranked by RfD values, was 0.00103 mg/kg (the "Most Toxic" Use Group accounting for 10 percent of total pounds applied; see Chapter 3 for methodological details).

Comparing the average RfDs shows that the six pesticides that EPA reviewed but largely left on the market are approximately as toxic as the use-weighted average for the most toxic group of all products on the market. The conclusion—EPA had the chance to restrict use of six high risk pesticides in the last decade but chose not to do so. Pesticides representing 10 percent of the market in 1992 pose comparable chronic risks on a pound for pound basis. While these comparisons are simplistic, they still make a valid point—differences in average chronic toxicity between pesticides that have been singled out for scrutiny by EPA and others on the market have narrowed markedly since the 1970s.

Impacts of Regulation on Insecticides

Out of 22 regulatory actions initiated by EPA from 1971 to 1977, 15 involved insecticides and 10 resulted in near or complete cancellations. The impact on insecticide use was significant. Products accounting for nearly 25 percent of total pounds of insecticides applied in 1971 were regulated off the market in the 1970s.

From 1978 to 1985, EPA initiated only four new actions dealing with insecticides—aldicarb (Temik), carbofuran (Furadan), chlordimeform (Galecron) and dicofol (Kelthane). In contrast to 1971-1977, regulation in the 1980s had a light touch. Cancelled uses and other restrictions placed on these four active ingredients reduced applications by about 3 million pounds in an average year. This reduction accounted for about 2.6 percent of the total pounds of insecticides applied in 1982.

Since 1986, EPA has initiated 11 regulatory actions (now called Special Reviews) involving insecticides. Regulation has had moderate to significant impact on a few products, but almost no impact relative to total insecticide use. We estimate that regulatory actions started since 1986 and completed through spring, 1996 will result in an average annual reduction in total insecticide use of about 0.5 million pounds—well below one percent of total pounds applied in 1992 (Gianessi, 1992).

In summary, in the three time periods studied since 1971, the impact of regulation on insecticide use has declined from about 25 percent, to 2.6 percent, to about 0.5 percent of pounds of insecticides applied at the time the regulatory actions were initiated.

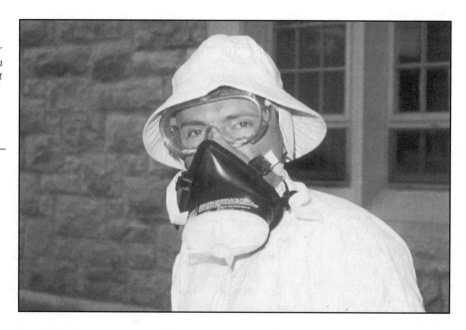

The cost of personal protective equipment is one of the cost categories projected to rise sharply through the year 2000. The need for costly full-body safety equipment should then decline as high risk pesticides are phased out of use, sales of biopesticides increase and more growers make progress along the IPM continuum. Credit: Mike Weaver, Virginia Tech Pesticide Programs

In some cases EPA has registered new high-risk pesticides. The most recent example was a controversial decision announced March 11, 1994 to grant a conditional registration for the herbicide acetochlor. In its decision document, the agency acknowledges that acetochlor is "a probable human carcinogen" and is likely to appear in drinking water in the Midwest. The EPA's reluctance to register this high risk product was evident in its statement at a briefing on the decision:

> "EPA's registration of acetochlor is dependent on a number of unprecedently stringent conditions: automatic cancellation if within 18 months there is not a reduction of 4 million pounds of certain herbicides (alachlor, metolachlor, atrazine, EPTC, butylate and 2,4-D) now used on corn, an overall reduction of 66.3 million pounds in five years (equal to a 33 percent reduction in the use of these herbicides in corn from 1992 levels)."

In registering acetochlor, EPA hoped that the new herbicide would displace older products that posed roughly equal risks but which are applied at higher rates and are more prone to leach into groundwater. Acres treated with acetochlor have come largely at the expense of acres treated with alachlor, as EPA anticipated, but the change in herbicides has resulted in little change in average rates of application (USDA, 1994b, 1995b; Benbrook, 1996). Corn farmers applied 1.78 pounds of acetochlor active ingredient per acre treated in 1994 and 1.98 pounds per acre of alachlor. There were more than 20 million acres treated with acetochlor in 1995 and further growth in its market share is expected in 1996 (USDA, 1996c).

After just one season of use in the summer of 1995, acetochlor was found in drinking water in several Midwestern communities (EPA, 1995d; Cohen et al., 1995a, 1995b). The registrants have petitioned the agency to relax several restrictions initially imposed as part of the conditional registration, which has not been enforced. It is doubtful that the required reduction in pounds of other herbicides applied in 1996 and subsequent years will occur, in part because of the increase in corn acres planted this year because of high market prices and the major changes in farm programs passed by Congress (see Chapter 6).

Monitoring compliance with the acetochlor conditional registration and responding to registrant petitions to change the conditions commits EPA to what could be several years of resource intensive reviews and risk assessment activities. All this energy will be spent on a product that is nearly identical to two major herbicides already on the market. EPA's action makes farmers no less reliant on herbicides and has done little or nothing to reduce risks associated with chemical-dependent weed management systems in the Midwest.

3. Plenty of Choices for Growers

Regulatory restrictions on a pesticide's use typically induce farmers to switch from one pesticide to another. Sometimes the alternative product is less risky, sometimes more. An assessment of pesticide substitution patterns following EPA cancellations in the 1970s, 1980s and 1990s clearly shows that net reductions in toxicity and risk have been modest; moreover, those reductions in risk have steadily declined relative to the risks associated with pesticides remaining in use.

For example, most cotton farmers in the 1970s first switched from one organochlorine insecticide to another, then to organophosphates and carbamates. Between 1975 and 1985, many of the same farmers then switched from one organophosphate or carbamate to another, and in the 1980s, they moved on to synthetic pyrethroids. On many farms each switch left growers a little more reliant on insecticides, as the adverse impacts on beneficial organisms worsened. Some product substitutions have resulted in a net reduction in some categories of risks, but overall cotton insecticide reliance and risk have probably risen.

Since the early 1970s, EPA actions have removed from the market some uses of 60 active ingredients—on average, less than three per year. Over the same period, the agency has granted registrations for an average 16 new active ingredients per year. The array of pesticide choices available to farmers has risen and is likely to continue rising. While there are many more reduced-risk products on the market today than there were 20 years ago, most are not successfully competing for market share. Old pesticides are generally the least expensive per acre treated. They also tend to be more toxic and potent—desirable characteristics for pest managers using chemical-intensive methods and systems. The fact that these same properties make them among the riskiest choices is not captured by the price system.

> Today, state pesticide regulatory programs spend about $1.46 for every dollar spent by EPA. We project that by 2020, the margin will rise to $2.38 for each dollar spent by EPA.

Until passage of the "Food Quality Protection Act of 1996," it was safe to predict that the net effect of regulation in future years would be modest relative to the overall levels of risk stemming from contemporary pesticide use in America. Passage of this bill raises the chance that progressive lowering of tolerances could lead within 5 to 10 years to some fundamental changes in the way organophosphate and carbamate insecticides are used. Since these classes of compounds represent a large portion of total pesticide risk, the magnitude of future benefits of regulation will depend significantly on whether this scenario is realized or not.

An additional logical response by food processors and growers to passage of this bill would be to accelerate efforts now to develop and adopt biointensive IPM systems, so that if some pesticides become unavailable a few years hence, viable alternatives will be accessible.

4. The Costs of Regulation and Pesticide Risk Management

Developing the data and risk assessments needed to make risk-benefit judgments on pesticide uses is expensive. Costs in the next 25 years are likely to be even higher.

The EPA completed a study in 1990 called *Environmental Investments: The Cost of a Clean Environment* (Carlin, 1990). The "Cost of Clean" project estimated the cost of full implementation of various environmental statutes, including FIFRA. The report's Appendix J estimates the public and private cost of pesticide regulation from 1972 to the year 2000. Cost projections from 1989 through 2000 were based on an assumed "full implementation" of FIFRA (i.e., completion of reregistration, etc.)

Implementation costs were estimated at $697 million in 1989 (9.5 percent of total industry sales) and were projected to rise to about $1.3 billion by 1995 (12 percent of sales). By the year 2000, they were projected to exceed $1.6 billion[5] (Carlin, 1990, Appendix J). These estimates include the costs of EPA expenditures, state regulation, pesticide industry safety and health data generation and regulatory compliance, cancellations, farm worker protection, record keeping, fees, USDA training programs and various other costs. But the estimates do not cover all direct and indirect costs of dealing with pesticide risks. (There are no costs included for USDA or EPA research carried out to document and learn how to manage pesticide risks, nor costs associated with dealing with pesticides in drinking water, for example.)

EPA analysts now believe that some of the projections in the *Cost of Clean* report for expenditures from 1990-2000 are too high, given current program priorities and activities (Aspelin, personal communication). With the help of EPA experts, we revised the *Cost of Clean* figures for 1990-2000 to reflect current program levels and polices, and extended the projection to 2020. In addition, we added two cost categories not included by EPA—public and private testing for residues in food, and USDA research on pesticide risks and environmental impacts. We projected the same categories of expenditures for two 25 year periods: 1971-1995 and 1996-2020.

A large investment has been made over the past 25 years to understand and manage pesticide risks. Table 4.3 presents public and private sector expenditures in several categories from 1971 through 1995, and Table 4.4 pre-

Table 4.3 Private and Public Sector Expenditures on Pesticide Regulation and the Management of Pesticide Risk: 1971 to 1995 (million dollars*)

	1971	1981	1991	1995	Total ('71-'95)
Pesticide Industry					
Regulatory Compliance	57.43	183.25	372.56	559.47	6,077.56
Other	28.55	48.39	82.37	102.18	1,500.58
Food Industry					
Residue Testing	17.03	28.44	51.00	58.64	859.65
User Level					
Farmers	18.85	67.05	83.43	97.88	1,448.12
Industry	5.35	17.33	15.29	18.14	330.31
Consumer	4.24	14.16	16.38	19.45	303.24
Regulatory Agencies					
Federal EPA	35.03	88.34	85.42	98.39	2,041.03
State	41.32	69.01	115.26	141.95	2,048.65
USDA					
Research** and data	31.05	42.11	57.10	64.50	1,146.04
Training and Other	0.00	19.27	8.88	7.47	442.66
Government Residue Testing[+]					
Pesticide Data Program	0.00	0.00	13.27	11.50	61.82
USDA FSIS	27.00	36.00	45.00	45.00	855.00
FDA	7.52	10.22	17.98	10.99	293.52
Subtotal Private Sector	131.45	360.63	621.03	855.76	10,519.45
Subtotal Public Sector	141.93	264.95	342.92	379.80	6,788.72
Total Expenditures	273.38	625.58	963.95	1,235.56	17,308.17
As Percent of Sales	4.8%	6.3%	10.7%	11.6%	7.4%

* 1995 Constant dollars.

** Research on pesticide environmental fate, toxicity, worker safety, consumer risks, and impacts on wildlife.

+ The Pesticide Data Program is managed by the USDA Agricultural Marketing Service; FSIS stands for Food Safety Inspection Service; FDA for the Food and Drug Administration.

sents projections for the next 25 years. Appendix 1 contains details on data sources and the assumptions and methods used in making the projections.

Understanding and managing pesticide risks cost more than $17 billion from 1971 through 1995, about 7.4 percent of gross pesticide sales. EPA and the pesticide industry have estimated that the costs to industry of compliance with EPA's requirements for safety and health data—the first row in Table 4.3—exceeded 3 percent of gross sales (Aspelin, 1994, 1996; American Crop Protection Association, 1996, 1994). Private costs total more than $10.5 billion and public costs, $6.8 billion. Overall costs have grown steadily from 4.8 percent of sales in 1971 to 11.6 percent in 1995.

Table 4.4 Private and Public Sector Expenditures on Pesticide Regulation and the Management of Pesticide Risk: 1996-2020 (million dollars*)

	1996	2000	2010	2020	Total ('96-'20)
Pesticide Industry					
Regulatory Compliance	542.68	460.82	518.40	752.67	13,557.51
Other	108.31	136.74	233.55	380.43	5,573.89
Food Industry					
Residue Testing	60.28	67.34	89.12	118.40	2,151.76
User Level					
Farmers	99.65	130.42	106.45	104.86	2,945.88
Industry	18.47	24.17	19.73	19.43	545.92
Consumer	19.80	25.91	21.15	20.84	585.33
Regulatory Agencies					
Federal EPA	102.28	119.69	130.89	137.58	3,172.32
State	149.04	181.16	243.47	327.20	5,837.50
USDA					
Research** and data	67.73	82.32	134.10	218.43	3,232.42
Training and Other	7.56	7.94	11.75	17.40	284.65
Government Residue Testing+					
Pesticide Data Program	11.50	11.00	13.00	16.00	345.50
USDA FSIS	45.00	45.00	49.50	49.50	1,215.00
FDA	11.16	12.51	12.96	12.96	318.15
Subtotal Private Sector	849.18	845.42	988.40	1,396.63	25,360.29
Subtotal Public Sector	394.27	459.62	595.67	779.07	14,405.53
Total Expenditures	1,243.45	1,305.04	1,584.07	2,175.70	39,765.82
As Percent of Sales	11.4%	11.1%	12.2%	16.0%	12.6%

* Projections are in 1995 dollars. See Appendix 1 for data sources and projection methods.

** Research on pesticide environmental fate, toxicity, worker safety, consumer risks, and impacts on wildlife.

+ The Pesticide Data Program is managed by the USDA Agricultural Marketing Service; FSIS stands for Food Safety Inspection Service; FDA for the Food and Drug Administration.

Costs imposed on the private sector have risen faster than public sector costs.

We estimate in Table 4.4 that the costs of regulation and managing pesticide risks will increase over the next 25 years, totaling almost $40 billion—2.3 times the expenditures in the previous 25 years. Our projections show that expenditures on risk management will aver-age 12.6 percent of total pesticide industry sales over the next 25 years; the split between public and private costs will remain about the same as in 1995; and there will be a significant shift in public regulatory costs from the federal government to state regulatory programs. Today, state pesticide regulatory programs spend about $1.46 for every dollar spent by EPA. We project that by 2020, the margin will rise to $2.38 for each dollar spent by EPA.

Our projections also indicate that USDA research expenditures on the properties and environmental impacts of pesticides and on developing safety precautions will rise appreciably, especially after the turn of the century. Our estimates of both public and private residue testing expenditures assume no sudden changes in public concern over food residues. This assumption is worth noting because in the three years following the Alar episode, public expenditures more than doubled and private testing costs rose more than five-fold. These costs have since declined to pre-Alar levels (Jones, 1996).

Some people will argue that individual cost elements included in our estimates are either too high or too low, and that better data are needed to refine the analysis. When making projections based on limited data and considerable uncertainty, we were conservative. Our estimates should therefore be interpreted as "costs are not likely to be less than…." Some important cost categories are not included or are incomplete (for example, community and water district and public utility costs associated with water quality monitoring, filtering and seeking uncontaminated supplies, which were not included because we could not find any consistent data on which to base national estimates).

Further analysis is needed to sharpen the assumptions used to project costs over the next 25 years. For example, the passage of the Food Quality Protection Act of 1996 is certain to alter the costs of managing dietary pesticide risks, but at this point we can offer only an educated guess that near-term costs (i.e. over the next decade) will rise somewhat more than projected in Table 4.4, and long-term costs may then decline faster than now estimated.

Notwithstanding the need for further work in refining these cost estimates, we can draw several important conclusions from them. First, the costs of coping with pesticide risks are high and likely to rise. Nearly one out of eight dollars earned from pesticide sales is spent on managing their risks. Second, the private sector already pays a large share of the costs and is likely to pay more in the future. Third, the role of the states, and the cost of state program efforts, is likely to continue growing, raising questions about how a growing state role will be financed.

Most important, although not displayed in the

> **The best way to save on the costs of regulating pesticides is to avoid creating risks that need to be regulated.**

tables, is the fact that as the nation spends billions of dollars a year dealing with pesticide risks, we have devoted pennies, in comparative terms, to developing and promoting IPM, priorities that must shift in order to accelerate progress along the IPM continuum.

F. Summary and Conclusions

The laws that established federal pesticide regulation programs sought to preserve the economic and food-supply benefits of pesticide use, while protecting against "unreasonable" risks of adverse effects on public health or the environment. The tension inherent in this balancing act pervades the regulatory process. Congress, with input from regulated parties, has also perceived a need to restrain the EPA from being too aggressive in reducing pesticide risks, and has created innumerable procedural hurdles and conditions that the agency must observe in reaching its decisions.

The strictures Congress has placed on EPA have made pesticide regulation a slow and difficult process, in which registrants have almost endless opportunities to delay and challenge EPA judgments. The enormous task of reregistering pesticides already on the market when EPA was created moved at a snail's pace for nearly 20 years. Although significant progress has been made in the past few years, a huge backlog of this work remains, and it is expected to take another 20 years to complete.

Reforms are still needed, to make tolerances for residues in foods more consistent with health and safety needs, to reduce delays in carrying out risk reducing steps once EPA has issued reregistration decisions, and to relieve EPA of the unfair burdens placed upon it to referee economic competition among pesticide manufacturers, among other problems. The just-passed Food Quality Protection Act of 1996 has set the stage for many needed improvements in tolerance setting, but needs for further reform still exist in other areas.

Regulation has not reduced pesticide use, overall. More pounds of products are applied each year today than at any time in the period since EPA began regulating pesticides. EPA's actions, especially during its early years, have removed several of the highest-risk products from use, and sharply restricted use of a few dozen other high risk ingredients. But many high risk pesticides remain in wide use, in part because they are inexpensive compared to registered alternatives. Because of changes in usage patterns, new routes of public exposure, and growth in overall reliance on pesticides, the aggregate risks of pesticides have not decreased appreciably. They have not increased dramatically, either, which attests to the beneficial impact of regulation. But we are basically running in place.

Pesticide regulation is a costly process, and costs are rising. When the benefits of this regulatory effort are measured in terms of reduced health risk (average mammalian toxicity of pesticides in use in a given year), it is clear that the benefits of regulation are declining. EPA got far more "bang for the buck" from its early bans of DDT and related insecticides than it has been able to attain with any recent actions.

The 1996 Food Quality Protection Act has created an opportunity for EPA to set tolerances for high risk pesticides that more closely approximate "safe" levels. Progressively lowering tolerances should make it more difficult and costly to use riskier ingredients, and should drive usage toward safer choices, including biopesticides and IPM. Significant reductions in public-health risk achieved in this manner could also increase the marginal benefit of EPA's regulatory costs. Whether this scenario

occurs or not will depend on how effectively EPA can implement its new mandates. Given that the legal, procedural and political hurdles that have produced gridlock in the past are still largely in place, success is by no means guaranteed.

While the need to protect public health and the environment makes it essential to continue to regulate pesticides, the recognition that the costs of the regulatory effort are rising while its benefits are declining is reason to examine the goals of pesticide regulation. The most valuable role for regulation in coming years may well be to increase the costs of reliance on and use of the riskier pesticides, and press the market to provide safer, cost-effective IPM alternatives. By actively pursuing a transition to biointensive IPM, we can escape from the pesticide regulation treadmill. The best way to save on the costs of regulating pesticides is to avoid creating risks that need to be regulated.

The remaining chapters of this report describe the transition to biointensive IPM, which is well under way in many areas, and lay out our vision of how policy can be structured to accelerate progress in that direction.

[1] Endosulfan was first registered in 1954. Almost 800,000 pounds were applied in 1966 (Gianessi, 1992). Use rose steadily through the mid-1970s and reached 1,653,000 pounds in 1976. The emergence of resistance in cotton insects forced farmers to switch to other products. Pounds applied fell to 977,000 in 1982 but has since almost doubled—reaching about 1,800,000 pounds in 1992 (Gianessi and Anderson, 1995). Cotton remains the biggest use, followed by several major food crops—apples (200,000 pounds applied on one-quarter of the nation's apple acreage), potatoes (180,000 pounds on 16 percent of acreage), pecans and tomatoes. Use of methoxychlor has dropped sharply since the mid-1970s when, like endosulfan, it hit its peak usage—4,057,000 pounds applied in 1976. By 1982, use had dropped to 643,000 pounds, again largely due to resistance. Only 89,000 pounds

were applied in 1992, with almost 70,000 pounds of that total on Washington state apples (Gianessi and Anderson, 1995).

[2] The fungicide applied was metalaxyl (Ridomil).

[3] USDA Press Release No. 0732.95, "USDA Announces New Crop Insurance Pilot Project."

[4] Also, the pesticide active ingredient must be "off-patent" and the period of exclusive use of the data must also be expired.

[5] All *Cost of Clean* cost estimates are reported in 1986 dollars. All the data in Tables 4.3 and 4.4 are in constant 1995 dollars.

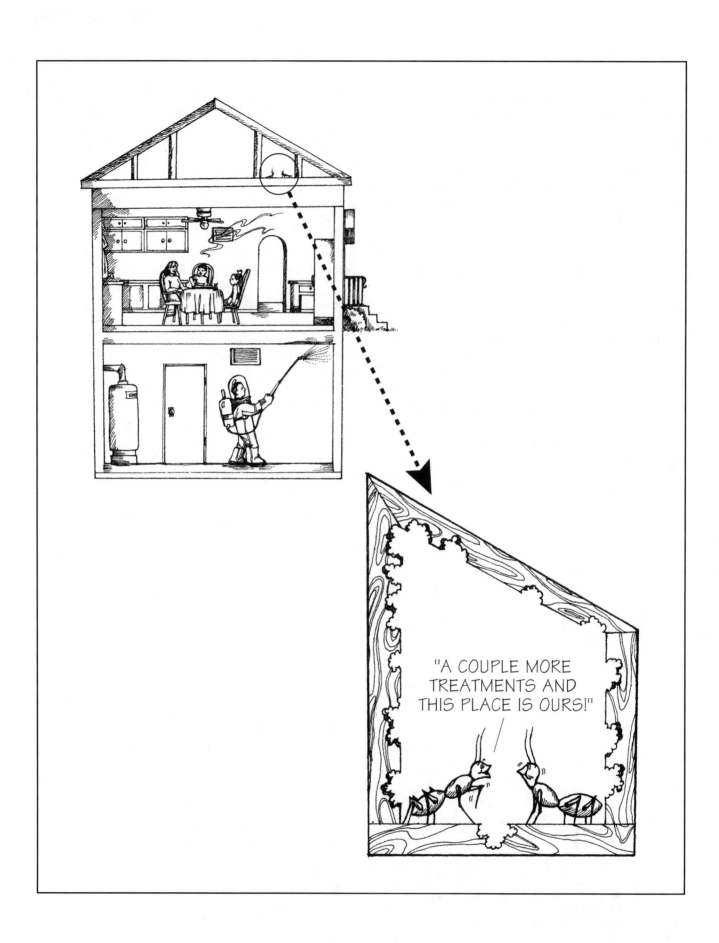

Government Adoption of IPM

Federal agencies should end use of risky pesticides and adopt biointensive IPM. Progress achieved by some agencies needs to be matched government-wide.

The federal government is not just a regulator of pesticides. It is also a major *user* of pesticides and the nation's largest contractor for pest management services. As the steward of our National Parks and monuments, the manager of national forests and rangelands, and owner of innumerable office buildings and other structures where people live, work and recreate, the government has enormous potential clout in the pest management marketplace. In this chapter we review the generally timid and isolated steps the government has taken to implement the recommendations in the 1979 CEQ report, as well as other reports reviewed in Chapter 4. In Chapter 9 we recommend additional steps needed to accelerate progress.

Directives in the 1970s ordered federal agencies to explore and implement Integrated Pest Management (IPM) as an alternative to unilateral reliance on pesticides. A 1972 IPM report by the President's newly formed Council on Environmental Quality states (CEQ, 1972):

> "To demonstrate the effectiveness of IPM, the President has ordered a review of the more than 3,800 Federal pest control programs to determine which of them may utilize this technique. Further, the USDA is expanding its pilot field scout program to reduce further the volume of pesticides used."

A coordinated interagency effort to encourage IPM adoption was set in motion by an August 2, 1979 "Memorandum from the President" signed by Jimmy Carter which stated in part (quote in Bottrell, 1979):

> "… IPM has both economic and environmental benefits and should be encouraged in both research and operational programs of federal agencies …"

The rhetorical embrace of IPM by Presidents and federal officials has still not been matched by tangible changes in federal pest management systems in many places and circumstances around the country. As with government procurement policies that give preference to products made in part with recycled materials, both state and federal pest management guidelines and contracts need to more clearly specify biointensive IPM approaches. This will help build the infrastructure needed to offer all pest managers, including homeowners, improved and lower-cost biointensive IPM services and products. And by practicing IPM in its

tens of thousands of buildings and sites across the country, the government would also be playing a key educational role—each facility serving as a local demonstration site for IPM.

Some agencies are leading the way effectively. The National Park Service began working on IPM 15 years ago, and has achieved considerable success, reducing annual pesticide use by an estimated 80 percent over pre-IPM levels. More recently, in 1993, the Department of Defense, which currently uses an estimated 1.2 million pounds of pesticide active ingredients annually on its facilities worldwide, has made a commitment to halve its pesticide use by the year 2000. The Forest Service, formerly a heavy user of pesticides on millions of acres of national forest under its control, has now adopted IPM and in at least one of its 10 regions has sprayed no herbicides at all since 1990.

However, most federal agency responses to the Carter and subsequent Presidential IPM-related directives have had mixed or modest results. Pest management on public lands and in public buildings is typically handled by full time staff or under contract to a pest management service. Pest management "by the book"—routine inspections and spraying, check-list approaches—makes it easier to plan and stay within budgets and comply with rules, and remains far too common among public sector pest management professionals. Biointensive IPM is more complex and site-specific and calls upon professionals to exercise greater judgment and accept greater responsibility regarding actions needed to assess and lessen pest populations when they rise above acceptable levels.

One constraint is widespread—not enough government pest management specialists have been given the training and encouragement needed to implement IPM. Nor do they have control over how land or buildings are used, constructed, managed or maintained. This limits the steps specialists can take to reduce pest pressure or otherwise avoid problems.

Clearly we have a distance to go before all federal agencies are practicing biointensive IPM in all their facilities and on all lands under their control (see the box, "Status of Agency Efforts to Promote IPM"). But some successful urban and recreational area IPM strategies and training programs have evolved, and are now reducing pesticide expenditures, decreasing human exposure to pesticides and lessening the government's liability. Encouraging progress made by the Department of Defense, General Services Administration and National Park Service, described here, shows what can be accomplished when government agencies choose to act and are permitted to do so.

A. The National Park Service

The U.S. National Park Service (NPS), a bureau within the Department of Interior, has led the Executive Branch in the adoption of IPM since the release of the 1979 CEQ report on IPM and the circulation of the August, 1979 Presidential Memorandum.

NPS is responsible for managing pests on over 80 million acres that make up the nation's 370 national parks and monuments. These lands include diverse geographic and climatic ecosystems—isolated pristine

Through the first half of the century elm trees graced the streets of thousands of American cities and public parks and facilities. In 1931, a shipment of elm tree logs from France to Cleveland, Ohio introduced the Dutch elm disease fungus Ophiostoma ulmi *into the United States (Becker, 1996). It spread first along the railroad route the logs were shipped over. By 1980 the disease had nearly wiped out America's 77 million elm trees.* Credit: Scott Bauer, Agricultural Research Service

Status of Agency Efforts to Promote IPM

Arecent joint project by the National Coalition Against the Misuse of Pesticides (NCAMP) and the Government Purchasing Project (GPP) surveyed the effectiveness of IPM programs adopted by 41 federal agency programs or offices (NCAMP, 1995). Those surveyed included the General Services Administration, Department of Veterans Affairs, National Park Service (Department of the Interior), U.S. Forest Service (Department of Agriculture), the Architect of the Capital (U.S. Capital and Supreme Court buildings) and the U.S. Postal Service.

The groups used stringent criteria to judge an IPM program's adequacy, including whether it contained a written policy emphasizing non-chemical pest management methods, established explicit pesticide use reduction goals, offered IPM-based training and certification programs and spelled out a method to monitor progress. The survey concluded that only four of the 41 IPM programs were "adequate" based on the list of essential program ingredients (NCAMP, 1995).

The groups found that some of the pesticides applied were actually illegal. For example, phostoxin and calcium cyanamid were used in Atlanta, Georgia's Peachtree Summit Federal Building despite the fact that phostoxin is not labeled for indoor use and all uses of calcium cyanamid were canceled between 1984 and 1991. Alloxydim-sodium, which is not registered for any use in the U.S., was applied in Dublin, Georgia's Veterans Administration Medical Center. NCAMP/GPP data showed that 64 pesticides were used at the 41 facilities, including nearly two dozen high risk active ingredients.

mountain parks, open ranges, ornamental gardens, museums, camping facilities, concession stands and agricultural areas managed cooperatively with farmers.[1] In addition, NPS must balance multiple missions to "conserve the scenery and natural and historic objects and wildlife …" while also ensuring the general public's access to the land and leaving it "… unimpaired for the enjoyment of future generations …."

1. First Steps Toward IPM

Integrated pest management activities in the National Park Service (NPS) intensified in the early 1980s when the Environmental Protection Agency (EPA) awarded NPS an $80,000 grant to initiate an IPM-based pest management pilot project in the National Capital Area (NCA) of Washington D.C., Maryland and Virginia. EPA's grant provided NPS with direction in the pest management arena and reinforced the agency's interest in protecting "the resources within parks in an effective and ecologically sound manner" (U.S. NPS, 1977). The grant also provided NPS with technical support in assessing pesticides recognized as potentially hazardous to park visitors, wildlife and local ecosystems.

The National Park Service was the only agency in the early 1980s making a serious attempt to implement recommendations directed toward it in the 1979 Council on Environmental Quality report *Integrated Pest Management* (Bottrell, 1979). While out of step with the political priorities of the time, implementing IPM coincided well with NPS's interest in ecologically sound resource protection. The agency's concerns regarding pesticide use were based on the premise that "most pesticides by design are toxic and therefore should not be considered safe" (NPS, 1977).

NPS soon developed the following definition of IPM:

"Integrated Pest Management (IPM) is a process for determining if pest management is needed; when management should be initiated (at what population level the pest becomes intolerable and at what population level action should be taken); where and at what frequency treatments should be applied; and what physical, cultural, biological, or chemical strategies should be employed and how effective these treatments are in achieving management objectives."

"IPM integrates compatible techniques to maintain pest damage below an unacceptable injury level while providing protection from threats to public health and safety and to the natural environment. IPM makes maximum use of such naturally occurring pest population regulating factors as weather, predators, parasites and pathogens. It also utilizes genetically resistant hosts and environmental modification, as well as various physical, cultural, biological, and chemical control techniques."

NPS policy also allows "native pest species that were evident in historic, pesticide free times …to function unimpeded except where control is desirable…" in particular situations.

> The warm rhetorical embrace of IPM by Presidents and federal officials has still not been matched by tangible actions in the field in many places and circumstances around the country.

NPS began work in 1979 on national IPM guidelines to govern actions in all parks when a "pest" problem arises. NPS staffers Mike Ruggiero and Gary Johnston hired a division of the John Muir Institute, a California-based non-profit organization now called the Bio-Integral Resource Center, or BIRC, to develop

The nation's Capital has been hard-hit by Dutch elm disease since 1947 when the first infected tree was found at the Lincoln Memorial. Over 10,000 trees have been removed from the National Capital Area, including this stately 80 year old American elm on the Mall, removed in 1966 (Sherald, 1982). Credit: H.V. Wester, U.S. Department of Interior

IPM guidelines and a 40-hour training course and demonstration project in the National Capital Area. BIRC was challenged to develop and demonstrate practical and reliable IPM systems to manage key pests in five areas: mosquitoes in the heavily visited zones of the C&O Canal, which flows from Washington, D.C. to Cumberland, Maryland; rodents in Lafayette Park (directly in front of the White House); insects in the azalea flower beds around several monuments; cockroaches in various federal buildings; and yellowjackets at the concession stand in Great Falls National Park in Virginia.

As a first step, the BIRC-led team developed policy guidelines on how IPM should be used to determine whether pest control actions are needed, and whether and when pesticides should be applied. Perhaps most important, the guidelines call for regular pest monitoring and establishment of action levels prior to applying control measures (such as spraying a pesticide). In addition, the guidelines describe other essential IPM program components: education in basic IPM principles, and on biological, cultural and mechanical control options, as well as a review process for major pest management strategic decisions at the regional and national levels. The review must find that prevention and biologically based IPM options are either unacceptable or not practical before a decision is made to apply a pesticide.

> Drawing on its work with several government agencies, BIRC believes that the major stumbling block slowing government adoption of IPM is getting pest managers in the field to use injury and pest population action levels in determining treatment needs and strategies. Once a program manager has a directive and budget to control pests, that is what most tend to do, even in some cases when no action is needed.

Each National Park was directed to appoint a Park IPM Coordinator responsible for implementing IPM policy. Decisions to apply a pesticide, however, would have to be approved by the national IPM Coordinator based in Washington, D.C., with special consideration given to avoiding uses that fall in the following four categories:

1. Use of any pesticide classified as a "Restricted Use" product by EPA. This classification is based on risk to either applicators, consumers or the environment and requires special training or precautions.
2. Pesticide uses that involve aquatic application or situations in which the applied pesticide could reasonably be expected to get into water resources.
3. Pesticide uses that can be expected to affect threatened or endangered plant or animal species.
4. Pesticide uses that consist of one application to more than 2,560 acres (four square miles).

Because of recent pressure to decentralize decision-making, NPS regional IPM Coordinators now make most decisions to deny or permit pesticide use in individual parks and facilities. Any person in this position must have completed the NPS IPM training course or its equivalent, be certified as a pesticide applicator in at least one state and be qualified as an IPM specialist, according to NPS guidelines.

2. The National Capital Area Demonstration Project

The NPS's first pilot IPM program was carried out in the National Capital Area (NCA), a location encompassing most federal monuments and parks in and around the nation's capital. The program sought to reduce "conventional" calendar-based pesticide sprays, educate site managers and establish long term "Best Management Practices" (BMPs) (U. S. NPS, 1990).

At most NCA locations, pesticides had been applied for years as a preventive measure whether or not they were needed. The basic approach was "spray and pray," according to NPS IPM Coordinator Carol DiSalvo. No records were kept of pesticide applications, no pre-treatment scouting of pest levels was carried out, no economic thresholds were considered and no one checked post-treatment efficacy. Dr. Jim Sherald, a NPS plant pathologist, remembers it as "a pesticide program, pure and simple." If a given pest was on a product label and someone felt action must be taken, the pesticide was applied, often according to a schedule or through a contract with a pest management service.

The NCA IPM program has produced dramatic improvements. Merely by halting preventive sprays, NCA pesticide use dropped 78 percent in the first few years. Incomplete pre-IPM pesticide logs for 1975 indicate 26,270 pounds of active ingredients were used, while 1982 log books report just 5,630 pounds. The trend is consistent and ongoing—NCA pesticide use declined to 3,110 pounds in 1992.

The National Mall—the long, grassy area that runs between the Lincoln Memorial and the U.S. Capitol building—was designed at the turn of the century. It includes 309 acres of turf (just under one-half a square mile) plus more than 2,000 elm trees, hundreds of cherry trees, dogwoods and ornamental planting beds. The area bears the heavy foot traffic of millions of visitors attending special events, parades and displays. Soil on the Mall is seriously compacted—its bulk density coefficient is 1.8, compared to 2.1 for cement (bulk density is a measure of the volume of soil particles per unit area). Compacted soil has minimal space for air and water particles—both essential for healthy roots and plant growth. No herbicides are used on the turf unless a renovation is needed. NPS uses spot treatments of glyphosate (Roundup) only on areas adjacent to light poles and benches. NPS is working to eliminate these uses of herbicides on sidewalks and along walls.

NPS manages the turfgrass with a vigorous regime of watering, top dressing with mulch, aeration (to improve water penetration) and fertilization. The mowing schedule keeps grass three inches high, helping it withstand the hot, humid weather and compaction from visitors while preventing the roots from drying out. The National Turf Grass Test Plots revealed that the best seed type for this busy zone is a mixture of bluegrass with tall fescue and rye. More focus on turf management at a local NPS-

Progress is being made in identifying Dutch elm disease tolerant trees by screening the genetic characteristics of the few elms that have survived. Here, Dr. Alden Townsend, an Agricultural Research Service (ARS) geneticist is injecting the fungus that causes Dutch elm disease into a tree to check its resistance to the disease. Dr. Townsend estimates that just one in 100,000 American elms is resistant to Dutch elm disease (Becker, 1996). Several government agencies are cooperating with an effort led by the U.S. National Arboretum and ARS to identify and breed resistant cultivars so that a new generation of disease resistant American elms can grace the landscape.
Credit: Scott Bauer, ARS

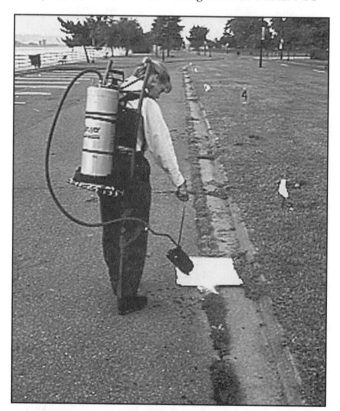

Heat from torch flamers like the one above is among the non-chemical weed management alternatives gaining wider use. Steam and electricity are also used in machines that use heat to manage weeds.
Credit: Carol DiSalvo, National Park Service

operated public golf course is needed as well. The largest quantities of pesticides applied in 1995 include chlorothalonil, bensulide, glyphosate and iprodione.

Ornamental trees on and around the Mall, such as cherry and dogwood, were plagued in the past by cankers and other plant diseases requiring treatments with pesticides and in many cases, costly replacement. Careful study revealed the source of the problem and a simple solution—a common occurrence when pest management professionals work to understand the situation before developing a treatment strategy. The disease outbreaks were caused by injuries to tree trunks by the careless operation of large "gang mowers" (with multiple arms).

The bark of a tree is its skin. When this covering is broken, secondary problems such as insects (borers) and disease-causing organisms have a direct route into the tree's vascular system—the equivalent of a person's circu-

The National Park Service greatly lessened the yellowjacket problem at the Great Falls National Park concession stand simply by putting a lid on garbage cans. Park staff keep the rats out by using strong plastic containers rather than plastic garbage bags.
Credit: U.S. NPS

latory system. The mechanical wounding caused disfigurement as well. Lawn mowing crews were educated about the problem and given better training in machinery operation, and corrugated pipe was installed around the base of young trees to protect their thin bark. The problem has been largely solved.

Another successful effort to reduce pesticide use involved management of elms along the Mall plagued by Dutch elm disease, a fungal growth transmitted from tree to tree by bark beetles. NPS quit spraying about 2,500 elms with methoxychlor, an insecticide used to kill the beetles, because the agency had no evidence that spraying was any more effective than removing dead and dying trees. NPS vigorously monitored disease incidence and aggressively pruned or cut down infected trees. At first this seemed a risky strategy since, as Sherald says, "the Mall is the backbone of the Monumental Core—if you lose these (elms) you're in big trouble. It's like losing the Washington Monument." Confidence has grown in the elm program. An experienced tree crew monitors for Dutch elm disease and practices proper sanitation—pruning, cutting back infected branches and removal of seriously infected trees.

In addition, NPS has gone on the offensive, restoring lost trees by planting newly bred varieties resistant to Dutch elm disease. Recently released cultivars with improved disease resistance and hardiness include Liberty, Valley Forge and New Harmony: "...the first commercially available new Dutch elm disease-tolerant American elm trees," according to ARS scientist and elm breeder Dr. Alden Townsend (Becker, 1996).

A Stinging Success

At nearby Great Falls park along the Potomac River, yellowjackets became a serious problem each summer, especially near the beverage sales area. The solution—installation of enclosed garbage containers and regular cleaning of cans with soapy water to remove the sticky sugar residues in and from beverage containers that attract bees. Another simple and helpful step—concessionaires were instructed to hand customers their soft drinks in cups with lids and straws inserted so that yellowjackets could not get to the sugar left in discarded cups. The same strategies work in and around the home to lessen problems with a number of opportunistic, sugar-loving pests. Few mice, ants, cockroaches or flies will pass up the chance to get into garbage, feed on compost piles or enter homes. But if pests cannot find food, water or habitat, they will stay away. As the NPS has learned several times, it is often easier to avoid pest problems than to treat them, especially once pests get well established.

The third test case of a pesticide-intensive area was the C&O Canal, stretching 185 miles from Georgetown in Washington, D.C. to Cumberland, Maryland. The canal's 75 locks ensure the slow movement of water, which created not only an idea channel for moving coal and grain vessels, but, unfortunately, also excellent habitat for mosquitoes. Concern grew that mosquitoes along the canal could transmit encephalitis to humans. To calm public fears, malathion and oil had been sprayed over the canal on mosquitoes' presumed breeding areas. But no

Use of malathion for mosquito control on Washington, D.C.'s C&O Canal was eliminated by the National Park Service by switching to biointensive IPM based on monitoring, natural predators and the use of the biopesticide Bti *as a last resort.* Credit: NPS

one really knew where the insects bred, nor was there solid evidence that they carried a dreaded disease.

BIRC developed a plan to train the NCA staff in population monitoring and selective treatment with *Bacillus thuringiensis israelensis (Bti)*, a biological control tool effective only on mosquito and fly larvae. Staff members were trained to treat a limited target area, "…and then only if it's a real problem," says Mr. Pat Toops, Chief of Natural Resources Management for NPS's C&O Canal National Historical Park. The monitoring program showed that most of the biting mosquitoes were originat-

ing from a nearby sewage treatment plant, not the C&O Canal. The plant ponds were treated regularly with *Bti*, largely solving the problem. On an ongoing basis, NPS staff check the mosquitoes with the assistance of the Centers for Disease Control to make sure they are not carrying encephalitis. NPS also tries to maintain a water level adequate to support enough larvae-eating fish to control the adult mosquito population.

The mosquitoes that remain are food not only for swallows, martins and other birds and bats, but also frogs, dragonflies and what DiSalvo calls the "non-charismatic predatory minifauna" of the area—beetles, mice and other wildlife that "people don't like but which form the basic building blocks of the food chain." The presence of these species helps NPS achieve another of its objectives—sustaining biological diversity.

In the spirit of President Carter's 1979 IPM Directive, few if any pesticides are used at the Jimmy Carter National Historic Site in Plains, Georgia, which is maintained by the NPS. The agency controlled lake algae, the site's biggest pest problem, by switching from pesticides to sterile grass carp with "excellent" results, says Park Ranger Lloyd Hoffman. The Carters, who live on the site, avoid pesticide use by planting native trees, shrubs and grasses around their home. Site staff use mostly petroleum oil to suppress mites and scale on apple, peach and other fruit trees. Because of its high quality IPM program, the Carter Historic Site was one of only four sites to receive a passing grade in the NCAMP/GPP IPM review of federal facilities. (see box on page 126).

Former President Jimmy Carter and wife Rosalynn rely on grass carp instead of pesticides to control algae in the lake on their property and allow native trees, shrubs and other vegetation around their house to grow undisturbed, eliminating the need for herbicides and diversifying the species that help make biological control work. Credit: NPS

3. Going Nationwide

In 1980, the NPS broadened the NCA program to apply to parks nationwide. In the years that followed, 10 regional IPM coordinators were trained.

The NPS developed contract specifications in the 1980s for any people or companies hired by the agency to help manage pests. The first priority was for parks to cancel any calendar spraying contracts in favor of those focusing on non-chemical management alternatives. Until recently, NPS also discouraged or prohibited the use of pesticides for which EPA has documented environmental or health risks. For example, NPS eliminated the use of the widely applied triazine herbicides (including atrazine) and the fumigant methyl bromide. The agency prohibited the use of some high risk pesticides on park properties before EPA cancellation (e.g., chlordane, the tributyltins and pentachlorophenol).

NPS applies fewer restricted use pesticides now than in the 1980s, and Dursban (chlorpyrifos) is used for termite control only on rare occasions when lower risk products such as boron-treated lumber or termite bait stations are ineffective. DiSalvo predicts that Dursban use is likely to decrease in the future due to the registration of low risk baits and biopesticides. Examples include biopesticides containing the fungus *Metarhizium anisopliae* and a new sulfluramid bait product (Bio-Integral Resource Center, 1996a, 1996b).

Unfortunately, with the decentralization of the NPS decision-making process, regional IPM Coordinators now will be able to approve the use of previously prohibited pesticides. NPS IPM specialist Terry Cacek notes hopefully that IPM coordinators should "… know the history of not approving (high risk products)." When NPS does approve applications of conventional pesticides like the fungicide benomyl (Benlate) or the weed-killer 2,4-D, applications are made when pests are most vulnerable and steps are taken to reduce application rates as far as possible. Calendar spraying is rarely carried out and strongly discouraged.

The Department of Interior (DOI) is now working to promote preservation and restoration of native plants, both to beautify the landscape and promote biodiversity. Establishing plants once native to a region is a step toward biointensive IPM, since native plants tend to be hardier and often harbor beneficial insects and other organisms that can help with pest management. DOI is taking the lead in responding to an April 1994 memorandum from President Clinton directing federal facilities and federally funded projects to use IPM and native plants for land-scaping and, wherever needed, to prevent pollution by reducing fertilizer and pesticide use (White House, 1994).

4. Training Activities

NPS began developing an in-depth IPM training program in 1979, with BIRC and EPA working together to create a program for the NCA. The program was expanded in 1980 to include park IPM coordinators nationwide, and at least 700 employees have received IPM training since then.

The training sessions are held two to three times a year and consist of a 40-hour hands-on course. Organizers include NPS IPM Coordinators Carol DiSalvo, Terry Cacek and Jerry McCrea. Instructors include former EPA IPM specialist Bill Currie and two to three other experts, some from universities. Sessions are often set in a hypothetical "Solitude Park," an area where virtually every conceivable pest management problem is represented for both indoor and outdoor environments—mosquitoes and wasps in trash storage areas, weeds and insects on croplands, aquatic pest management and control of slimes and molds. The course also addresses problems created by the design of structures and landscapes (such as planting shade-loving plants in full sun), and how to educate people to change their actions and habits.

The training focuses on identification of pests and an in-depth discussion of IPM strategies for specific situations in various locations. The program encourages IPM coordinators to properly identify pests and base control interventions on action thresholds and a good understanding of IPM options. Coordinators are urged to seek professional input on pest management options, build consensus among affected parties, monitor changes in pests and their environment with emphasis on why pest problems occur, and create short and long term goals. The training program provides examples of proper NPS IPM guideline implementation, including the approval process when a pesticide application is necessary, and required record keeping.

> Reestablishing plants once native to a region can be a helpful step toward biointensive IPM, since native plants tend to be hardier and provide habitat for native beneficial insects and microorganisms that can also help keep other potential pests in check.

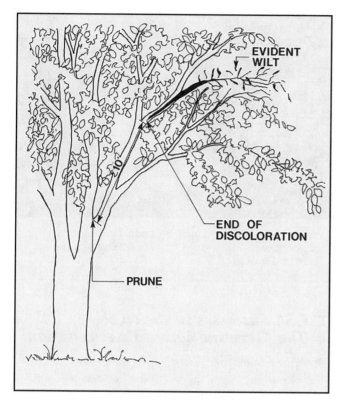

The Dutch elm disease fungus is spread by two primary insect vectors, the smaller European elm bark beetle and the native elm bark beetle. After World War II, the insecticide DDT was used to help slow the spread of the disease, but environmental impacts were unacceptable and the insecticide was banned for such uses in the late 1960s. Other pesticides were then tried but have proven ineffective, costly and also damaging to the environment and risky for people. Sanitation is now the recommended management strategy and rests upon aggressive pruning of infected trees. This diagram from a 1982 Department of Interior pamphlet on the disease provides suggestions for pruning therapy (Sherald, 1982).

As a result of budget cuts, NPS was unable to offer the training program in 1995, the first year without training sessions since the early 1980s. Classes were scheduled to being again in September 1996.

5. *Record Keeping*

NPS is diligent about record keeping for its pest management program. Each park is required to keep records, which are then compiled and analyzed in a nationwide database. Until 1996, all use of pesticides was reported annually on a Pesticide Use Log Form, which was submitted through the regional IPM coordinator to the Washington office. Any request for pesticide use triggers the need to submit an annual Pest Management Program Report.[2] Systemwide records were collected, computer-

ized and analyzed in Washington until 1990. Since then, budget cuts have ended NPS's ability to compile national totals.

A new computerized system was installed at most national parks in 1996, and NPS should be able to maintain and analyze pest management data far more efficiently. Start-up problems such as including information about newly registered products and ensuring that all parks use the system will make 1996 data "less than perfect," says Cacek. But he believes the agency will make solid progress in 1997.

Nationwide reporting has enabled program coordinators to determine the areas of greatest use, target environmental monitoring activities and focus on ways to mitigate risks and adverse impacts. By consulting the database, for example, NPS determined that pesticide use is highest on agricultural lands leased by the agency to farmers. Steps are underway to encourage these farmers to adopt biointensive IPM practices.

Although few formal pesticide use records were kept prior to initiating the IPM program, NPS estimates it has reduced pesticide use by at least 80 percent between 1975 and 1982, from approximately 207,360 pounds of active ingredients to between 25,000 and 40,000 pounds. Elimination of calendar-based sprayings has resulted in major reductions. Prior to the IPM program, managers lacked a systematic approach to pest management. "We were spraying in case something was there, without knowing what we were doing to the environment, or ourselves," says DiSalvo.

Many of the products used by NPS today are low risk pesticides including boric acid (for cockroach control), soaps, petroleum or paraffin oils, gels and insect growth regulators. The modest amounts of synthetic pesticides now applied by NPS demonstrate the potential to reduce pest problems through simple changes in management and attitudes and occasional applications of bio-pesticides.

B. General Services Administration

The General Services Administration (GSA) has achieved striking success reducing pesticide reliance in the buildings it manages in the National Capital Region (NCR). GSA hired entomologist Dr. Albert Greene in 1988 to begin and manage the agency's IPM program, placing him in charge of pest management in 612 federal buildings including the National Archives, the Old and New Executive Office Buildings, the Departments of Justice and State, and the East and West Wings of the White House.[3]

Dr. Greene brought to his assignment a strong desire to reduce pesticide use and implement biologically based IPM, which he defines as a "systems approach" to pest management stressing three essential elements:

■ Pest control must emphasize prevention by decreasing the resources that pests need to infest a structure—food, water, shelter and access.

■ When corrective measures are necessary, non-chemical or the most "chemically-conservative" (i.e., least toxic and disruptive) solutions are strongly preferred over conventional pesticides.

■ Pest control must be a multidisciplinary endeavor that coordinates a wide range of complementary technologies and interventions carried out in partnership with the departments responsible for the care, maintenance and operations of a facility.

According to Dr. Greene, most major Federal agencies and several dozen state and municipal agencies are now using GSA information bulletins and training documents. Many other government bodies are using IPM contract specifications developed and used by GSA (U.S. GSA, 1993). The GSA effort to influence pest management decision-making in the 8,000 buildings the agency leases or manages nationwide began in 1993. About one million tenants live in or use these buildings. Dr. Greene stresses that pest control needs vary greatly across the country, as does the availability of biointensive IPM systems. GSA recognizes the need to invest time, effort and funding for effective biointensive IPM methods to be developed, implemented and maintained.

Dr. Albert Greene directs the General Services Administration's IPM program, which has achieved significant reductions in pesticide use in participating federal buildings. Credit: GSA

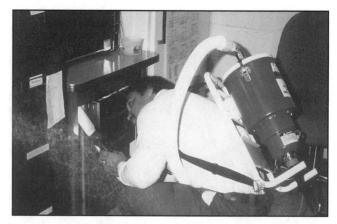

A trained pest control technician uses a vacuum cleaner instead of pesticides to remove cockroaches from office hiding places.
Credit: Dr. Al Greene

1. GSA Successes in the NCR— The "Termination of Extermination"

The *Federal Managers Quarterly* used the phrase "termination of extermination" in describing progress made in GSA IPM programs in the National Capital Region (GSA, 1992a). An average of 30 gallons of insecticides were being applied per month in 1987 in GSA's NCR facilities. The most widely used formulated products contained two insecticides, fenvalerate (Pydrin, now discontinued) and chlorpyrifos (Dursban). The preventive measures instituted since then have reduced reliance and use so that more than 99 percent of all insecticide now applied consists of low risk bait products containing principally hydramethylnon (Amdro), boric acid and abamectin.[4] Toxic pesticides are no longer used to deter birds from nesting in historic structures. Instead, Dr. Greene uses special netting with peripheral cabling that when stretched tight, cannot be seen by people passing by (Alderson and Greene, 1995).

The IPM program has dramatically changed how GSA responds to calls for pest management services in its buildings. In the year before the IPM program began, almost 100 percent of pest-related calls from building maintenance personnel led to a pesticide application. Dr. Greene refers to this inclination to spray, and then forget about pest management needs for a month or two, as the "invisible shield syndrome."

Since the beginning of the program, requests for services have decreased almost 25 percent. Of all pest-related calls, slightly more than 40 percent have resulted in a pesticide application. Almost 60 percent have been dealt with satisfactorily through an assessment of pest identity and population levels, placement of traps or structural repairs to eliminate pest access, use of non-chemical control products to disrupt the life cycle or reproductive success of the pest and client education. Despite progress in application of IPM techniques, however, Greene expects the calls to continue because GSA works mostly with "massive old buildings with too many avenues of penetration."

Records show that the pest management costs of GSA's IPM programs are similar to the former pesticide-intensive methods, running about $60 to $65 per hour for routine contracted services. But when looking for a good contractor, cost is just one factor Greene takes into account. He also assesses the skill and experience of contractors in applying biointensive IPM concepts and practices, as well as who can deliver the "greatest value," not necessarily the lowest cost, per visit or per application. Often higher costs per visit or per building are justified in order to cover salaries for better trained and motivated people.

> **GSA's Dr. Greene calls the inclination to spray a building and then forget about pest management needs for a few months the "invisible shield syndrome." It remains a problem in many places.**

Greene prefers to work with contractors who have been certified by their state pest control program. He seeks out individuals with up-to-date training in IPM techniques in relevant facilities and pest problems. The best contractors recognize the need to spend time with building managers and maintenance staff, investigating the causes of pest problems and what can be done to lessen them through simple, non-chemical control options. In order to identify commonsense solutions, contractors must understand how a building is used and by whom. Implementing solutions thus requires cooperation coupled with understanding and new tools.

2. Promoting IPM through Contract Specifications—GSA Sets the Pace

Under the guidance of Dr. Greene, GSA developed IPM "contract specifications" in 1989 for all GSA-managed facilities in the NCR. Success with these specifications led to their adoption by GSA nationwide in 1993. Since then, the agency's IPM contract specifications have become the standard for pest management contracts, whether with Federal or state facilities, hospitals or schools (GSA, 1993).

The specifications include several rigorous requirements. Contractors must complete a thorough inspection of each building prior to starting the contract. They also must submit to a Contracting Officer's Representative (COR) a Pest Control Plan that:

1) identifies pests found and names any pesticide, bait or other trapping or monitoring device(s) to be used.

2) describes methods and procedures for identifying sites where pests live and gain access and for determining population levels. Sets a schedule for weekly or monthly visits.

Cockroaches are bashful insects that move around mostly at night and when people are not around. A key step in developing better control strategies is to learn more about cockroach behavior. The Agricultural Research Service (ARS) has built a special building outfitted with sensors and other electronic equipment to monitor cockroach activity and test new bait and control methods. Here, technician David Milne is preparing a data logger prior to release of a batch of cockroaches.
Credit: Barry Fitzgerald, ARS

3) describes site-specific solutions for observed sources of pest food, water, harborage or access.

4) provides proof that any contracted employee would be a certified pest control operator—not just "operating under the supervision of a certified applicator" as allowed by EPA regulations.

In addition, GSA IPM contract specifications require that:

■ the contractor use non-pesticide methods of control wherever possible. For example, instead of spraying, the contractor would use portable vacuums to remove cockroaches and trapping devices for indoor flies.

■ applications of insecticides to exposed surfaces or use of aerosol foggers in an enclosed space be restricted to unique situations where no alternative measures are practical. No "tenant" personnel may be present during these procedures.

> **Blocking pest access to food, breeding habitat and water are examples of the simplest and often the most effective IPM strategies, and should always be among the first steps taken by anyone managing pests.**

■ strategically placed bait formulations be used for cockroach and ant control wherever appropriate as opposed to broadcast applications (spraying a pesticide through a whole area).

■ indoor rodent control be accomplished with trapping devices. If a rodenticide must be used in an exceptional situation, it must be placed in sites inaccessible to children, pets or wildlife. Outdoors, any rodenticide may be applied directly into a particular burrow.

■ the contractor is responsible for advising building personnel about any structural, sanitary or procedural

modifications that would reduce pest food, water, harborage or access.

■ the contractor must maintain a pest control log book or file for each building or site specified in the contract.

Dr. Greene recognizes the limitations of progressive contracts—"Contracts are just a bunch of words. If oversight is not there, if contractors are not skilled in this type of service, you will get the same old stuff. We also need to ensure that the Quality Assurance people are trained."

Success in Managing Rats and Roaches

GSA has been particularly successful in controlling rats and roaches with minimal reliance on pesticides (GSA, 1995). Greene found that outdoor rat populations could be reduced markedly in and around many buildings and facilities by a combination of commonsense practices. Steps include replacing uncovered or poorly sealed trash compactors with self-contained units fitted with pest-proof covers, identifying and then removing breeding sites and restricting rodent access to water (or placing control measures in breeding or watering locations). These are examples of the simplest and often the most effective IPM strategies, and should *always* be among the first steps taken by anyone managing pests.

GSA pest managers dramatically reduced cockroach populations in food service and trash holding areas through use of portable electric pressure washers. The washers spray hot water into areas where grease and

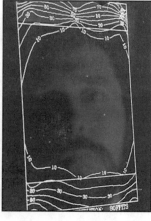

ARS entomologist Dr. Richard Brenner (left) uses microclimate and movement sensors to collect data on cockroach behavior. Computer-generated maps (right) are then developed with the data to assess patterns of movement within the experimental attic space. Credits: Barry Fitzgerald, ARS

debris accumulate. The high pressure spray kills any roaches in the area and removes the majority of their food source. Combined with caulking and a good sanitation program, these measures have almost eliminated stubborn roach problems in facilities including cafeterias, rest rooms and commercial kitchens.

3. Taking the NCR Program Nationwide

GSA launched an initiative in 1993 to extend its NCR IPM program nationwide to all 8,000 GSA owned or managed buildings. Through 10 regional offices, Dr. Greene is trying to encourage progress in implementing IPM and has found that such progress depends "… on the interest and enthusiasm of front line personnel." Greene has held IPM training sessions in several regions, but he "has no idea how much pesticide is used in GSA buildings nationwide" because no records are compiled at the national level. While funds are limited for compiling and analyzing data, Greene is working on a list of "approved pesticides" to be issued in late 1996 that will help building managers keep track of what is being sprayed.

> When first published, General Services Administration IPM contract requirements were not popular. Dr. Greene was criticized at training workshops in 1988 and 1989 by pest control company officials who claimed that the new GSA requirement to have an entomologist on staff would cost them business.

Since more and more government buildings include child care facilities, Greene also has developed anti-rodent recommendations for playgrounds. These include installation of synthetic play surfaces not prone to fungal or insect pests, minimization of dense landscape cover, play equipment supported on piers rather than platforms and security fences that thwart rat entry.

Recognizing the progress made by GSA, the Department of Defense has drawn on the agency's contract specifications in developing its own program and has asked Dr. Greene to attend Armed Forces Pest Management Board meetings. The National Park Service also has used the GSA specifications in developing NPS contracts.

When first published, GSA IPM contract requirements were not popular with pest control operators. Dr. Greene was sharply criticized at local industry training recertification workshops in 1988 and 1989 by pest control company officials who claimed that the requirement to have entomologists on staff would unfairly exclude some businesses from government pest control contracts. The requirement is still in place for NCR operations, but not for other parts of the country where entomologists may not be available.

The IPM concepts and strategies emphasized in GSA contracts are far more accepted today (GSA, 1992b). Most have even been adopted as recommended approaches by the National Pest Control Association (NPCA), the trade group representing pest control operators. The NPCA is launching a voluntary program for pest control operators, and Greene helped develop the course of instruction and the testing exam.

The Future

Greene believes pest management policies and practices carried out by all public institutions eventually will be subject to review by those affected and other concerned citizens—parents, veteran's groups, unions and regulatory agencies, to name a few. He feels that "GSA has helped make constructive change possible by demonstrating that IPM is practical, pragmatic, efficient and cost effective on a giant scale."

C. Department of Defense.

Driven by growing concern over pesticide exposure and risks at its facilities, the U.S. Department of Defense (DOD) made a commitment in 1994 to reduce pesticide use on military facilities by 50 percent by September 2000 as measured against 1993 baseline use levels. A year later, in November 1995, DOD signed a Memorandum of Understanding with EPA. Key elements included "eliminating unnecessary pesticide use by fully implementing IPM, substituting safer pesticides, and fostering research on non-chemical and `least toxic' control methods" (U.S. DOD, 1996b).

DOD interest in promoting IPM actually began years earlier. President Carter's 1979 memorandum on IPM triggered a process within DOD that culminated in 1983 when the department officially adopted IPM as its pest management method of choice (DOD, 1983). One of DOD's first steps was to prohibit prophylactic or scheduled pesticide treatments.

But according to Lt. Col. Robert McKenna with the Armed Forces Pest Management Board (AFPMB),[5] DOD's emphasis on IPM really took off after the 1993 release of the National Research Council report on the effect of pesticides on infants and children (NRC, 1993a).

The report received widespread media and scientific

attention during the same period DOD was studying the possible role of pesticides among the causes of Gulf War Syndrome neurological problems. Interest within DOD also was heightened by President Clinton's August 3, 1993 Executive Order 12856 outlining "Federal Compliance with Right-to-Know Laws and Pollution Prevention Requirements" and his April 26, 1994 memorandum to executive departments and agencies urging support for the use of native plants, reducing pesticide use and employing IPM techniques (White House, 1994).

1. The Department of Defense Plan

On August 11, 1994, Secretary Perry announced DOD's plan to reduce pesticide use by 50 percent by the year 2000 as part of the Department's "Comprehensive Pollution Prevention Strategy." A December 23 memorandum issued by Deputy Under Secretary of Defense for Environmental Security Sherri Goodman set three main goals in a section describing "Pest Management Measures of Merit:"

1. By the end of fiscal year (FY) 1997, all DOD installations will have pest management plans prepared and reviewed. The plans will be updated annually by service pest management professionals.
2. By the end of FY 2000, the amount of pesticide applied annually on DOD installations will be reduced by 50 percent from the 1993 baseline in pounds of active ingredient applied.
3. By the end of FY 1998, 100 percent of all DOD installation pesticide applicators will be properly certified and have at least two years of employment experience.

Current Pest Management Activities

In 1993, the four branches of the Armed Forces—the Air Force, Army, Defense Logistics Agency and Navy (includes the Marines)—used approximately 1.2 million pounds of active ingredient on the more than 400 major bases around the world.

Current DOD policy requires that each installation develop an annual pest management plan that is approved by the pest manager at the command level. Once the plan is approved, applicators must record the amount of pesticide product and active ingredient applied per application and submit the information to pest management officials on a quarterly basis. The records must be kept at the base level. DOD's record keeping requirement applies to all pesticides, not just restricted use active ingredients as is the case with farm

application under EPA/USDA record keeping rules.

Of the approximately 1.2 million pounds of active ingredients applied in 1993 at both domestic and overseas bases, 214,300 pounds were used by the Air Force, 595,000 pounds by the Army, 277,150 by the Navy and 23,000 by Defense Logistics. The Army's record keeping system is not automated, limiting its ability to analyze and transfer data. The Navy and Air Forces systems are automated, however, making more information available. In the future, McKenna says that all reports will be automated and easier to analyze at all levels, from a single military installation to DOD as a whole.

All pesticide applicators must be certified within two years of employment in the safe handling and application of pesticides, either by a DOD or state training program. Approximately half of the pesticides are procured from the Federal Supply System, which stocks conventional products as well as low risk biopesticides and insect growth regulators. Certain products have been taken out of use over the years due to risk concerns and the development of alternatives. These formulations include lindane, dacthal, pentachlorophenol, creosote, propoxur, paraquat and the liquid formulations of DDVP.

2. Meeting the Year 2000 Challenge

DOD is the only U.S. government organization to commit to a concrete pesticide use reduction goal as part of its formal IPM policy. McKenna acknowledges that achieving the goal will be hard, and DOD is "... a big boat to turn around." To help reach its target, DOD has developed the following definition of IPM:

"A planned program, incorporating continuous monitoring, education, record keeping, and communication to prevent pests and disease vectors from causing unacceptable damage to operations, people, material, or the environment. IPM uses targeted, sustainable (effective, economical, environmentally sound) methods including educational tactics, habitat modification, biological control, cultural control, mechanical control, physical control, and, where necessary, the judicious use of less-hazardous pesticides."

DOD senior management has voiced strong support for the IPM and pesticide use reduction initiative. In July 1994, the Armed Forces Pest Management Board (AFPMB) published an overview of IPM in and around buildings, developed in cooperation with GSA's Dr. Greene. DOD's January 1995 pest management workshop was entitled, "Sustainable Integrated Pest Management for the Department of Defense: Vision for the 21st Century." According to Under Secretary Goodman, the DOD initiative's "key elements were: eliminating unnecessary pesticide use by fully implementing integrated pest management, substituting 'safe' pesticides, and fostering research on non-chemical and least-toxic chemical control methods ... We see IPM as a pollution prevention tool to help reduce pesticide risk and use" (DOD, 1995).

Mr. William Bennett, Chairman of the AFPMB, reinforced this message, saying, "Pollution prevention is key! Ask yourselves, 'Is what I am doing, or recommending be done today, going to be problem later?' Think! What is the fate of the material I am using and recommending for use today? Will residues be a problem later?"

The November 1995 DOD-EPA Memorandum of Understanding outlines further steps that DOD has taken or is planning:

■ promoting IPM on DOD-controlled golf courses, with the objective of eventually having all DOD courses practicing IPM.

■ providing a suitable location on DOD installations where innovative IPM techniques can be perfected and demonstrated to interested parties.

■ dedicating the personnel and equipment necessary to implement IPM techniques including physical, mechanical, cultural and biological resources, educational activities and use of less toxic pesticides such as biopesticides.

McKenna reports that DOD also is exploring ways to preferentially seek out food supplies grown under IPM, a step that will require agreement on an acceptable defini-

tion of "IPM-Grown" food. Reaching such agreement is bound to take time and effort, but some commodity organizations already are working with EPA as part of its pesticide environmental stewardship program to come up with commodity and region specific definitions of IPM. These definitions then could be used to certify food produced under IPM. As an alternative, DOD may seek produce certified by third parties as "pesticide free" or grown using organic production methods.

3. Matching Words and Actions— Challenges Persist for DOD

Although the DOD has committed itself to an ambitious agenda for change, problems persist:

■ The AFPMB currently collects data only on overall pesticide use by individual branch. Further detailed data such as product use and specific formulations are not reported for all of DOD, although they are available at individual bases. While these data will eventually become available DOD-wide, there are no plans to do a Department-wide analysis of it by base, pesticide and problem to determine "hot spots" and primary use areas, information seemingly key to developing baseline use and risk data and determining where military personnel may be exposed to the greatest quantity or most toxic combinations of pesticides.

■ DOD requires individuals applying pesticides to be certified and trained, and also is providing IPM instruction as a component of certification and training programs. Approximately 2,000 pest management technicians are trained annually. But unlike GSA, DOD

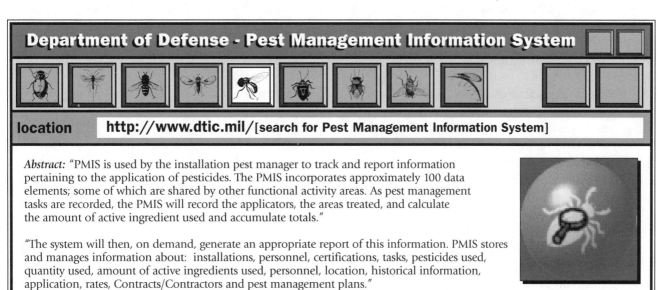

Department of Defense - Pest Management Information System

location   http://www.dtic.mil/[search for Pest Management Information System]

Abstract: "PMIS is used by the installation pest manager to track and report information pertaining to the application of pesticides. The PMIS incorporates approximately 100 data elements; some of which are shared by other functional activity areas. As pest management tasks are recorded, the PMIS will record the applicators, the areas treated, and calculate the amount of active ingredient used and accumulate totals."

"The system will then, on demand, generate an appropriate report of this information. PMIS stores and manages information about: installations, personnel, certifications, tasks, pesticides used, quantity used, amount of active ingredients used, personnel, location, historical information, application, rates, Contracts/Contractors and pest management plans."

does not require compliance with basic IPM concepts and practices in contract specifications, nor are officials overseeing contracts instructed to assure adequate knowledge of IPM. Still, DOD is taking more steps to augment IPM skills and system choices. For example, the Air Force recently distributed to all its facilities a copy of "Common Sense Pest Control" (BIRC, 1996a).

■ Budget cuts mean that more outside contractors will be hired to perform pest management programs. While DOD has copies of the GSA specifications for indoor pest management and is aware of GSA's success in reducing pesticide use in its buildings, DOD does not currently require contractors to follow the specifications. However, DOD is currently developing standard guidance for contracting IPM consistent with the GSA's guidelines.

■ Individual base pest management professionals can authorize the use of pesticides not approved for use by the AFPMB. Such purchases already constitute about 50 percent of all pesticide acquisitions and seem to be increasing (DOD, 1994). This authority makes it more difficult for the AFPMB to limit use of toxic pesticides.

■ Pesticide use reduction goals may not occur uniformly throughout DOD. For example, golf courses, which historically have been major pesticide users, could turn out to be "sacred cows."

■ There is no official DOD policy requiring that service personnel or the public be notified of pesticide applications, even indoors. Notification is supplied "under some circumstances" such as large scale aerial applications, and if required under state or local regulations or law.

On April 22, 1996 DOD issued new instructions to adhere to basic IPM principles (DOD, 1996a). While certain features appear to contradict one another, it contains a new definition of IPM close to our notion of biointensive IPM:

"IPM is the method of choice for DOD pest management and disease vector control. IPM is a sustainable approach to managing pests and controlling disease vectors by combining applicable pest management tools in a way that minimizes economic, health, and environmental risks. IPM uses regular or scheduled monitoring to determine if and when treatments are necessary and employs physical, mechanical, cultural, biologic, genetic, regulatory, chemical, and educational tactics to keep pest numbers low enough to prevent unacceptable damage or impacts. Treatments are not made according to a predetermined schedule; they are made only when and where monitoring has indicated that the pest will cause unacceptable economic, medical, or aesthetic damage. Treatments are chosen and timed to be most effective and least disruptive to natural control of pests. *Least hazardous, but effective, pesticides are used as a last resort* (Emphasis added)."

4. Success Stories

The DOD has been a pioneer in certain areas of pest management research and development. Each month the department ships between 200,000 and 1,000,000 pounds of commodities to the Pacific Rim, much of it perishable food. Methyl bromide, a very hazardous fumigant that depletes the ozone layer and poses health risks, has been used in the past as a pre-shipment fumigant to kill any insects in perishable fruits and vegetables, despite high costs and an average 30 percent loss of useable product per shipment to pests and shipping damage (Gay, 1996). The phase out of methyl bromide use by 2001, plus growing concerns about efficacy and cost, led DOD to search for alternatives. The search led the Defense Logistics Agency, private industry and universities to collaborate on developing "controlled atmosphere" technology to replace pre-shipment fumigation with pesticides (see Lt. Cmdr. Robert Gay's presentation in U.S. DOD, 1995).

Controlled atmosphere shipping containers work by lowering the oxygen content to only 0.5 percent for 96 hours at the beginning of a trip, or before a ship leaves port. "One hundred percent mortality has been observed for nearly all insects tested," according to Gay, a U.S. Navy staff entomologist (Gay, 1996). Ethylene content also is lowered when certain commodities are shipped, and experimentation continues with ways to manipulate other parameters such as temperature and moisture in conjunction with oxygen, ethylene and nitrogen content.

DOD is now using controlled atmosphere technology to ship a wide variety of commodities and is saving an estimated $2.9 to $5.0 million annually as a result, despite the higher up front cost of containers suited for the treatments. The savings come largely from DOD's ability to switch from air transport for perishables—at a cost of $1.25 per pound—to surface transport, which costs $0.43 per pound. Work is progressing on ways to fine-tune controlled atmosphere shipping techniques and equipment so that this approach will work reliably with hard-to-ship fruits like Asian pears and kiwis.

DOD also has joined EPA's Pesticide Stewardship Program and is working with various associations and commodity groups to develop IPM programs for specific applications. DOD is focusing attention on golf courses, parade grounds and other managed turf locations. Several other programs are underway on individual bases, although little information is available to document concrete changes in pest management systems or pesticide use levels.

It remains to be seen whether DOD will reduce pesticide use 50 percent over the next four years. Education of base personnel remains a key goal since, according to McKenna, some people may misinterpret a reduction in pesticide use as "...another erosion of benefits."

5. Base Conversion Trends

An encouraging trend is emerging involving the use of current and former military bases and installations for experimental pest management projects such as urban IPM and rangeland weed control. The Berkeley, California-based Bio-Integral Resource Center (BIRC), which assisted with the Park Service's IPM program, has received a grant from the State of California's Department of Pesticide Regulation to work with DOD on the 290-acre Moffet Field, where 140 buildings house the National Aeronautics and Space Administration's Ames Research Center and other organizations. BIRC is leading a team of facility managers, pest control operators and other specialists in developing cost-effective indoor IPM programs. The team has set ambitious goals for reducing pesticide use and is making solid progress toward attaining them.[6]

Other organizations including local environmental groups are working to restore native prairies and improve wildlife habitat in and around military facilities. The World Bank is considering placement of an international IPM and sustainable agriculture training center at the emerging science and technology park at Fort Ord in Monterey, California. The University of California at Santa Cruz may also participate in the center through its agroecology program. In addition, the Committee for Sustainable Agriculture, California's most well established organization supporting onfarm research on organic and sustainable production methods, hopes to establish a world-class demonstration and research farm and meeting center on the old base and its adjacent Salinas Valley farmland.

Similar plans and projects are taking shape in other states, many partially financed through federal base conversion funds. The ability of the DOD to draw upon its resources in working with experts around the world can rapidly advance the technology development process. Several technologies critical to national defense and

> The ability of the DOD to draw upon its resources and work with shipping experts around the world accelerated development of closed atmosphere shipping techniques that are not reliant on pesticides and are saving taxpayers money. This is a good example of how government can exercise leadership in development of pest management technology needed to progress along the IPM continuum.

IPM Innovators CA Department of Pesticide Regulation

location http://www.cdpr.ca.gov/docs/ipminov/ipmmenu.htm

THE 1995 AWARDEES
The Napa County Resource Conservation District local growers, community groups, private citizens, and governmental agencies working on problems they all share.. (Dennis Bowker, 707 252-4188)
The Magalia Nursery of the California Department of Forestry and Fire Protection
has succeeded in finding a solution to controlling soil pests without using fumigants such as methyl bromide. (Bill Krelle, 916/873-0400; David Adams, 916/332-0126)
The Imperial County Whitefly Management Committee (David Ritter, 619/339-4314)
The California Clean Growers' Association: a group of 150 farmers and others who share information on family farming, soil health, and methods to minimize reliance on pesticides. (Paul Buxman, 209/897-7547)

"IPM (Integrated Pest Management) Innovators are groups exhibiting leadership in adopting techniques that increase the benefits and reduce the risks of pest control."

developed by DOD also can be valuable when applied to civilian pest management challenges. Examples of possible applications include:

■ remote sensing methods to track pest movement and detect water, nutrient and mineral deficiencies that may be a sign of root diseases, drought stress, excessive salinity or soil fertility imbalances.

■ automated weather stations and associated expert systems to help pest managers predict disease spore growth, insect flight, mating behavior and key weather related parameters that influence crop-pest interactions.

■ application of night-vision technologies to electronically detect movement of nocturnal pests, creating a new tool for scouting fields for pests or assessing pest pressure in crawl spaces and other hard-to-reach places.

■ biological control of mosquitoes and other insects that can transmit diseases.

■ use of electrical pulses, heat and other non-chemical methods, possibly in combination, to mange weeds and help reduce soil-borne insect and plant pathogen pressure.

■ building construction and maintenance methods that reduce problems with termites, ants, bees and wasps, other bothersome insects and rodents.

Some former military contracting firms specializing in telecommunications, robotics and sensor technology are now applying their expertise in the design and refinement of automated weather stations, sensors to detect conditions favorable to disease or the spread of disease and other technologies that will help pest managers move along the IPM continuum.

[1] Much of the information reported in this chapter is not available from published sources. It was obtained through a series of Freedom of Information Act requests, meetings and conversations between CU project team member Sandra Marquardt and government agency officials.

[2] This NPS requirement is similar to those imposed by the General Services Administration (GSA) and the Department of Defense (DOD), and is more comprehensive than the record keeping requirement applicable to agriculture. Certified applicators, which can include farmers, are required only to compile records on applications of restricted use pesticides.

[3] General information on the GSA Integrated Pest Management Program in this section and quotes from Dr. Greene were from a series of conversations and faxes between Sandra Marquardt and Dr. Greene in October-December 1995. Key items are cited and appear in the bibliography.

[4] Abamectin in pure crystal form is actually quite toxic but when formulated into consumer market end-use products, the active ingredient is present in very low concentrations and hence these products pose limited risks. Also important, there is little or no resistance yet to abamectin in most urban IPM uses, but given the current extent of reliance on abamectin in some areas, resistance remains a serious worry.

[5] Information on Department of Defense pest management programs and policies has been provided through a series of conversations between Sandra Marquardt and Lt. Col. McKenna, who also provided copies of a number of memoranda and supporting documentation. Key items are cited and appear in the bibliography.

[6] Description of project is in "Innovations in Pest Management Grants 1996" issued by the Department of Pesticide Regulation, Cal-EPA, Sacramento, California (see web page box on page 220).

Institutional Barriers

*A change in research focus, policy and more open markets
are needed to help pest managers leap over barriers in the way
of progress toward biointensive IPM.*

Government scientists, research agencies and private companies have worked for decades to promote the development and adoption of Integrated Pest Management (IPM). Federal agencies have pledged to rely on IPM, and the U.S. Department of Agriculture (USDA) has promoted IPM as "official" policy since the early 1970s. The pesticide industry has sought more selective products compatible with IPM and some have been registered. Still, overall pesticide use and reliance has been growing since the 1940s. Why?

One reason is that the federal government has promoted IPM with one hand and pesticides with the other. Another is that the pesticide industry has placed most

> As public institutions worked to show pest managers that pesticides were the "modern" solution, research on the genetic and biological foundations of biointensive IPM languished.

of its scientific and marketing resources behind conventional pesticides.

Public sector efforts to promote IPM always have been founded on good intentions but piecemeal and inadequately funded. Since the 1940s, the main focus of most federal government research has been finding a better chemical solution, not trying to lessen reliance on pesticides in general.

Overview

Four government programs and related policies—pest eradication, commodity price supports, produce grading standards, and research and education—have required or indirectly encouraged reliance on pesticides. Throughout the cotton belt, for example, farmers have been struggling for years with half a dozen difficult-to-control insects, several induced to major pest status by pesticide spraying. Serious trouble with cotton insect pest management led to the first federal appropriations for IPM research and education in the early 1970s. Much progress has since been made in establishing a science base for cotton IPM; yet across the cotton belt USDA is still supporting chemical-based boll weevil eradication programs that typically draw farmers farther onto the pesticide treadmill.

Eradication programs help justify and finance intensive

pesticide use in defined areas for generally short periods of time. Government commodity price support programs, on the other hand, have heightened pesticide reliance incrementally over large areas, leading to contamination of drinking water and widespread ecological damage. They have done this by rewarding specialization and intensification of production while penalizing crop rotations—the foundation of cropping and pest management systems that can greatly lessen reliance on pesticides.

In the marketing arena, USDA works with food processors, the retail sector and commodity organizations to shape and regulate grading standards and access to the market. In the process, grading and quality standards for fruit and vegetables have been adopted that foster late-season "peace of mind" applications of pesticides. These standards and policies impact pest management systems much as eradication programs do—by requiring or rewarding heavy reliance on pesticides, they draw farmers farther onto the pesticide treadmill, triggering secondary pests and making primary ones harder to control.

Some of the most important contemporary barriers to IPM adoption were erected one year at a time over four decades, as the USDA and Congress provided support for the public research and education activities needed to bring on the "golden age of pesticides." But as public institutions worked to show pest managers that pesticides were the "modern" solution, research on the genetic and biological foundations of biointensive IPM languished. Now, a surprising portion of research funding is locked up trying to keep chemical-based pest management systems from collapsing, while at the same time also dealing with their growing adverse economic, public health and environmental consequences.

As a result, pest managers and farmers wanting to get off or stay off the pesticide treadmill have had little help from public institutions. There is lots of information available on how to use pesticides, steps needed to avoid resistance, safety precautions, and ways to protect water quality, but much less up-to-date information on non-chemical and biointensive IPM solutions.

Looking to the future, this chapter describes the need for reordering priorities in pest management research and technology development, especially in the area of biotechnology. We also stress the need for innovative ways to engage farmers and IPM practitioners in field-level participatory research and education efforts. Around the country, IPM's roots are spreading fastest where farmers have created ways to come together, discussing common problems, sharing ideas and experiences, and moving beyond barriers to progress along the IPM continuum.

> **Across America IPM's roots are spreading fastest where farmers have created ways to come together to discuss and solve common problems.**

A key need in fostering grass-roots-driven IPM innovation is finding—and financing—new ways to collect and synthesize information encompassing scouting methods, pest status, thresholds, effectiveness of control strategies, and how to enhance beneficial organism survival. To maximize progress, such information must come from many farms, field practitioners and disciplines, and it must be timely, region-specific, easily accessible and delivered interactively so that information, ideas and experience always flow two ways.

The Internet will be a valuable resource in this process

and indeed could, in time, revolutionize information flows critical to IPM. The web page boxes shown throughout this book provide a glimpse of a pest-management future when information is a common good and where progress toward biointensive IPM is a function of the ease with which information flows from those who have it, or know where it can be obtained, to those who need it. In such a future, public institutions would be able to focus steadily more of their effort on improving people's abilities and skills in using information to guide day-to-day pest management decisions.

A. Eradication Programs

The USDA has periodically supported efforts to "eradicate" pests since the 1940s, typically through widespread and concentrated pesticide spray programs. Such programs initially were focused on non-native pest species introduced into the United States, like the Medfly and the screwworm. Success depended on early detection, fast action to contain an infestation in one or a few areas and immediate steps to kill 100 percent of the population or prevent reproduction. Over the years the pest challenges addressed through eradication

The Medfly (left) is not welcome in Southern California because if established, it could move north, threatening the state's multi-billion dollar orchard and fruit industries. International food shipments are carefully inspected for Medfly because this pest can threaten both crops and markets. Extensive efforts are made throughout Southern California (right) to monitor Medfly populations and remove fruit from abandoned trees. Credits: APHIS

The spread of the boll weevil into the Lower-Rio Grande Valley led to establishment of a new Boll Weevil Eradication Program Area. But early season malathion spraying triggered secondary pest problems and growers lost an estimated $150 million. Credit: Animal Plant and Health Inspection Service

programs have grown to include some well-established and troublesome pests, including the boll weevil—the American cotton farmer's major insect pest for most of a century.

Success usually has been temporary at best. The pink bollworm program in California cotton regions is an exception. This program has been based predominantly on trapping and extending the period between cotton crops. While eradication programs based on biological and cultural controls have had some success, attempts to eradicate pests through heavy pesticide use are inimical to the principles of IPM, almost never work for long and often make matters worse.

> **Attempts to eradicate a well-established pest through heavy reliance on pesticides are inimical to the principles of IPM, almost never work for long and often make matters worse.**

1. Medfly and Screwworm Programs

Several well-publicized efforts have been made to eradicate the Mediterranean fruit fly (Medfly) from Southern California through aggressive monitoring, removal of infected fruit and localized treatments. In cases where Medfly populations appear poised to spread, aerial applications of malathion have been ordered, including over urban areas. Experts disagree over whether the program has been successful. Some believe the pest has been established for years in parts of Southern California. Others claim that eradication efforts have been successful temporarily, but that the pest is continuously reintroduced in the thousands of tons of produce and ornamentals shipped into California from Mexico, the Caribbean and other tropical regions where the fly is endemic.

Perhaps the most successful eradication program carried out by the USDA targeted the screwworm, a damaging external insect pest of cattle and other livestock in the Southwest. The effort was successful in suppressing the screwworm, although it has not eradicated the insect. The program is ongoing and scientists must remain vigilant in tracking the pest's movement into new areas. The relative success of the screwworm program can be traced to its reliance on a largely biological approach—release of sterile male screwworm flies. Also contributing to the program's effectiveness is the fact that monitoring and tracking infected cattle is easier than dealing with a pest like the boll weevil, which is able to move several hundred miles in a season and can become a problem almost anywhere cotton is grown.

2. The Lower-Rio Grande BWEP

A costly example of what can go wrong with eradication programs occurred in Texas in 1995. When the boll weevil spread west in the spring, nervous cotton farmers asked the Texas Department of Agriculture to establish a new zone in the state-federal Boll Weevil Eradication Program (BWEP) already underway in several cotton

> *"I was a reviewer of the ARS report on the Lower-Rio Grande Valley episode prepared for the annual cotton conference proceedings and find it very difficult to believe why there is any debate. It is clear cut; the BWEP spraying triggered the beet armyworm outbreak!"*
>
> **Dr. Dale Bottrell,** *Department of Entomology University of Maryland—College Park*[1]

growing states and other parts of Texas. A new boll weevil eradication zone was approved, and aerial spraying of some 200,000 acres of cotton began in the spring of 1995 using the organophosphate insecticide malathion, the same pesticide sprayed periodically in Southern California in response to Medfly detections.

Trouble arose quickly. Texas cotton farmers in the eradication zone incurred devastating losses in 1995 from secondary pests triggered largely by the absence of beneficial insects wiped out by the malathion spraying. First, cotton aphids spread quickly west and north, then beet armyworms began to spread as well, causing serious losses. The sweet potato whitefly delivered the knock-out punch on several farms. Many growers lost their entire crop despite as many as 25 insecticide applications, up to 15 of them by the BWEP. In the Lower-Rio Grande Valley area, cotton farms usually harvest more than 300,000 bales of cotton. But in 1995, they managed only 54,000 bales—over an 80 percent drop (Meister, 1996).

A team of ARS scientists studied the infestation and prepared a report documenting the heavy losses in the eradication zone compared to surrounding areas, which did not incur unusual losses (USDA, 1995e). At first, USDA officials in Washington raised questions about the draft ARS report. Following additional data collection, analysis and full peer review, the final ARS report vindicated the draft report's findings, which concluded:

> "The (data) overwhelmingly implicate heavy pesticide usage as the primary causal factor for dramatic differences observed in pest and beneficial insect complexes. Furthermore, these differences were primarily responsible for the catastrophic crop losses experienced" (USDA, 1995e).

As scientists tried to determine the causes of the outbreak, farmers struggled to cope with the program's financial consequences and the resulting beet armyworm crop damage. Since the worms are difficult and costly to control with pesticides, the program turned into a "total fiasco," according to John Christian, a crop consultant active in the area (Meister, 1996). A similar scenario unfolded in 29 eastern Mississippi counties where

"Everybody in the district had a crop failure in 1995, and some lost millions" because spraying by the regional boll weevil eradication program knocked out beneficials that normally help control the tobacco budworm (Meister, 1996).

Anger mounted among growers, citizens and concerned organizations in the Lower-Rio Grande Valley when ARS scientists and cotton pest management experts confirmed that just across the Colorado River in Mexico, cotton farmers had gotten through the season without serious losses by sticking with their traditional IPM system.

The contrast in outcomes triggered sharp criticism of the BWEP and a group of farmers certain that the early spraying had cost them most of their 1995 crop started a campaign for a referendum on whether to continue the program in 1996. An at times emotional debate unfolded. Meetings and demonstrations were held during which growers explained what had happened on their farms in 1995 and why they held the BWEP responsible. Several officials and experts working for the foundation carrying out the BWEP—the USDA, Texas A&M University, and the state department of agriculture—argued that unusual weather patterns were largely to blame, made worse by delays in getting new pesticides registered by the EPA. But these arguments were not persuasive. Cotton farmers in the Lower-Rio Grande Valley voted by a three-to-one margin in early 1996 to end the eradication program.

The Lower-Rio Grande Valley's boll weevil eradication disaster could have been avoided had a 1993 state law been obeyed that requires adopting IPM in eradication programs and taking measures to avoid resistance and secondary pest problems. Those who designed and carried out the eradication plan ignored both the law and warnings from environmental and consumer groups, Reggie James in CU's Southwestern Office in Austin, Texas, prominently among them.

> *"The immense value of natural biological control was not fully appreciated by entomologists or cotton producers until after the introduction of synthetic organic insecticides. When the effectiveness of the approximately 600 species of predators and parasites found in cotton is disrupted, often by a single insecticide application, many secondary pests do considerable damage to the crop."*
>
> **Pest Control: An Assessment of Present and Alternative Technologies,** *Report of the Executive Committee (NRC, 1975)*

Two Responses

While the 1995 season was in progress, both farmers and scientists tried to find ways to slow the spread of the beet armyworm and lessen damage to the 1995 crop. One group turned to chemical-intensive solutions, and either sprayed more frequently or sought out supplies of two new pesticides (Provado, imidacloprid; Alert or Pirate, a pyrrole compound). While not fully registered by the EPA, the products were granted "emergency exemptions" covering application to Texas cotton fields, justified on the basis of the otherwise hard-to-control secondary pest outbreaks. However, there was not enough of these new pesticides to meet the demand and an acre-treatment cost about $150—much more than Texas cotton farmers could afford given the crop's value and relatively narrow per-acre profit margins.

> As losses mounted in Texas, the search for a scapegoat intensified and EPA proved a convenient target. Several organizations complained to the Congress and the media that EPA had dragged its feet in approving requests for "emergency exemptions." But EPA responded by pointing out that it had approved each of four requests within 48 hours of its receipt.

As losses caused by the beet armyworm mounted to as much as $150 million at the farm level, the episode attracted national attention. Some began looking for a scapegoat, and EPA proved a convenient target. Several organizations complained to the Congress and the media that EPA had dragged its feet in approving requests for "emergency exemptions" as called for in Section 18 of the FIFRA statute. Responding to these charges in a letter to the *Washington Post*, Dr. Lynn Goldman, the EPA's Assistant Administrator in charge of the pesticide program, wrote:

"The U.S. EPA moved swiftly to meet the needs of Texas cotton growers. Beginning last year and continuing through this past August (1995), EPA responded to four different emergency requests from Texas to deal with the unusually large infestation of beet armyworm. In each instance, the agency responded within 48 hours" (quoted in *Pesticide and Toxic Chemical News*, 1995a).

Experts in Texas, including state IPM coordinator Dr. Tom Fuchs, agree that both the state and EPA acted swiftly once the growers asked for emergency exemptions. One source of delay was the requirement that the state document the existence of an emergency and provide data to EPA showing that no acceptable registered pesticide or IPM alternative was available. Ironically, this proved difficult. According to Dr. Fuchs, "The beet armyworm is such a sporadic pest in Texas that little data was available when the Section 18s were asked for" (*Pesticide and Toxic Chemical News*, 1995a).

Another group of farmers recognized that excessive pesticide use had triggered the problem and decided to seek solutions through IPM and biological control. Interest grew among a small segment of the grower community in a new biological control organism that the USDA had been studying for several years—the tiny parasitic wasp *Catolaccus grandis* (Becker et al., 1992). The region's many organic cotton producers hoped this wasp could be estab-

Female Catolaccus grandis *wasps (left) attack the boll weevil larva in two stages. They first draw nourishment from the larva. Later, other wasps will deposit eggs near the larva that will feed on it when they hatch. The wasp is a native of Mexico and is being developed as a biological control agent by USDA scientists—and none too soon. The USDA has plans to include more than 9 million acres of cotton in the Boll Weevil Eradication Program over the next three years. On a cotton farm in Aliceville, Alabama, Agricultural Research Service entomologists Juan Morales-Ramos and Ed King (standing) release canisters of* Catolaccus grandis. Credits: Left, Scott Bauer, ARS; Right, David Nance, ARS

lished and provide another tool for coping with the boll weevil. These farmers feared that secondary pests triggered by heavy BWEP insecticide spraying would undermine their generally successful biointensive IPM system.

While the wasp and other biological control organisms for cotton insect pests in Texas are promising alternatives, supplies are grossly inadequate. There is little hope for increased public or private investment in biointensive IPM and biological control infrastructure until a decision is made to halt heavy BWEP insecticide spraying.

Our Conclusion

An objective review of the record shows that most eradication programs generally have failed to eliminate pests. Most have suppressed pest populations for a period of time through what can be viewed as publicly funded areawide pesticide cost-share programs. The pattern of spraying has often accelerated the emergence of resistance or triggered secondary pests. A few programs have caused serious environmental damage. In the case of boll weevil eradication programs, although public researchers have discovered more than 50 different parasites, parasitoids and pathogens that can help control the boll weevil, these beneficials cannot get established until use of and reliance on broad-spectrum insecticides is curtailed substantially.

Eradication programs are expensive, for both farmers and public institutions. After financing the BWEP, state institutions and local growers had few resources to invest in biointensive IPM solutions, despite the promising field

performance of some such approaches. The same holds true in other areas where farmers and government place their faith—and resources—in eradication programs.

The notion of eradication is incompatible with biointensive IPM, which seeks to mange pest populations, not eradicate them. The heavy spraying required by chemical-based eradication programs almost always thins the diversity and lowers the populations of beneficial organisms such that biointensive IPM becomes impossible for a period of time. This incompatibility of eradication and IPM is supported by sound science and widely accepted, but rarely acknowledged by those who design and promote eradication programs or defend their budgets to the general public.

B. Policies that Shape Pest Management

Federal policy has shaped pest management systems in many ways. Two of the most important occur at opposite ends of the chain linking farmers and consumers. The commodity price support programs have helped determine what crops get planted, where they get planted and in what rotations with other crops. These are among the first decisions a farmer makes, and few choices have a more profound impact on pest pressure and pesticide use.

Toward the end of the farmer's production cycle, another set of polices and institutions shapes market access and price, particularly for growers of fruits and veg etables. Marketing orders and grading and cosmetic standards impose strict limits on pest damage and hence place a premium on near-perfect pest control. In many areas a significant portion of a year's total pesticide use is applied for "peace of mind" in an effort to eliminate any chance of receiving a lower quality grade and price.

1. Commodity Programs

As crop yields and production rose in the 1920s and early 1930s, surpluses and low prices were recurrent problems. Agricultural commodity price support programs began in the late 1930s and applied to major field crops and small grains—cotton, soybeans, the feed grains corn and sorghum and the small grains wheat, rice, oats and barley. These programs strove to support farm income by offering direct payments to producers in return for their periodically holding out of production a percentage of their land. This is why USDA commodity programs are also referred to as "supply control" programs.

> Growing different crops in sequence breaks pest cycles by denying pests access to the food, space or habitat they need to thrive. The "rotation effect" produces a boost in yields typically ranging from 10 to 15 percent from improved root system health and plant growth.

Payments through commodity programs have been important in ensuring a participating farm's long-run economic viability. In years of surpluses and depressed prices, USDA payments made the difference between scraping by and bankruptcy on thousands of farms. Inadvertently though, commodity programs have created a host of indirect economic incentives that are obstacles to non-chemical pest control.

In any given year, a farmer's payment is a function of market prices, program rules for that year and the acreage the farmer is eligible to enroll, often referred to as the *base acreage allotment.* The "base" for each crop reflects enrollments and plantings in previous years. Most farmers do whatever they can to build their base allotments for future years. Some buy more land, others move toward more specialized cropping patterns and some plow up highly erodible pasture and rangeland or drained wetlands. A few pursue all four strategies. But the key is planting as many acres as possible of qualifying crops year after year.

Importance of Rotations

While many changes were underway on farms in the 1950s and 1960s, the most important in terms of pest management was the move away from crop rotations. Maximizing commodity program benefits meant farmers had to specialize. The biological consequences of the shift to continuous cropping patterns (planting the same crop year after year) were masked by the discovery and growing use of new-generation pesticides. The discovery of dozens of new herbicides made possible a shift toward reduced tillage systems that helped lower soil erosion rates. According to an editorial in *Science*:

> "Substantial advances have been made in enhancing the ability of plants to combat enemies that attack above ground. But comparable progress has not been achieved in safeguarding plants against the biological warfare that rages in the soil. Nematodes and micro-organisms attack the roots of plants, limiting the effectiveness of fertilizers and lowering the yields of many crops" (Abelson, 1995).

"Biological warfare" is more likely in soils when the same crop is grown year after year. Planting different crops in sequence breaks pest cycles by denying pests access to the food, space or habitat they need to thrive. In addition to helping manage above-ground insects and weeds, this "rotation effect" produces a boost in yields typically ranging from 10 to 15 percent from improved root and plant health (NRC, 1989a; Cook and Veseth, 1991; Crookston, et al., 1991). The biological processes and interactions that create or contribute to this largely below-ground rotation effect include:

■ improved root health from suppression of soil-borne pathogens.

■ enhanced microbial biodiversity and activity, leading to more nutrient cycling through the soil and greater opportunities for biological control of pests (Bezdicek and Granatstein, 1989).

■ improved soil structure and water holding capacity (NRC, 1993b; Hudson, 1994).

Corn, soybeans and cotton accounted for 65 percent of the total pounds of pesticide active ingredients applied in 1992 for agricultural use (Anderson, 1994). Rotations would greatly lessen reliance on herbicides applied to all three crops, and reliance on insecticides now used to manage the corn rootworm also would fall. Rotation reduces pest pressure effectively nearly everywhere in the

Contour strip cropping systems are effective in controlling soil erosion and also can increase yields through impacts on soil microbial communities, pest pressure and nutrient availability. The Leopold Center for Sustainable Agriculture Research at Iowa State University has carried out extensive research on these systems and documented major water quality and agronomic benefits (i.e., see Mayerfeld et al., 1996). Credit: Leopold Center for Sustainable Agriculture

U.S. as long as the crops in the rotation are selected based on knowledge of local soil and climate conditions and pest populations.

One worrisome trend undercutting crop rotation is the growing market share of some two dozen sulfonylurea, imidazolinone and other herbicides that can carry over in the soil until the fall or following spring, limiting the grower's selection of cover and rotation crops (Ahrens and Fuerst, 1990; Loux et al., 1989; Liebman and Dyck, 1992; Fletcher et al., 1993). Persistent grass herbicides, for example, often include restrictions on the label forbidding a grower from planting a grass hay crop or a small grain crop for a period of time long enough for the residues in the soil to thoroughly break down—usually three to 10 months for relatively persistent herbicides (Meister, 1996).

Herbicide carryover damage to subsequent crops is a growing problem in all sectors of agriculture and triggers hundreds of lawsuits every year. The likelihood of trouble can be heightened by a variety of conditions, including a cold spring when microbial activity in the soil does not break down last season's herbicide residues to the expected extent (Ahrens and Fuerst, 1990). A 1995 poll asked 1,000 soybean producers what factors most often influenced their selection of herbicides. Possible rotational restrictions was the most frequent answer given (30 percent of those surveyed), followed by control of

> The new farm bill provides growers 100 percent flexibility to plant for the market. But now some commonly applied low dose herbicides impose a new sort of barrier to rotations—crop rotation restrictions on labels for up to 10 months and the fear of carryover injury to subsequent crops.

broadleaf weeds (29 percent) and effectiveness on herbicide tolerant weeds (21 percent) (*Farm Chemicals*, 1996).

The USDA's Natural Resources Conservation Service (NRCS) has announced plans to focus in the years ahead on helping landowners, farmers and communities establish grass filter strips along streams, rivers and lakes, and grass waterways on the landscape where needed to reduce gully erosion, improve water quality and enhance wildlife and stream habitat. The economic benefits of filter strips and grass waterways are well documented; such steps complement existing erosion control policies and programs. They work by trapping (i.e., filtering) sediment, nutrients and pesticides carried by surface water that runs off farm fields, especially after hard spring and early summer thunderstorms. Properly designed grass waterway and filter strip systems remove 70 to 90 percent of the sediment and nutrients in surface water runoff, and are among the most effective ways farmers can protect water quality and rebuild native fisheries (NRC, 1993b).

But their longevity, and hence cost-effectiveness will be jeopardized if farmers rely increasingly on low dose persistent herbicides and crop varieties genetically engineered to resist such persistent products. These changes in weed management technology will lead to additional and later-in-the-season applications of herbicides. Rainfall will wash some of the applied herbicide off the land and down slopes. Surface runoff containing herbicide residues will flow through and across grass waterways and filter strips, weakening, and in some instances killing the grass species that are most effective in waterways and filter strips.

Policy Enhances Reliance on Herbicides

Applying herbicides has emerged as the weed management technology of choice on most farms participating in government programs. Applying herbicides is indirectly encouraged by conservation policy and preferred by most farmers as a matter of convenience, cost and compatibility with large scale operations (see box).

In 1971, conservation tillage was used on less than 10 percent of acreage planted to corn or soybeans, and crop rotations of three years or longer were common (Anderson, 1994). Tillage and rotations carried a significant share of the weed control burden at the time. Farmers were, on average, about equally reliant on herbicides and cultural practices (rotations, tillage, cultivation) in managing weeds.

But the booming market years of the early 1970s and high prices led many farmers to bring thousands of acres of fragile soils into production and intensified production on land already in use. Erosion and the loss of soil quality worsened, as did pest pressure, particularly in areas where government programs underwrote intensification in land use patterns through monoculture (many acres of a genetically uniform crop) or irrigation in areas

with fragile soils and shallow water tables.

The farming bust in the early 1980s placed most farmers in serious financial jeopardy. Land prices collapsed and government program payments became a key to survival. Almost all eligible land was enrolled in commodity programs and their cost soared, peaking in 1986 at about $26 billion (Anderson, 1994). Subsequent cuts in agriculture's share of the federal budget have been from a baseline inflated during the mid-1980s to about twice the historical level of annual program spending.

To link receipt of payments to land stewardship, the 1985 farm bill included several key new provisions. The "swampbuster" and "sodbuster" provisions discouraged farmers from draining wetlands or plowing highly erodible land to expand production. "Conservation compliance" requires producers growing program crops on "highly erodible land" to meet erosion control goals, if they want to remain eligible for maximum government benefits. Most farmers meet their conservation compliance obligation by adopting conservation tillage systems that reduce the degree of soil disturbance so that more of the ground is covered by crop residues. Reducing tillage to control erosion can and often does make weed control harder because it limits tillage and management options. The result has been steadily higher reliance on herbicides.

In 1995, the majority of cultivated cropland in the Midwest was planted to corn or soybeans. USDA's 1994 Cropping Practices Survey collected data in the Midwest's top 10 producing states to determine the prior use of land

Conservation Tillage

Conservation tillage refers to a set of reduced tillage methods used to prepare cropland for planting. All types of tillage operations—moldboard plowing, off-set disking, chisel plowing—disturb the soil and bury a portion of crop residues. As tillage buries more of the residue left from the past season's crop, the surface of the soil becomes progressively more fully exposed to the erosive forces of wind and rain, and hence erosion risk and rates increase.

Conservation tillage systems minimize the depth and degree of tillage needed to prepare a seedbed for planting, and hence help sustain residue cover and reduce erosion losses. To meet government commodity program erosion control standards, farmers in most areas are required to retain a minimum 30 percent residue cover when planting highly erodible cropland.

The most extreme form of conservation tillage is "No-till," a planting system that requires no tillage at all. No-till planters are heavy and designed to cut through residue on the surface so that seeds can be planted through the residues left by the previous crop. In general but not in all situations, conservation tillage systems increase reliance on herbicides, especially if they stir up the soil just enough to bring weed seeds to the surface but not enough to bury any seeds left from the last crop season.

that was planted to corn in 1994 (USDA, 1995b): 21 percent was continuous corn since 1992, 48 percent was in corn-soybean two-year rotations, 10 percent was in longer corn-soybean rotations and 21 percent was managed with some other rotation, including 8 percent that was corn land idled as a requirement of the commodity programs.

About half of the acreage in corn and soybeans is now planted using some form of conservation tillage (USDA, 1995b; Anderson, 1994). Herbicides bear most of the weed control burden on a majority of farms producing crops covered by commodity price support programs.

The 1996 Farm Bill

The 1996 farm bill continues the trend toward greater flexibility for farmers. Its principal commodity program provisions include an end to individual crop base acreage allotments and fixed but declining payments that are not linked to the market. With a few exceptions, farmers are now free to plant whatever crops they feel offer the best chance for profits. Thirty years ago, such a change in policy would likely have triggered a return to more diversified rotations to recapture their agronomic and pest management benefits.

Today, most farmers are planning to take advantage of greater planting freedom by growing more of their most profitable crop. Specialization is likely to increase. Given recent and current policy, the agronomic and pest management benefits from more diverse rotations are likely to be outweighed by the economies of scale associated with highly specialized machinery and marketing infrastructure.

Pesticide and fertilizer use is bound to rise sharply in

> "A number of federal programs inhibit use of IPM, including the commodity programs, agricultural loans, defect action levels [levels set for insect parts and other detritus in food], and disaster assistance...marketing orders and water subsidies. Most of these programs either unintentionally or indirectly resulted in constraining IPM adoption by altering crop prices, input prices or the input mix."
>
> **The 1992 National IPM Forum Policy Team**
> *(Sorensen, 1992)*

1996 (and probably again in 1997) in most major farming areas in response to record high crop prices and growth in planted acreage. Corn acreage is expected to rise by about 10 million acres in 1996—an almost 14 percent increase from 1995. Wheat acreage is expected to rise by 2.6 million acres (USDA March 1996 "Prospective Plantings" report).

If the trend toward planting flexibility and a lessened role for government continues as prices and farm income fall, the cash production costs for fertilizers and pesticides will grow as a share of per acre gross income. This trend is evident on some Midwestern soybean farms in 1996, where more will be spent per acre on herbicides than any cost other than land (*Top Producer*, 1996).

The cost of herbicides in Iowa has risen steadily from less than 5 percent of non-land production costs in 1970 to about 25 percent today (Liebman and Gallandt, 1996). If soybean prices reach $7.50 a bushel in 1996, herbicide expenditures of $35.00 per acre would account for about 18 percent of net returns per acre (assuming a

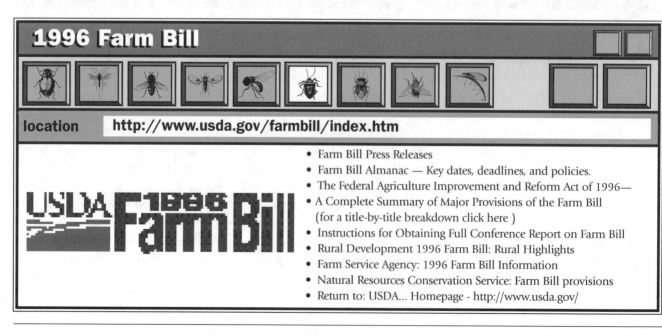

1996 Farm Bill

location http://www.usda.gov/farmbill/index.htm

USDA 1996 Farm Bill

- Farm Bill Press Releases
- Farm Bill Almanac — Key dates, deadlines, and policies.
- The Federal Agriculture Improvement and Reform Act of 1996—
- A Complete Summary of Major Provisions of the Farm Bill (for a title-by-title breakdown click here)
- Instructions for Obtaining Full Conference Report on Farm Bill
- Rural Development 1996 Farm Bill: Rural Highlights
- Farm Service Agency: 1996 Farm Bill Information
- Natural Resources Conservation Service: Farm Bill provisions
- Return to: USDA... Homepage - http://www.usda.gov/

40 bushel average per acre). But if prices slip back to recent levels—about $5.50 per bushel—herbicide costs would rise to around one-third of net returns per acre, which might stimulate interest in integrated weed management systems that lessen reliance on herbicides.

2. Shaping the Market—Grading and Cosmetic Standards

Commodity programs are not the only avenue through which policy influences farming systems. The government also impacts fruit and vegetable farmers, indirectly but significantly, through shaping access to and prices in the marketplace. USDA grading and quality standards, for example, have both created and reinforced consumer expectations for cosmetically "perfect" (unblemished) or near-perfect produce.

There are an array of cosmetic and grading standards, some set by the federal government, some by states and others by private sector marketing and retail organizations. "Defect action levels" are set by the federal Food and Drug Administration (FDA) and govern the allowable levels of pest parts in processed foods and produce headed for processing. States establish quality standards for marketing fresh produce, often in cooperation with grower groups. Through contracts with growers, food cooperatives, processors and retailers often set quality standards for produce, in addition to those imposed by government.

In California, state processing tomato grading standards allow up to 2 percent damage, but processors generally insist on zero percent damage. Some processors are considering accepting 0.5 percent damage as part of their efforts to promote IPM but are proceeding slowly because of concern among some in the industry that such a change might require more inspectors and slower line speeds in processing plants.

Growers sometimes impose quality and cosmetic standards on themselves through marketing orders approved by USDA, with compliance typically enforced by state departments of agriculture (see box). Sometimes these standards also play a role in restricting supply and enhancing prices. Top prices go to produce that is essentially free of any visible pest damage, even if the damage has no effect on taste or nutritional quality. In years when supplies are ample and prices low, inspectors sometimes become even stricter, trying to keep prices from declining further.

Unforgiving, excessively strict quality standards force farmers to leave nothing to chance, and most do what-

ever it takes to keep pest levels low and damage from occurring. Pesticides are a logical way for growers to hedge their investment and lower their risk of income loss. Those who lose income because of failure to make quality grades learn "it's better to be safe than sorry." As a result, additional late season pesticide applications are often made on fruit and vegetable crops (Olkowski and Olkowski, 1996). Farmers gain peace of mind at the expense of consumers and farm workers, since late season applications of insecticides and fungicides account for a large share of dietary and farm worker exposure to pesticides.

Marketing Orders

Marketing orders govern the supply, quality and price of many perishable fruits and vegetables, and strive to even out volatility in the production and marketing of perishable commodities. Marketing order quality standards typically encompass produce size, shape, ripeness, and freedom from defects such as disease scars or insect parts. Most orders include supply and marketing provisions designed to either directly set or influence prices and the pounds of produce sold into specific markets. Growers subject to orders often have production and marketing quotas which are adjusted periodically in response to supply and demand.

Federal law establishes a referendum process, whereby growers, food processors and others involved in the growing and marketing of food must come together, structure the terms of the order, and then gain its passage. Once an order is in place, grower-participants pay a small per pound check-off fee that finances order administration, advertising and often research. In the pest management arena, most marketing orders have focused on efforts to obtain additional pesticide registrations. But now some are financing pest management research committees focusing on IPM. A few have helped organize and finance cooperative research and demonstration projects that have successfully overcome barriers to progress along the IPM continuum (e.g., see Randall Island Project box in Chapter 1, pages 14-15).

C. Building and Sharing the Knowledge Base

By the mid-1960s, new fertilizer and pesticide technologies had begun to reshape the American landscape. Coupled with the mechanization of agriculture, pesticides made it possible for farmers to cover more ground and specialize in the production of one or a few crops. Herbicides freed farmers from time-consuming chores—cultivating row crops and hand weeding high value crops. Plant breeders and fertilizer technology pushed attainable yields upward. It was a time of optimism and change.

Most farmers, scientists and public officials saw no reason to look back. Yet as early as 1967, scientists were looking ahead to a third generation of pesticides based on highly specific biological control agents.[2] Dr. Carroll Williams, Professor of Biology at Harvard University, wrote in *Scientific American* (Williams, 1967):

> "Man's efforts to control harmful insects with pesticides have encountered two intractable difficulties….(they are) too broad in their effect … (and) insects have shown a remarkable ability to develop resistance to pesticides … Plainly the ideal approach would be to find agents (called 'Third Generation Pesticides') that are highly specific … Recent findings indicate the possibility of achieving success along these lines is much more likely than it seemed a few years ago. The central idea embodied in these findings is that a harmful species of insect can be attacked with its own hormones."

> *"Unfortunately, for the past fifty years most pest management research has centered on the development and use of pesticides."*
>
> **Pest Management in Iowa: Planning for the Future** *(Mayerfeld et al., 1996)*

1. USDA Pest Management Research

During the late 1950s and 1960s, publicly funded pest management research programs in USDA and land grant universities shifted focus. With few exceptions, less emphasis was placed on plant breeding for pest resistance, the ecology of plant-pest interactions and biological control strategies. Researchers invested progressively more effort in understanding pesticide modes of action; how to apply pesticides cheaply and effectively (rates, timing, methods); the compatibility of pesticides with various farming practices, soil types and technologies; pesticide environmental fate and toxicity; and impacts on non-target organisms.

Plant breeders spent more time and effort selecting for varieties that would respond to high levels of fertilization, dense plantings and other variables correlated with high yield potential (Robinson, 1996). Promising work in California on identifying nematode-resistant grape varieties was shelved in the 1960s because the soil fumigant ethylene dibromide worked so well and seemed so afford-

able. Work on alternative approaches like steam sterilization and microbial biocontrol was largely stopped as another highly toxic, broad spectrum soil fumigant—methyl bromide—gained near-universal adoption in high-value cropping systems (*IPM Practitioner*, 1994). The result was that farmers received progressively more information and assistance pointing them toward how to use pesticides; the flow of technical information, new technologies and improved systems incorporating non-chemical alternatives all but disappeared.

USDA Priorities

Deputy Secretary of Agriculture Richard Rominger has been the champion of IPM research and education in the Administration since 1993. During his presentation on February 27, 1996 at the Third National IPM Forum, the Deputy Secretary reported that USDA had committed about $135 million this year to IPM and pest management research and education. He predicted the Administration would seek a substantial IPM funding increase in its FY 1997 budget request, but correctly predicted a tough time convincing Congress to appropriate the additional funds. Chapter 8 includes a more detailed discussion of the USDA's recent IPM initiative budget requests and outcomes. Here we place into perspective the $125 to $135 million Congress has appropriated in recent years for IPM and pest management research and education. (Average annual average IPM research and education funding has been about $130 million since 1994, so this is the level of funding we use in the discussion that follows).

Federal IPM funding represents about 7.5 percent of the annual USDA science and education budget, which has totaled about $1.8 billion in recent years. In addition to these federal funds, states appropriate additional fund-

ing to land grant university and state agricultural experiment stations.[3] System-wide expenditures from both federal and state funding sources totaled $2.97 billion in FY 1993. Most of the support for IPM and pesticide-related research falls within the "crop" category which accounted for $1.03 billion of the $2.97 billion spent in FY 1993, according to data in the USDA's "Current Research Information System," or CRIS (USDA, 1994a). Other USDA funding supports research on pesticide risks and impacts and is reviewed in the box "USDA Research Also Focuses on Pesticide Risks."

IPM Initiative Funding

The federal IPM Initiative was announced in December of 1994, and was USDA's first agency-wide response to the President's June, 1993 pledge to gain IPM adoption on 75 percent of cropland acreage. The first requested increase in funding for IPM research and education was contained in the USDA's proposed FY 1995 budget sent to Congress in February, 1994.

In the USDA's 1994 budget summary, a special table appeared in the Appendix entitled "Selected Pesticide Related Activities." In each budget since, the USDA has updated this table, which is now called "Integrated Pest Management and Related Programs" (USDA, 1996a). This budget table (see Chapter 8) includes IPM research and education, plus "Related Programs" including pesticide use data collection, pest management programs carried out by the Animal and Plant Health Inspection Service (APHIS) and the Forest Service (FS), and pesticide registration, assessment and clearance programs.

Total IPM Initiative funding in 1994 and 1995, as reported in USDA budget summaries, was about $192 million, of which research and education totaled about

---

USDA Research Also Focuses on Pesticide Risks

In addition to sponsoring IPM research and education, pesticide risk and impacts research is carried out through several USDA programs, as well as other government agencies. We reviewed CRIS data on seven categories of USDA research projects assessing farm pollution; pesticide residues in food; farmer, applicator and farm worker safety; ecological impacts; and watershed management. USDA allocated about $158 million in federal funds to research in the seven categories reviewed, which include research on pesticides, fertilizers, sediment, heavy metal residues in food, watershed management to protect water quality and hazards to wildlife (USDA, 1994a). Based on review of project reports and budget documents, we estimate that about 40 percent of the overall research effort in these seven categories is largely focused on pesticide risks and impacts, or $63 million annually.

$130 million. In each fiscal year since, USDA has sought an increase in IPM research and education on the order of $14 million, but has been unable to convince Congress to appropriate increased funding.

FY 1997 Budget

The Administration's FY 1997 budget request proposed increasing USDA IPM research and education funding by $14.2 million to $145 million, as part of the National IPM Initiative. Increased funding would be split between new multidisciplinary IPM research team grants focusing on major crops and pests, and IPM extension education activities. The "Biological Control" program area would be restored within the competitive grants program.

> Congress again failed to appropriate the modest $14 million increase sought by the Administration in the FY 1997 budget for IPM research and education, but it did find ways to fund more than $50 million in research buildings and special grants not sought by the Administration. The National IPM Initiative has languished for four years because of Congressional priorities, not because of efforts to reduce the federal budget deficit.

In final action on the FY 1997 budget, Congress again failed to appropriate the modest increase sought by USDA. In its FY 1997 science and education budget proposal, USDA had sought two significant increases totaling $47 million—$14 million for the IPM Initiative and $33 million for the competitive research grants program. Neither was approved. Instead Congress used the money in the USDA's proposed budget to fund more than $25 million in buildings and facilities not requested by USDA, as well as much of $27 million in Special Grant projects also not requested. Hence, failure to appropriate increased funding

for IPM reflects different priorities in the USDA and in Congress, not the availability of funds or determination by the Congress to reduce the deficit.

The Focus of the IPM Initiative

We also assessed the kinds of activities funded by the IPM Initiative in the last three years. Within the $192 million commited to the Initiative, about $130 million is appropriated for IPM research and education, $40 million supports pesticide-based pest management activities in the field, and $22 million funds collection of data needed to assess pesticide use trends and risks, and gain new pesticide registrations.

We consulted with experts and assessed pest management and pesticide-related projects in the USDA's CRIS system to determine what portion of the $130 million devoted to IPM research and education is supporting work on the biological and ecological foundations for biointensive IPM, in contrast to chemical-based pest management systems. About half of the $130 million is spent on research designed principally to improve the efficiency or prolong the effectiveness of pesticide-intensive systems. This $65 million is invested in research on reduced rate pesticide application systems and equipment, interactions between pesticides and fertilizers that alter their environmental

National IPM Initiative FUNDING 1996

location http://www.nysaes.cornell.edu:80/ipmnet/init.factsht.html

TOTAL IPM INITIATIVE AND OTHER IPM-RELATED PROGRAMS BUDGET REQUEST
FY96 = $189.7 MILLION;
FY97 = $204.9 million, an increase of $15.1 million

- **IPM Initiative Budget Information**
- **Budget Requests for Other Ongoing IPM-Related Programs**
- **IPM Budget Request Totals**

- IPM and Biological Control Research (PL89-106 Special Research): (1997 budget request is $8.0 million, an increase of $5.3 million over 1996.)
- Pest Management Education (Smith-Lever 3(d)): (budget request is $15.0 million, an increase of $4.2 million over 1996.)
- National IPM Implementation Program: (1997 budget request is $4.5 million, an increase of $2.5 million)
- Areawide IPM Research: (1997 budget request is $6.0 million, an increase of $2.2 million)
- Economic Research Service (ERS) (1997 budget request is $0.5 million, no increase over 1996)

fate (and sometimes adversely impact soil microbial communities or plant growth patterns), resistance management, discovery of new pesticidal modes of action, techniques to use genetic engineering to produce crops tolerant of herbicides or expressing *Bt*, ways to limit adverse impacts on beneficials, and encapsulation and other new ways to formulate pesticides so they are less likely to leach to groundwater. None of these research endeavors supports the preventive practices that form the core of biointensive IPM.

The remaining $65 million focuses on tactics, methods, technologies and information needs that are more directly relevant to prevention-based IPM systems than to pesticide-based systems (see Chapter 7 for a discussion of the progressively more prevention-oriented practices needed to advance along the IPM continuum). Of this $65 million, about half focuses predominantly on "Low" or "Medium" level IPM tactics, practices and technologies, and the other half on steps and knowledge needed to progress into the biointensive, or "High" level along the continuum. Accordingly, we estimate that USDA is now investing only about $32.5 million annually to directly support biointensive IPM development and adoption. This level of funding is well under 20 percent of the $192 million in annual expenditures through the IPM Initiative, and is just 12.7 percent of total USDA

> If USDA's $64 billion annual budget were sliced into 2,000 equal pieces, one would represent biointensive IPM research and education funding—a meager investment given that about 30 percent of total U.S. agricultural production is still lost to pests and that rising reliance on pesticides poses serious risks to the environment and public health, as well as agricultural sustainability in some regions.

expenditures on all pest management, pesticide use and related risk research (this total is $255 million—$192 million through the IPM initiative and another estimated $63 million on pesticide risks and impacts [see earlier box]).

If USDA's $64 billion annual budget were sliced into 2,000 equal pieces, one would represent biointensive IPM research and education funding. All IPM research would be just two of 2,000 slices—a meager investment, considering that about 30 percent of total U.S. agricultural production is still lost to pests each year, that hard-to-control pests threaten the sustainability of agriculture in many regions and that rising reliance on pesticides poses serious risks to the environment and public health.

2. *Trends in the Focus of University Research*

Beginning in the 1960s, the chemical era of pest management unfolded with remarkable speed and unanimity. In response to recommendations from farm groups, professional societies and the pesticide industry, Congress pushed along the shift in research priorities from cultural and biological pest management to pesticide-based systems. This shift continued through most of the 1980s, as

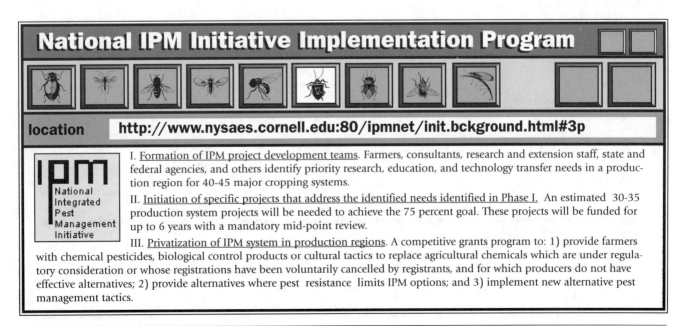

National IPM Initiative Implementation Program

location http://www.nysaes.cornell.edu:80/ipmnet/init.bckground.html#3p

IPM National Integrated Pest Management Initiative

I. Formation of IPM project development teams. Farmers, consultants, research and extension staff, state and federal agencies, and others identify priority research, education, and technology transfer needs in a production region for 40-45 major cropping systems.

II. Initiation of specific projects that address the identified needs identified in Phase I. An estimated 30-35 production system projects will be needed to achieve the 75 percent goal. These projects will be funded for up to 6 years with a mandatory mid-point review.

III. Privatization of IPM system in production regions. A competitive grants program to: 1) provide farmers with chemical pesticides, biological control products or cultural tactics to replace agricultural chemicals which are under regulatory consideration or whose registrations have been voluntarily cancelled by registrants, and for which producers do not have effective alternatives; 2) provide alternatives where pest resistance limits IPM options; and 3) implement new alternative pest management tactics.

is evident in a review of citations in technical and scientific literature published since the 1960s.

Two Texas A&M weed scientists analyzed worldwide weed management research priorities (Abernathy and Bridges, 1994). They found that herbicide-related citations accounted for almost 76 percent of the citations. Ecological or cultural approaches to weed management accounted for about 24 percent. The largest category was herbicide activity/selectivity/efficacy, accounting for slightly less than 39 percent of total citations.

We carried out analyses of the USDA's Agricola database of research articles and reports focusing on weed management (reported later), entomology and plant pathology research from the early 1970s to the 1990s (see Tables 6.1 and 6.2). To assess research priorities and trends over time, citations in the Agricola database were analyzed in two-year periods, at five-year intervals beginning in 1970-1971, and then 1975-1976, 1980-1981 and so on to 1993-1994, the last period when complete Agricola records were available. We used total citations in two-year periods to limit the chance that unusually high or low levels of citations in a given year would skew the results. Results show that entomologists and plant

> "We strongly recommend that the U.S. Department of Agriculture and the State Agricultural Experiment Stations (SAES) support and encourage additional application of contemporary theory in population biology and ecosystem analysis to pest control problems; and, reciprocally, that the USDA, SAES, and other mission-oriented agencies with responsibilities in pest control support and encourage further interactions between theory development and applied research in pest control."
>
> "We recommend that the agencies concerned with pest control problems recognize their dual responsibility to the support of basic research on ecosystem dynamics and the biology of pest organisms, and to the training of the pest management specialists who will be needed to guide growers in the application of new knowledge."
>
> **Pest Control: An Assessment of Present and Alternative Technologies** *The Report of the Executive Committee (NRC, 1975)*

pathologists have been less focused on insecticides and fungicides than weed scientists have been on herbicides, and that the number of citations in all three disciplines

Table 6.1 Entomology Research Priorities Evident in Research Article Citations

	1970-71	1975-76	1980-81	1985-86	1990-91	1993-94	Total 1970-94
Insects: Total Citations*	3,522	4,631	4,182	6,677	5,992	3,840	28,844
Control Approach							
Insecticides	339	512	768	1,133	897	549	4,198
IPM	0	7	117	192	184	125	625
Biological Control	146	291	299	1,140	1,004	528	3,408
Tactics⁺							
Economic Thresholds	0	1	0	4	16	18	39
Mating Disruption	0	0	31	28	23	19	101
Pheromones/Semiochemicals	0	0	16	12	23	19	70
Bacillus thuringiensis	115	190	281	337	375	287	1,585
IGR/Juvenile Hormones	121	373	285	241	228	195	1,443
Host Plant Resistance	0	6	13	13	17	5	54
Natural Enemies	0	0	9	11	107	104	231

Source: Agricola Citations, 1970-1994.

* The number of citations involving insects far exceeds the number of citations to all control approaches and tactics because of the popularity of insects as experimental models for genetics research and other types of research advancing basic biological sciences.

⁺ Some articles address multiple tactics and control strategies, in addition to the use of insecticides. Therefore, some articles may appear under multiple categories.

Table 6.2 Plant Pathology Research Priorities Evident in Research Article Citations

	1970-71	1975-76	1980-81	1985-86	1990-91	1993-94	Total 1970-94
Plant Diseases or Pathogens: Total Citations	255	416	505	2,234	1,267	930	5,607
Control Approach							
Fungicides	167	280	725	798	405	264	2,639
IPM	0	0	2	22	25	31	80
Biological Control	2	18	22	131	211	115	499
Tactics+							
Rotations	1	4	3	8	24	82	122
Antagonists	18	30	49	152	287	286	822
Antibiosis	5	11	6	19	58	35	134
Population Dynamics	88	133	249	995	690	361	2,516

Source: Agricola Citations, 1970-1994.

+ Some articles describe multiple tactics and control strategies, and thus some articles may appear under multiple categories.

peaked in the mid-1980s and have declined appreciably since. This decline roughly tracks reductions in the number of scientists working in these fields (NRC, 1989b).

Out of 28,844 citations on insects, just 4,198 involved insecticides. The number of citations involving insects far exceeds the number of citations for all insect pest control approaches and tactics because of the popularity of insects as experimental models for genetics, physiological and other types of research advancing basic biological sciences. In terms of insect pest management tactics, there were about 6.7 articles involving insecticides for each one citing IPM. Through the early 1980s there were about two citations on insecticides for each one on biological control, but since then the focus on biological control has been comparable in terms of numbers of citations. Articles involving *Bt* account for about one-third of all articles on insecticides.

Less than 50 percent of citations involving plant disease or plant pathogens also involved fungicides. Major focuses of plant pathology research include antagonists and population dynamics—both critical areas in develop-

> Budget cuts and the redirection of funding to microbiology and genetic engineering in the early 1990s led the University of California to dismantle its Division of Biological Control, for years one of the nation's premier centers conducting biointensive IPM research.

ing biointensive IPM systems. There has been some erosion in focus and funding on classical biological control of plant pathogens and non-chemical control options since the early 1990s. In the mid-1980s there were almost 1,000 citations over a two-year period involving population dynamics but by 1993-1994, the number of citations had dropped to 361. Biological control citations dropped by almost half from a peak in 1990-1991 to 1993-1994.

Comparable reductions are evident in insect pest management research—biological control citations peaked in 1985-1986 at 1,140 and dropped to 528 in 1993-1994. These steep reductions are a reflection of changing funding priorities and levels. In order to redirect resources to microbiology and biotechnology, applied field pest management and biocontrol research have been cut deeply at most institutions. One of the telling consequences of this shift was the decision a few years ago by the University of California to dismantle the Division of Biological Control, one of the nation's premier research centers of excellence on biointensive IPM.

3. Collecting and Sharing Information

Biointensive IPM is information intensive. Research must unravel the details of pest ecology and how farming systems impact pests, beneficials, crops and their interactions. But then, additional data and effort are needed to deliver information to field practitioners in forms tailored to meet their specific needs. Pests and beneficials must be properly identified and their numbers monitored over time. Pest levels and potential damage must be evaluated relative to stages and rates of crop growth and development.

And then the key step—and looming challenge—real time pest, crop stage and beneficial organism data collected in the field on a Tuesday morning must somehow be interpreted and translated into control recommendations if populations are over thresholds, ideally with the benefit of all existing information and experience, in time to guide actions needed Wednesday, if not Tuesday afternoon. Information on IPM systems and tactics that cannot be brought to bear quickly in such situations is not of much value to the field practitioner.

Meeting such real time biointensive IPM information needs will place new demands on cooperative extension agents, crop consultants and others working to give pest managers the information they need. The focus of agri-

> **The key hurdle for IPM practitioners is integrating real time field data collected on a Tuesday morning with all existing knowledge about the crop, its pests and their interactions to craft control actions needed on Wednesday, if not Tuesday afternoon.**

cultural extension agents, in particular, will need to change since, according to the National Research Council's study on ecologically based pest management, "Historically, extension agents focused predominantly on recommendations using pesticides…"(NRC, 1996). Since pesticide-based systems were receiving the most attention from researchers and farmers, extension followed suit.

Two overall trends seem inevitable—funding for cooperative extension will continue to lag far behind need, and second, the role of independent crop consultants working for growers and others in need of pest management services is bound to grow. In response to these trends, cooperative extension is likely to play an increasingly important role as a link between research scientists and crop consultants and other field level practitioners delivering IPM services. This change in the role for extension has implications for the skills extension agents will need in the future.

Another important insight has emerged in the last decade from experiences around the world in developing and promoting adoption of IPM systems. Farmers and other pest managers possess valuable experience which, when systematically tapped and shared with other farmers and pest managers seeking solutions to similar pest problems, can rapidly accelerate progress along the IPM continuum. This suggests another new role for marketing

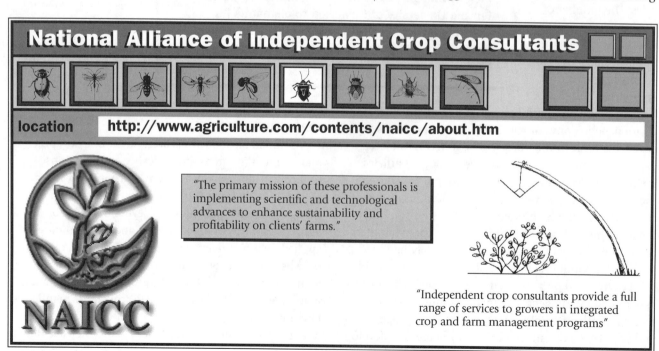

National Alliance of Independent Crop Consultants

location http://www.agriculture.com/contents/naicc/about.htm

"The primary mission of these professionals is implementing scientific and technological advances to enhance sustainability and profitability on clients' farms."

NAICC

"Independent crop consultants provide a full range of services to growers in integrated crop and farm management programs"

orders, food processors and cooperative extension—organizing and facilitating opportunities for farmers and other pest managers to come together and share ideas about how to overcome hurdles that arise in implementing biointensive IPM solutions.

First Things First

Correct pest identification prior to taking action, especially prior to applying a toxic pesticide, is central to the success of biointensive IPM. Government, product suppliers, consultants and retailers need to tackle this need first, and as a matter of some urgency.

Because pests are constantly evolving ways around the control measures used against them, pest managers need up-to-date information on the strains of pests in a population, the emergence and levels of resistance to commonly applied pesticides, if any, and information about key beneficials or other tactics that could play a role in control. Often, sophisticated taxonomic skills and equipment are needed to make such identifications and to run assays checking resistance.

Below-ground pests and plant pathogens can be especially tricky to identify and understand. Some problems will be traced to imbalance in the relative numbers of microorganisms in the soil, rather than the absence or presence of a given species. Developing, refining and applying such diagnostic techniques will remain a key

role for extension pest management specialists. Efficiently transferring these techniques to the field will require new methods, strategies and more funding.

In urban and other settings, "do-it-yourself" pest managers often need help identifying pests. New tools are emerging to help. The Virginia Polytechnic Institute (VPI) Department of Entomology has developed a fun and informative "Household and Structural Pest Identification" system (see web page boxes on pages 40 and 41). Accessible with a World Wide Web (WWW) browser, it starts, for example, with simple questions like—Does Your Pest Fly or Crawl? Too Tiny to Tell? Four Legs or Eight Legs?—and progresses through a series of easy to understand queries and graphics that make it possible to quickly and accurately identify most common pests.

Once the species is identified, the user clicks on the name to get basic information about the pest's life cycle, habitat needs, the type of damage it can cause, control alternatives, interesting facts and where to get more information or help. To alert people to the availability of such systems, USDA and states should provide assistance and modest funding to libraries, schools, veterinarian offices, pest control business offices, and other places that already have the basic hardware and software needed to use the WWW. Retailers should be encouraged to make such systems available in stores selling consumer pesticide products, just as many drugstores now offer

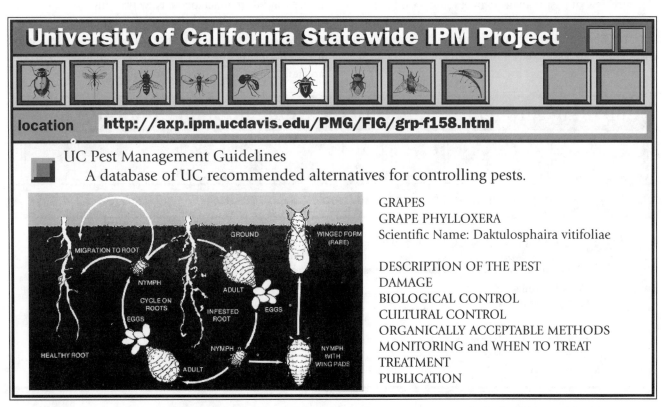

consumers access to computer terminals with either CD-ROM or Internet access to information about drugs, health problems and treatment options. Good print pest management resources also exist and can supplement information accessible over the Internet (e.g., *Pest Control for Home and Garden* [Hansen, 1993], the *IPM Practitioner* and *Common Sense Pest Control* published by the Bio-Integral Resource Center [Olkowski et al., 1991]).

Tapping the Internet

Many valuable sources of IPM information available on the Internet are featured in the World Wide Web boxes displayed throughout this book. Much of the potential of the Internet is yet to be realized because databases needed to help pest managers deal with many common management decisions have not yet been compiled. For example, regional information systems and services could provide up-to-date information on pest status, levels of resistance, control options and the effectiveness of alternative methods. Nearly all pest managers would benefit from basic data on pesticide properties and toxicity, environmental fate, and toxicity to beneficial organisms. Once such data systems are developed, they can be drawn upon and adapted to address many other situations. The capacity to do so raises an interesting new set of issues regarding ownership, control and the sharing of information.

A review of pest management resources on land grant university WWW sites displays a bias toward insects. There is relatively little information on plant diseases and even less on weed management. By its nature, the WWW makes it easy for users to move from one information system and database to another. There is no need for 50 land grant entomology departments to develop slightly different taxonomic identification tools and pest life cycle descriptions. Everyone needs such taxonomic resources but their development, refinement and upkeep needs to be a more cooperative and shared system-wide activity.

The resources now being used to develop largely duplicative sources of the same information could be invested in compiling new information. The lack of information on non-chemical weed management options needs to be rectified by USDA as a first priority, given the need across much of the Midwest to reduce reliance on herbicides (see the box "Focus on Non-Chemical Weed Management Alternatives"). Information on pesticide impacts on beneficials, performance of forecasting models and trends in resistance are among the topics well-suited to dissemination through the Internet.

In the past extension agents have drawn mostly upon published experiment station reports based on replicated field trials carried out on research farms—a one-dimensional and expensive way to generate new information and insights about commercial farming and pest management systems. Today, most of the innovation in pest management is occurring on farms. It is brought about by the day-to-day efforts of farmers, consultants, academics and others who are cooperatively working toward better ways to manage pests. New ways are needed to tap this enormous well of onfarm innovation. Doing so can greatly accelerate the generation of new knowledge, refine ideas and test novel approaches to pest management, accelerating progress along the IPM continuum.

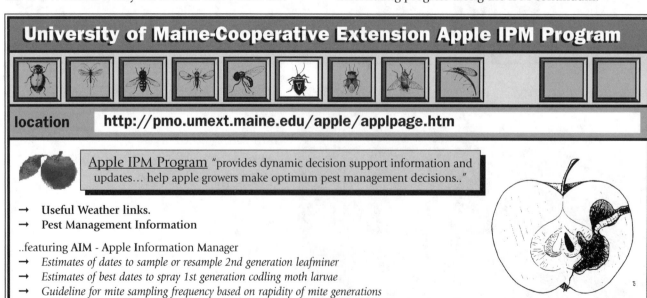

University of Maine-Cooperative Extension Apple IPM Program

location http://pmo.umext.maine.edu/apple/applpage.htm

Apple IPM Program "provides dynamic decision support information and updates... help apple growers make optimum pest management decisions.."

→ Useful Weather links.
→ Pest Management Information

..featuring AIM - Apple Information Manager
→ *Estimates of dates to sample or resample 2nd generation leafminer*
→ *Estimates of best dates to spray 1st generation codling moth larvae*
→ *Guideline for mite sampling frequency based on rapidity of mite generations*

Focus on Non-Chemical Weed Management Alternatives

Consultants, extension agents and other IPM experts draw upon a common knowledge base in guiding growers on alternatives to pesticides. Reliance on herbicides has grown steadily since the 1960s for several reasons—convenience, cost-effectiveness, growth in the average size of farm, incentives for conservation tillage, promotional efforts by manufacturers and the lack of serious effort in developing non-chemical alternatives.

Table 6.3 surveys trends in weed science research priorities as evident in citations in the USDA's Agricola database. Throughout the 24 years surveyed less than 20 percent of the articles addressing weeds involved control strategies other than herbicides. While starting from a low base, the number of citations on common cultural practices like rotations, tillage, cultivation and cover crops has risen gradually over the whole period from 3.2 percent of citations to weeds, to 14.5 percent in 1993-1994. Still, the dominace of research on herbicides is striking.

Table 6.3 Change Over Time in Weed Management Research Priorities, Agricola Citations, 1970-1971 through 1993-1994

	1970-71	1975-76	1980-81	1985-86	1990-91	1993-94	Total
Weeds*	1,528	2,552	3,352	2,825	2,692	1,526	14,485
Herbicides*	1,438	2,515	2,725	2,209	2,089	1,212	12,188
- as % of Weeds	94.1%	98.5%	81.3%	78.2%	77.6%	78.9%	84.1%
Reduced Chemical Control Approach+							
Weeds and Tillage	8	26	60	115	135	92	436
Rotations and Weeds	10	23	46	39	58	49	225
Mechanical Cultivation	3	7	10	0	2	4	26
Rotary Hoe	0	4	2	2	2	0	10
Weeds and Cultivation	24	24	8	66	38	37	197
Weeds and Mulch	4	4	5	10	10	10	41
Weeds and Cover Crops	0	2	0	21	50	30	103
Total Alternatives	49	88	131	253	295	222	1,038
- as % of Weeds	3.2%	3.5%	3.9%	9.0%	11.0%	14.5%	7.2%

Source: Compiled by BCS from Agricola Citations, 1970-1994.
* Total number of citations that include the word "weed" or "weeds," some of which address weed physiology, genetics and impacts without any reference to control options or herbicide use.
+ Some articles address multiple control approaches and so the total number of citations to control approaches exceeds the number of articles.

The contrast in research on herbicides and non-chemical methods is striking:

■ "Mechanical cultivation," "rotary hoe" and "weeds and cultivation" accounted for 233 citations over the six periods studied—about 1 citation for every 52 involving herbicides.

■ Rotary hoeing accounted for only six citations since the end of the 1970s.

■ "Mulch" and "cover crops" accounted for 117 citations—less than one for each 100 on herbicides.

> *"As one looks back, the meshing of university research, universtiy extension, industrial research, and crop producers to introduce chemical weed control, is a model for propellling new technology into the mainstrean of society…Most of the resources devoted to herbicide research have been used to develop and evaluate herbicide effectiveness, and only a limited amount of resources has been devoted to research on the effect of herbicides on agriculture and the environment, non-chemical weed control, and weed ecology…Non-chemical methods of weed control have not been researched extensively for almost 30 years."*
>
> **Dr. Don Wyse,** *University of Minnesota*
> *"The Future of Weed Science" (Wyse, 1992)*

In the future both the generation and sharing of pest management and IPM system information should become more open, cooperative and interactive. It should draw upon all of agriculture's innovators, not just those working for research institutions. Sharing analytical tasks and information management and dissemination activities across state and institutional lines has always proven difficult in the agricultural research community. Such sharing and collaboration is much easier using the tools of the Internet and will produce more valuable networks of information and decision support systems. Perhaps most important, such steps will help reconnect USDA and extension IPM specialists with the general public seeking practical help managing pests.

The Role of Crop Consultants

One of the many reasons that farmers use crop consultants and pest control advisors (PCAs) is to gather field-specific information that can be used in "real time" as the cropping season progresses. In most states, including California, the majority of scouts and PCAs derive most of their income from companies selling or applying pesticides. Bonuses often are linked to the volume of pes-

> *"We'd expect industry to concentrate on herbicide development because of the profit motive. And when public sector scientists also jumped on the herbicide bandwagon, we created a lop-sided weed management system in the U.S. But now it's time to regroup and develop alternatives … Weed control should move from a largely chemical approach to a systems approach …The one thing I have learned from 35 years of weed research is that there's no panacea weed control method."*
>
> **Dr. Orvin Burnside,** *University of Minnesota*[4]

ticide and fertilizer sales in a season.

Many PCAs realize that IPM can reduce pesticide use and grower costs and improve the safety conditions for workers in the field. But some PCAs are reluctant to become IPM experts or base their advice to grower-clients on IPM because of the impact it would have on pesticide sales and their employer's profitability:

> "In fact, one long-time PCA admitted that he could not afford to participate in a [IPM] monitoring program that encouraged pesticide reduction, since he depended on pesticide sales to stay in business" (Olkowski and Olkowski, 1996).

The need to sever this link has been a recurrent political issue in California and a few other states. The importance of independence from income based on product sales led the nation's primary professional association of crop consultants to call itself the National Alliance of **Independent** Crop Consultants (NAICC). In the early 1990s, NAICC went through a two-year process defining what the term "Independent" means and specifying criteria to evaluate new voting members. The key requirement is independence from any income directly connected to the sale of a product as a result of a pest management recommendation made to a client.

Advertising and the Struggle for Market Share

Consultants and cooperative extension are not the only sources of information farmers receive on pest management alternatives. Indeed, the most frequently encountered form of information in major farming regions is pesticide product advertising. The corn-soybean herbicide market is where pesticide companies have invested most heavily in the discovery and registration of new active ingredients. As a result, competition is fierce. Advertising expenditures have risen and product guarantee and respray programs have been used as marketing tools (see Chapter 2).

The extent of pesticide advertising in farm magazines—the majority for herbicides—is remarkable during the late winter and early spring months. In nine issues of *Top Producer* magazine, full-page pesticide advertisements accounted for slightly less than 44 percent of the total pages in each issue. Table 6.4 presents data on 26 issues of farm magazines published in 1995 and 1996. Only full-page advertisements were counted, so the table somewhat understates total pesticide advertising content.

Agricom, a Missouri-based company, compiles information annually on total pesticide industry print advertising.[5] In 1994, pesticide manufacturers spent

> *"Although farmers may be skeptical about specific advertising claims, the fact remains that for most farmers, much if not most of the information they see and hear about pesticides is in the form of advertising or advice from chemical dealers."*
>
> **Pest Management in Iowa: Planning for the Future** (*Mayerfeld et al., 1996*)

$54 million on all agrichemical print advertising, which includes generic "feel good" advertisements as well as those for service centers. Herbicide advertising expenditures were estimated at $32.1 million, insecticide ads at $9.7 million and fungicide ads at $3.6 million. Advertisements for the biopesticide *Bt* totaled $992,180, well above Bt's approximate 3 percent market share among all insecticides (Gianessi, 1995b).

Agricom's estimate is similar to the pesticide industry's. The American Crop Protection Association (ACPA) 1995 *Industry Profile* reports print advertising expenditures in 1994 of $61.6 million. Pesticide companies spent $35.5 million in 1995 on television advertising, $34.2 million on the radio, and also sent most commercial scale farmers several mailings each year, costing more than $27 million annually (ACPA, 1996). These typically include detailed product performance information, testimonials from regional land grant university specialists and information on sales promotions and incentives. Another $29.7 million is spent on point-of-purchase promotional literature, bonuses and incentive programs for major customers.

Total advertising expenditures grew 2 percent in 1995, reaching $246 million. Expenditures on television

advertising dropped $9.35 million, down almost 21 percent from the year before. Expenditures in the category "Product Publicity and Public Relations" rose $5.3 million—an almost 30 percent increase.

In addition to the $246 million spent on advertising and promotional mailings, pesticide industry in-house advertising personnel account for an estimated $11.1 million in expenditures and market research, another $28.5 million (ACPA, 1996). Total advertising and marketing expenditures are about $285 million—more than twice what USDA spends on all pest management research and education and almost nine times what USDA spends on biointensive IPM research.

D. Genetic Engineering and Biointensive IPM

Biotechnology gives scientists powerful new methods to identify, isolate, understand and manipulate the genetic traits of plants, animals and microorganisms. It offers new tools for enhancing a plant's ability to defend itself and grow vigorously. Genetic engineering could help raise the economic threshold level for pest populations before pesticide treatments are warranted, and in some crops for some pests, might help eliminate the need for pesticide applications altogether, at least in most years.

Unfortunately, this potential is largely unrealized to date. More than half of the biotechnology field trials approved by USDA since 1987 have involved breeding herbicide tolerant plant varieties (30 percent of total releases) or transgenic plants that manufacture their own insecticides (21 percent) (Kaiser, 1994). These biotechnology applications are intended to improve the efficiency and

Table 6.4 Space Devoted to Pesticide Advertising in Major Farm Magazines

Magazine (Number of Issues)	Average Number Pages per Issue	Average Advertising Pages per Issue Total	Pesiticides	Full Page Pesticides as % of Total Pages
California Farmer (4)	86	25	11	12.8%
Farm Journal (9)	59	19	7	11.9%
Top Producer (9)	64	36	28	43.8%
Wallaces Farmer (4)	83	25	13	15.7%
All Issues (26)	73	26	15	20.5%

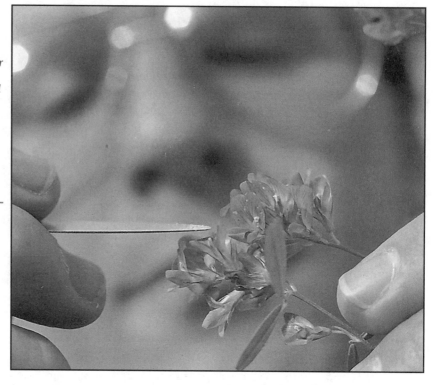

University of Wisconsin postdoctoral researcher David Johnson is working with plant pathologist Dr. Robert Goodman to identify plant genes that enhance the affinity between roots and beneficial soil microorganisms. According to Goodman, "Our ultimate goal is to breed varieties whose roots will be a 'magnet,' attracting and supporting beneficial microbes that are already present in the soil" (Gallepp, 1994). If such genes can be identified, cloned and moved into commercial cultivars, breeders may attain a wholly new mechanism to help plants protect themselves. Here, David Johnson is hand pollinating alfalfa.
Credit: Wolfgang Hoffman

range of applicability of chemical-dependent pest management systems. Pesticide manufacturers have invested heavily in these technologies, not simply because of their potential to lessen pest pressure, but primarily to preserve or expand pesticide market share, especially for proprietary products and technologies.

There is much less commercial interest in using biotechnology to help identify and refine microbial biocontrol processes and opportunities. Many natural compounds are known to play a role in microbial biocontrol and in triggering or strengthening plant defense mechanisms. But just a few have been characterized and studied in depth. Biotechnology is making it easier to take advantage of these compounds. Novel compounds produced by plants or microorganisms have been discovered that act like pesticides or antibiotics. For example, a University of Wisconsin research team has identified a previously unknown antibiotic, Zwittermicin A, produced by a common strain of the soil microorganism *Bacillus cereus* (Stabb et al., 1994). This *Bacillus cereus* strain helps suppress "damping off" in alfalfa, a root disease caused by *Phytophthora medicaginis,* and shows promise in suppressing similar root diseases in soybeans and other major crops (Osburn et al., 1995).

> Genetic engineering could help raise the economic threshold level for pest populations before pesticide treatments are warranted and might help eliminate the need for some pesticide applications all together. Unfortunately this potential is largely unrealized.

Once isolated and understood, such natural compounds could have several uses in pest management systems. One approach is to engineer plants to "supercharge" their existing natural defense mechanisms. Another involves altering the flow and composition of root exudates—the waste products plants return to the soil through their roots—in ways that favor beneficial soil microorganisms. A third is to produce seed treatments or biopesticides that alter the composition of microbial communities in ways that disadvantage damaging pathogens (Gilbert et al., 1993; Bezdicek and Granatstein, 1989).

While exciting possibilities have been discovered in laboratory experiments, much work must be done to improve the reliability of these approaches in the field. The vast majority of soil microorganisms—some scientists think well over 99 percent—have not been identified. Little is known about how they interact with other organisms and roots, or how these interactions influence pathogen pressure, the attractiveness of plants to insects and the vigor of plant defense mechanisms (Dr. Jo Handelsman, personal communication). But this knowledge is slowly building and new techniques drawing upon biotechnology are speeding the process of discovery and lowering its costs. These advances will greatly broaden the science base for microbial biocontrol strategies in the context of biointensive IPM.

In the future, pest managers are likely to pursue microbial biocontrol in several ways simultaneously. These may include altering the mix and competitiveness of species within indigenous microbial communities, applying specially produced composts and other soil amendments, planting varieties which have affinity for certain beneficial microorganisms, and use of seed inoculants, including some engineered to be more competitive in the typically hostile environment in the soil.

> About half the biotechnology applications approved by USDA to date that are relevant to pest management involve herbicide tolerant plant varieties. Pesticide manufacturers have invested heavily in these technologies to preserve or expand sales of proprietary herbicides.

1. Bt-Transgenic Plants

Bacillus thuringiensis (Bt) biopesticides are the foundation of lepidopteran insect pest management systems on many large and small commercial vegetable and fruit farms as well as on most organic farms. These biopesticides are produced by bacteria. They work by eroding the lining in the insect gut. *Bt* is formulated into several foliar insecticides that are sprayed much like conventional insecticides. They are among the safest insecticides on the market, breaking down quickly and posing almost no risk to farm workers, applicators and non-target organisms (except other lepidopteran species). These advantages of *Bt* insecticides triggered interest in the private sector once a method was found to introduce genetic material that codes for *Bt* endotoxin.

Bt-transgenic plants are engineered to produce *Bt* endotoxin systemically (inside the plant) at high enough levels to control feeding insects. The *Bt* toxin is produced in nearly all growing tissues of transgenic plants, regardless of whether pests have reached economic threshold levels; they are the genetic-engineering equivalent of calendar spraying. *Bt*-transgenic plants violate one of the key ecological principles underlying IPM. They are bound to accelerate the emergence of resistance to *Bt*, reducing the effectiveness of this safe biopesticide and possibly forcing farmers to return to using more hazardous carbamate and organophosphate insecticides. Companies developing and marketing *Bt*-transgenic plants have proposed management schemes to slow the emergence of resistance, but there are little or no data to indicate that these plans will succeed.

Independent pest management experts have raised serious doubts over *Bt*-transgenic plant resistance management strategies and efficacy (Gould, 1991; Harris, 1991). Some are skeptical that farmers will adhere to the complex restrictions required governing where, how and how often transgenic varieties can be planted (Kennedy and Whalon, 1995).

A Cornell scientist who has worked for years developing *Bt*-transgenic plants commented to the EPA concerning a pending application from Ciba Corporation to field test "Event 176," a *Bt*-transgenic corn variety approved in 1995 and now in commercial use:

> "Ciba's assessment of the risk of resistance is incomplete and underestimates potential problems … I am alarmed at the prospect that *Bt*-transgenic corn could reach the marketplace without some restrictions on use.
>
> "Pest resurgences due to pesticide use are a common phenomenon. With nearly 80 million acres of corn production in the U.S., unbridled use of *Bt* corn could potentially lead to a resurgence of European corn borers on a geographic scale unprecedented in history."[6]

> *"First, resistance is inevitable … If Bt toxins are simultaneously deployed against Helicoverpes in cotton, corn, and sorghum, I predict perhaps 25 to 75 generations (3 to 9 years) will elapse before resistance renders the technology useless."*
>
> **Dr. Marvin Harris, Entomology Research Laboratory Texas A&M University** (*Harris, 1991*)

> *"Thousands of acres of cotton bioengineered to make its own insecticide have fallen victim to cotton bollworms, one of three pests that the crops were supposed to kill…the result … has revived calls for tougher federal biosafety regulations … says Fred Gould 'no entomologist was really surprised' by the Bt cotton failure."*
>
> *"… the reasons behind the disappointing results serve as a reminder to researchers that Mother Nature still has a few tricks up her sleeve."*
>
> **Jocelyn Kaiser,** *Science, July 26, 1996*

> *"I am concerned about the development of resistance to* Bt *engineered plants."*
>
> **Dr. Mark Atwood, American Cyanamid Company**
>
> *Speaking before the American Crop Protection Association's Spring 1996 conference*[7]

Experience in the field in 1996 confirms that *Bt*-transgenic plants are already accelerating *Bt* resistance in insect populations. Many thousand acres of transgenic cotton have required insecticide applications because of either uneven or inadequate production of the *Bt* endo-toxin in plant tissues. In regions where conventional *Bt* formulations are relied upon, newly resistant strains of insects will more quickly develop higher levels of resistance, requiring more frequent applications and hastening the day when *Bt* products of any sort are no longer effective. Many other insects that feed on *Bt*-transgenic crop varieties are bound to gain *Bt* resistance faster than they otherwise would, now that EPA has approved widespread use of several such varieties.

> The rapid increase in the number of herbicide resistant weeds should prompt farmers to reconsider the wisdom of planting herbicide tolerant plants. Regulation and resistance are likely to lessen the number of triazine (i.e. atrazine and cyanazine) and acetanilide (i.e. alachlor, metolachlor and acetochlor) herbicides available for widespread use.

Plants genetically engineered to produce *Bt* toxins may prove to be a short-lived application of biotechnology. The inevitable loss of the *Bt*-susceptible gene pool in common lepidopteran insects will markedly increase reliance on and use of more toxic materials and set back long-overdue efforts to reduce pesticide residue levels in food and water. This in turn could undermine farmer and public confidence in biotechnology.

By helping identify and understand genetic traits and interactions among organisms, biotechnology could play a much more important role than it has so far in support of biointensive pest management strategies. But for that to happen, R&D priorities will need to shift to emphasize ecologically grounded, systems-based pest management strategies rather than maximizing short-term profits from sales of proprietary pesticide-based technologies.

2. Herbicide Tolerant Plants

Herbicides are the pesticide industry's growth sector. The quantity of herbicide active ingredient applied per planted acre grew from 0.28 pounds in 1964 to 0.93 pounds just seven years later. Use is now about 1.6 pounds per acre. Chapter 2 presents more detailed information on herbicide use and reliance.

A new generation of low dose sulfonylurea and imidazolinone corn and soybean herbicides have gained significant market share in recent years. These pesticides are highly active biologically and tend to be persistent—two reasons why a fraction of an ounce per acre (or even much less) can control weeds as effectively as 1.5 pounds of older products. But this combination of properties—high activity and persistence—can spell trouble with carryover damage to nearby or subsequent rotational crops. For this reason, product labels often contain explicit instructions and limitations on use to protect rotational crops.

Some new herbicides also react in unexpected ways if the water used to mix the products is too acid, especially if insecticides are also included in tank-mixes. Some become more active, others degrade and become ineffective. While these herbicides can work well when all conditions are right, when they are not these products can be unforgiving for farmers, turf managers or those living near where they have been applied.

These products are generally far less toxic to mammals than older herbicides, and the switch to them should reduce human health risks, to the extent we understand them. The largest reduction in risks should be brought about by less exposure through drinking water to older herbicides like atrazine and alachlor. But other risks will rise, including impacts on aquatic ecosystems and the economic and ecological risks borne by farmers and others who apply these new herbicides.

To solve the problem of carryover injury in corn-soybean rotations, a number of herbicide manufacturers with new products registered for soybean application are working to develop herbicide tolerant corn varieties. Herbicide tolerant corn is needed to reduce the chance of carryover damage to corn grown in rotation with soybeans—the Midwest's most common crop rotation. Other companies have pursued herbicide tolerant plant varieties so that broad-spectrum herbicides can be sprayed "over the top."

Approval already has been granted for a number of herbicide tolerant transgenic plant varieties, and companies are now marketing seed-herbicide "packages of technology." More are scheduled to reach the market within the next few years, despite the rapid spread of resistance to the sulfonylurea herbicides. The recent discovery of a first-ever ("not possible") glyphosate-resistant weed species in Australia should prompt farmers to reconsider the wisdom and sustainability of these technologies (see Chapter 2 for more discussion of herbicide resistant weeds). Regulation and resistance are, by the turn of the century, likely to markedly reduce the number of older herbicides accessible for routine use (EPA, 1996g). The problems posed by resistance and the "escape" of herbicide tolerance genes from crops to related weeds are discussed further in Chapter 8, in the context of EPA's evolving "plant pesticide" policies.

Most pesticide industry R&D has focused on developing crop varieties tolerant to glyphosate and aceto-hydroxyacid synthase (AHAS) inhibitors. AHAS is a key enzyme unique to plants and necessary for the production of several essential amino acids. Twelve pesticide manufacturers have commercialized herbicides that disrupt the AHAS or the related acetolactate synthase (ALS) enzyme system, a factor that heightens the chance and seriousness of cross-resistance and multiple resistance. (ALS is another plant enzyme that plays a role in the biosynthesis of certain amino acids.)[8]

Three problems will be made worse if herbicide tolerant plant varieties expand use and reliance on low dose herbicides with common mechanisms of action: adverse impacts on grass filter strips and grass waterways (and hence, efforts to enhance water quality); resistance; and impacts on soil microbial communities. The adverse impacts on microorganisms may prove to be a more significant problem than resistance, since these highly active and persistent herbicides appear to trigger significant shifts in microbial communities.

Studies have shown that some of today's most popular corn and soybean herbicides depress populations of certain beneficial rhizobacteria that must colonize plant roots in order for soil phosphorous to be bioavailable. Despite ample levels of soil phosphorous, many soybean fields have experienced yellowing and other classic symptoms of a phosphorous shortage. These herbicides also lead to a shift in microbial communities, since only about 25 percent of the species of microorganisms appear to be affected. In some comparative field trials, the shifts in microbial communities resulted in a reduction in yields (Forlani et al., 1995).

In May 1995, EPA approved a controversial application for a genetically engineered herbicide tolerant plant—cotton bred to resist the herbicide bromoxynil—

> *"In recent years, the principles of IPM have come under attack as a result of the introduction of new products such as the systemic fungicides, systemic insecticides, and now the transgenic 'potato.' It is clear that these products exist because of the opportunity for profit from their sale. The reason they are being purchased and used is because our university research system has allowed a void to exist that has been filled by the agri-chemical (and now, bio-engineering) companies."*
>
> **Chris Holmes,** *New Penny Farm, Presque Isle, Maine* *"Farmer's Perspective on Food Technology"* Bangor Daily News, *February, 1996*

despite serious concerns about human and environmental risks. Bromoxynil is a possible human carcinogen, a developmental toxicant and highly toxic to fish.[9]

In granting a conditional registration for bromoxynil tolerant plants, EPA is requiring the applicant, Rhone-Poulenc to submit data demonstrating that the new variety will lead to a reduction in total cotton herbicide use.

Other registrants have inserted herbicide tolerance genes into certain plant varieties where they are used as "marker genes." Their role is to make it possible to determine whether another trait, such as production of the *Bt* toxin, has been expressed within a transgenic plant. The engineered plants are grown in the laboratory and treated with the herbicide. Those that survive are assumed to have expressed both genes. EPA is considering several applications to approve herbicide tolerance genes used as markers as "plant pesticide inert ingredients," and has already granted two such applications for *Bt* corn involving a gene conferring glufosinate resistance. This would exempt the engineered plants from further safety evaluation and prevent disclosure of herbicide-tolerance related information. Pesticide law requires EPA to protect a pesticide product's confidential statement of formula, including the identity of most inert ingredients.

3. Overview of Biotech Priorities

Table 6.5 summarizes information on over thirty genetically engineered seed products planned for commercial introduction by the year 2000 and is developed from a list compiled by *Dealer Progress* magazine and the Union of Concerned Scientists (*Dealer Progress*, 1995; Union of Concerned Scientists, 1996). A majority will be available by 1998. Note that 16 involve breeding herbicide tolerance into crop plants. Another seven bioengineered seed products are *Bt*-transgenic plants. Three are corn plants engineered to change processing characteristics. Only three plants engineered for virus resistance may be compatible with biointensive IPM.

EPA will face a number of difficult decisions in the years ahead when a series of conditional registrations covering crop-specific transgenic and herbicide use reduction requirements run their course and become eligible for full registrations. If use reduction triggers are not met, EPA will either have to cancel registrations or ignore a fundamental component of its initial decision to grant conditional registrations.

4. *How Biotechnology Can Support Biointensive IPM*

Genetic engineering greatly expands our ability to manipulate the genetic profile of organisms and hence change the ways they interact with each other or with their environment. As a set of scientific tools, genetic engineering has the *potential* for positive impacts on biointensive IPM. But as currently used in most private sector, government and university laboratories, genetic engineering

inherently predisposes scientists to look for simple genetic traits that by and large do not advance biointensive IPM.

When breeders successfully isolate single genes associated with pest resistance and move them into a commercial cultivar, they are exploiting a comparatively narrow form of resistance sometimes called "vertical resistance." Biotechnology applied to pest management in this way will usually prove disappointing, since pests have a relatively easy time developing ways around single-gene resistance (NRC, 1986). "Horizontal resistance," on the other hand, is a more broad-based form of resistance. It is based on traits that are multigenic, and pests have a much more difficult time overcoming it (Robinson, 1996).

Crowding Out Ecological Research

Since the early 1980s, the effort to develop and commercialize herbicide tolerant and *Bt*-transgenic plants have together commanded the lion's share of public and private investment devoted to pest management biotechnology applications (see Table 6.5).

There are big differences between *treatment-oriented* applications of biotechnology in pest management and

Table 6.5 New Characteristics Associated with Genetically Engineered Crop Varieties Planned for Introduction by the Year 2000

Crop	Number Designed For—			*Bt*-transgenic Plants	Herbicide Tolerance *		
	Chemical Intensive Systems	Biointensive IPM	Other Goals		1	2	3
Corn	8	0	4	4	6**	3	2
Cotton	6	0	0	2	4***	2	1
Soybeans	3	0	0	0	3	2	1
Potatoes	0	0	0	1	0	0	0
Canola	0	0	2	0	2	2	0
Other	3	3[+]	5	0	1	1	0
Total[++]	20	3[+]	11	7	16	10	4

* These columns refer to different herbicide active ingredients involved in herbicide tolerant crop varieties: (1)=Total herbicides; (2)=Glyphosate (Roundup) and glufosinate-ammonium (Liberty); (3)=Imidazolinone and sulfonylurea active ingredients.

** Includes "Poast Compatible Corn" resistant to sethoxydim.

*** Includes bromoxynil resistant cotton.

[+] Includes virus tolerant varieties of squash and papaya; some scientists have raised ecological concerns about these transgenic plant varieties (Rissler and Mellon, 1994; Greene and Allison, 1993).

[++] Some plant varieties are engineered to include more than one new trait.

Source: Adapted from "High Tech Seed Products," *Dealer Progress*, November, 1995.

applications that will advance knowledge useful in *avoiding* pest management problems in the first place. The later approach will help farmers and consumers progress toward biointensive IPM, while the former simply brings the new tools of biotechnology to bear on the task of sustaining the efficacy of pesticide-based management systems.

Treatment-oriented biotechnology is attractive to private companies because it is product-based. There is something to sell and a concrete technology that can be protected through patents and trade secret laws. Preventive, management-based pest management solutions from biotechnology research are not nearly so attractive to the private sector because there is often no simple way to capture profits or protect intellectual property.

If IPM-relevant biotechnology applications are to emerge, they need to be pursued by public research institutions or by new types of grower-private sector partnerships working in conjunction with public research institutions. But most public research agencies and programs are not in a position to take on new, long-term projects, and most private sector funding is moving into other sorts of biotechnology applications.

New Public-Private Partnerships Needed

The pesticide industry is currently funding significant biotechnology research in publicly funded research insti-

> *"We've seen what the industrial sector has in mind for agricultural genetic engineering and it's not a pretty picture. We don't need more biotechnology research focusing on turning plants into pesticide factories—or protecting them from potent and persistent herbicides. These approaches are fundamentally flawed and dominate industrial ag biotech today because they will increase sales of proprietary products, and for this reason, profits. What we need instead is more good old fashioned ecologically-grounded multidisciplinary applied field research. While sometimes difficult to coordinate and increasingly hard to fund, this is the sort of research farmers and consumers will really benefit from because these projects can lead to permanent solutions to pest problems."*
>
> **Sheila Daar, Executive Director**
> **Bio-Integral Resource Center** *(BIRC)*[10]

tutions. Most private sector support comes with at least some strings attached. In most instances, industry sponsored research starts out with a product or single technology focus, or soon evolves in that direction. Joint research contracts nearly always require pre-publication review and this sometimes leads to constraints on what can be published and when. Most industry contracts support graduate students and postdoctoral researchers who will soon be looking for jobs. The students' choice of topics studied, hypotheses tested, probes developed, and

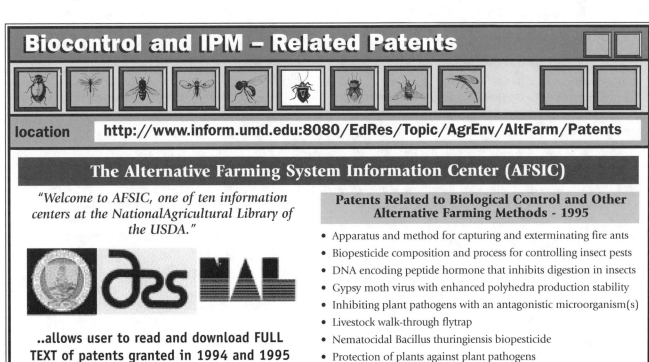

Biocontrol and IPM – Related Patents

location http://www.inform.umd.edu:8080/EdRes/Topic/AgrEnv/AltFarm/Patents

The Alternative Farming System Information Center (AFSIC)

"Welcome to AFSIC, one of ten information centers at the NationalAgricultural Library of the USDA."

..allows user to read and download FULL TEXT of patents granted in 1994 and 1995

Patents Related to Biological Control and Other Alternative Farming Methods - 1995

- Apparatus and method for capturing and exterminating fire ants
- Biopesticide composition and process for controlling insect pests
- DNA encoding peptide hormone that inhibits digestion in insects
- Gypsy moth virus with enhanced polyhedra production stability
- Inhibiting plant pathogens with an antagonistic microorganism(s)
- Livestock walk-through flytrap
- Nematocidal Bacillus thuringiensis biopesticide
- Protection of plants against plant pathogens

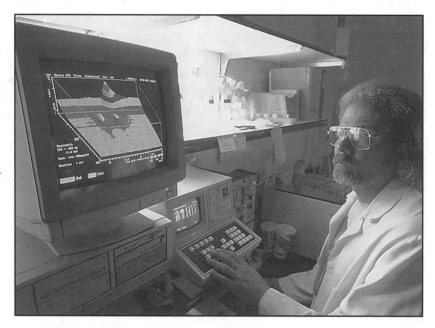

One of the most promising applications of biotechnology is identifying and utilizing natural compounds that can suppress pathogenic microorganisms. Biochemist Bob Bonsall works with a team of ARS researchers in Washington state looking for microbial biocontrol agents to combat the region's principal wheat root diseases (Stelljes and Hardin, 1995). Here he is analyzing the spectral characteristics of a natural antibiotic produced by soil bacteria that may help manage Pythium *and* Take-all. Credit: Jack Dykinga, ARS

genetic maps completed often are influenced more by the interests of the company sponsor than the needs of pest managers or science. The goal is typically to discover new or improved products or show that some product or technology works, while hopefully also showing why they work. Students working on specific, product-based applications of biotechnology may not have much chance to learn about ecological and systems-based research needs and methods.

But the money is now lacking to discover, develop and refine applications of biotechnology more suited to advance biointensive IPM in both the public and private sectors. New partnerships among grower groups, food processors, academia and pest control companies are needed to share the burdens and risks of developing this important component of future biointensive IPM infrastructure. Consumers and farmers will have to vote with dollars and political initiative to bring government

> *"How many universities, desperate for research funds, will be able to withstand the increasingly tough bargains being driven by some corporations? ... [In this incident involving the Boots pharmaceutical company and the University of California-San Francisco] ... the victim is obvious: the university. Each infringement on its unwritten contract with society to avoid secrecy whenever possible and maintain its independence from government or corporate pressure weakens its integrity."*
>
> **Dr. Dorothy Zinberg** "A Cautionary Tale"
> (*Science*, 1996)

and industry to the table, a necessary first step. Several other challenges will then follow.

Promising Applications of Biotechnology

Many biotechnology applications could significantly enhance the understanding and viability of biointensive IPM systems. Genetic engineering can be used to understand plant-pest interactions and the genetic foundation for both positive and negative interactions. It also gives plant breeders powerful new tools to exploit knowledge of plant-pest interactions. For example, one team of researchers discovered that some pea varieties protect themselves from certain insects by producing a natural protein that blocks the action of a starch digesting enzyme in the insect's gut (Schmidt, 1994). The scientists isolated the genetic sequence that produces the protein, as well as the switch that turns it on, and this multigenic trait has now been moved into new pea plant varieties.

Perhaps even more important in the long run, biotechnology research methods can identify traits within holistic farming systems that strengthen a plant's defenses, increase the diversity of organisms and the effectiveness of biocontrol mechanisms, or trigger pests and pest-induced problems. Few such applications are being pursued seriously. The science is difficult and costly, and few laboratories have the skills and equipment needed. The private sector has been slow to respond because the science needed to support biointensive IPM requires a radically different mix of skills and disciplines and is currently more difficult to capitalize on in the marketplace. Profitable private sector applications will often require major changes in the biology and ecology of farming systems and in the skills, attitudes and expectations of pest managers, farmers and consumers. Neither the public nor private sector is doing much to promote these vital changes.

In the public sector, research priorities are particularly slow to change when increased funding for one approach necessarily means less for another. The few academic and ARS laboratories that have secured stable funding for applying biotechnology in ways supportive of biointensive IPM are making encouraging progress. Still, many hurdles arise when the time comes to move new ideas, products and systems into the field for testing and refinement, and then

> **The commercial interests of pesticide and seed companies do not coincide with the needs of farmers and consumers, who will benefit most from holistic, management-based solutions to pest problems that will sometimes, but not always, involve purchasing a product.**

through regulators and ultimately, into the marketplace.

The tools of genetic engineering could support progress toward biointensive IPM in different ways. The most promising ones focus on identifying and understanding organisms, genetic traits and interactions. Gaining knowledge should be given top priority for the foreseeable future. In time new ways will emerge to apply this knowledge through classical breeding, changes in farming systems, or genetic engineering. Some include:

- Diagnostic tools to determine the microbial composition of weed- and disease-suppressive soils, and the structure of microbial communities on plant leaves and fruit leading to reduced prevalence and severity of plant diseases.

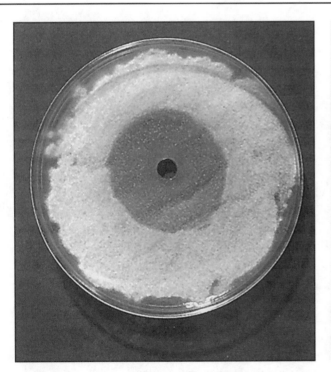

Phytophthora, *the white growth ringing the petri dish on the left, is a common root pathogen that attacks many major field and forage crops. Note the lack of growth in the center, which contains a newly discovered antibiotic, Zwittermicin A, produced by UW85, a strain of* Bacillus cereus. *This strain was discovered by Dr. Jo Handelsman and colleagues at the University of Wisconsin-Madison. The antibiotic may someday be commercialized as a low risk biopesticide (Gilbert et al., 1993). Graduate students Eric Stabb and Laura Silo-Suh work in Dr. Handelsman's laboratory and have made key contributions. Stabb identified a virus that binds to bacterial strains that produce Zwittermicin A, which can help control damping-off disease in alfalfa and soybeans (Stabb et al., 1994). Silo-Suh discovered that UW85 actually produces two distinct antibiotics, including one never before isolated (Silo-Suh et al., 1994). Credit: Wolfgang Hoffman*

■ Use of nuclear markers for studying microbial population structure or genetic variation within and among pest populations.

■ Identifying and mapping multigenic traits that can enhance a plant's innate hardiness and ability to overcome pests.

■ Systems to identify, understand and, if possible, deliver and sustain the viability of microorganisms applied as foliar sprays to combat plant diseases.

■ Developing strains of natural enemies, nitrogen fixing bacteria and biocontrol agents engineered to be more competitive in a given environment and better able to crowd out or compete with more damaging pest species or marginally helpful beneficial strains.

■ Identifying and characterizing natural plant growth regulators like auxins, gibberelins and cytokinins that regulate physiological processes (maturation, ripening,

sugar content and evapotranspiration) and may trigger systemic acquired resistance.

■ Formulating location-specific seed inoculants from microorganisms adapted to a given region and found to compete successfully with damaging root diseases like *Pythium* and Take-all.

Understanding complex systems is key to unlocking the potential contributions of biotechnology in supporting progress toward biointensive IPM. Much more research is needed on the basic biology and ecology of farming systems and the organisms that play a part in governing plant-pest interactions. Recommendations in Chapter 9 return to this theme and address the role biotechnology can play in accelerating progress toward biointensive IPM.

[1] Dr. Bottrell made this comment in his review of a draft of this book.

[2] According to the Williams *Scientific American* article, "The first generation is exemplified by arsenate of lead; the second, by DDT. Now insect hormones promise to provide insecticides that are not only more specific but also proof against the evolution of resistance."

[3] The best source of detailed information on research projects and funding is the USDA's "Current Research Information System"(CRIS) (USDA, 1994). This system includes project-by-project summaries that include research objectives, who is carrying out projects, funding levels, project duration, and milestones. USDA publishes an annual report with summary tables that we used the FY 1993 report to compile an overview of research spending levels and priorities. The CRIS system reports funding levels in several different ways. "National Total" or "system-wide" data include both USDA and state funding for agricultural research and extension carried out at state land grant colleges and universities, 1890 institutions and Tuskegee University, as well as schools of veterinary medicine and forestry. System-wide expenditures also include USDA's in-house research agency, the Agricultural Research Service, other federal funding awarded through competitive grants and research contracts from the National Science Foundation, National Institutes of Health, and the Department of Energy. It does not include most federally funded research on pesticide toxicity, risks or environmental fate carried out by the EPA, the National Cancer Institute, or other health-based agencies.

[4] Quote from Guest Editorial, "WANTED: An Integrated Approach to Weed Management", in *Dealer Progress*," February-March, 1996. This magazine serves the fertilizer and agrochemical retail sector.

[5] We commissioned a special report from Agricom dated March 13, 1995, covering expenditures from 1980 through 1994.

[6] Dr. Rick Roush, Cornell University, letter to Office of Pesticide Programs Docket accompanying the "Event 176" transgenic corn application.

[7] Pesticide industry companies and R&D leaders are deeply divided over the wisdom of some current applications of biotechnology. Dr. Atwood's April 25, 1996 speech before ACPA was one of the first public airings of such divergent views within industry. He also raised serious concerns over resistance to AHAS (acetohydroxyacid synthase) inhibiting herbicides for which resistance crop varieties have been developed.

[8] Point made in address April 25, 1996 by Dr. Mark Atwood before the spring conference of the American Crop Protection Association.

[9] These adverse impacts of bromoxynil were among those noted in the EPA decision document explaining the decision to approve bromoxynil tolerant cotton.

[10] Sheila Daar made this comment in her review of a draft of this book.

Baiointensive IPM and the IPM Continuum

Our goal should be ambitious—100 percent biointensive IPM by the year 2020. The strong and sustained effort needed to attain it will deliver major dividends even if, in some circumstances in some years, we fall short of the goal.

In Chapter 1, we described an array of proven IPM systems that have succeeded in managing a variety of farm, urban and indoor pest problems. Nevertheless, biointensive IPM remains an underutilized approach. In this chapter we set forth our definition of biointensive IPM, describe the distinguishing characteristics of IPM systems long a continuum, and discuss and apply methods developed by USDA and Consumers Union to measure IPM adoption. Our results define the scope of the challenge ahead and show how we can set goals and monitor progress.

Again and again, it seems, we must relearn the lesson that reliance on pesticides as a primary pest control approach will ultimately fail to control pests, that effective long-term strategies depend on ecologically sound, safe, biology-based IPM techniques and systems. In 1978, Dr. Robert van den Bosch documented that 24 of the 25 major insect pests in California were "secondary pests," that is they were induced to pest status by the absence of natural enemies as a consequence of insecticide spraying (van den Bosch, 1978). In 1995, after early spraying for the lygus bug, the season unfolded without major problems through midsummer on Richard Enns' cotton farm. But in mid-July his fields were overrun by flushes of mites and aphids that "seemed to come out of nowhere," according to Enns (Merlo, 1996).[1]

After incurring almost $200.00 per acre in additional insecticide and miticide costs, Enns still had not brought mite populations back down below thresholds, and his crop started to suffer damage because there were insuffi-

cient numbers of beneficial insects left in his fields to help keep mid-summer pests under control. He and many cotton growers in California's San Joaquin Valley saw yields drop from an expected 2.75 bales per acre to 1.75 or lower. Cotton yields across the whole valley dropped an average 21 percent despite two to eight extra miticide applications (Merlo, 1996). "Last year was an expensive lesson for us," declares grower Greg Palla, who lost half his normal yield after early spraying for lygus bugs with a broad spectrum insecticide. Sadly, it was a lesson van den Bosch had documented in the 1970s.

University of California IPM specialist Dr. Peter Goodell studied the Valley's insect problems in 1995, a year that convinced him "our IPM system is out of whack." According to Goodell (Merlo, 1996):

> "Over the last four years, we've moved cotton onto an insecticide treadmill, and to get off it, we're going to have to tread lightly with broad-spectrum materials…We've created our own problems with insects…It takes discipline and courage to stare down pests and 'draw' only when a true threat exists. And it takes faith in the biological system that it will respond and repair itself."

Reflecting on the Nature of Pests

Consumers also need to learn what makes an unwanted organism a pest and when the presence of a pest warrants a pesticide application. Tons of herbicides are sprayed on lawns each year in America for dandelions and other "weeds" that some people and cultures revere as beautiful, or harvest as a resource. At the first sight of crawling insects inside a home, some consumers call a pest control service and insist that their home be sprayed, without even asking what harm might come from the intruder, what its life cycle is (will it be gone on its own in a few days?) or whether there are simple, cheap and safe ways to deal with the problem.

Managing pests with little or no reliance on broad-spectrum and toxic chemicals is almost always technically feasible, although special attention and effort often will be needed during periods of transition away from regular pesticide use. It takes time for the diversity and effectiveness

---

"In California's San Joaquin Valley, two important cotton pests are Lygus and Heliothis. The former, a plant-feeding bug that appears in early- and mid-season, is often treated with organophosphate insecticides. Heliothis, the bollworm, is a lepidopteran pest that appears late in the season, and its outbreaks are particularly severe when earlier chemical treatments for Lygus have been heavy."

Pest Control: An Assessment of Present and Alternative Technologies, *Report of the Executive Committee (NRC, 1975)*

Facing an early infestation of lygus bugs, California cotton farmers got nervous and began spraying broad-spectrum insecticides earlier then usual. The results were a disaster for area cotton growers— average yields dropped 21 percent. Credit: Catherine Merlo

of biological control processes to become reestablished. It needs new tools and knowledge, different approaches and often changes in attitudes. There is still "no free lunch." But once consumers and farmers gain experience and confidence, pest management can become easier, more reliable, safer and less costly.

A. The Nature and Roots of Biointensive IPM

The term that best captures safe and sustainable pest management is "biointensive IPM." The genesis of this term is a story in itself. Much of the tale is told in a December 1993 report entitled, "Integrated Pest Management: The Path of a Paradigm," written by Dr. James Cate, a USDA entomologist, and Ms. Maureen Hinkle, pest management expert working for the National Audubon Society in Washington, D.C. They note that the term IPM initially appears in scientific literature in 1967. IPM's intellectual roots and scientific grounding come from the term "integrated control," first used in 1959 and defined as (Cate and Hinkle, 1993):

"Applied pest control which combines and integrates biological and chemical control. Chemical control is used as necessary and in a manner which is least disruptive to biological control."

Over the years various efforts were made to mold the definition of IPM to fit reality in the field, where pesticide use and dependence were rising steadily. But during a 1972 conference, Dr. R.L. Rabb, an academic expert, felt compelled to remind his colleagues that "pest management deals primarily with populations, communities, and ecosystems. Thus, the basic biological discipline involved is ecology, and there should be no 'fuzzy thinking' about this fact" (Cate and Hinkle, 1993). Later in their report, Cate and Hinkle amplify this point:

"IPM is not about tactics, but about the manner by which communities of organisms are managed. We can call these communities farms, pastures, forests, homes, gardens, agro-ecosystems, or landscapes. Regardless of the pests, the many organisms that help limit their abundance interact in the context of these communities or ecological systems and the surrounding environment. IPM is an ecological enterprise which must be practiced in the context of basic ecological principles regardless of new tactics or technology at hand."

Our View of IPM

IPM is holistic, complex and responsive to change. A pesticide-intensive management system is more reductionist, one-dimensional and predictable. IPM is knowledge-based and depends on many skills and types of information. A pesticide-intensive system depends on correct selection of purchased products, timing, and proper calibration and operation of spray equipment.

IPM's knowledge base rests on genetics, population dynamics, phenology, biology and ecology. Pesticide-based systems rely on chemistry to discover and synthesize active ingredients, on chemical engineering to formulate products that mix well and last long enough in the field to work, and on other engineering fields to handle and deliver pesticides across large expanses of land (or many individual lawns) as cheaply and safely as possible. The infrastructure of pesticide-based systems is designed to lower the cost of delivering properly formulated chemicals. The infrastructure of biointensive IPM must be information and management-based. The key is helping people integrate resistant varieties and diverse tactics and practices into a prevention-oriented system— what two weed ecologists call the "many little hammers

Bakersfield, California cotton grower Greg Palla lost half his normal yield in 1995 to secondary pests made worse by early season synthetic pyrethroid spraying. He called the year "… an expensive lesson for us." Credit: Catherine Merlo

approach" (Liebman and Gallandt, 1996).

IPM relies at times on the "art" of farming and pest management. This art is the innate ability of some experienced farmers, gardeners and homemakers to understand and anticipate interactions between plants, pests and beneficial organisms within a given, often changing environment. Pesticide-based systems depend on a simpler sequence of steps—identify the pests present, pick the right products, choose the best time and method to apply them and observe the results. If less than hoped for, pick

a stronger product, spray more often, or both.

As the definition of IPM evolved in the 1970s and 1980s, tension grew over efforts to stretch the definition from its ecological and biological roots to accommodate rising levels of pesticide reliance. Cate and Hinkle state in their report's executive summary that over the years, "IPM has come to mean many different things … As a result, IPM lacks any clear identity, unless it is the one most commonly held: that it is an efficient use of pesticides based upon monitoring of pest abundance and decisions to treat based upon economic thresholds."

In working toward an IPM paradigm for the future, Cate and Hinkle offer the following definition:

> "**Integrated Pest Management** is the judicious use and integration of various pest control tactics in the context of the associated environment of the pest in ways that complement and facilitate the biological and other natural controls of pests to meet economic, public health, and environment goals."

This definition is close to one advanced in a 1994 speech by Dr. James Cook, then Senior Scientist of USDA's National Research Initiative and a recognized international expert in the biological control of soil-borne root diseases (Cook, 1994):

> "IPM as applied in agriculture, ideally, is the use of the most effective, economical, safest, ecologically sustainable, and sociologically acceptable combination of physical, chemical, and biological methods to limit the harmful effects of pests on the health and performance of crops, livestock, and other agriculturally important organ-

---

Northeast Region Integrated Pest Management Page

location http://www.nysaes.cornell.edu:80/ipmnet/[part of Northeast IPM Network]

What is Integrated Pest Management?

"Integrated Pest Management (IPM) is a sustainable approach to managing pests by combining biological, cultural, physical and chemical tools in a way that minimizes economic, health and environmental risks. What you can learn about IPM is limited only by your own time and interest. *Click here to see a quick overview, delve into a little more detail, or access an electronic textbook of IPM.*

isms. In practice, IPM is developed around knowledge of the ecology of the pest agent and takes maximum advantage of natural mechanisms of pest suppression."

By broadening the definition of IPM to encompass promoting plant health, Cook achieved a conceptual leap and opened up a broader array of tactics and practices to utilize in progressing toward biointensive IPM. There are many more ways to promote plant health than those that simply manage pest populations. Promoting plant health and vigorous growth increases the crop's inherent ability to resist pest attack or simply outgrow whatever damage pests inflict. A key non-chemical weed management strategy, for example, is to select fast-emerging varieties and plant them more densely so that the crop's canopy closes early, shading the ground and limiting weed seed germination and growth. Promoting plant growth and strong defense mechanisms is clearly integral to sound pest management, just as good health and a sound immune system help people resist the flu and recover more quickly from health problems when they occur.

While many leading scientists, farmers and environmentalists have worked to bring the definition of IPM back to its roots in ecology, other voices in both the public and private sectors have worked in the opposite direction. Tugged back and forth, the definition of IPM has become elastic and progressively all-encompassing, and in the process it has become less meaningful for purposes of policy dialogue, goal setting and analysis.

In an attempt to bridge the rhetorical gap, which was seen as undermining public support and confidence in IPM, two Texas A&M University entomologists, Dr. Ray Frisbie and Dr. J.W. Smith, Jr., suggested the term *"biologically intensive IPM"* at a 1989 symposium sponsored by the Entomological Society of America. Frisbie and Smith did not specifically define the term, but its meaning was clear. They used the term "biologically intensive IPM" to distinguish systems more true to IPM's original roots in ecology and the management of population dynamics, in contrast to what they labeled "chemically dependent IPM" (Frisbie and Smith, 1989).

1. Definition of Biointensive IPM

Biointensive integrated pest management systems differ greatly according to the landscapes and mixes of pests they address. But the basic principles of biointensive

IPM apply equally to agricultural and urban locations, even when tactics differ markedly.

Farmers can manipulate a field for weed management in ways a forester or park manager cannot. Pest management options in a food storage and processing facility differ from those acceptable in a kitchen or retail store, or in the home. Insect pests of livestock and pets have to be managed much differently than insects attacking plants. Indoor pest management, especially in tightly sealed buildings or where likelihood of human exposure is high, has to be carried out with greater attention to safety than in locations with lots of air movement and

Monitoring the interaction between pests and their natural enemies, both in trees and cover crops (shown here), is a necessary first step toward biointensive IPM. Credit: Richard Steven Street

few people around. Biointensive IPM systems for mosquito management in urban areas obviously will require different strategies and knowledge than managing aphids in a cotton field. Aquatic pest management is particularly tricky where children like to swim or where downstream communities draw their drinking water. Pest management in schools requires special attention to safety for obvious reasons.

Biointensive IPM in Agriculture

We have recognized these differences and developed definitions to suit the setting. The following is our definition of biointensive IPM in agriculture:

> **Biointensive IPM** is a systems approach to pest management that is based on an understanding of pest ecology. It relies on resistant varieties and promoting plant health, crop rotation, disrupting pest reproduction, and the management of bio-

logical processes to diversify and build populations of beneficial organisms. Reduced risk pesticides, including biopesticides, are used only as a last resort and only in ways that minimize risks.

Biointensive IPM Outside Agriculture

In urban environments, the kitchen, a backyard garden or lawn, biointensive IPM is a four step process:

■ Get to know the life cycle of a pest, and why and how the pest thrives in a particular place where it is a problem.

■ Remove easy access to food, water, air and places where pests live, reproduce or overwinter.

■ Disrupt pest behavior or life cycles by forcing pests to coexist with their natural enemies or competitors.

■ Use the same IPM strategies farmers rely on—resistant varieties, promoting plant (and pet) health, and the safest pesticides available, but only as a last resort.

While the information base, tools and technologies underlying IPM systems differ greatly across pests, regions and circumstances, biointensive IPM systems are all shaped by common concepts and strategies that form the core of our definitions of biointensive IPM: understanding the biology and ecology of the pest, prevention, full use of resistant varieties, promoting biodiversity, conserving and building populations of beneficial organisms and enhancing the capacity of plants, animals and trees to defend themselves.

Allowing certain species of wasps to get established around a garden, for example, can eliminate the need for pesticides often relied on to control worms that attack cabbages and other crops. Weed or disease problems in a lawn sometimes can be traced to over-fertilization, an imbalance in trace minerals in the soil or mowing too low. Consumers, landlords and public health departments spend hundreds of thousands of dollars on insecticides that do not work well because of resistance in cockroaches, termites, mosquitoes and other common insect pests.

Is a New Definition of IPM Really Necessary?

Some argue that IPM is practiced when a home is scouted for termites or a lawn inspected for weeds before spraying is carried out. In agriculture, some people believe that IPM is practiced when pesticide use is cost-effective or a herbicide tolerant or Bt-transgenic plant variety is planted.

A June 1996 *California Farmer* article on cotton insect pest management quotes a farm advisor describing a

Scouting is the single most essential ingredient in biointensive IPM systems. As farmers progress along the IPM continuum, the complexity of the challenge facing scouts increases from just identifying pests and determining whether thresholds are exceeded, to complex monitoring of plant-pest-beneficial organism interactions. Here, University of Maine graduate students are sharpening their scouting skills assessing the interactions of Colorado potato bugs and the predatory stink bug. Credit: Dr. Matt Liebman

"strict IPM program" as one starting with an early season application of aldicarb, the most acutely toxic insecticide on the market, followed several weeks later, just before bloom, by a spray with a new insecticide such as Provado (imidacloprid). Midseason applications would include one or more of the organophosphate insecticides used on cotton. The program would conclude with a late season application of a synthetic pyrethroid (Rehrman, 1996). If a spray program including four different chemical families and six to eight applications can be called "strict IPM," especially in California, a new definition of IPM is needed.

If government policy and consumer preferences are to promote IPM adoption as we believe they must, it is essential to define what it is we wish to promote. We need to identify from among the many possible IPM systems those most likely to deliver significant long-run health, environmental and economic benefits.

A central feature of biointensive IPM is its reliance on information as the key input in reaching timely management decisions. The raw material of biointensive IPM is accurate field data, which often must be collected weekly, or even several times in a week in some highly sensitive crops. This information must then be interpreted insightfully in projecting trends in pest and beneficial population levels, crop phenology (growth stages) and plant-pest interactions. Growth in both the types and quantity of information needed to make

Information is Key

Biointensive IPM systems are more information and management intensive than chemical-based systems. It takes effort and skill to replace chemicals with the management of pest and beneficial organism habitat and interactions (Olkowski and Olkowski, 1996). It is remarkably easy in some settings, however, once the underlying cause of a problem is understood and alleviated.

The Nature of Scouting

Scouts have a much tougher and more important job on farms working toward the biointensive zone of the IPM continuum. Controlling pests with minimal pesticide use while also avoiding significant crop losses requires a more complex set of tools, tactics and economic thresholds than those used in chemical-intensive systems.

Under biointensive IPM, scouts must be sensitive to the early signs of infestations or disease pressure so that preventive steps can be taken soon enough to avoid trouble through largely biological means (Olkowski and Olkowski, 1996). Scouts must understand what beneficial organisms to look for at different stages of the crop's development and be aware that thresholds may need to change as a function of crop stage, weather conditions and other factors. In combating root diseases, scouts must pay close attention to plant nutrition, irrigation scheduling, soil structure and the diversity and activity of soil microorganisms (Cook and Veseth, 1991; Huber, 1994; Gilbert et al., 1993).

In chemical-intensive systems, scouts monitor target pest population levels and life stages to determine when a pesticide application is necessary and justified in order to increase net profits, after paying for the application. Experienced scouts looking to reduce pesticide use check fields for beneficials as well as pests and try to select a pesticide and application method that spare as many "good bugs" as possible.

In assessing the effectiveness of sprays, scouts will look for signs of resistance or secondary pest problems. When these problems seem to be emerging, alternate products will be selected or the search for biocontrol options intensified. These steps are part of what we regard as low level, or chemical-dependent IPM. As prevention-based measures are adopted and reliance on pesticides declines, progress is made into the medium and then biointensive zones along the IPM continuum.

Whenever a pesticide is applied, scouts must collect information on results. Scouts in chemical-intensive systems will focus on whether the expected degree of control was attained and if not, what went wrong. A scout in a biointensive IPM system would be equally concerned about the survival of key beneficial species.

biointensive IPM work is highlighted in the box "Information is Key."

Pesticides and Biointensive IPM

The need to apply pesticides routinely is a sign that more effort is needed in structuring pest and beneficial organism habitats and interactions in order to reach and remain within the biointensive zone of the IPM continuum. Pesticides play a role in biointensive IPM, but they are used only as a last resort, to help get through a period when pest populations balloon to levels that threaten significant economic loss. Biointensive IPM practitioners seek out the least toxic and most specific pesticide available to limit adverse impacts on non-target beneficial species, biological processes and ecosystem interactions. (Pesticides that are soft on beneficials and safe for IPM

systems are generally also less likely to pose human health risks.) While pesticides will be necessary sometimes, a goal of biointensive IPM is to eliminate reliance, even on biopesticides.

Our emphasis on designing IPM systems with minimal pesticide reliance is not based on a judgment that all pesticides are hazardous or ecologically disruptive. Healthy and sustainable farming systems tend to be both biologically balanced and diverse. The need to apply pesticides reflects imbalance among species and pesticide use often makes matters worse, since most pesticides, especially insecticides, are toxic to many organisms beside the target pest.

The toughest challenges facing American farmers and the pest management profession arise in dealing with plant diseases caused by fungi, bacteria, viruses and other plant pathogens. For these pests, the gap between control that can be achieved using contemporary pesticide-based systems and what biointensive IPM can do is often wide, especially where high value crops are grown in hot and humid regions and there is little tolerance for less than 100 percent successful control. Such conditions exist nearly year round in Florida's vegetable producing regions, for parts of most years in New England apple orchards and wherever fresh market produce is grown where the weather is periodically hot and humid.

The tools, technologies, market incentives and policies needed to bridge the gap between current pesticide-dependent systems and biointensive IPM will vary across the country, as will the difficulty and time needed to accomplish this task. Biointensive IPM systems must evolve in step with new pests; changes in the economics of crop production, tillage and planting systems; technology and the many other factors that can influence pest populations. Systems that work in one region often will not in others and the goals of pest managers also vary greatly as a function of the level of damage they, their clients and markets can tolerate, as discussed in the box "Keywords and Caveats."

2. Transitions and Adapting to Change

Dealing with pests during periods of transition is both a technical and an economic challenge. In order to acceler-ate progress despite hurdles and barriers, farmers will periodically need help from policymakers and support in the marketplace. In addition, transition periods can resurface after years of success with biointensive IPM if a new strain of plant pathogen emerges or a new insect species gets established. Examples include the tough-to-control new late blight fungus that has plagued potato producers since 1991 and *Thrips palmi*, a tiny but devastating insect pest that got established in South Florida in 1990.

In setting policy and working with growers, the goal should be a ***managed transition*** from conventional agriculture to high-yield sustainable systems incorporating biointensive IPM. Policy and marketplace support is needed because the risk of crop losses is greater during transitions (even well managed ones). It takes time for complex food chains to become established, an essential step in building populations of beneficials. Diverse microbial communities in the soil are critical, yet are often undermined during key periods of the growing season (early spring and summer) by pesticides or tillage. One class of organisms, the decomposers, build soil quality and cycle nutrients. A second class are the foot soldiers of biological control—predators and parasites that feed on the decomposers. Other organisms play intricate roles in food chains and nutrient cycles. Scientists recognize that the productivity of the whole system is much more than the sum of its parts and are working hard to explain why.

Ultra-low-volume herbicide application equipment reduces the amount of pesticide applied to about one-quarter of conventional sprayers. Advanced and efficient pesticide application systems should be used at all points along the IPM continuum. ARS plant physiologist Dr. Chester McWhorter (now retired) helped develop such application methods.
Credit: Keith Weller, ARS

Key Words and Caveats

To **"Promote Plant Health"** is to ensure that plants have access to fertile soil with adequate nutrient levels, a hospitable soil profile for root development, adequate but not excessive moisture and protection against weed and insect pests, pathogens and chemical contaminants that can cause a variety of physical or physiological damage to roots, stems, leaves, and the plants' natural defenses.

Livestock producers may promote animal health, which refers to pet or livestock feeding, husbandry, grooming, health, pest and disease management practices that do not cause other health complications and help assure an animal is vigorous and able to overcome exposure to pathogens and pests that are a normal part of its environment.

"Functional Diversity"

Biointensive IPM practitioners manage biological processes and ecological interactions through the promotion and manipulation of "functional diversity," a term used in the ecological sciences. Dr. James Cook, USDA plant pathologist and member of the National Academy of Sciences, stated in a recent speech (Cook, 1994):

> "Experience teaches and ecological theory predicts that the more diverse the cropping systems, cultivars, genes for pest resistance, natural enemies for biological control, and pesticides, the more resilient the agroecosystem in response to pest pressures."

It is often said that in "diversity there is stability." This ecological rule-of-thumb is not always true in agroecosystems (see the box "A Mixed Blessing"), despite the importance of biodiversity. That's why ecologists created the concept of "functional diversity" to describe the behavior of natural and managed ecosystems.

"Damage"

"Damage" encompasses a range of physical insults brought about by pests that can translate into health or economic losses—yield reductions, quality losses, property losses (such as a wood structure or stored grain), higher pest management costs and longer-run slippage in productivity levels or the ease of managing pests. In making judgments about whether damage is "minimal" or "acceptable," farmers and pest managers typically focus on damages relative to a level considered unavoidable or too costly to avoid.

"Under Control"

The notion of "control" is linked to a farmer's sense of acceptable or unavoidable damage. "Under control" means managing population levels of insects, pathogens, invertebrates, vertebrates and competing weeds so that damage to crops, animals, property or people is minimal or simply inconsequential (scattered weeds in a 60-acre soybean field or a few flies in the backyard).

Farmers have different notions of acceptable control. In Florida, for example, some clients of the independent consulting firm Glades Crop Care seek 95 percent control (i.e., 95 percent of the pounds harvested in a field make the top grade and have no pest damage). Other more risk-averse clients expect Glades Crop Care to deliver 99 percent control in most years. Based on 20 years' experience with Florida winter vegetables, Dr. Charles Mellinger, Glades Crop Care scientific director, estimates that the growers seeking 99 percent control would typically incur pesticide costs ranging from $600 to $800 an acre. In most crop cycles (usually two per year), 10 to 15 fungicide applications would be needed to control plant pathogens.

Florida growers willing to accept modestly greater risk—90 to 95 percent control instead of 99 percent—can get by with pesticide expenditures of $300 or less per acre, with some as low as $100. Fungicide applications would be cut back to no more than seven where disease pressure is high, compared with more than 15 applications on farms with little tolerance for quality grade reductions. In most years the farmer seeking 90 to 95 percent control will achieve nearly 100 percent control, just as his more risk-averse neighbor will. Some of Glades Crop Care's more adventurous clients have grown pepper and tomato crops successfully and profitably with just one or two applications of insecticides and fungicides (Mellinger, 1995).

Florida-based IPM expert Dr. Charles Mellinger has developed several special scouting techniques. Here, he is scouting tomatoes for the larval stage of beet armyworms. If the threshold is exceeded, he will recommend an application of the biopesticide Bt. Credit: Glades Crop Care

Biodiversity above the ground is important in protecting plants from a host of mobile pests, such as insects and plant diseases. Diversity also is needed inside plants. By drawing upon different genotypes (genetically distinct parental varieties) for major cultivars like the hybrid seed corn planted in the Midwest, plant breeders help ensure that growers are less likely to face widespread disease outbreaks such as those caused by a new strain of pathogen.

Biodiversity and its structured management is a cornerstone of biointensive IPM but is incompatible with chemical-intensive systems, especially those that rely on soil fumigation. In those parts of the country where soil fumigation is a common practice, the impacts are profound on the soil and organisms within agroecosystems. In Santa Cruz County, California, 633,000 pounds of methyl bromide were applied in 1995 on 1,865 acres of cropland, an average of 340 pounds per acre. Strawberries, the state's most pesticide-dependent crop, accounted for about 80 percent of the

A Mixed Blessing

Pierce's disease is a devastating grape pathogen that has become a major problem in recent years. When young vines are infected, the disease is nearly always fatal. The new challenges posed by Pierce's disease can be traced, in part, to steps taken over the last five years in response to another major grape pest, the insect *Phylloxera*. Hundreds of acres of new plantings in the North Coast wine region have been completed in an effort to replant vineyards with *Phylloxera*-resistant root stock. The insect has caused enormous economic losses in most of the state's premium wine producing regions.

But now the green sharp shooter, generally not a significant problem, has emerged as a major threat. This species of leafhopper can spread *Xylella fastidiosa*, the organism that causes Pierce's disease. The tiny leafhopper picks up the pathogen from infected weeds and shrubs, usually in riparian areas (stream banks) near vineyards, then flies into vineyards to feed and inserts the pathogen into the grape plant's vascular system through its mouthparts (Purcell, 1993). Both the sharpshooter and the plants that harbor the *Xylella fastidiosa* pathogen are a normal part of diverse and healthy ecosystems in this part of California. But their combination in an area with young and vulnerable new grape plantings already has cost more than $18 million in losses (Oltman, 1996).

Two strategies are emerging to manage Pierce's disease. One is close scouting and special steps to control the green sharpshooter, especially between riparian areas and the edges of vineyards. The second involves changing the mix of species in riparian zones to eliminate other host plants and trees that can harbor *Xylella fastidiosa*.

Grape growers in the North Coast have intensified trapping and scouting activities in and near riparian zones, which are the native habitat for the green sharpshooter, the vector carrying the Pierce's disease pathogen into vineyards. In many cases the only way to manage a plant disease is targeting the insect vector that moves it around.
Credit: *California Farmer*

pounds applied (California Department of Pesticide Regulation, 1996). Biointensive IPM is not possible on cropland that is routinely fumigated.

Adapting to Change

There are many ways a farmer or pest management specialist can respond in dealing with a case where a biological control or conventional pesticide-based system is not working as well as hoped. One common response involves seeking a better chemical solution—improved timing, a switch to a more potent chemical or combination of active ingredients, or more frequent applications at higher rates. A second response—still uncommon—entails changes in farming systems to alter the environment and habitat occupied by pests and their natural enemies. This is what Dr. Goodell means when he says cotton farmers in the San Joaquin Valley need to have "faith in the biological system that it will respond and repair itself" (Merlo, 1996).

Pruning is sometimes all it takes to make a fruit tree, berry bush or hedge healthy enough to withstand a degree of pest pressure. Opening up a grape vine or rose bush—referred to as canopy management—can limit the chance of trouble with botrytis (a common plant fungal disease) or other moisture-sensitive diseases. Such approaches work by increasing air flow through foliage and allowing more sunlight to penetrate into the middle and lower parts of plants.

The key change that makes biointensive IPM work in growing vegetables, fruit, roses or a lawn is sometimes so simple that it eludes even experienced gardeners and farmers. Many people believe that spraying is a necessary and responsible thing to do when what is really needed is some reflection on why a pest has become a problem and how to eliminate the problem permanently, without

The University of California "Foundation Plant Materials Service" in Davis, California imports and evaluates plant varieties from around the world in search for pest resistant germ plasm. Here, Deborah Golino inspects a grape vine under evaluation. Credit: *California Farmer*

> *"The multiple ways in which fumigants destroy the environment and threaten public health convinces me that fumigation should not be allowed as a general policy, period. I am not saying that everyone should farm organically. But I think every farmer should have a soil that is alive, and that farms where every living thing in the soil is killed every year cannot be sustainable. These farms rob California of its future."*
>
> **Brian Baker,** *Technical Director, California Certified Organic Farmers, Quote from* Challenge and Change: A Progressive Approach to Pesticide Regulation in California *(Benbrook and Marquart, 1993)*

the ongoing expense and risk of pesticide reliance. Asking these sorts of questions, and gathering information in the field to answer them, is the crux of biointensive IPM.

But in many cases, especially large-scale, specialized cropping systems, the changes required to move from pesticide dependence to biointensive IPM are difficult and time consuming. Reducing applications of broadly toxic pesticides is always an essential step in order to give beneficial organisms a chance to become reestablished. Then new scouting techniques must be devised, coupled with new thresholds that take into account interactions between beneficials and pests and cultural practices. The role of scouts and regional cooperative extension specialists becomes more important, as does experience in identifying pest species, following their life

In the early spring when there is ample soil moisture, some grape growers in California let wild mustard grow (left), since it appears to help suppress below-ground nematode damage through allelopathic activity. In late spring, the mustard is either mowed and managed as a cover crop, or plowed under between the rows. Above the ground, different practices are used to prevent problems with plant diseases. Managing the canopy to allow ample air flow (right) is a key cultural practice that can minimize problems with the common disease botrytis. Good air movement helps keep leaf surfaces dry and retards botrytis growth. Credits: Richard Steven Street

cycle, understanding whether and when they might do damage and drawing upon the full range of tactics to keep populations below thresholds.

In chemical-based systems, erratic weather, new pests, resistance, new farming techniques or a change in irrigation scheduling will alter the selection and timing of pesticide applications. But the goal remains the same—reducing pest populations by exposing them to chemicals that make their life short and reproduction improbable.

Strawberries grown in Santa Cruz County are among the most pesticide dependent crops grown anywhere. Slipping efficacy, the cost of pesticides, worker safety and environmental concerns have placed a premium on IPM innovation in the region Here, Frank Ramos, who runs Ramos Farms in Watsonville, California, is scouting spider mites in order to time an application of the biopesticide, abamectin. Credit: Merck & Co., Inc.

In biointensive IPM, the same sorts of changes typically trigger a more complex and varied response. Pest managers will intensify scouting routines to see how the competitive balance among organisms has shifted in the field. They will incorporate a different mix of tactics into their systems as needed, with the goal of shaping the outcome of interactions among pests and natural enemies while remaining mindful of the underlying ecological and biological dynamics unfolding in the system. It is a more subtle intervention than applying a pesticide but can be equally or more effective. Biointensive IPM also can save money, lessen risk and—most importantly and in sharpest contrast to spraying—avoid creating more trouble in the future.

Thresholds Also Can Change

The concept of "economic thresholds" translates acceptable damages into pest population "action levels." When pests exceed an action level, experience suggests it is time to take action to avoid serious losses. But thresholds are not static across the landscape. Farming and pest management systems alter the level of pests that can be tolerated without jeopardy of economically significant losses. (For an excellent review of the factors influencing economic thresholds, see Pedigo and Higley, 1992).

One of biointensive IPM's positive consequences is its tendency to raise economic thresholds for many types of pests. "Good" bugs eating "bad" bugs is a basic tactic relied on in biointensive IPM. For the "good" bugs to survive and attain population levels adequate to limit damage, there must be enough of their prey, the "bad" bugs, to sustain their population. In systems with high levels of beneficial organisms, higher levels of pests cannot only be tolerated, but may be essential, especially during the part of the season when they can do little damage but are needed to build the population of their natural enemies.

Scientists studying weed management are just beginning to establish thresholds for weeds and weed seedbanks in the soil profile. Most farmers strive for nearly complete weed control since just a few escaped weed plants can produce hundreds of thousands of seeds, possibly causing problems for years to come. But recent onfarm research has challenged conventional wisdom. Scientists have discovered that microbes and arthropods can play important roles in weed management by eating weed seeds directly or breaking them down through microbial processes (Liebman and Gallandt, 1996). In a study of no-till soybean systems, arthropods and mice consumed substantially greater numbers of weed seeds than on conventionally farmed plots (Brust and House, 1988). Until recently, the role of biological degradation and herbivore consumption of weed seeds has not been assessed or thought important, but this thinking among weed scientists is changing.

Most soils also contain natural pathogens that survive by attacking the roots of weeds rather than plants (Kremer, 1996; Harris and Stahlman, 1996). Scientists are discovering that a combination of such biological mechanisms can create "weed suppressive soils" like those on the Thompson farm discussed in Chapter 1. By tapping biological mechanisms that reduce the number of weed seeds remaining viable, or by encouraging natural pathogens to attack vulnerable young weed seedlings, farmers may be able to raise the economic threshold applicable to some weed species later in the season.

"Extension personnel alone cannot bring about widespread implementation of IPM and ICM [Integrated Crop Management]. If these approaches are to become the norm, the state [Iowa] will need more independent crop consultants, and/or crop advisers affiliated with dealerships who can provide full time IPM and ICM services."

Pest Management in Iowa: Planning for the Future *(Mayerfeld et al., 1996)*

The big-eyed bug is one of the most valued general predators on farms working toward biointensive IPM. It is found in several crops and preys upon many major insect pests including whiteflies (shown here). Credit: ARS

3. Soil Quality: The Foundation of Sustainable Agriculture

To farmers and backyard gardeners, "soil quality" can be defined as the capacity of soil to take in, hold and make available to plants the moisture, nutrients and healthy environment needed for roots to spread and function. To society, "soil quality" takes on added dimensions—the ability to hold, cycle, and purify water; the capacity to recycle nutrients; and many additional valuable ecological and environmental functions, each discussed in the 1993 National Research Council (NRC) report *Soil and Water Quality: An Agenda for Agriculture* (NRC, 1993b).

Soil quality vitally influences pest management and plant health and hence, the viability of biointensive IPM. For farmers, the capacity of soil microbial communities to suppress root disease and promote full development of root systems is a key component of soil quality (Burpee, 1990; Werner and Dindal, 1990; Bezdicek and Granatstein, 1989; Cook and Veseth, 1991). Soil microbes within the rhizosphere (the area very close to the surface of plant roots) play a direct role in plant

Delano, California organic grape grower Steve Pavich is recognized for his expertise in making high quality compost. As scientists and farmers understand the characteristics of soil microbial communities in disease and weed suppressive soils, new methods will emerge to formulate customized composts that will help provide microbial biocontrol.
Credit: Richard Steven Street

nutrition by making soil phosphorous and other essential nutrients available to roots.

Through mechanisms not fully understood but under active exploration, soil microbes can either trigger or strengthen plant immune systems so that later in life plants can better withstand a degree of plant pathogen pressure or insect attack (de la Cruz et al., 1992; Gilbert et al., 1994; Handelsman et al., 1990; Huber and MacCay-Buis, 1993; Kuc, 1995). This phenomenon is referred to as systemic acquired resistance (SAR), an area receiving much research attention that may lead to a new generation of biopesticides (Malamy et al., 1990; Delaney et al., 1994; Amir and Alabouvette, 1993). Some scientists, including Dr. Robert Goodman in the University of Wisconsin-Madison Department of Plant Pathology, are exploring the linkages between plant genetic traits and soil microbial communities. The hope is that certain genes in plants can be identified, isolated and then cloned into commercial cultivars (plant varieties) that make it possible for plants, through their root exudates (liquids that plants excrete through their roots), to more efficiently trigger positive changes in microbial communities, in turn benefiting the plant through enhanced nutrition or ability to withstand pest pressure.

The Roots of Soil Quality

Soil microbial activity also plays a direct role in the biocontrol of nematodes, soil-borne insects and associated plant pathogens (Amir and Alabouvette, 1993; Huberand McCay-Buis, 1993; Gilbert et al., 1994; Werner and Dindal, 1990; Burpee, 1990; de la Cruz et al., 1992). Scientists have documented the role played by root exudates in stimulating the activity or expanding the populations of certain microorganisms, which can in turn play a direct or indirect role in combating pests or strengthening plant defenses. Common modes of action of microbial biocontrol agents include:

■ *Antibiosis*—some microorganisms produce natural antibiotics that are toxic to other microorganisms.

■ *Competition*—insects, microorganisms and other beneficial or pest species need space, moisture, air and nutrients to thrive in the soil. Aggressive and well-adapted species can sometimes out-compete others for one or more of these essential resources.

■ *Predation* and *Parasitism*—some microbes, bacteria, fungi and viruses directly feed on pests (predation); others reproduce in pest organisms.

With few exceptions, the basic biology of soil microbial interactions is poorly understood, in part because few research dollars have been invested in studying them and in part because they are so complex and dynamic. Nearly all aspects of farm management influence the hundreds of thousands of micoorganism species present in the soil, the majority of which are not even characterized or identified. Still, farmers continue to pioneer

Wheat is the most profitable crop on much of the highly erodible cropland in the Pacific Northwest. When wheat is grown continuously, soil-borne pathogens build up and attack root systems. ARS plant pathologist Dr. James Cook (left), has pioneered microbial biocontrol methods involving the identification of indigenous microorganisms that work through antibiosis and by out-competing more damaging pathogens. Here, Dr. Cook and John Aeschliman (right), a Colfax, Washington wheat grower, inspect the difference between a healthy (left) and diseased (right) root system. Healthy roots are able to more fully extract available moisture and nutrients from the soil. Promoting root health and microbial biocontrol of soil pathogens are key components of biointensive IPM. Credit: Jack Dykinga, ARS

research and experimentation on what can heighten the chance a given soil will become "disease (or weed) suppressive." They do it empirically, through observing from year to year those parts of fields that seem prone to disease and those parts that are not, and sorting out what seems to explain the difference.

Progress has accelerated appreciably in recent years as the tools of biotechnology have been brought to bear on the same empirical challenge in partnership with growers, drawing on their skills and years of experience. One promising practical application is unfolding in the Pacific Northwest, where farmers and scientists are isolat-

ing beneficial soil microbes that can colonize the roots of young wheat plants and protect them from the ravages of the common root pathogens *Pythium*, Take-all and *Rhizoctonia* (Stelljes and Hardin, 1995; Cook, 1991, 1994).

B. The IPM Continuum

Integrated Pest Management systems exist in almost infinite variety, ranging from those scarcely distinguishable from pesticide-dependent systems to those that rarely, if ever, require pesticides. It is useful to think of IPM sys-

California PestCast

location http://www.cdpr.ca.gov/docs/ipminov/pestcast/pestcast.htm

A Weather Network To Support Crop Disease Management Decisions

California PestCast is a collaborative project of the University of California, Department of Pesticide Regulation (DPR), and the California agricultural industry to expand the use of computer-based crop disease forecasting to reduce unnecessary pesticide use. This project will provide an infrastructure to collect appropriate weather data, facilitate the research and validation of models of crop diseases, demonstrate their utility, and further local implementation efforts. Data will be gathered centrally, quality controlled, stored, and made available to users.

tems as falling along a continuum. The distinguishing characteristic of IPM systems along the continuum is their degree of reliance on biologically based, prevention-oriented practices relative to reliance on pesticides and treatment-oriented practices.

1. Four Zones

As we explained in Chapter 1, analysts who have studied IPM adoption have divided the IPM continuum into four levels or zones, each corresponding to progressively greater reliance on biologically based practices rather than pesticides. The USDA has adopted a comparable approach (described below). The World Wildlife Fund uses the continuum in its IPM measurement work (Hoppin, 1996; Hoppin et al., 1996; Benbrook, 1996). While different analysts and organizations use different labels, the four levels or zones generally can be described as:

- **No IPM**, or **Chemical Control**, corresponding to systems essentially dependent on pesticides and not employing basic IPM practices such as pesticide application in accord with economic thresholds.

- **Low Level IPM**, where farmers employ at least the most basic IPM practices—scouting and application in accord with thresholds, for example—but few, if any, preventive measures.

- **Medium Level IPM**, systems in which farmers have adopted some preventive measures, coupled with efforts to cut back on broad spectrum pesticide use, protect beneficial organisms and assure that pesticides are applied most efficiently.

- **High Level**, or **Biointensive IPM**, the zone farthest along the IPM continuum, where farmers have integrated multiple preventive practices and as a result, have become able to control pests without relying routinely on pesticides.

Figure 7.1 displays the IPM continuum graphically. It also highlights degrees of change, both qualitative and quantitative, along the continuum for two basic features of IPM—scouting, and application of pesticides in accord with thresholds. Note how both the volume and qualitative nature of information changes along the continuum. In the left half of the continuum, pesticides carry most of the pest management burden and practices needed to use them cost-effectively are key; in the right half, practices needed to enhance populations of beneficial organisms, and manage their interactions with pests, become the dominant feature of management systems.

A significant portion of grape production destined for vintners in California is grown using biointensive IPM systems, including a sizable acreage that is certified organic or in transition to organic. This Buena Vista vineyard uses cover crops, drip irrigation, aggressive scouting for pests and beneficials, and biopesticides approved for organic production in managing pests and promoting profitable yields. Credit: Richard Steven Street

Scouts often have to look closely to detect signs of pests and natural enemies. Here, Pat Weddle, an independent consultant based in Placerville, California, is inspecting a small pear for signs of the codling moth. The trap in the foreground contains a small capsule of codling moth pheromone and is used to monitor moth flights and population levels. Credit: Richard Steven Street

Figure 7.1 The Integrated Pest Management Continuum

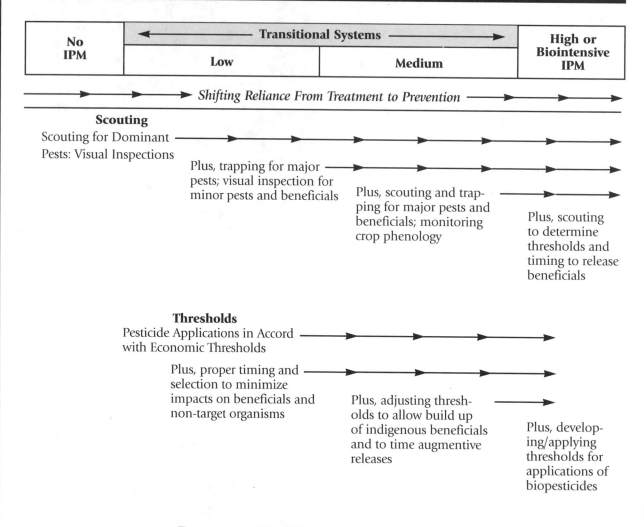

No IPM	Transitional Systems		High or Biointensive IPM
	Low	**Medium**	

Shifting Reliance From Treatment to Prevention

Scouting

Scouting for Dominant Pests: Visual Inspections

Plus, trapping for major pests; visual inspection for minor pests and beneficials

Plus, scouting and trapping for major pests and beneficials; monitoring crop phenology

Plus, scouting to determine thresholds and timing to release beneficials

Thresholds

Pesticide Applications in Accord with Economic Thresholds

Plus, proper timing and selection to minimize impacts on beneficials and non-target organisms

Plus, adjusting thresholds to allow build up of indigenous beneficials and to time augmentive releases

Plus, developing/applying thresholds for applications of biopesticides

Representative IPM System Characteristics

No IPM:
- proper calibration, operation and cleaning of spray equipment
- scouting for pests
- sanitation and good agronomic practice

Low Level IPM:
- scouting plus applications in accord with thresholds
- avoid or delay resistance and secondary pest problems
- optimally time applications
- some preventive practices (short rotations, resistant varieties, cultivation)

Medium Level IPM:
Multitactic Approaches to:
- limit or remove pest habitat and augment biodiversity
- resistant varieties, use of cover crops and longer rotations
- enhance beneficials, use of soil amendments, disease forecasting models

Biointensive IPM:
Reliance on Preventive Measures to Limit Pest Pressure and Enhance Beneficials:
- multiple steps to enhance plant health and soil quality
- focus on conservation of beneficials and habitat
- microbial biocontrol of root pathogens
- release of beneficials

2. The Pear Pest Management System Continuum in California: A Case Study

Pear and apple producers in California's Sacramento and San Joaquin Valley have struggled for years with a dominant insect pest—the codling moth. In the 1980s, most farmers settled on the organophosphate Guthion (azinphos-methyl) as the insecticide of choice. But because of repeated use of this pesticide over a wide area, resistance began to emerge in the late 1980s. Pest management professionals like Pat Weddle, an independent IPM consultant, knew that steps had to be taken quickly to keep his clients in business. Returning to calendar spraying of broad-spectrum insecticides was not an option in this environmentally sensitive area (Weddle, 1994).

A search ensued for new technologies that would lessen reliance on Guthion as a way to slow, or even reverse Guthion resistance (see the box "Resistance Drives Search for Alternatives" and also Chapter 1). Codling moth mating disruption (CMMD) emerged as the most promising new approach, and since the late 1980s has

made possible major strides toward biointensive IPM in pear and apple production regions from California, to the Hood River region in Oregon, Washington State, the Kelowna area of British Columbia, South Africa and Italy's Poa River Valley. (For general overviews of pheromone-based management systems, see Barnes et al., 1992; Howell et al., 1992; Kirsch, 1988).

To gain a perspective on the IPM adoption process, we commissioned Pat Weddle to describe the pear IPM systems now in place in the Sacramento and San Joaquin Valleys. The tables and figures that follow cover pear pest management and draw upon the records of Weddle, Hansen, and Associates, as well as other crop consultants in this region who together cover a significant percentage of the area's pear acreage.

Pat Weddle estimates that in 1996 about 15 to 20 percent of pear acreage in the Delta and Valley region was managed using conventional, chemical-intensive systems; between 50 and 60 percent under "Low" level IPM; 20 to 30 percent under "Medium" level, or transitional IPM systems; and, from 5 to 10 percent under biointensive IPM. Accordingly, based on Pat Weddle's assessment of

Resistance Drives Search for Alternatives

In the early 1990s, 93 percent of California's pear acreage was sprayed three to five times with Guthion (azinphos-methyl). On average, a total quantity of 3.77 pounds of a.i. per acre was applied (Gianessi and Anderson, 1995). Guthion poses significant risks to farm workers and non-target organisms and is one of the most frequently detected pesticide residues in pears.

Resistance is monitored by tracking changes in the "Lethal Concentration" (LC) of pesticides like azinphos-methyl. The LC-50 is the concentration needed to kill 50 percent of codling moths in a laboratory assay. Traps are used every season in commercial orchards to monitor moth population levels. Some insects are captured and taken to the laboratory where they are tested for susceptibility to Guthion and other commonly used insecticides.

LC-50 values have risen more than eight-fold since the late 1980s, as shown in the graph (Weddle, 1994). Codling moth trap counts (an indicator of pest population size) started going up in 1988 despite heavier and more frequent applications of Guthion in California's Sacramento River Delta region. Monitoring and field research were intensified, and a regional project was started in 1994 by growers, pest management consultants and University of California researchers that became known as the Randall Island Project (see Chapter 1).

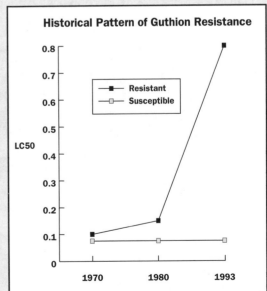

Source: Weddle, 1994.

IPM adoption in San Joaquin Valley pear production, growers already have achieved the USDA's goal of 75 percent adoption of IPM, which encompasses all three levels of IPM adoption.

As argued in the next chapter, we think "Low" level IPM is essentially just using pesticides cost-effectively and typically includes too few preventive practices to lessen reliance on pesticides. For this reason, in Chapter 9 we call for reconsideration of both the IPM adoption goal in agriculture and how its attainment will be monitored.

> **Early adopters in the Valley improved the cost-effectiveness of CMMD, learning from mistakes and each season's unique combination of circumstances. According to Weddle, "Every season is an adventure but every year we learn more..." that will make the transition easier for others in the future.**

Based on his clients' experience, Weddle estimates that the transition from chemical control to "Low" level IPM takes about one year; another one to two years is needed to progress into the "Medium" zone. He projects that it commonly takes another two to three years, at a minimum, to make the final transition to biointensive IPM. Few growers in the Valley have progressed from "No" IPM to biointensive IPM in less than five years, but he feels it can be done if growers are committed to making the change and are able to get the assistance needed. The transition is likely to be smoother in the future compared to five to seven years ago, when mating disruption was first introduced to the Valley. Early innovators have worked many kinks out of CMMD technology, learning from mistakes and each season's unique combination of

circumstances. According to Weddle, "Every season is an adventure but every year we learn more."

Yields on pear farms in the "Low," "Medium" and biointensive zones generally fall in the 12 to 25 tons per acre range (the difference is largely a function of tree density and health). Orchards at the chemical-intensive end of the continuum generally harvest 10 to 15 tons per acre. Table 7.1 summarizes the basic scouting and pesticide application criteria used by pear pest managers at various stages along the IPM continuum.

System Performance

After three years of CMMD implementation, pear growers in the Randall Island Project, all of whom are in the "Medium" or biointensive zones along the continuum, have achieved impressive results. The 1995 pear harvest moved into packing sheds with an average of less than one percent worm damage. While some blocks had higher damage, few exceeded 1.5 percent.

The efficacy achieved with CMMD is at least comparable to, and in many instances better than that achieved in orchards still largely reliant on Guthion, in which three to five applications were made, totaling 4 to 7.5 pounds a.i. per acre per season. Randall Island Project participants applied only about 0.5 to 0.7 pound of a.i. per acre over approximately 90 percent of the acreage

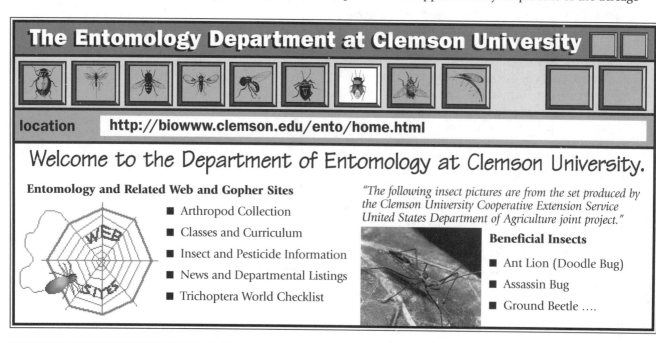

Table 7.1 California Pear IPM Scouting and Pesticide Application Criteria

	No IPM	Transitional Systems		High or Biointensive IPM
		Low	**Medium**	
Scouting for Major Pests	Limited visual inspections for major pests; no or minimal effort in trapping codling moths and monitoring population levels	Moth traps, plus non-systematic visual spot checking for mite, psylla and other pests; 1 to 2 traps per 40 to 80 acres	Moth traps, systematic monitoring of multiple pests and beneficials (phenology, population histories, statistical analysis of trends); 1 to 2 traps per 20 to 40 acres	Intensive trapping and systematic monitoring of pests and beneficials, plus statistical analyses of factors affecting pest-beneficial interaction; 1 to 2 traps per 10 to 20 acres
Pesticide Application Criteria	CRITERION A: Pesticides applied routinely, often on a calendar schedule	CRITERION B: Pesticide applications timed for optimal efficiency and based on scouting data and presence of target pests	CRITERION C: Criterion B, plus increased use of biopesticides and selection of pesticides/timing of applications to minimize adverse impacts on beneficials; aggressive resistance management	Criterion C, plus mating disruption and use of biopesticides when needed; avoidance of broad-spectrum chemicals; release of natural enemies and other steps to augment populations of beneficials

Source: Pat Weddle, pear pest management case study for Consumers Union.

also treated with CMMD—on average nearly an 85 percent reduction from pre-CMMD levels. Part of the remaining 10 percent of acreage was not sprayed at all, and part was sprayed more often, typically because the blocks, or portions of blocks, are small or isolated from larger areas treated with mating disruption (CMMD works best in large, contiguously treated areas).

Table 7.2 presents data showing the change in reliance on pesticides as progress is made along the continuum. "Dose Equivalents" are a measure of the number of times the full label rate of a pesticide was

> Reliance on and dose equivalents of broad-spectrum toxic pesticides in biointensive pear pest management systems in California are well less than one-quarter of the levels typical of pest management systems at the "No" and "Low" end of the pear IPM continuum.

sprayed in the orchard. It equals total pounds applied over all applications divided by the maximum allowable one-time rate of application. Synthetic pesticides used by pear growers in the region include herbicides; the insecticides Guthion, Lorsban (chlorpyrifos) and various pyrethroids; and when needed (as in 1996), abamectin for fire blight control. Biopesticides include oils, *Bt*, and the codling moth pheromone. Table 7.2 reports both dose equivalents and the number of applications, because application costs are a significant share of total costs, as shown in the bottom line in of the table.

Table 7.2 California Pear Pesticide Use and Pest Management Cost Summary Along the IPM Continuum

	No IPM	Low IPM	Medium IPM	High IPM
Dose Equivalents (Number)				
Synthetics	14-27	13-20	10-15*	9-12*
Biopesticides	1	1-2	1-4	2-6
Application Equivalents (Number)				
Synthetics	10-15	10-15	10-15*	10-15*
Biopesticides	0**	0**	1	1-2
Synthetics Range lbs a.i./acre	25-40	20-40	10-25	6-20
Best Estimate a.i./acre	35	30	20	13
Cost Ranges ($/Acre)				
Materials	$320-$532	$250-$385	$193-$473	$224-$500
Average $/Acre	$425	$320	$330	$360
Applications	$150-$225	$150-$225	$150-$245	$150-$265
Average $/Acre	$190	$190	$198	$207
Scouting	0	$10-20	$20-40	$40-50
Average $/Acre	0	$15	$30	$45
Total Cost Range	$470-$757	$410-$630	$363-$738	$414-$815
Average $/Acre	$615	$525	$558	$612

* Heavy spray oil equivalent for mite control.
** Biopesticides applied with synthetic products in tank mixes.
Source: Pat Weddle, case study.

As progress is made along the IPM continuum, the intensity and scope of scouting increases, as do scouting costs. The table shows scouting expenditures per acre rising from nothing under "No" IPM (chemical company representatives, or Pest Control Advisors [PCAs] working for businesses selling pesticides typically scout at no extra charge), to $45.00 per acre under biointensive IPM. This increase in scouting costs, though, is more than offset by the reduction in expenditures on pesticides.

Figure 7.2 highlights the shift in reliance—measured as dose equivalents—from synthetic pesticides to biopesticides as progress is made along the pear pest management continuum. Under chemical control, over 20 dose equivalents are needed on the average acre, and almost

> **In the world of pest management, the advances envisioned for CMMD could make this approach to codling moth management an example of precision farming at its best.**

no use is made of biopesticides; under biointensive IPM, the average number of synthetic dose equivalents has dropped by almost half, from 20.5 to 10.5 (including several dose equivalents of non-toxic spray oils for mite control), and the average four dose equivalents of biopesticides is almost a third of the total number of pesticide dose equivalents. Reliance on and dose equivalents of broad-spectrum toxic pesticides in the biointensive system are well below one-quarter of the levels typical of pest management systems at the "No" and "Low" end of the pear IPM continuum.

In working with clients, Weddle stresses a key point that is clear in Table 7.2 – the transition along the IPM continuum generally does not significantly change total

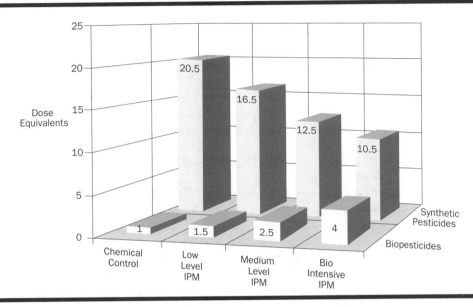

Figure 7.2 Comparison of Synthetic Pesticide and Biopesticide Dose Equivalents* Along the IPM Continuum: California Pear Producers (Number of Dose Equivalents Per Acre)

*In this example, one dose equivalent for a pesticide active ingredient is application of the full label rate on one acre, possibly over more than one applications. (For example, two applications at one-half the label rate equals one dose equivalent). Source: Pat Weddle.

pest management expenditures but it does shift the distribution of expenditures. By far the biggest change behind the numbers in Table 7.2 is the shift from reliance on Guthion to use of mating disruption. This shift also accounts for a large change in the toxicity and environmental impacts of pesticides applied in the orchard, as well as significant change in the split of pes-ticide expenditures between synthetic and biopesticide products. As in all biointensive IPM systems, the effort to discover and apply new pest management technologies must be ongoing to improve effectiveness and lower costs. Some of the more promising CMMD technical innovations are reviewed in the box "Lowering the Cost of New Technology."

Peach and pear growers have reduced the pounds of pesticide applied by adopting "alternate row spraying." A high-pressure airblast sprayer is used to gain good coverage of trees in two rows. Then the sprayer moves over two full rows instead of one for its next pass. This method of spraying cuts the amount of pesticide needed per acre by about 20 percent to 40 percent. Credit: Keith Weller, ARS

Lowering the Cost of New Technology

Science will steadily broaden the range of tools and tactics used by IPM practitioners. Technical progress and innovation will foster wider adoption by reducing the cost of information-based pest management systems and improving their effectiveness. New techniques have been developed in the last three years, for example, to more cost-effectively deliver minute quantities of insect pheromones in orchards and fields. The pheromone itself is the most expensive component of mating disruption systems—over $600.00 per ounce—so steps to reduce the amount needed can markedly lower CMMD costs. An automated aerosol dispenser is being developed that will periodically emit a small quantity of pheromone.

An even more dramatic step in the CMMD innovation process is just beginning to take shape—an automated method to adjust pheromone levels in orchards as a function of weather conditions, especially temperature and wind. Temperature in the orchard has a major impact on codling moth hatching and mating activity. Scouts routinely monitor the number of eggs hatching and the number of adults being caught in traps. These data are being used to develop and calibrate models that predict moth flight as a function of temperature data, which can be automatically collected by weather stations placed in orchards.

Wind is another key variable in the orchard when moths are flying to locate a mate. Under windy conditions, the pheromone disperses too quickly, triggering the need for greater quantities and frequency of dispersion. Researchers are working to develop a new pheromone delivery mechanism, much like a spray dispenser, that is controlled by a computer linked to weather tracking stations that measure temperature and wind direction and speed. When a calculated threshold is crossed—a combination of degree days and wind speed—the program increases the frequency and dosage of pheromone dispensed into the orchard but then, when conditions change, it also reduces the amount released into the orchard. Frequent scouting and trap counts will help refine the system and calibrate how farmers deal with unique field conditions, locations and circumstances.

In the world of pest management, the advances envisioned for CMMD could make this approach to codling moth management an example of precision farming at its best.

C. Measuring IPM Adoption: USDA and CU Definitions and Estimates Differ

A central element in the Clinton Administration's National IPM Initiative, reviewed fully in Chapter 8, is helping growers adopt IPM on 75 percent of the nation's cropland acreage by the year 2000. As soon as this goal was announced in June, 1993, many people—agricultural leaders, politicians, environmentalists, the media—asked USDA and EPA officials what percent of crop acreage is already under IPM, obviously a key question in gauging the significance of the Administration's pledge, and the likelihood of meeting the goal.

Here, we conclude this chapter by describing and contrasting the measurement methodologies USDA and Consumers Union (CU) have used to estimate current national IPM adoption along the continuum. When the goal was first announced, Administration officials actually did not have a solid basis to estimate acreage under IPM. Senior USDA officials directed the Economic

Research Service (ERS) to develop a method as quickly as possible for estimating current IPM adoption, based on data available at the time (early 1994). The ERS report, *Adoption of IPM in U.S. Agriculture,* was released in September 1994 (Vandeman et al., 1994). Its stated purpose is to establish a baseline estimate of IPM adoption for use in monitoring progress toward the Administration's 75 percent goal. The report's basic empirical finding is that:

> "IPM has been adopted on 50 percent or more of the crop acreage in the fruits and nuts, vegetables, and field crops studied for at least one of the three pest types: insects, diseases, and weeds."

Unfortunately, the USDA's definition of IPM and its adoption criteria were quite lax, and we believe the ERS analysis overstates actual progress along the continuum by a wide margin. ERS analysts have acknowledged that further work is needed in order to refine their IPM adoption criteria and measurement methods, and the agency is pursuing several collaborative research activities toward this end.[2]

IPM Adoption Criteria in the ERS Report

The report includes separate measures of IPM adoption for weeds, insects and plant diseases. For an acre to count as "under IPM," a farmer must have used an "IPM approach" which requires, at a minimum, scouting for a pest and a subsequent pesticide application in accord with some threshold. In the case of corn, the use of a crop rotation in combination with no use of soil insecticides is also deemed IPM, regardless of whether a field was scouted.

The report explains that IPM systems are highly variable and run along a continuum from chemical-dependent to biologically-based. The USDA chose to divide all farmers into three categories: "IPM," "No IPM," and "Not Classified." The "Not Classified" as to IPM adoption category includes the generally small percentage of growers who did not apply pesticides. (These growers were not classified because the Department could not apply its basic criteria—scouting and spraying in accord with thresholds—to acreage never sprayed.)

USDA analysts then further divided all acreage considered under IPM into three levels of adoption—"Low," "Medium" and "High." In structure, these categories roughly correspond to the "Low," "Medium,"

and "Biointensive" zones along the CU continuum, and the CU "No IPM" zone roughly corresponds to "No IPM" under the USDA's classification system. Simple rules were used by USDA in dividing pest management systems into the four categories.

Acreage that was scouted and sprayed in accord with thresholds was judged by USDA as falling in the "Low," "Medium" and "High" IPM levels based on the number of practices "indicative of an IPM approach." For each major category of pests (weeds, insects, plant diseases) and three major crop groupings (fruits and nuts, vegetables and field crops [corn, soybeans, potatoes]), the ERS identified seven to nine practices deemed "indicative of an IPM approach." The distribution of acres managed under varying levels of IPM systems was projected according to the following criteria:

- "Low" level IPM requires only scouting (S) and pesticide applications in accord with thresholds (T) for one type of pest

- "Medium" level IPM requires S+T plus one or two additional practices from those identified as "indicative of an IPM approach"

- "High" level IPM requires S+T plus three or more additional practices

Data Sources for Measuring IPM Adoption

Researchers in the United States have extensive data on several major crops to draw upon in estimating IPM adoption. Despite our criticisms of their analysis, ERS deserves recognition for creativity in using cropping practices and pesticide use survey data that was compiled several years earlier for completely different purposes. Fruit and nut data came from a 1991 survey. Information on vegetable crops came from a 1992 survey, which included a follow-up survey on selected IPM practices done on a subset of farms. These practices were among those identified in 1994 as "indicative of an IPM approach." Field crop data was derived from the 1993 Cropping Practices Survey, which collected considerable IPM practice data on a subset of field crops and states contained in the nationwide chemical use surveys.

In developing its methodology for measuring IPM adoption at various levels, ERS was constrained (as we were) by the supply and nature of the data USDA compiles on pest management practices and systems through its various chemical use and cropping practices surveys. National information on IPM practices has been collected only since the early 1990s. Growing interest in IPM convinced ERS and the National Agricultural Statistics Service (NASS), the part of USDA that carries out field surveys, to include additional questions in surveys that had changed little over the years up to that point.

As a result of the steady increase in pest management system questions, the database available to evaluate IPM systems has expanded since the early 1990s. The 1995 and 1996 surveys will provide the richest data yet for studying IPM system adoption and the consequences of IPM on pesticide use, reliance and risk outcomes.

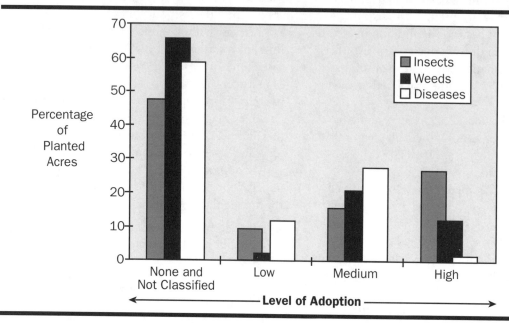

Figure 7.3 IPM Adoption by Major Pest Type Along the IPM Continuum: USDA Estimates for Vegetable Production

Source: Derived from Vandeman et al., 1994.

Drawing on national cropping and chemical use surveys carried out in the last five years, ERS identified 24 practices "indicative of an IPM" approach—eight in fruit and nut IPM; nine in vegetable IPM; and seven in the production of field crops. Of these 24 practices:

■ 10 are part of all well-managed cropping systems and are adopted for several reasons besides increasing the effectiveness of pest management systems or reducing their cost.

■ Eight are necessary either to apply pesticides cost-effectively or to extend the useful life of a pesticide active ingredient by slowing the emergence of resistance.

■ Only six are biologically based preventive pest management practices commonly found on farms practicing or moving toward biointensive IPM.

The box "Data Sources for Measuring IPM Adoption" on the previous page explains how ERS compiled a database to measure national IPM adoption. We used the same data sets (but different criteria) in our own estimates of IPM adoption presented later in this section.

1. ERS Estimates of IPM Adoption

ERS concluded that IPM was practiced on 50 percent or more of overall crop acreage in the early 1990s. This estimate represents a synthesis by ERS of its results in the three crop groupings and across the three major types of pests.

In terms of individual field crops, ERS found that IPM was used in managing insects on 74 percent of corn acreage and 53 percent of corn acreage was under IPM in managing weeds (and 59 percent in soybeans). Potato producers used IPM on 72 percent of acreage in managing insects and about two-thirds of acreage in managing weeds and plant diseases (Vandeman et al., 1994).

In the case of vegetable pest management, ERS estimated IPM adoption by major class of pests. Figure 7.3 summarizes these findings. Insects were managed under IPM on about 52 percent of vegetable acreage and plant diseases, on 41 percent. Only 1 percent of vegetable acres were considered under "High" level IPM in managing plant diseases, a concern given the frequency of fungicide residues found in some fresh and processed vegetable products (USDA, 1995f, 1996b; Wiles and Campbell, 1993b).

Galen Frantz (left), an independent consultant working with Glades Crop Care in Jupiter, Florida, is scouting this Florida strawberry field for two-spotted spider mites (TSSM) and its predator, Phytoseiulus persimilis, another species of mite. Until recently, Florida strawberry fields were typically sprayed with abamectin when TSSM populations exceeded the threshold of one or more mites on 5 percent or more of the leaves, but now the predatory mites are often purchased and released to augment natural populations. Gary Omori, a pest control advisor working for Agrichemical and Supply in Salinas, California, and Tim Krueger, a Merck & Co. sales representative, (right) are assessing spider mite damage in this Watsonville, California strawberry field. The pest problems facing strawberry growers in California and Florida vary greatly, as does the information scouts gather in the fields, but the tactics used are often the same.
Credits: Left, Dr. Charles Mellinger; Right, Merck & Co., Inc.

ERS found that 50 percent of fruit and nut acreage was under IPM, 42 percent was not and 8 percent was not classified as practicing IPM because no pesticide was applied. Most but not all farmers who use scouting also apply pesticides in accord with thresholds. The report notes that "although 54 percent of apple acreage is professionally scouted, fulfilling the monitoring criteria for IPM, only 43 percent of apple acreage meets both the monitoring and threshold criteria for IPM." Similar differences were found in most other crops—about 20 percent of the acreage scouted is sprayed without regard to thresholds.

Discouraging Insights from Crop-by-Crop Results

ERS estimated IPM adoption by individual crops, resulting in a number of surprising findings:

■ More than 45 percent of apple acreage and 53 percent of peaches was not scouted for any pests. Across all fruit and nut crops studied, 35 percent of acreage was not scouted.

■ On 17 percent of fruit and nut crop acreage, not one of nine pest management practices "indicative of an IPM approach" was used.

■ About 90 percent of vegetable acreage was not treated with any of three pest management practices typically found in biointensive systems.

■ Resistant varieties were used on only 22 percent of fruit and nut acreage, and water management practices on 31 percent.

■ Almost two-thirds of vegetable crop acreage was sprayed with pesticides without regard to impacts on beneficials.

2. Consumers Union's Estimates of IPM Adoption

Farmers move incrementally along the IPM continuum as they shift toward progressively greater reliance on preventive practices. At all points along the continuum, our measurement method is based on the relative reliance on biologically based preventive measures in contrast to treatment-oriented interventions. If pest pressure worsens in a given region, farmers committed to biointensive IPM might apply pesticides more often than in the past, but not without also increasing the number and scope of preventive measures designed to bring pest populations back under control, both during the current season and in future years, through largely biological and ecological processes.

Our methodology is more complicated than USDA's and requires more data and judgment in evaluating the relative importance of various pest management practices. In applying its point system, USDA counted all practices "indicative of an IPM approach" as equal in weight and importance, an assumption we do not make. In developing our methodology we sought ways to overcome shortcomings in the USDA methodology, including failure to take into account the intensity of pesticide use, criteria insufficiently grounded in the ecological roots of IPM, and counting practices needed to use pesticides cost-effectively as "indicative of an IPM approach" and equal in importance to biologically based practices.

The CU methodology rests on three variables that need to be calculated for each field included in a given dataset. NASS/USDA surveys and the even more detailed field-level crop-specific datasets compiled in several states by food processors, crop consultants, commodity associations and research teams working on IPM adoption, can be used to calculate these factors:

■ *"Dose-Adjusted Acre Treatments"* (DAAT) is a measure of the intensity of pesticide applications on a given acre. It is defined as the number of acre treatments with distinct pesticide active ingredients at common rates of application per acre, and serves as a generic measure of reliance on pesticides.[3] (In future analyses, methods should be explored to calculate toxicity-adjusted DAATs).

■ *"Preventive Practice Points"* (PPP) is the sum of points assigned to a set of prevention-based practices that are "indicative of an IPM approach" (to borrow USDA's term) in producing a given crop in a given region. "Preventive practices" include planting resistant varieties, crop rotations, cultural practices, biocontrol, release of beneficials, composts, pheromone confusion and mechanical cultivation for weeds. Point values for practices need to be proportional to each practice's importance across all identified preventive practices in reducing target pest pressure or minimizing pest damage.

■ *"IPM System Ratio"* captures the relative reliance on biologically-based preventive measures (PPP) in contrast to treatment-oriented practices (DAAT). It is measured as PPP divided by DAAT. The higher the value in a given area—a field, farm, lawn or region—the closer to the biointensive IPM zone along the continuum.

For a given crop in a state, region, or the nation, the distribution of the values of the variable "IPM System Ratio" can be used to divide all fields and farms into one of the four zones along the IPM continuum. The methods used to calculate PPP and DAAT and to divide farms into the four zones can get complicated and different approaches should be explored. The tough step is assigning points to preventive practices, a process that requires in-depth knowledge of how different practices lessen pest pressure.[4]

> At all points along the IPM continuum, our measurement method is based on the relative reliance on biologically based preventive measures in contrast to treatment-oriented interventions.

Nematodes as Biological Control Agents of Insects

location http://129.93.226.138/nematode/WORMHOME.HTM

.."if the entomopathogenic (insect-parasitic) nematode attacks insect pest; kills or hampers the development of the insect host; and is capable of mass production it can be used as an effective biological control agent (Poinar 1979)."

■ Mermithidae can be used to control mosquitos

■ Steinernema and Heterorhabditis nematodes can be used to control garden and insect pests

■ Retail Suppliers of Beneficial Organisms

University of Nebraska - Lincoln (UNL) Lincoln, Nebraska 68583-0722 Institute of Agriculture and Natural Resources

• Nematology Mailing List (NEMA-L)
• Nematodes of the Northern Great Plains
• Nematodes of Quarantinable Concern
• Nematode Diagnostics
• Nematology Lab at UN-L
• Nematode Images
• National Needs and Priorities in Nematology

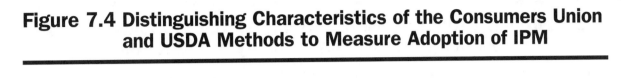

Figure 7.4 Distinguishing Characteristics of the Consumers Union and USDA Methods to Measure Adoption of IPM

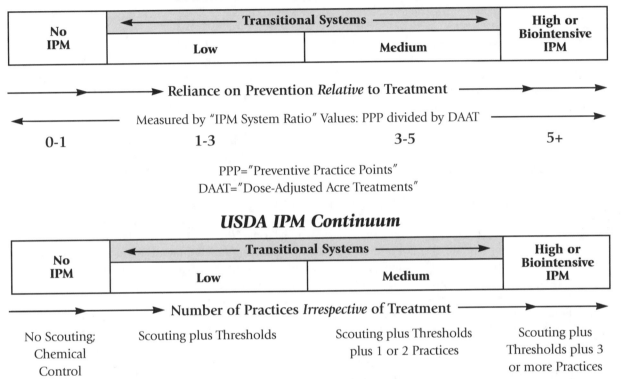

Consumers Union IPM Continuum

No IPM	Transitional Systems		High or Biointensive IPM
	Low	Medium	

Reliance on Prevention *Relative* to Treatment

Measured by "IPM System Ratio" Values: PPP divided by DAAT

| 0-1 | 1-3 | 3-5 | 5+ |

PPP="Preventive Practice Points"
DAAT="Dose-Adjusted Acre Treatments"

USDA IPM Continuum

No IPM	Transitional Systems		High or Biointensive IPM
	Low	Medium	

Number of Practices *Irrespective* of Treatment

| No Scouting; Chemical Control | Scouting plus Thresholds | Scouting plus Thresholds plus 1 or 2 Practices | Scouting plus Thresholds plus 3 or more Practices |

The most complete application of the methodology to date is a study of weed management in corn and soybean cropping systems (Benbrook, 1996). Researchers and IPM experts in USDA, Wisconsin, Florida, Maine, California, and possibly elsewhere are now adapting and applying the methodology to specific crops, pests and pest management systems. An example of some of the major differences that will emerge in applying our method to the same crop in different regions is presented in the box on the next page assessing tomato plant disease management in California and Florida.

Figure 7.4 above summarizes the distinguishing characteristics of the criteria and decision-rules incorporated in the CU and USDA methodologies for measuring IPM adoption. In our method, the value of the variable "IPM System Ratio" rises as progress is made along the IPM continuum toward the biointensive IPM zone. In the example presented in Figure 7.4, farmers in the "Low" zone would have "IPM System Ratio" values between 1 and 3 (i.e., 1 to 3 "Preventive Practice Points"

per "Dose-Adjusted Acre Treatment"). Those that progress into the "Medium" zone would have "IPM System Ratio" values between 3 and 5, indicative of more significant use of preventive practices relative to each DAAT with a pesticide. In the biointensive zone, we would expect a preponderance of preventive practices in contrast to pesticide applications, as reflected in "IPM System Ratio" values of 5 or more.

Estimating IPM Adoption Using the CU Measurement Methodology

One of the major differences between the CU measurement methodology and the USDA's is that we assign preventive practice points as a function of a practice's importance in lessening pest pressure. USDA counts practices that are prevention-oriented as well as those necessary to manage pesticides cost-effectively. While the data are not available to apply our methodology to all crops addressed in the 1994 ERS report, we have made preliminary estimates of IPM adoption in the four zones

Biointensive Tomato Disease Management in California and Florida: The CU Methodology in Practice

In California fresh market and processed tomato production systems, pest management professionals typically rely on resistant varieties and a half-dozen major sets of preventive practices to limit plant disease pressure (Olkowski and Olkowski, 1996). Years of university research and the region's predictable and dry climate have made it possible for some producers to limit fungicide applications to one Dose-Adjusted Acre Treatment (DAAT) or less in most years.

In Florida, tomato producers face a much tougher complex of insects and plant diseases and much less predictable weather. Insects are important in managing diseases because they are often the vector transmitting disease from field to field, and within fields. In addition, almost all Florida tomatoes are grown for the fresh market and must meet strict USDA and packer quality standards. Fruit that is not essentially perfect is downgraded and receives a lower price.

The biointensive plant disease management program used by Glades Crop Care, a Jupiter, Florida crop consulting firm, includes dozens of preventive practices. In a given field and year, 10 to 20 practices might be needed, depending on pest pressure and weather trends. By assigning points to these preventive practices, Glades Crop Care could calculate "Preventive Practice Points" (PPP) for each farm. Total PPPs might fall, for example, between 18 and 36.

In a good year, the Crop Care tomato disease management program reduces fungicide DAATs from 10 to 16 to as few as four to six (Mellinger, personal communication). Accordingly, in this hypothetical example involving Florida tomato farms, plant disease management values for the variable "IPM System Ratio" might fall between 3 ("Low" level IPM) and 9 or more—probably well within the biointensive zone, based on the IPM System Ratio values shown in Figure 7.4 corresponding to the four zones along the continuum.

Florida growers in the biointensive zone, though, will still need to apply four to six times more fungicide than their California counterparts, at least in most years. Most California tomato producers successfully mange plant diseases in early-planted tomatoes with one or no fungicide applications, and hence on average, just a fraction of a DAAT (Olkowski and Olkowski, 1996). But in years with higher than normal disease pressure when two or three applications are made, some growers might still fall in the "Low" IPM zone (even "No" IPM), however, because of a lack of preventive practice points.

This leads to a key point—the CU measurement methodology is based on the relative reliance on preventive practices in contrast to treatments within a region and thus takes into account each region's unique combination of pests, climate, soil conditions and cropping systems. For this reason, we believe our method is better suited than USDA's to compile national estimates of IPM adoption and to compare IPM systems across regions.

New York State Integrated Pest Management Program

location   http://www.nysaes.cornell.edu/ipmnet/ny/

New York State
Integrated Pest Management Program
Cornell University
Cornell Cooperative Extension
New York State Department of Agriculture & Markets

Find the NY State IPM program 1996 annual report at:
http://www.nysaes.cornell.edu:80/ipmnet/ny/program_info/AR_96.html

Links to other Integrated Pest Management

PARASITOIDS

Web page prepared by Cheryl TenEyck, IPM Program, cnt1@cornell.edu

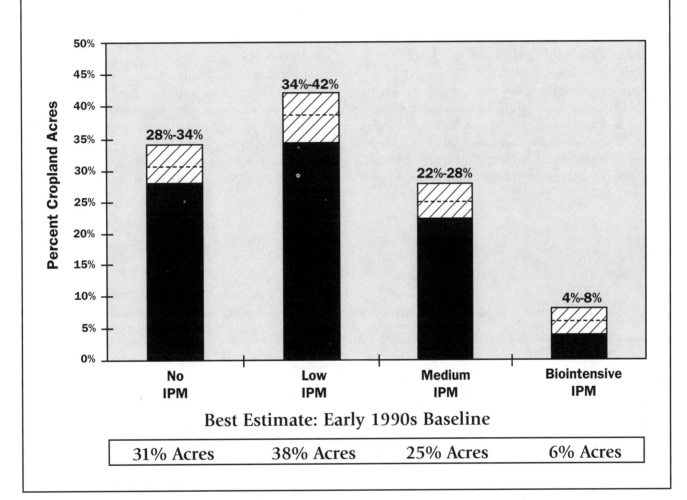

Figure 7.5 Consumers Union's Estimate of IPM Adoption: Early 1990s Baseline

Best Estimate: Early 1990s Baseline

31% Acres	38% Acres	25% Acres	6% Acres

along the IPM continuum based on data that are available and through analyses of the ERS method and findings.

Figure 7.5 presents our estimate of national IPM adoption in the early 1990s. Each bar shows high and low estimates of the percent of crop acres that were managed under various IPM levels. The ranges included in the bars reflect differences between crops and regions, and the need for more specific data on a greater variety of crops and further analytical applications focusing on specific crops. Still, we are confident that our "best estimate" of early 1990s IPM adoption, presented in the bottom line of Figure 7.5, is a good approximation of the distribution of cropland acreage in the four zones along the IPM continuum, based on CU's definition of

biointensive IPM and our methodology for measuring IPM adoption.

Our criteria and methodology show between 62 and 76 percent of cropland acreage in the "No IPM" and "Low" level zones, compared to between about 40 and 75 percent using the USDA methodology.

At the biointensive IPM end of the continuum, CU estimates vary more dramatically from USDA's (as reported in Vandeman et al., 1994):

■ We estimate that between 4 and 8 percent of acreage falls in the biointensive IPM zone, compared to USDA results suggesting that between 20 and 30 percent falls in "High" level IPM.

■ We estimate that between 26 and 36 percent of acreage falls within the combined biointensive and "Medium" level IPM zones, compared to USDA's estimate of between 45 and 65 percent.

We argue in our recommendations chapter that the nation should strive for 75 percent of cropland acreage under the "Medium" plus biointensive levels of the IPM continuum by the year 2010, and 100 percent under biointensive by the year 2020. Comparable goals should be set and achieved for urban and other nonagricultural pest management challenges. USDA interprets the President's IPM goal for agriculture to mean 75 percent of acreage should fall under *any* level of IPM—a goal American farmers almost certainly have already achieved. "Low" level IPM has more to do with efficient pesticide use than biologically based, prevention-oriented systems.

Acres under "Low" level IPM are only marginally consistent with the goals or spirit of the President's IPM pledge and should not count toward its achievement.

We return to measurement issues in Chapter 9. Our best estimate of IPM adoption in the early 1990s, shown in Figure 7.5, is the baseline we use in suggesting IPM adoption goals in agriculture. In that chapter, we urge pest managers in the public and private sectors and in agriculture and urban settings to pursue achievement of an ambitious goal—100% biointensive IPM by the year 2020, or as close to it as people can come. The fact that it will take time and much effort for all Americans to reach this goal does not lessen its importance or validity. Such a goal is needed to realistically confront the scope of the challenge we face in reaching biointensive IPM, so that what now seems inconceivable will someday become commonplace.

[1] Quotes and facts on insect problems in California cotton in the 1995 from "Expensive Lessons: A System that Relies Too Heavily on Broad-Spectrum Pesticides May Have Contributed to Last Season's Insect Problems in San Joaquin Valley Cotton Fields" (Merlo, 1996). Ironically, this article on cotton insect loses caused by early season lygus bug spraying with synthetic pyrethroids starts on page 51 of the May issue of *California Farmer*, followed by a two-page advertisement on pages 52-53 for the synthetic pyrethroid insecticide bifenthrin. The advertisement states: "The data is in. Acres treated with Capture Insecticide/Miticide from FMC yield 20-27% more cotton than acres treated with [competing insecticides]. That's because Capture controls lygus better than any other…"

[2] Economic Research Service (ERS) analysts discussed the problems with their 1994 IPM measurement methodology, and possible solutions, with a team of IPM experts convened in July, 1995 by the World Wildlife Fund (WWF) (Hoppin, 1996), as well as at several sessions during the Third National IPM Forum held in March, 1996. ERS staff members, especially Merritt Padgitt, have contributed significantly to the development of CU's methodology.

[3] "Common" one-time rates of application are recommended for use in calculating DAATs instead of maximum one-time label rates because in the case of many, but not all pesticides, maximum one-time label rates are quite high relative to average or routine application rates (USDA, 1995h). (For example, some herbicide application rates are much higher in high organic matter soils in humid regions [for a detailed discussion of methods to calculate DAATs and an empirical application, see Benbrook, 1996].) Use of maximum one-time label rates, therefore, would bias DAAT estimates downward for pesticides with relatively high one-time maximum allowed label rates. Instead, we recommend use of average or routine one-time

application rates in an area, or some increment above average rates (like 125 percent of the average rate, or one standard deviation above the average rate). Most important though is use of a method consistently in calculating DAATs across all pesticides.

[4] In our analyses of baseline IPM adoption reported in Figure 7.5, we focused on the same crops, acreage and major pest management challenges covered in USDA's study of IPM adoption, i.e. the major field crops corn, soybeans, cotton, and fall potatoes; 25 fruit and four nut crops, and 16 vegetable crops (Vandeman et al., 1994). These crops and pest management needs account for over 75 percent of total agricultural pesticide use. We calculated DAATs for selected crops and pesticide uses from USDA cropping practices and chemical use surveys (USDA, 1994b, 1995b), and USDA chemical use reports (USDA, 1993b, 1994d, 1995d, 1995g). In the most complete application of the methodology, we identified preventive practices and points for weed management in corn and soybean production, as well as IPM system ratio values. A full discussion of the methods used, the role of expert judgment and data sources is presented in Benbrook, 1996. Calculations of weed management PPPs in other field crops (cotton and potatoes) were limited by available data; we relied on the practices reported and estimates made by USDA (Vandeman et al., 1994). Along with USDA data on pesticide use noted above, we used the fruit and vegetable IPM practices data compiled by USDA (Vandeman et al., 1994) to estimate acreage in the four zones of the IPM continuum using the IPM system ratio methodology. We also commissioned a case study of pear pest management in California. In Figure 7.5 we report ranges of agricultural IPM adoption along the continuum, reflecting the need for better data and more analyses. Our work is ongoing and we encourage others to refine the analysis for specific crops and pest management challenges, and for overall progress.

The Clinton Administration IPM Initiative

8

The Administration embraced IPM as a national goal in 1993 but Congress has not made it a priority. Federal funding for IPM is now about half what chemical companies spend advertising pesticides.

On Friday, June 25, 1993, the Clinton Administration released a statement that began:

> "The Clinton Administration today announces its commitment to reducing the use of pesticides and to promote sustainable agriculture. ...We will intensify our efforts to reduce the use of higher-risk pesticides and to promote integrated pest management.... We will work side by side with American farmers to help test and implement improved and safer methods of pest management ..."

> "We will promote development of safer pesticides by reforming our regulatory program to encourage registration of safer pesticides and by providing incentives to pesticide manufacturers to develop safer pesticides ..." (USDA, 1993a).

Overview

Since the 1993 pledge there has been a flurry of planning and a great deal of dialogue but a paucity of funding to move new initiatives along in the field. USDA has proposed $14 million to $35 million increases in IPM research and education funding in each of the four budget cycles since 1993, but Congress has approved none of them. None of the requested $14.2 million increase sought in FY 1997 was approved. Funding since 1994 has barely kept up with inflation.

While the USDA has been unsuccessful in convincing Congress to appropriate additional funding, it has moved forward with other aspects of the Administration's IPM Initiative. Great effort has been invested in developing a strategic plan to guide IPM research and education. As a part of this effort, 23 commodity-specific regional task forces were established. More than 4,000 people took part in priority-setting exercises around the country. But much of the planning effort focused on newly emerging and unmet needs. Without new funding little new effort is likely in these areas since there remains modest capacity within the system to redirect money from one area to another.

EPA has pursued two policy initiatives to help achieve the Administration's IPM adoption goal. It has established partnerships with several pesticide user groups focusing on voluntary measures to promote IPM, in an attempt to apply generally successful industrial pollution prevention strategies in the pesticide use and risk arena. EPA has also created a new division responsible for registering low risk biopesticides and given it the mandate and resources to reduce the time required to get a registration application through the process. The new division has been in place about a year and has made progress in speeding the decision process, reducing the time required by about 50 percent.

Both EPA policy initiatives are moving in the right direction. It appears EPA has overcome the initial reluctance of grower groups to join the pesticide stewardship program. Now that several partnerships are in place and activities are gaining momentum, EPA needs to encourage groups to set concrete goals for IPM adoption and reduction in the use of pesticides (especially where risks are high per treated acre). Given the experimental nature of this program and limited funding, the number of partnerships in place is less important than making sure that a few achieve tangible progress toward meaningful goals.

For these new programs and policy directions to make a major difference, both USDA and EPA will have to invest significantly more resources in them. Given the pressure to balance the federal budget, new money is not likely to be appropriated. So federal managers face the always unpopular task of deciding what programs and categories of spending can be cut to find money for new initiatives. But as USDA has learned, even taking this painful step and proposing a redirection of resources in the President's budget is no guarantee of success. Congress has its own priorities and has shown no hesitation to take money allocated in the President's budget for IPM and spend it restoring cuts in its favorite programs.

The Administration captured the attention of farmers, food processors and the academic community with its pledge to get 75 percent of cropland acreage under IPM by the year 2000. Most constituencies and people have responded enthusiastically and with a spirit of hope that progress toward IPM can make a real difference in reducing pest problems and lessening reliance on pesticides. That promise remains, but it takes more to accelerate progress along the IPM continuum than a series of challenges, planning activities and encouragement. If the federal government cannot provide more effective leadership and follow

through on pledges to increase public sector IPM investment, rallying others to hasten progress along the
continuum will be more difficult.

Timing of the Pledge

The timing of the Administration's IPM adoption goal
and pledge was no accident. The Administration wanted
to get ahead of the wave of publicity it knew would follow the release on Tuesday, June 28th of a long-awaited
National Academy of Sciences report, *Pesticides in the
Diets of Infants and Children* (NRC, 1993a). The June 25th
press release and language of the three-agency statement
was covered prominently in dozens of national news stories that began appearing Monday, June 27 in most
papers across the country. Heavy coverage of the NRC
report, reaction to it, and the Administration's pledge
continued for months.

Release of the report elevated pesticide issues on the
Congressional agenda. Environmental Protection Agency
(EPA) Administrator Carol Browner was called upon in a
Joint Congressional hearing on September 21, 1993 to be
more specific regarding the Administration's commitment to IPM. To demonstrate solidarity within the three
key Executive Branch agencies, a joint appearance was
scheduled with Ms. Browner; Mr. Richard Rominger,
Deputy Secretary of the U.S. Department of Agriculture
(USDA); and Mr. Michael Taylor, then Food and Drug
Administration (FDA) Deputy Commissioner for Policy.
In her testimony, EPA Administrator Browner announced
an unprecedented EPA-USDA-FDA initiative focusing not
just on IPM, but also specifically calling for pesticide use
reduction goals.

For the first time the link between IPM adoption and
pesticide use reduction was prominently embraced by
government leaders representing *both* the environmental

> *"We consider this a major shift in policy that will finally
> move the nation in the direction of a responsible and
> comprehensive approach to reducing the risks of pesticides
> to human health and the environment."*
>
> *"We congratulate the Clinton Administration on the prin-
> ciples set forth, which are at once bold and pragmatic.
> Clearly, the Administration intends to reinvent federal
> pesticide policy; and the entire nation will benefit."*
>
> **Kenneth A Cook,** *President, Environmental Working
> Group. Statement released June 25, 1993 in response
> to the Clinton Administration IPM Pledge*

and agricultural communities. Speaking on behalf
of the Administration, EPA Administrator Browner said
at the hearing:

> "We are setting a goal of developing and imple-
> menting IPM programs for 75 percent of total
> crop acreage within the next 7 years. We believe
> Congress should endorse the goal…"

> "Today, EPA and USDA are announcing the
> beginning of a one year process to develop specif-
> ic pesticide use reduction goals for various seg-
> ments of production agriculture to be achieved by
> 2000.…" (U.S. EPA, 1993).

A. Trouble from the Start

Problems with the Clinton Administration's initiative
soon surfaced. Administrator Browner was pressed by
members of Congress during the September 1993 hearing to define the term "Integrated Pest Management"
(IPM) as used in her statement and in the three-agency

*A key goal of the IPM initiative is
encouraging large scale operations to
progress along the IPM continuum.
This sprayer can cover over 80 acres
in a day. Much work is needed by
agricultural engineers and the farm
equipment industry to develop application equipment and techniques so
that biopesticides, beneficial organisms and other biologically based pest
management interventions can be
made over large areas quickly and
cost-effectively.* Credit: USDA

"In late June [1993], the Administration announced its commitment to reducing use of pesticides and promoting sustainable agriculture in this country... Since that announcement... we [EPA, USDA and FDA] have developed a three part program involving both legislative and administrative initiatives."

"First, we want to strengthen existing statutory authorities governing pesticides. Second, we pledge to upgrade the science related to pesticides and food safety, especially as it applies to the protection of children. We are addressing the recommendations put forth in the 1993 National Academy of Sciences report, Pesticides in the Diets of Infants and Children. Third, we are reorienting our efforts to focus on preventing problems at the source, through appropriate reduction of pesticide use. History teaches us that in all aspects of life, prevention saves time, energy, and resources. By stressing prevention, we not only safeguard today's children, we look beyond to protect the health and environment of future generations."

Carol M. Browner, *Administrator, EPA*
Congressional Testimony September 21, 1993 on Behalf of EPA, USDA, and FDA

pledge to promote IPM. Congress and others were curious about the definition for obvious reasons (e.g., where the nation currently stood relative to the IPM adoption goal, see Chapter 7). Questions during the hearing returned several times to the definition and what the Administration really was calling for in terms of change in pest management systems and what it might take to get there.

In the week before the Administration's announcement and the release of the NRC report, EPA and USDA staff held nearly non-stop meetings, trying to hammer out a national initiative worthy of a presidential statement and pledge. EPA agreed that IPM should be featured but also wanted the statement to include tangible pesticide use reduction goals, patterned after successful European programs.[1] USDA negotiators were nervous about concrete use reduction goals for both technical and political reasons. They also hoped to avoid triggering outright opposition from farm organizations and agribusiness.

The deadline arrived and the negotiating team struck a deal. The statement would call for a firm target for IPM adoption—75 percent of cropland acreage by 2000—coupled with a reference to pesticide use reduction and sustainable agriculture, but would include no measurable use reduction goals.

Disagreements Surface

Through the fall of 1993 and early 1994, the Administration worked hard to complete a legislative package that had been promised to Congress during the September 1993 hearing. The package was transmitted to Congress in April 1994 with the following statement on the IPM goal:

"The Secretary of Agriculture, in consultation and cooperation with the Administrator, shall establish a national goal for the adoption of integrated pest management techniques ... [and] shall implement research, demonstration, and education programs to support meeting the goals of adoption of IPM."[2]

The quantitative goal was nowhere to be found. According to USDA and EPA staff who participated in the negotiations on the legislative package, agreement still could not be reached on how to define and measure IPM.

In the meantime, a variety of groups, constituencies and individuals continued to ask the Administration what it was doing in response to its June 1993 pledge. Some urged announcement of a concrete definition and IPM adoption goals, crop by crop if need be, coupled with pesticide use reduction goals. Others raised concerns over whether IPM systems could be codified and measured and wondered out loud whether government getting involved would do more harm than good.

Measuring IPM is difficult even in relatively simple cropping systems. While most IPM systems share a number of common strategies and tactics—scouting, use of thresholds and preserving beneficial organisms—it is difficult to identify a set of practices that are always needed or that if present, always constitute IPM (see Chapter 7 for more discussion). If such a definition were formulated, it would need to be site specific and contingent on various changeable factors—the weather, pest pressure, new technology or emergence of resistance to a frequently used pesticide.

Farm community skepticism over prescriptive approaches was summed up by Texas cotton grower Jim Ed Miller, speaking before the 1992 (First) National IPM Forum (Sorensen, 1992):

High value fruit and vegetable production systems entail high per acre cash costs. Florida fresh market tomato producers can spend over $10,000 per acre in getting a crop through the season and to market, and they can either make or lose nearly that much per acre, depending on yields and market prices. With so much at stake, pests are managed aggressively and IPM systems include dozens of practices—making the measurement of IPM adoption a complex task. Credit: Glades Crop Care

"Let IPM start at the farm and work up to Washington. Don't decide here in Washington what we're going to do and shove it down to the farms."

1. No Yardstick Applicable to IPM

The lack of a concrete definition of IPM and a way to measure adoption was a real problem for USDA and EPA policy officials. The Administration tried to fill the void, calling in its September 21 testimony for a one-year cooperative process working with commodity organizations and professional groups to develop crop-by-crop, sector-by-sector IPM adoption and pesticide use reduction plans. Such crop-specific plans would include:

■ concrete definitions of IPM so that progress toward it could be monitored and research needs specified.

■ a process to establish an up-to-date pesticide use baseline from which to monitor changes in use levels.

■ goals for IPM adoption and pesticide use reduction, including clear explanations of the ways IPM will lead to pesticide use reduction.

EPA's call for a cooperative process turned out to be a hard sell. Most commodity organizations and farm groups anticipated (and feared) a costly and time-consuming process that ultimately would lead to more regulations. Few in agriculture thought IPM could be defined and many feared the definition would be used to

demonstrate that growers in some regions, or on particular farms, were lagging in IPM adoption. Moreover, most groups were reluctant to establish pesticide use baselines or reduction goals for fear that they would later be held accountable for achieving them.

In response to concerns and complaints from farm groups and professional associations involved in pest management, the EPA started to modify program goals and "essential" ingredients. EPA dropped its requirement that cooperating partners agree to establish pesticide use baselines and reduction goals, and blurred the requirement that IPM adoption goals be set and progress monitored. As a result, about 20 commodity groups agreed during 1994 and 1995 to work with EPA and USDA in developing an assessment of IPM techniques and needs. Few groups, if any, have thus far offered an IPM adoption baseline or set goals for progress, although several are getting close to this key step.

2. EPA's "Pest SMART" Effort

EPA chose the name "Pest SMART" for its program focusing on establishment of IPM partnerships. The first issue of the *Pest SMART Update* newsletter was disseminated in August 1994 to inform a wide range of interested parties about the EPA initiative. The front page of *Update* #1 included in the upper right hand corner the logo of EPA's program, "Partnership in Prevention: Government-Industry-Community." The *Update* begins by explaining the purpose of the "Pesticide Use/Risk Reduction Initiative:"

"…to reduce the use of pesticides that pose unreasonable risks to humans and the environment … Two early focal points: The development of commodity-specific use/risk reduction goals by October 1994; and the enrollment of 75 percent of agriculture acreage in IPM programs by the year 2000."

The *Update* touched a nerve in the pesticide industry and agriculture communities. Chemical industry representatives opposed any mention of "use reduction" as a goal, favoring instead risk reduction based on "sound science." Industry had expressed similar viewpoints two months earlier at a June 13-15, 1994 workshop sponsored by the Office of Pesticide Programs to discuss the EPA's risk reduction initiative and the just announced "Pest SMART" program. Several industry representatives said the agency had no business trying to shape farmers' pest management decisions—a task that "USDA is handling quite adequately." Pesticide registrants said that EPA's top goal and priority should be speeding up the pesticide registration process to assure American farmers quicker access to new crop protection chemicals.

"Industry doesn't need incentives to make safer products because that is our goal too," one industry presenter asserted.[3] A trade association representative said the reduced risk initiative would introduce new concepts into an already bogged down process, and warned, "…we'll have a field day in court." Registrants also argued strongly that it was inappropriate and possibly illegal for EPA to embrace use or risk reduction goals since all registered pesticides have been determined by the agency to pose acceptable risks when used in accord with labels. Industry alleged that by advocating use and risk reduction goals, EPA might undermine public confidence, both in the agency and the safety of registered pesticides.

The grower community was nervous about cooperating with EPA in pursuit of risk reduction and pollution prevention, which entailed an implicit admission that risks existed and that pollution was occurring. Growers feared one step would lead to another, and soon EPA would be dictating their choice of pest management technologies. Most groups felt that EPA lacked the expertise to deal with site-specific pest management issues and had no business intruding on USDA "turf."

Environmentalists Voice Concerns

Industry and agricultural groups were not the only ones speaking out about EPA's proposed initiative. In the 1990s, a growing segment of the environmental community came to distrust risk assessment as a regulatory tool for several reasons. In public meetings, reports, letters to EPA and Congressional testimony, they argued that:

> **Pesticide industry representatives argued that it was inappropriate—and possibly illegal—for EPA to set pesticide use and risk reduction goals. Industry alleged that such goals might undermine public confidence in the agency and the safety of registered pesticides, and they promised "…we'll have a field day in court."**

USDA NRICGP Abstracts of Funded Research, FY 1995

location http://www.reeusda.gov/new/nri/abstract95/weedsci.htm

PEST BIOLOGY, BIOLOGICAL CONTROL, AND INTEGRATED PEST MANAGEMENT

WEED SCIENCE

9502217 An Ecophysiology Approach to Understanding Maize Tolerance and Weed Suppressive Ability
Mortensen, D.A.; Lindquist, J.L.; Johnson, B.E.
University of Nebraska, Lincoln; Department of Agronomy; Lincoln, NE 68583-0915

Panel Manager - Dr. Jodie S. Holt

Herbicide resistance, public concern over agrichemicals in our water supply, and a national initiative to implement integrated pest management (IPM) on 75% of the nations farmland will limit chemical weed control options in the future. Cost effective alternative strategies must therefore be developed….

■ Exposure and risk estimates done by industry remain the primary basis for EPA regulatory decisions, and many gaps persist both in scientific knowledge, the completeness of exposure assessments and toxicological databases.

■ Risk assessment depends upon many assumptions, subjective judgments and choices regarding which data are the most relevant and reliable; and, the industry is often successful in challenging EPA analyses and proposed regulatory actions by raising arguments in support of an alternative set of assumptions, judgments and choices.

■ Pesticide registrants have access to a vast array of information sources, most of which are private or proprietary, and registrants may selectively submit such information to EPA.

■ Use reduction is far easier to measure and monitor than risk reduction.

EPA Regroups

Negative reactions from all sides convinced EPA to regroup. Four months after release of the first *Update,* the second newsletter described a very different sort of effort. The "Partnership in Prevention" logo was gone. The newsletter's subheading had changed from "Information on EPA's Pesticide Use/Reduction Initiative" to "Information on EPA's Pesticide Environmental Stewardship Program." *Update #2* states that the purpose of the initiative is to work toward "… achieving the Administration's goal of reducing the use and risks of pesticides in the United States." The President's 75 percent IPM adoption goal—the flagship of the whole

> *"Environmental protection requires a formidable array of analytical tools, but it is not purely a technocratic affair. Cost benefit and risk analysis are vitally important, but there is something more fundamental too: an ethical imperative to restore and conserve the natural order."*
>
> *"One of the first concerns of a moral order must be to clarify and uphold principles of conduct that promote the survival and fulfillment of the species. That compels us to recognize and correct the disharmony in the relationship between nature and humankind …"*
>
> **William K. Reilly,** *Then-Administrator, EPA*
> *From June 21, 1991 Address Before the "Conference on the Environment for Europe," Dobris Castle, Czechoslovakia (Quoted in* Washington Post, *July 10, 1991)*

> *"The pest control policy of the U.S. Department of Agriculture embraces the concept of integrated pest management. The policy of the Department of Agriculture is to practice and encourage the use of those means of effective pest control which provide the least potential hazard to man, his animals, wildlife, and the other components of the natural environment."*
>
> **Earl L. Butz,** *Secretary of Agriculture*
> *Excerpt from* Integrated Pest Management,
> *A Report by the Council on Environmental Quality, 1972*

program—is no longer mentioned.

Update #3 was issued in April 1995. It goes even further in distancing the agency from any specific reduction goals. It states that the Pesticide Environmental Stewardship Program "… is EPA's overall program designed to address the use and risks associated with pesticides." *Update #3* contains not a single reference to the need to *reduce* use or risks. Pesticide user-friendly language includes the need to "address" use and risks and the need to "encourage the use of safer pesticides,… use the safest, cost-effective, pest management practices…," and "…promote and implement pesticide environmental stewardship."

B. USDA Responds to the President's IPM Pledge

USDA announced a "National Plan to Increase the Use of IPM" at a December 14, 1994 press briefing. Materials distributed at the briefing provided the first official details of USDA's strategy to deliver on the President's June 1993 pledge "to help agricultural producers implement IPM methods on 75 percent of total crop acreage by the year 2000." USDA's press release included this definition of IPM (USDA, 1994e):

> "Integrated pest management is a systems approach that combines a wide array of crop production practices with careful monitoring of pests and their natural enemies. IPM practices include use of resistant varieties, timing of planting, cultivation, biological controls and judicious use of pesticides. These IPM practices are used in greenhouses and on field crops. IPM systems anticipate and prevent pests from reaching economically damaging levels."

In announcing its "aggressive IPM initiative," USDA said the plan "delivers on the Clinton Administration's commitment to help agricultural producers implement IPM methods on 75 percent of total crop acreage by the year 2000." The basic principles of USDA's IPM initiative were described in a "Backgrounder" distributed at the December 1994 press briefing:

- "Involving farmers and practitioners in the development and assessment of IPM programs improves USDA customer service and increases the adoption of IPM practices."

- "Streamlining and coordinating USDA IPM programs."

- "Increasing the use and adoption of IPM enables farmers to achieve both economic and environmental objectives."

In response to questions, USDA Deputy Secretary Richard Rominger said that the Administration was hoping to propose a modest increase in IPM funding in the FY 1996 budget, but acknowledged that resources were tight and likely to grow tighter in future fiscal years.

1. New Funding Proves Elusive

In its proposed FY 1995 budget, the USDA included among the "Highlights" a pesticide initiative that read in part:

"During 1993, the Administration announced plans to reform the Nation's pesticide laws to reduce the risks of pesticides to Americans, especially infants and children ... Scientific advances make it possible to rely more heavily on biological controls and advanced farm management systems. An important part of the USDA program

for 1995 is a $12 million increase for research and extension specifically targeted to developing and demonstrating the effectiveness of improved IPM systems and biological controls."

The increase in funding sought by the Administration, while modest, would have supported a significant increase in the nation's equally modest investment in IPM research and education. Never as enthusiastic about IPM or biological control as the Executive Branch, Congress actually cut funding for several IPM research and education activities in FY 1993 and FY 1994 and total funding remained nearly constant. The FY 1995 budget as passed increased total IPM funding from $187.1 to $194 million—just 3.7 percent and barely ahead of inflation.

Another Try in the FY 1996 Budget Cycle

The Administration again sought increased funding for IPM research and education activities in the USDA's FY 1996 budget request. The summary section of the request document states under "Highlights":

"The budget includes the funding needed to move ahead on the IPM initiative announced by the Department in December 1994. These are the programs that will deliver on the Administration's commitment to help agricultural producers implement IPM practices on 75 percent of total crop acreage by 2000."[4]

In the detailed section on science and education programs, the proposed FY 1996 budget calls for several changes in funding pertinent to IPM. Table 8.1 sets forth major changes in funding of IPM and related programs

USDA Deputy Secretary Richard Rominger has led the effort in USDA to shape and pursue a National IPM Initiative.
Credit: USDA

from FY 1994 through the FY 1997 budget. Note that the column in Table 8.1 marked "FY 1996 (Proposed)" is the funding levels sought by USDA and the Administration. The other columns report actual funding levels appropriated by Congress (or the best available estimate of funding, as appropriated).

The Administration's proposed FY 1996 budget called for a 13.5 percent increase in total IPM activities, a spending jump of $26.2 million. But this increase is less than meets the eye. About two-thirds would have focused on research and education activities designed to develop IPM systems and biological controls. The other one-third would support:

- efforts aimed at getting more pesticides registered or expanding product registrations to additional minor use crops.

- research used predominantly to assess the risks and benefits of pesticides under regulatory scrutiny, including work on pesticide physical and chemical properties and how they impact environmental fate, their modes of action, their toxicity to wildlife and pesticide benefits assessments.

- pesticide applicator safety and training activities.

Again showing its lack of enthusiasm for IPM, Congress actually reduced overall IPM and related program funding in the final FY 1996 budget, decreasing it by about $2 million below FY 1995 (see column "FY 1996 [Actual]" in Table 8.1). The research and education programs slated for the biggest percentage increase in the President's budget—a doubling from $18.3 million in FY 1995 to $36.3 in FY 1996—received less than a $3 million increase.

In its FY 1997 budget proposal, USDA called for a modest increase in overall IPM funding but a significant redirection of spending from "Applications" (down from $41 million to $27 million) to the IPM research and education activities (up from $21 million to $34 million).

But even these proposals and USDA's willingness to face the difficult task of internal redirection of funding were largely ignored by Congress. In final action on the FY 1997 budget, Congress held all IPM spending levels roughly at the same level as FY 1996.

C. EPA's Reduced Risk Initiative

The EPA announced in September 1993 a "Pesticide Use/Risk Reduction Initiative," a joint effort with USDA and the FDA. In her Congressional testimony September 21, 1993, EPA Administrator Browner framed one of the key issues—should the policy goal be reducing pesticide use, reducing risk or both?

"We are committed to making a concerted inter-agency effort to reduce pesticide risks and associated use ... We realize that ... a 25 percent reduction in the use of a highly toxic pesticide may be preferable to an 80 percent reduction in use of a relatively safer pesticide." (EPA, 1993)

The testimony laid out the basic components of EPA's reduced risk, safer pesticide initiative and its three goals: "to discourage the use of high risk pesticides," "to provide incentives for the development and commercialization of safer products," and "to encourage use of alternative control methods which decrease the reliance on toxic and persistent chemicals."

In an October 25, 1994 "Constituents Meeting" to discuss goals for the Office of Pesticide Programs (OPP), EPA Assistant Administrator Lynn Goldman stated the premise for ongoing regulatory reform efforts in OPP: "We feel there is a need for fundamental reform in the way we regulate pesticides in this country...." Dr. Goldman went on to say that EPA saw great promise in the application of pollution prevention strategies in reducing pesticide risks and felt that sustainable agriculture systems offered the best way to produce safer food and protect ecosystems.

1. A New Division Takes Over

Responsibility for EPA's Pesticide Environmental Stewardship Program (now called "Pest SMART") was transferred, on a pilot-program basis, to the Division on Biopesticides and Pollution Prevention, formed in November 1994 and initially composed of 33 employees. The program's major focus was expediting registration of "reduced risk" biopesticides (we define this term later). The division has developed criteria registrants are to use in making the case that a given application should be

Table 8.1 USDA IPM Initiative Funding Levels, FY 1994 through FY 1997 Budget Cycles (Millions of Dollars)
(*Actual* = Approved by Congress; *Proposed* = USDA Proposed Budget)

	FY 1994 (Actual)	FY 1995 (Actual)	FY 1996 (Proposed)	FY 1996 (Actual)	FY 1997 (Proposed)
IPM Initiative: Producer Identified Needs*					
IPM and Biological Control Research Grants	$3.0	$2.7	$7.0	$3.0	$8.0
Alternatives to Pesticides and Critical Issues	0.0	0.0	4.5	2.0	4.0
IPM Extension Education	8.5	10.9	15.0	11.0	15.0
ARS Areawide Research	3.8	4.5	9.5	4.0	6.0
ERS IPM Research	0.2	1.0	0.3	1.0	1.0
Total	15.5	18.3	36.3	$21.0	34.0
Ongoing Research					
Formula and Grants**	39.6	43.0	38.0	$37.0	65.0
ARS Research	55.0	60.0	58.4	62.0	37.0
Forest Service, ERS	10.1	11.0	10.8	9.0	9.0
Total	104.7	114.0	107.2	$108.0	111.0
IPM Applications in the Field					
APHIS Programs	18.6	15.0	15.6	14.0	13.0
FSA-ACP	8.5	6.0	11.8	7.0	8.0
Forest Service	18.4	18.0	7.1	20.0	6.0
Total	46.0	39.0	34.5	41.0	27.0
Pesticide Registration, Clearance, Assessment and Training					
Minor Use Clearance	8.4	7.8	17.1	8.0+	13.0
Pesticide Impact Assessment	6.4	6.2	7.8	6.0	6.0
Applicator Training	0.0	0.0	2.0	0.0	0.0
Total	14.8	14.0	26.9	14.0	19.0
Data Collection	6.1	7.0	15.3	8.0	12.0
Total, IPM/Related Programs	$187.1	$194.0	$220.2	$192.0	$203.0

*Acronyms in this table stand for the following USDA agencies and programs: ARS, Agricultural Research Service; ERS, Economic Research Service; APHIS, Animal and Plant Health Inspection Service; FSA-ACP, Farm Services Agency—Agricultural Conservation Program.

**Pest management related special grants in FY 1994 totaling $6.2 million are counted under "Ongoing Research"; special grants totaling $3.0 million in FY 1995 are counted under "Ongoing Research."

+ Includes $1.3 million special grant and $3.3 million in additional funding through the Extension 3(d) program.

Source: USDA Budget Summary FY 1996, Appendix "IPM and Related Programs" (page 107); USDA Budget Summary FY 1997, Appendix "IPM and Related Programs" (page 62).

EPA Sets "Safe Food" Goals for 2005

Progress toward biointensive IPM will be essential if EPA is to attain an ambitious set of goals set forth in late 1995 as part of an agencywide "Goals Report." EPA set the following milestones for the year 2005 (*Pesticide and Toxic Chemical News*, 1995b):

■ "Illegal residues of pesticides detected in FDA (Food and Drug Administration) monitoring of the food supply will be reduced 25 percent from current levels."

■ "There will be a significant reduction in use in food production of those pesticides which have the highest potential for carcinogenic effects."

■ "There will be no instances, in either adults or children, where pesticide reference dose (RfD, i.e. safe levels above which adverse effects would be expected in humans) is exceeded."

■ "90 percent of crop acreage and pesticide usage will be under IPM."

■ "The use of safe biological pesticides will increase 100 percent from the 1995 levels."

reviewed under a "fast-track" process. The division has exempted 32 biochemical pesticides from further regulation and drafted a "Pheromone Regulatory Relief Strategy" that is now being implemented.

A second goal has been working with agricultural commodity and pesticide user groups in voluntary partnerships promoting IPM adoption. As of early 1996, commodity and trade associations representing the corn, potato, pear and apple sectors; lawn care professionals and 17 utility companies have signed on to this voluntary program. Most of the participating associations have agreed to continue or expand their IPM research. In addi-

tion, the new division has helped provide seed money for a number of onfarm research and demonstration projects.

The box "Supporting Partnerships to Advance IPM" describes two promising efforts underway in California—the Biologically Integrated Orchard Systems Project (BIOS) and California Clean Marketing Group. Both are generating effective exchange among growers, researchers, IPM consultants, regulators, buyers and consumers. In an interview with *Farmer to Farmer*, a newsletter published by the Community Alliance with Family Farmers, a group that helped start the BIOS project, USDA Deputy Secretary

EPA (Press Releases) NTC EPA Awarded Grants

location http://www.epa.gov/PressReleases/

NTC EPA AWARDED GRANTS AIMED AT REDUCING PEST. USE AND RISK *FOR RELEASE: THURSDAY, AUGUST 8, 1996*

To improve public health and strengthen food safety protections from harmful pesticides, EPA has awarded grants totaling almost $740,000 aimed at reducing pesticide use and risk. The grants are part of the Pesticide Environmental Stewardship Program (PESP) *http://es.inel.gov/partners/pest/pest.html*

Partners for the Environment

The 1996 PESP Partnership grant winners are: (partial listing)
Hood River Grower-Shipper Association (Odell, Ore.): $30,000 for standardized pesticide record-keeping
Monroe County Community School Corporation (Bloomington, Ind.): $30,000 for IPM programs in Monroe County, Ind. schools.
The 1996 Regional Pollution Prevention Initiative Grant winners under PESP are: (partial listing)
Wisconsin Potato and Vegetable Growers Association (University of Wisconsin, Madison): $38,694 to enhance potato biological pest control.

Supporting Partnerships to Advance IPM

The Biologically Integrated Orchard Systems Project (BIOS) promotes biointensive IPM and soil fertility management systems, principally in almond and other orchard crops in several California counties. BIOS provides growers technical support in designing and carrying out participatory research centered on practical, customized farm plans that each grower develops and pursues. The BIOS project was recognized for its accomplishments in August 1994 by the Cal-EPA Department of Pesticide Regulation (DPR), which awarded one of its first "IPM Innovators" awards to the BIOS team.

The Lodi-Woodbridge Winegrape Commission, winner of a 1995 DPR "IPM Innovator" award, has pledged that 100 percent of its 650 growers will adopt at least six of nine environmentally friendly practices by the year 2000. These practices include a mix of the old and new—native grasses and cover crops, owl boxes, composting, leaf pulling, computer disease forecasting models, release of beneficials, reduced risk biopesticides, habitat restoration and drip irrigation (Lodi-Woodbrige, 1996).

The "California Clean Marketing Group" is another farmer-led organization that focuses on reducing reliance on high risk pesticides. Its mission is to "strengthen the connection between the customer and the farmer." Also recognized by a 1995 "IPM Innovator" award, California Clean is developing practical biointensive IPM systems that will help meet the needs of family farmers who are committed to the principles cited in the organization's 1995 "Guidelines." California Clean members pledge to:

- "Use ecologically sound practices.
- Strengthen their soils through a program of natural enrichment.
- Arrange their farms in ways that encourage wildlife to take up permanent residence.
- Create farm environments that encourage natural biological pest control.
- Create good working conditions for their workers and promote farm atmospheres which recognize the worker's individual contributions and worth.
- Deliver produce with superior taste and nutrition.
- Take time to communicate with consumers."

Each farmer-member of California Clean has a special label the family places on produce boxes. The label for one of the group's founding farm families, Paul and Ruth Buxman, features a painting of a ranch in the area. Paul Buxman also painted this book's cover.

Richard Rominger, a fourth-generation California family farmer, was asked what the department is doing to promote IPM:

> "Research in [pest management], helping farmers develop IPM systems. We're working with EPA to get softer pesticides registered more rapidly. We're looking for non-chemical alternatives for biological control, and getting biocontrol agents approved on a fast track. We're trying to get as many of these new pest control techniques available as fast as possible, so farmers will have a wider selection."

2. Focus on Registering Reduced Risk Biopesticides

The top priority for the new EPA division is expediting the registration of "reduced risk" biopesticides, which may be either microbial or genetically engineered products, or biochemical pesticides. EPA defines a "biochemical pesticide" as a pesticide active ingredient (or ingredients) made from natural sources like a pheromone (or close synthetic analogues that work the same way and pose essentially identical toxicological risks), that works through a non-toxic mode of action and is free of possibly toxic impurities or metabolites. Microbial and genetically engineered biopesticides can include bacteria, fungi, viruses and natural toxins produced by microbes. *Bacillus thuringiensis (Bt)* is perhaps the best known example. The *Bt* toxin can be produced in a fermentation vat by bacteria and then extracted and formulated as a foliar pesticide product or it can be engineered into transgenic plants that then produce the *Bt* toxin in leaf tissue (see below and Chapter 6 for more discussion).

Administrator Browner's September 1993 testimony points out that: "Biological pesticides comprise the single fastest growing segment of registration activity…In the past two years [1992-1993] 50 percent to 70 percent of all new pesticide active ingredients registered have been biologicals" (EPA, 1993a). A key goal for the new division is to simplify the registration process for biopesticides. This will mean altering some data requirements and decision criteria to reflect biopesticides' unique properties and modes of action—and comparative safety, in most cases—in contrast to synthetic chemicals.

Biopesticides include compounds that are complex mixtures of natural substances, making it difficult to determine exactly what constituents account for a product's efficacy. This complicates the EPA's pesticide registration process, which is driven by the evaluation of active ingredients' properties. The agency is still trying to determine how to evaluate and regulate biopesticides that contain multiple active agents derived from natural sources, many of which may be present at very low levels and have unknown biological activity, or those that work through multiple modes of action, some of which may be triggered only under specific sets of circumstances

Cindy Lashbrook (left) is a licensed Pest Control Advisor (PCA) in California and works closely with several growers participating in the BIOS project. Here Cindy is discussing the beneficial insects just captured in her sweep net during a BIOS project field day. Credit: Community Alliance with Family Farmers (soil temperature, fertility status, the presence of certain microorganisms). The goal of expediting registration of such materials has proven elusive, although EPA recommitted itself July 13, 1995 to speedier action on reduced risk pesticides that show promise, such as alternatives for methyl bromide.[5]

The EPA registered 40 new active ingredients in FY 1995, 21 of which are biopesticides. These included two "Plant-Pesticides" as EPA calls them—*Bt*-transgenic potatoes (Monsanto) and *Bt* corn (Ciba Seeds and Mycogen) (EPA, 1995d), in addition to one *Bt* foliar insecticide formulation, eight microbial pesticides and two pheromones.

Drawing the Lines: A Key Hurdle

EPA is working out the criteria it will use in judging whether a pesticide will receive expedited treatment as a "reduced risk" biopesticide (see the box "Not All Pesticides Are Created Equal"). As we noted in Chapter 3, there are vast differences in the mammalian toxicity of registered pesticides. The most hazardous group of insecticides used in agriculture today is more than 2,800 times as acutely toxic as the least toxic group. (The range in consumer products is much narrower since none of the most toxic active ingredients used in agriculture are approved for home use products.) There are also wide differences in the ecological risks posed by pesticides.

Thus, it is often possible and generally desirable for EPA to distinguish between "risky" and "reduced risk" products. And now there is a another challenge—distinguishing between comparatively "reduced risk" products and absolutely "low risk" biopesticides. A "reduced risk" pesticide product poses risks comparable in nature to other products but markedly lower; "low risk" biopesticides typically pose much more narrow and much lower risks in all conceivable circumstances when used in accord with product labels.

In addition to mammalian toxicity, EPA must consider both ecological and environmental risks when deciding whether a new pesticide, or a plant-pesticide, warrants "fast track" approval as a "low risk" biopesticide. Given the unique ecological risks posed by transgenic plants, we do not think plant-pesticides should be classified or reviewed as "low risk" biopesticides, at least not until much more is learned from well-controlled field studies under a wide variety of conditions routinely encountered on the farm—drought, floods and wet conditions, nutrient stress, and use in conjunction with other pesticides.

The Nature of "Low Risk" Biopesticides

Biopesticides and related biocontrol organisms can play particularly important roles in the transition from chemical-dependent systems to biointensive IPM. We believe that "low risk" biopesticides should include products and technologies:

■ that are applied by methods or at rates so low that they pose virtually no risk under the proposed label uses and restrictions. Pheromones, chemicals insects emit to attract members of the opposite sex, are a contemporary example.

The USDA's Agricultural Research Service (ARS) has begun to focus a share of its pest management research effort on biopesticides, especially in situations where there are no effective conventional pesticides. This Maricopa, Arizona cotton field is being sprayed with a combination of soap and vegetable oil to manage sweetpotato whiteflies, a serious and relatively new cotton insect pest in many states.
Credit: Jack Dykinga, ARS

Many Florida vegetable growers have been using pheromones to manage tomato pinworm since the early 1990s, one of the earliest large scale field applications of mating disruption technology. Here, Galen Frantz (right), a crop consultant with Glades Crop Care, is attaching pheromone-containing cards onto tomato plant stakes, with a representative of the firm supplying the product. Prior to the introduction of this biopesticide, most Crop Care clients controlled pinworms with multiple applications of a tank-mix of Lannate (methomyl) and Monitor (methamidophos), a high-risk combination of products.
Credit: Glades Crop Care

■ that quickly and harmlessly dissipate through interactions with microorganisms in the soil or on plant tissues, or break down into known, ubiquitous and non-toxic elements through well documented pathways. Likely candidates for this category include *Bacillus thuringiensis* when applied as a foliar spray, *Bacillus cereus* seed inoculants and fatty acid soaps.

■ whose residue levels in or on food at harvest, or in the home, garden or urban environment, are no more than 10 times above levels found naturally in or on plants, in the soil or in water, and there is no evidence of toxicity or reason to suspect health problems associated with consumption of the biopesticide or closely related natural or synthetic analogs.

Not All Pesticides Are Created Equal

A key goal of EPA's reduced risk initiative is to develop criteria to delineate safer, reduced risk pesticides, as well as better ways to identify high risk pesticides. Regulatory relief and streamlining measures would be focused on the former, and regulatory restrictions would target the latter. Pesticides that do not fall into either the reduced risk or high risk categories would continue to be reviewed and regulated under the current process, but on a slower schedule. The bulk of agency resources will be devoted to expanding the range of safer alternatives and cutting back on use of high risk chemicals.

The agency has held a number of public meetings, published Federal Register notices, and floated proposals of methods to delineate "safer," reduced risk pesticides. We think the essential elements of a refined classification scheme should include evaluation of a pesticide's active ingredient and inert ingredients in terms of:

■ Potential toxicity to consumers, applicators, farm workers, farmers and others who live in or near areas where the pesticide is being applied.

■ Capacity to kill or harm beneficial non-target organisms at the rates of application commonly needed to control target pests.

■ Impact on biodiversity and ecological interactions that play a role in nutrient cycling or biological control.

■ Persistence and environmental fate once applied—will use of the pesticide as called for on the label pose risks to water quality, ecosystem integrity or to wildlife?

■ that reinforce biological or ecological processes and interactions that undermine a pest's ability to reach damaging population levels, or otherwise enhance a plant's ability to overcome a level of pest pressure without sacrificing yield or crop quality.

EPA is working to accelerate registration of "reduced risk" biopesticides—those derived largely from natural sources, including plant extracts, microorganisms, viruses and natural chemicals made by insects that play a role in molting, energy utilization, the ability to find food or a mate, or complete stages of development. In Chapter 9 we offer suggestions regarding how EPA could sharpen its ability to distinguish between "reduced risk" pesticides and "low risk" biopesticides and provide additional incentives for the development and registration of the latter.

Modes of Action—A Key Criterion

Many categories of biopesticides are easy to classify as working through a non-toxic mode of action— pheromones, most soil microbial stimulants and inoculants that help protect plant roots from diseases by crowding out other damaging pathogens. A non-toxic mode of action does not depend on rendering direct harm or insult to target organisms, but nonetheless leads to reductions in the virulence or population levels of target pests. Given the vast diversity of organisms' interactions in the real world, it will be difficult in some cases to draw the line between a "toxic" and "non-toxic" mode of action.

Some microbial pesticides, including *Bt* toxin, attack the lining of an insect's gut, causing it to leak. The insect becomes progressively lethargic and eventually starves. Some microbial seed inoculants protect roots from pathogens by emitting antibiotics that are directly toxic to target microbes. A wide range of natural plant constituents, produced as a normal part of a plant's defense mechanisms, are toxic (directly poisonous) to certain pests—that is why the plant produces them. If a biopesticide contains such a natural constituent, or increases a plant's production of one, would the biopesticide be judged as working through a "non-toxic" mode of action?

EPA and USDA will need to rely on additional information and criteria in drawing distinctions in difficult cases. Two basic questions should be answered—to what is the biopesticide potentially toxic and with what consequence? In the case of most *Bt* strains, the mode of action is toxic, but it is also relatively specific. There is no comparable mode of action in organisms other than lepidopteran insects (although some lepidopteran species are

non-target organisms, including butterflies).[7] Hence, one criterion could be whether non-target organisms could be vulnerable to harm through the same or a similar mode of action under the proposed conditions of use.

> *"For 25 years, nobody used it—it was just an unusual product on the shelf. It took 25 years for it to get visibility."*
>
> **Dr. Louis Falcon,** *University of California–Berkeley*
> *Reflecting on the history of* Bt *discovery and commercialization*[6]

Other criteria applicable to microbial biopesticides might address the capacity of affected non-target microorganisms to recover quickly (within several days to a few weeks) to near pre-application population levels, and whether a short term impact on their population levels is of any consequence to the performance of the farming system, the integrity of food chains or ecosystem health.

Not all products that qualify as biopesticides are benign in agroecosystems. The insecticide neem, which contains azadirachtin and other biologically active natural compounds, is as toxic to some beneficial arthropods as the organophosphate and pyrethroid insecticides it replaces (Bottrell and Lim, 1994). Problems have also been documented recently in South Africa with certain insect growth regulators (IGRs) used in citrus pest management (Hattingh, 1996):

> "Widespread use of certain IGRs…has resulted in repercussion outbreaks of previously unimportant pests. Bioassays have shown that a number of economically important biocontrol agents are sensitive to some of these products."

Compared to most conventional pesticides, biopesticides clearly pose less risks on a pound-for-pound or acre-treated basis, but they are not risk free. Some biopesticides may trigger unexpected changes in species diversity and interactions, leading to different sorts of "secondary" pest problems. For example, a biopesticide seed inoculant that helps protect a plant from root diseases like the wheat disease Take-all might prove so competitive in some circumstances that it crowds out mycorrhizae needed to make phosphorous available to roots. Also, if relied upon too heavily, biopesticides can induce resistance in pest populations and trigger unwelcomed ecological problems. In the quest for survival, organisms are blind to the "synthetic versus natural" debate and deploy the same adaptive instincts and capabilities in overcoming any threats they face.

3. Special Caution Needed In Regulating Transgenic Plants

Several categories of genetically-engineered plants pose serious ecological and environmental risks, and need to be evaluated with a heightened sense of caution, especially given recent developments discussed here and in Chapter 6. One worry is that an herbicide resistance gene transferred into an agronomic plant variety may find its way into wild relatives of the crops, thereby enhancing their potential to become weeds (or making them harder to control if they are already weeds).

Such transgene flow to wild relatives has already been documented. Research with canola (*Brassica napus*) engineered to be herbicide tolerant has demonstrated that the tolerance gene can move from the canola into wild mustard (*B. campestris*), a close relative and serious weed pest of canola (Jorgensen and Andersen, 1994). Recent research demonstrated that the now transgenic weeds not only expressed the herbicide tolerance gene, but also were just as hardy and fit as their non-transgenic counterparts (i.e., they set the same number of seeds and were comparably competitive in the field) (Mikkelsen et al., 1996). Indeed, after two

> **Relying on biopesticides the same way many farmers use insecticides today will cause many of the same problems associated with conventional pesticide use. In the quest for survival, organisms are blind to the "synthetic versus natural" debate and deploy the same adaptive capabilities in overcoming the threats they face.**

generations over 40 percent of the wild mustard in surveyed fields contained the herbicide tolerance gene—a development that defeats the purpose of this technology and complicates certain herbicide-based weed management systems.

A more widespread concern with herbicide tolerant plants is the likelihood they will accelerate the emergence of resistant weed species. Now that Roundup-resistant weeds have been documented in Australia (see Chapters 2 and 6), resistance is a known problem with all the herbicide active ingredients associated with already approved herbicide tolerant plant varieties. Farmers planting herbicide tolerant varieties will typically rely more on the herbicide to which the crop variety is no longer susceptible. Gaining the ability to apply the herbicides more frequently or possibly at higher rates per acre is the major reason farmers are willing to pay the higher cost for transgenic seed. Such changes in the pattern of herbicide use, though, are almost custom-made for accelerating resistance. In addition, the clear evidence of multiple- and cross-resistance to sulfonylurea and imidazolinone herbicides in several weeds suggests that the planting of transgenic varieties tolerant to any herbicide active ingredient in these chemical families is likely to hasten the day when *all* products containing these or related (by mode of action) active ingredients will be marginally

Cal–EPA and DPR News Releases

location http://www.cdpr.ca.gov/docs/pressrls/newhaven.htm

NEW HAVEN SCHOOL DISTRICT TO GET AWARD FOR INNOVATIONS IN ENVIRONMENTALLY FRIENDLY PEST CONTROL | June 17, 1996:

"The award recognizes the work of the district's garden department in using environmentally friendly ways to fight insects, weeds, and other pests in school landscaping."

You can sign up to have news releases sent automatically to your e-mail address. (The subscription is free.)

Cal/EPA
Department of Pesticide Regulation

"In March, DPR distributed nearly $600,000 in grants to pursue projects in reduced-risk pest management. Among the 24 recipients statewide was the San Francisco Green Gardening Educator Training Program; a program to set up a model IPM program to control pests in buildings at Moffett Field; and a project to study controlled atmosphere as an alternative to methyl bromide post harvest fumigation in Santa Cruz, San Luis Obispo, and Yolo Counties."

effective. This is a sobering prospect given agriculture's current high and rising reliance on herbicides that fall within these chemical families.

Bt-Transgenic Plants—A Special Case

Similar concerns exist for plants engineered to produce pesticidal substances. If the engineered substances are foreign to the plant and close relatives, they may flow into related plants and enhance their ability to compete, in the process turning them into weeds. A greater ecological concern centers around the crop varieties engineered to produce the Bt endotoxin in their tissues. These transgenic plants greatly exacerbate the potential for resistance to Bt to emerge and spread among lepidopteran insects, thereby undermining the future efficacy of Bt foliar insecticides, which control lepidopteran insects during their larval (caterpillar) stage.

The loss of Bt to resistance triggered by Bt-transgenic plants would be a major setback for American agriculture, especially fruit and vegetable growers in the Southeast and organic producers nationwide. Insects that Bt can control include many difficult to manage pests leading to heavy reliance on insecticides in a wide range of crops—the cabbage looper, diamondback moth, major insect pests of cotton (bollworm, tobacco budworm), corn borer, the Colorado potato beetle, the beet armyworm, gypsy moth, spruce budworm and many other tough to control pests. Bt foliar products are the foundation of most biointensive

IPM systems in Florida fruit and vegetable regions. Organic farmers producing certified produce are even more reliant on Bt products than their conventional neighbors because they are not able to use conventional pesticides without sacrificing their ability to market produce as organic.

Bt is unlike synthetic insecticides, which are discovered, patented, developed and marketed for the purpose of pest management. A company which manufacturers and markets synthetic chemical insecticide products to which insects develop resistance will bear a major share of the financial consequences of a failed resistance management plan. When the costs of resistance are borne by the company that also stands to profit from the future sales of a product, there is a strong incentive for attention to resistance management.

But Bt is different. It is properly viewed as a valuable—and now vulnerable—natural resource uniquely useful and safe for the purpose of insect pest management. Companies selling foliar Bt products and marketing Bt-transgenic plants did not discover Bt nor its insecticidal properties. They have developed new and more efficient ways to produce and deliver this natural product into agroecosystems. But new transgenic delivery mechanisms threaten to undermine the efficacy of all Bt-based products. The slim prospects for managing resistance in areas where significant cropland is planted to Bt-transgenic varieties is reviewed in the box "Bt-Transgenic Plants and Resistance: Just a Matter of Time."

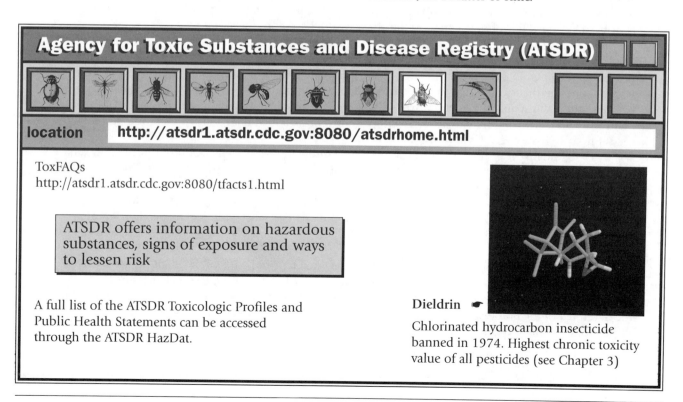

If *Bt*-transgenic plants quickly lead to resistance, as it appears they already are doing, do growers who lose their ability to control lepidopteran insects deserve compensation? Who will pay for the increased public and private costs that will accompany rising reliance on conventional, high risk organophosphate and carbamate insecticide alternatives to *Bt*?

Clearly, new criteria are needed to guide decision-making in identifying "low risk" biopesticides and in regulating transgenic plants. EPA must also quickly modify its past decisions in response to new insights gained from developments in the field. Serious concerns were raised by many experts that transgenic plant varieties would accelerate resistance if planted widely in the field. Their warnings are now reinforced by widespread problems with *Bt* cotton in the field in 1996. The emergence of Roundup resistant weeds is an ominous development, as is the dramatic increase in the rate of growth in herbicide resistant weed species—many displaying both multiple- and cross-resistance to two of the herbicide

chemical families most commonly the target of companies developing herbicide tolerant plant varieties. In light of these developments EPA should reconsider some past decisions and change policies governing future approval of transgenic plants. In Chapter 9 we recommend prudent steps EPA should take before the 1997 planting season to begin nudging agricultural biotechnology onto a path more solidly supportive of progress along the IPM continuum.

The task of identifying and granting fast-track approvals for "low risk" biopesticides is going to require attention to detail and the exercise of prudent caution. EPA must constantly question whether approval of biopesticides will lower one category of risk only to increase others. One of the fundamental criteria EPA should apply is whether a biopesticide or transgenic plant is inherently compatible with biointensive IPM, because it works through manipulation of largely biological processes and ecological interactions. Biopesticides or transgenic plants that simply make it possible to use pes-

Bt-Transgenic Plants and Resistance: Just a Matter of Time

Companies marketing *Bt*-transgenic plant varieties have developed and submitted resistance management plans to the EPA. The scientific review of these plans has generated much controversy. Many leading entomologists consider the plans unlikely to work and inadequately grounded in sound science. None of the plans has ever been shown to work in the field. Disappointing results in cotton producing regions in 1996 have severely undermined any prospect that the resistance management plans, as currently conceived, can be relied upon to preserve the efficacy of *Bt*-based products.

In seeking regulatory approval of *Bt*-transgenic plants, companies have rested their arguments on a "high dose" strategy, coupled with the planting of refugia (rows of the crop are planted to a variety not producing the *Bt* endotoxin in plant tissues, to serve as a refuge for *Bt*-susceptible insects to breed with resistant ones, in theory diluting the spread of resistance in a population). The "high dose" strategy is based on the premise that the *Bt* endotoxin will be expressed at such high levels and so evenly through all plant tissue that any lepidopteran larvae feeding on the plant will be killed with virtually 100 percent efficacy. If no insects survive, resistance will not emerge.

In 1996, the first year of widespread commercial planting of *Bt*-transgenic cotton, control failures have occurred across the cotton belt (Kaiser, 1996; see also discussion of *Bt*-transgenic plants in Chapter 6). The transgenic cotton appears to be working against the tobacco budworm, but has failed in many areas against the cotton bollworm. Preliminary research shows that the bollworm can tolerate much higher levels of *Bt* than the budworm. As Don Johnson, cotton insect specialist with the Cooperative Research Service, noted, "We had larvae in the lab you could feed *Bt* cotton, and they'd live off it just as well as regular cotton" (Associated Press, 1996).

In addition, it appears that bollworm larvae have learned to avoid parts of the plant expressing lethal concentrations of *Bt*, a mechanism referred to as "behavioral tolerance." (The insect changes its feeding behavior to minimize its exposure to a pesticide.) These two factors undermine the assertion by Monsanto, the developer of the *Bt*-transgenic cotton, that the endotoxin will be expressed at high enough levels throughout the plant to guarantee nearly 100 percent efficacy against all lepidopteran pests.

ticides or natural pesticidal compounds in new situations (herbicide tolerant plants for example), or deliver toxins in a novel way or in more potent forms (*Bt*-transgenic plants), do nothing to reduce reliance on pesticides. Their intent is to treat symptoms; biocontrol organisms and biopesticides compatible with biointensive IPM help relieve symptoms by altering the underlying circumstances that create or sustain an opening for pests. This distinction is of fundamental importance and EPA must become expert at recognizing it.

[1] European pesticide use reduction programs have decreased the total pounds of pesticides applied by 50 percent to 75 percent, yet about two-thirds of this reduction has been achieved by switching to lower dose products and more careful calibration and operation of equipment (Organization for Economic Cooperation and Development, 1996; Mateson, 1995). One-third or less of the reduction has been brought about through adoption of IPM practices and systems that have lessened reliance on pesticides. Steps are underway in several European countries to rectify this shortcoming.

[2] Section (i), page 71, draft bill dated April 13, 1994.

[3] EPA Workshop Summary, Day 2 session on the Reduced Risk Initiative.

[4] USDA FY 1996 Budget Summary, page 12.

[5] PR Notice 95-4, "Regulatory Status of Methyl Bromide and Priority Review of Methyl Bromide Alternatives."

[6] Quote from "Keeping Faith," an article on a biopesticide for control of codling moth, *California Farmer*, April 1996.

[7] *Bt* harms butterflies and moths during their larval stage. This has surfaced as a concern in some agricultural areas, as well as where *Bt* has been sprayed over large tracts of forests to control gypsy moth or spruce budworm. Impacts on butterfly and moth populations may also have adverse impacts on food chains and other species if *Bt* use is widespread and sustained. To date, the economic costs of *Bt*-based spray programs have limited adverse ecological impacts.

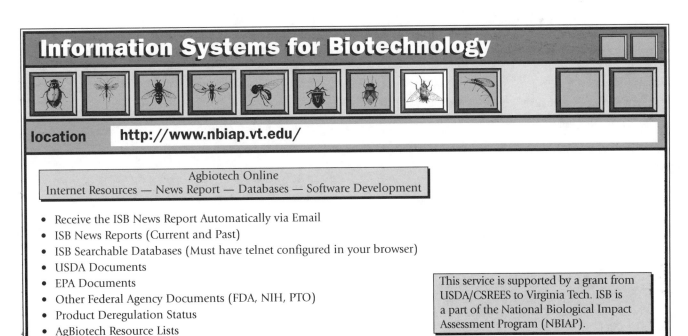

Information Systems for Biotechnology

location http://www.nbiap.vt.edu/

> Agbiotech Online
> Internet Resources — News Report — Databases — Software Development

- Receive the ISB News Report Automatically via Email
- ISB News Reports (Current and Past)
- ISB Searchable Databases (Must have telnet configured in your browser)
- USDA Documents
- EPA Documents
- Other Federal Agency Documents (FDA, NIH, PTO)
- Product Deregulation Status
- AgBiotech Resource Lists
- U.S. Biotechnology Centers
- Annotated List of WWW Sites Pertaining to Agricultural Biotechnology

This service is supported by a grant from USDA/CSREES to Virginia Tech. ISB is a part of the National Biological Impact Assessment Program (NBIAP).

Recommendations

Biointensive IPM is feasible and desirable, but many obstacles remain. Here, we map out ways to accelerate progress along the IPM continuum and concrete steps that consumers, business and government should take now.

The transition to biointensive IPM has begun but is moving far too slowly. This chapter sets forth an agenda to accelerate the pace of change by overcoming obstacles and rewarding innovation.

Public willingness to invest in IPM and support it in the marketplace is based largely on desire to lower pesticide risks to human health and the environment. The evidence reviewed in Chapters 3 and 4 shows that the policies of the last 25 years have not effectively reduced pesticide risks. In fact, many Americans today face greater pesticide risks than their parents did.

But there are also other important reasons to promote progress along the IPM continuum more aggressively. In a growing number of situations, pesticides are working poorly or making pest management more difficult. In agriculture, some chemical-intensive pest management systems are nearing the end of the line on the pesticide treadmill, placing the livelihood of farmers in jeopardy and sharply increasing pesticide use, risks and costs. Where reliance on insecticides is heavy, pest population resistance and negative impacts on natural enemies continue to worsen. The direct costs and hidden externalities of pesticide-based systems are rising, and costs of regulation, monitoring and other efforts to minimize pesticide risks are high and projected to rise. Many of these costs are borne by all consumers and taxpayers, not just by those using pesticides.

The public has consistently expected more from government regulation of pesticides than it can realistically deliver. Despite its inherent limitations and high cost, regulation has a role to play, but needs to fulfill it more decisively. Major legislation passed in July 1996 gives EPA clearer direction to adjust pesticide tolerance levels so that even vulnerable population groups like infants, children and the unborn will have a "reasonable certainty of no harm" from exposure to pesticide residues. But the task is complex, and EPA is likely to meet significant resistance as it tries to carry out this mandate.

Our Conclusion

The best way to lower pesticide risks is to reduce reliance on pesticides through a transition to biointensive IPM. That will take time, effort, innovation and investment. But collective efforts to adopt biointensive IPM offer major and sustained benefits in effective pest control, lower risks and costs, and reduced inefficiencies associated with pesticide regulation. Our recommendations focus on strategies to accelerate progress toward this goal.

A. Mapping the Transition to Biointensive IPM

Setting meaningful goals is the essential first step. Consumers, farmers and public officials need clear targets to aim for, and information on what is needed to attain them. The overriding goal of national policy should be to make progress along the IPM continuum, from wherever one begins, in all pest management contexts. Progress toward biointensive IPM is the surest, most cost-effective way to reduce reliance on pesticides, which in turn is the best way to reduce pesticide risks.

Government needs to set overall goals and help monitor progress, but the process of change will depend mostly on market forces and on the people, businesses and institutions closer to the action. Grower groups, commodity organizations, the research and education communities, food processors, the pesticide and biological-control industries, regulators and citizen groups will need to cooperate in translating broad, generally stated national goals into concrete and meaningful crop-by-crop, state and regional goals. From those more specific goals will emerge the iterative process of identifying and overcoming technical and economic hurdles to progress along the IPM continuum.

1. The Appropriate Role of Government

In 1993, President Clinton challenged the nation to adopt IPM on 75 percent of agricultural cropland by the year 2000. The President's declaration identified needs and set in motion many activities, which now need a sharper focus and a better sense of direction.

The "National IPM Initiative" has thus far generated much hopeful talk and useful planning activity, but Congressional opposition to redirecting funding to support IPM has truncated USDA's ability to follow through with

Eldon Lundberg and family produce organic rice in California. Over the years, the Lundbergs have developed several novel biointensive weed and rice weevil IPM practices involving water and rice straw management. Many conventional rice farmers in the region are adapting Lundburg farm innovations in their own operations as they progress along the IPM continuum. (See case study number 11 in the NRC report Alternative Agriculture *for further details, NRC, 1989a).*
Credit: Richard Steven Street

promises made to the grower and research communities. Many people in the field are frustrated and growing skeptical about whether IPM is really a national priority. For government to provide direction and needed leadership for ongoing IPM efforts, we must reassess what government can legitimately accomplish and realistically deliver.

"Government" includes a panoply of federal, state and local legislative bodies, executive agencies and other institutions that regulate pesticides, carry out research on pest management, administer training and certification programs, issue permits, and provide information. But two federal agencies—USDA and EPA—bear special responsibilities in setting goals, establishing priorities, adjusting policy tools and strategies, and taking actions that make the best use of available financial and technical assistance resources. Consequently, many of our recommendations focus on steps these two federal agencies should take.

Government must do more than set goals and issue challenges if it expects either to be taken seriously. We are not confident that two traditional approaches—stricter and more sweeping regulation, or offering new financial incentives to change behavior—will bring about all needed changes in pest management systems. New approaches are essential. We have focused on some we believe offer the greatest promise.

First, government can and should seek to shape and tap market forces to hasten progress toward biointensive IPM.

Second, government should also incrementally adjust policies and priorities as a function of whether acceptable progress is being made. The mileposts and timetables for the expected transition should be clearly articulated, along with descriptions of the expected policy responses if progress lags. By creating a predictable policy environment, government can help change private sector spending and investment patterns and broaden the foundation that will support biointensive IPM.

2. Goals for Progress Toward Biointensive IPM

We urge the next Administration, in partnership with Congress, to restate the nation's IPM goals for the next five, 10 and 25 years. The goals need to be more sharply focused and clearly articulated, broader in vision, and more directly linked to things the government pledges to do to help achieve the goals. We urge USDA to adopt the IPM measurement methodology outlined in Chapter 7, or one similar to it, when assessing progress.

A timetable is essential. Mileposts and monitoring methods and responsibilities—how and by whom progress is to be measured—must be set forth clearly. The plan should also specify how policy will be adjusted to accelerate progress where it is lagging.

In 1994, USDA estimated that at least 50 percent of agricultural acreage was already under one of three levels of IPM. We think USDA's criteria for defining IPM overstated where we are in the transition to biointensive IPM, and provided unduly modest national goals. The next Administration should work with Congress to reformulate the basic goals, plans and policy tools comprising the National IPM Initiative. Key elements should include:

Basic Goal *The overriding goal of policy should be to promote incremental steps toward biointensive IPM, from all points along the IPM continuum.*

An Overall Target *The overall long-term goal should be universal adoption of biointensive IPM in agriculture, forestry, urban and household settings by the year 2020.*

A New Foundation *The definition of IPM used in setting goals and developing action plans should be grounded firmly in the ecological roots of biointensive IPM.*

First Steps *An essential first step is to estimate baseline levels of IPM adoption, to determine where along the continuum of pest management systems specific crops, regions and the nation as a whole are at present.*

A Key Concept *The distinguishing characteristic of IPM systems along the continuum should be relative reliance on prevention-based practices and strategies compared to reliance on treatments with pesticides.*

And a Wider Scope *Goals for progress toward IPM should be developed for pest management challenges outside of agriculture—urban and indoor pest management, forestry, mosquito control, and other settings.*

In all sectors, initial efforts to promote progress toward biointensive IPM should focus on pest management systems where reliance on high risk pesticides is comparatively heavy. Examples include strawberries, cotton, termite control, golf course and urban lawn care, potato disease and insect pest management, weed management in corn and soybean crops, and major fruit and vegetable crops, especially those that play important roles in the diets of infants and children. Progress and experience gained from these high-priority cases can be applied in other circumstances and locations.

Specific Goals for Progress

As we have explained in Chapter 7, IPM adoption occurs incrementally along a continuum of pest management systems, from those largely reliant on pesticides to those in which biologically based preventive practices keep pest populations below levels warranting pesticide use.

Measuring IPM adoption and setting goals for progress in agriculture must be crop- and region-specific, since soils, climate, technology and pest pressure vary so greatly across the country. Our collective goal should be accelerating progress along the IPM continuum, from wherever on the continuum a crop or a region begins. Looking at U.S. agriculture in the aggregate, and based on our analysis in Chapter 7, we recommend the following goals:

By the year 2010, *75 percent of cropland should be under "Medium" or "High" (biointensive) IPM, including nearly 100 percent of fruit and vegetable acreage.*

By the year 2020, *all acreage in American agriculture should be managed under biointensive IPM.*

Similar goals can be set for IPM adoption in urban, suburban and household pest management contexts. In these settings, the potential for direct exposure of large numbers of people to pesticides is greater, but pest management is often easier. We therefore believe more rapid progress is essential and feasible here, and recommend that:

In urban, suburban, household and other indoor pest management, *biointensive IPM should be nearly universal by the year 2010.*

Our research shows that the largest reductions in pesticide use and risk are generally achieved by moving from the "No IPM" zone into the "Low" IPM zone, and from the "Low" to "Medium" zones along the continuum. We also believe that in most circumstances, the toughest transition will be from "Medium" level to biointensive IPM.

Figure 9.1 displays our recommended goals for progress along the IPM continuum in agriculture. The left column in the figure presents our best estimate of baseline adoption of IPM in the early 1990s (see Chapter 7). Goals for the year 2000 are in the second column, the third shows goals for 2010, and the fourth, our goal for 2020.

Changing circumstances may require revising goals, either for the nation or on a smaller scale. New technical and economic hurdles will emerge, while others will subside. New strains of pests come and go. New pesticide risk concerns may arise, or old worries abate. Breakthroughs may occur in microbial biological control, and in understanding how to build soil quality and productivity. If world food demand grows faster than supplies, foreign purchases of U.S. farm commodities may grow and prices rise. Increasing production could lead to shifts in land use patterns, pest problems, and pest management systems, and to renewed debate over the safest and most sustainable ways to increase agricultural productivity. While goals may need to be revised, we will always need credible methods to monitor IPM adoption, its impacts on pesticide reliance, and pesticide use and risk levels.

3. Reducing Pesticide Reliance, Use and Risks

One initial focus of the Clinton Administration's IPM Initiative was on developing targets for quantitative reductions in pesticide use (see Chapter 8). However, pesticide use reduction does not ensure progress toward biointensive IPM. Progress along the IPM continuum is the overriding goal, and should be given the greatest weight in shaping policy, planning exercises and priorities. We believe that progress toward biointensive IPM is the surest, most sustainable way to reduce pesticide risks from today's levels. If IPM adoption expands and there is significant collective progress made toward biointensive IPM, pesticide reliance, use and risks will inevitably decrease.

While we decline to recommend specific numerical goals for reducing pesticide use, reliance or risks, we

believe such reductions are implicit expectations of the transition to biointensive IPM. Progress toward these objectives needs to be closely monitored, so that policy makers and the public can tell whether progress in adopting IPM is having the expected economic and risk-reducing benefits. In some regions and for many crops, it will be easier to measure pesticide use and reliance than it will be to monitor progress along the IPM continuum, and the former can serve as a useful, if indirect, indicator of the latter.

To ensure that this critical information is provided, we recommend:

New Measurement Methodologies *USDA and EPA need to develop improved, scientifically rigorous techniques for measuring aggregate pesticide use, reliance and risks.*

Establishing Baselines and Documenting Progress *Initial effort should focus on determining current levels of use, reliance and risks for crops, regions and the nation as a whole. Thereafter, periodic reports should be issued to track progress as each of these indices of pesticide problems declines with progress along the IPM continuum.*

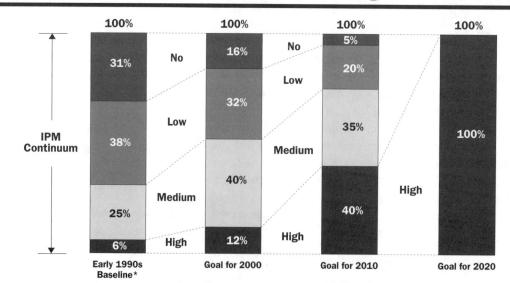

Figure 9.1 Consumers Union's Goals for Progress Along the IPM Continuum in Agriculture Through the Year 2020

Distribution of Harvested Acreage

* Based on Consumers Union's Best Estimates; see Chapter 7.

Establishing national goals for pesticide use reduction and getting all the stakeholders to agree to pursue them would be certain to involve EPA and USDA in a protracted and contentious political process. In contrast, measuring pesticide reliance and risks, and tracking progress as IPM adoption reduces both, are more clearly appropriate tasks for government, as well as essential to the overall process. USDA and EPA should lead the effort to develop appropriate analytical methods, with input from experts in the private sector, consumer and environmental organizations.

As we noted in Chapters 2 and 3, better methods are needed for measuring pesticide reliance and risks. Quantitative measures such as pounds applied can be misleading, since switching to a more potent pesticide can reduce pounds applied even if the intensity of reliance and the risks associated with applications actually increase. We presented our own methods for measuring reliance (in Chapter 2) and overall human health risk (in Chapter 3), and we believe those approaches, or similar ones that other analysts might develop, should be used for the monitoring effort we envision. In addition:

Compare Risks Per Area Treated *Efforts to monitor and reduce pesticide risks should be based on use and risks per acre, household, or other area actually treated, taking into account application rates and frequency, relative toxicity levels, and the properties of both the active ingredients and the inerts in each end-use product.*

Reduce Reliance on Types of Pesticides *To implement the mandates in the newly passed food safety bill (H.R. 1627), EPA must focus on reducing use of closely related active ingredients whose risks may add up because they have a common mechanism of toxicity.*

While government has a natural leadership role to play in measuring and tracking changes in pesticide use, reliance and risks, many other researchers and interested parties have knowledge and ideas to contribute to this mission. To facilitate the advancement of scientific methods in this field, the data needed to support analyses must be widely available. We therefore recommend:

More Open Access to Use and Risk Data
Regulators and government agencies should compile and make widely available pesticide use data and generic toxicity and environmental fate databases on pesticide active and inert ingredients.

Deborah Golino directs a center at the University of California—Davis, focusing on the collection and evaluation of plant germplasm with desirable qualities, including resistance to pests. As progress is made along the IPM continuum, the importance and economic return stemming from traditional plant germplasm collection, evaluation and storage programs will rise, necessitating the need to increase support for centers like this one. Credit: *California Farmer*

B. Rebuilding the Pest Management Infrastructure

Policies, institutions and government expenditures helped create and currently help sustain chemical-dependent pest management systems and services, as we have documented in Chapter 6. Changing this infrastructure to support biointensive IPM will take time, vision, leadership and money.

The infrastructure needed to support biointensive IPM encompasses human skills and knowledge, new-generation biopesticides, and expanded, more affordable access to biologically based tools, techniques, systems and services. Parts of the infrastructure that are hurdles to biointensive IPM include policies, programs and institutions that distort the market and promote reliance on chemical pesticides. A successful transition to IPM requires building up the former elements and dismantling or redirecting the latter ones. To do so, pest managers in the field need to be more effectively integrated into the process used to allocate funds, design and carry out research, and share results with other practitioners.

1. New Science and Technology

To date neither the public nor the private sector has succeeded very well in shifting resources away from science and technology that support pesticide-dependent systems, and toward support of biointensive IPM. Different sets of initiatives, each important, are needed to shift the focus of research in the public and private sectors.

Public Sector

USDA spends about $192 million annually under the IPM Initiative and another $63 million in research largely focused on pesticide risks, as discussed in Chapters 6 and 8. Of this $255 million, however, only about $65 million supports IPM research, and only about half of that is directly relevant to biointensive IPM. We estimate that only 12.7 percent of total USDA spending on pest management supports biointensive IPM, while nearly three-quarters of USDA's annual pest-management research money supports pesticide-based systems.

These priorities are backwards. Reversing them is essential both to invest in biointensive IPM and to separate USDA from the mission of propping up failing chemical-intensive pest management systems.

Increase Funding and Shift Priorities *The overall level of federal funding for pest management research and education should at least double over the next five fiscal years. The portion of funding supporting biointensive IPM should rise from the current 13 percent to at least three-quarters of total pest management research.*

Since the effort to balance the federal budget is likely to continue, new funding for biointensive IPM research and education activities will need to be redirected from within USDA's current $62 billion budget, of which about $1.8 billion supports science and education programs. In the last three budget cycles, USDA has proposed redirection of funding to IPM but Congress has refused to go along. In its FY 1998 budget request USDA should set forth a plan to shift the focus of its programs to biointensive IPM while doubling total IPM funding incrementally over the next five budget cycles. Congress should lend its full support to this key component of the National IPM Initiative.

Target New Funding to Critical Needs *New and redirected USDA funding should support the following objectives:*

- *A $25 million initiative focusing on biointensive IPM for urban, suburban and household pest management;*

- *Expansion of the crop- and region-specific grants under the National IPM Research Initiative from about a dozen to at least 50 multidisciplinary grants per year;*

- *Tripling research focusing on plant-pest interactions, pest physiology, agroecology and the impact of farming systems on natural enemies and biodiversity; and*

- *A $20 million increase in the USDA competitive grants program dedicated to microbial biocontrol of plant pathogens on major food crops, coupled with a complementary Small Business Innovation Research Program offering grants to private pest management service providers and biopesticide companies.*

In the past most farmers looked to agricultural experiment stations and USDA for pest management advice and technology. But now, out of necessity as funding for applied research has dried up, farmers have taken over much of the responsibility for developing and testing biointensive IPM systems and techniques. Many have joined new partnerships with crop consultants, food processors and others in the private sector. Those who have successfully moved along the IPM continuum have valuable lessons to share with others. It is appropriate to use government resources to systematically record, document and disseminate breakthroughs being made by such field practitioners.

Acquire and Share Knowledge *Public sector programs should devote more resources to the collection, synthesis and sharing of biointensive IPM information and experiences gained by private sector IPM-innovators. Such information-based activities and services will most efficiently foster progress along the IPM continuum if they are farmer-driven and focused on the most pressing needs in the field.*

The 1996 farm bill establishes a "Fund for Rural America," dedicated to investment in rural development and infrastructure, conservation and research on sustainable agricultural systems. Congress and USDA should build on this positive step:

Advance IPM Through the "Fund for Rural America" *This innovative program can invest in new partnerships with states, business, and local organizations. A significant portion of the fund should be dedicated to broadening the infrastructure needed to move toward biointensive IPM, especially where pesticides are known to contaminate drinking water or to threaten the integrity of ecosystems.*

Private Sector

The private sector invests significantly more in pest management and pesticide research and development than the public sector does. Billions of dollars have been invested over the past few decades in discovering and bringing to market new chemical pesticides and genetically engineered plant varieties. Major recent components of private-sector pest management R&D have been carried out by the biotechnology industry. Most biotechnology R&D has aimed at developing commercially marketable products that enhance reliance on chemical pesticides, by solidifying or building the market share held by proprietary pesticide active ingredients or opening up new markets for pesticides. To date, comparatively little effort has been focused on reducing pest pressure or tapping into biological and ecological forces that can be used to limit pest populations or the damage they inflict.

Shift Private-Sector Priorities *A shift in priorities to emphasize biotechnology that supports and enhances biointensive IPM is needed to provide a firmer foundation for long-term commercial success.*

For reasons set forth in Chapters 6 and 8, many of the transgenic plant products that have resulted from these private sector investment priorities are fundamentally flawed from an ecological perspective and are not compatible with IPM. For similar reasons, most of the recently introduced *Bt*-transgenic plants and herbicide tolerant crop varieties seem unlikely to be commercial successes in the long run. They may well work as intended under some conditions, but most are also likely to trigger unexpected problems, even when they appear to otherwise be working as designed.

While some major pesticide and biotechnology companies have been developing products incompatible with or irrelevant to biointensive IPM, other companies have focused on isolating microorganisms and genetic traits that might someday help pest managers progress along the IPM continuum. Much of the most promising

research is being done at small, recently established firms that seek to develop natural biopesticides and biointensive IPM systems for application in specific cropping systems.

Support Small, Innovative Companies *There are sound policy reasons for both public and private-sector investment patterns to favor small companies that are carrying out innovative research. Comparatively small investments here can have a great deal of leverage in advancing biointensive IPM methods.*

These firms will benefit from expanded opportunities to collaborate with farmers and field practitioners, in partnership with university specialists in pest management. Additional public and private financial support should be invested in developing IPM systems and tools. Cover crops, cultivation and planting systems for weed control should be priorities to lessen reliance on herbicides. Research should also focus on taxonomy, population dynamics, phenology, mating disruption, forecasting models, and new delivery mechanisms for biopesticides.

2. *Promoting Professionalism: Technology Transfer, Education and Certification*

Many individuals and companies provide pest management information and services to farmers, consumers, government, schools and building managers. Their ability and inclination to support progress along the IPM continuum depend on their training, experience, access to information and the goals of the people or institutions they work for. To accelerate progress, it is essential to promote and reward professionalism in the delivery of quality biointensive IPM services and assistance. Reordering USDA Extention priorities to focus on biointensive IPM, instead of pesticide-intensive systems, is essential to promote more rapid movement along the continuum.

Cooperative Extension *Through all their research and education programs, USDA and land grant universities should focus predominantly on how to help pest managers progress toward biointensive IPM.*

Successful IPM is very dependent on up-to-date field information. Lowering the cost of obtaining such information and enhancing its utility should be key priorities for cooperative extension pest management specialists. More funding is needed across the country for projects in which extension personnel can join as partners with farmers, crop consultants, commodity groups and food processors to advance needed elements of the IPM infrastructure. Examples of projects include developing and refining advanced diagnostic tools, expert systems, automated weather stations, and other technologies that will lower the cost and increase the timeliness and quality of information needed to apply biointensive IPM in the field. Public sector participants should also be given the support they need to systematically document the effectiveness and consequences of the pest management choices made possible by such projects.

Access to Information

Up-to-date information is essential to progress along the IPM continuum. The needed data include information on the costs and risks of pesticide use and reliance, as well as a wide spectrum of knowledge about biointensive IPM approaches to specific pest management problems. To foster the needed flow of information, we recommend:

Build on the IPM Network *The USDA and State agricultural experiment stations should build on their investment in the IPM Network on the Internet—already a valuable resource—by funding development of new databases providing current information on:*

■ *latest developments in automated weather stations, diagnostic tools, pest population forecasting models and other tools;*

■ *trends in pesticide resistance by type of pesticide, target pest, and region, in both agricultural and urban pest management;*

■ *pest species and pesticide-specific analyses of the severity of resistance and effectiveness of resistance management strategies; and*

■ *impacts of pesticides (active ingredients and formulated end-use products) on beneficial organisms including bees, earthworms, soil microorganisms and arthropod predators and parasites of important pest species.*

Summary tables with the above information, synthesized for easy comparison across pesticide-crop-pest combinations, should be accessible on the World Wide Web, in government and public libraries and through other sources. Electronic datasets should be continuously updated. Special attention should be directed toward high risk pest management systems, or those that have become unstable because of resistance or secondary pest problems. Other cost-effective mechanisms—published reports, newsletters, field days—should also be used to disseminate this information.

Field Practitioners

A growing number of crop consultants, diagnostic laboratories and other IPM experts serve as vital sources of information for farmers and others who need help managing pests. But several institutional barriers should be

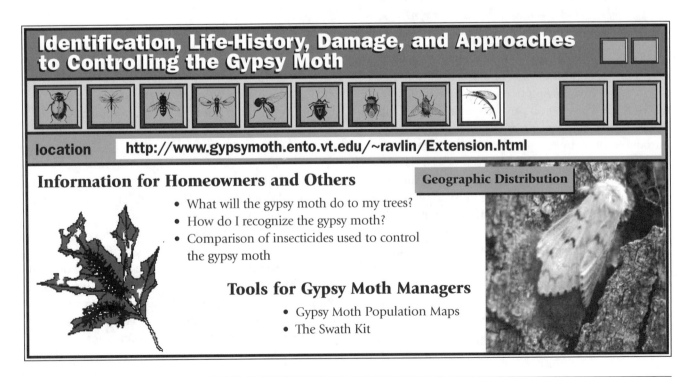

Identification, Life-History, Damage, and Approaches to Controlling the Gypsy Moth

location http://www.gypsymoth.ento.vt.edu/~ravlin/Extension.html

Information for Homeowners and Others

Geographic Distribution

- What will the gypsy moth do to my trees?
- How do I recognize the gypsy moth?
- Comparison of insecticides used to control the gypsy moth

Tools for Gypsy Moth Managers

- Gypsy Moth Population Maps
- The Swath Kit

Some farmers have been using organic farming methods for decades and have gained unique understanding of the essential ingredients needed to minimize pest problems with few or no applications of synthetic pesticides. Their farms are often valuable sites for applied field research and demonstration activities. The Sozzoni brothers (left) produce organic grapes for Fetzer winery, some in fields right next to houses. Frank Nola (right) has grown organic cherries near San Jose for 55 years and also has learned to live with an increasing number of neighbors. Credits: Richard Steven Street

addressed to improve the information and field-level scouting infrastructure needed to advance toward biointensive IPM.

Many potential clients can get similar assistance at no extra charge from individuals working for pesticide manufacturers, retailers or applicators. We believe carefully conducted research comparing the benefits and costs of relying on advice from different sources would clearly show the advantages of independent advice. An increasing number of pest management consultants have adopted a professional code of ethics that includes a pledge to sell only knowledge and advice, and not to depend in any way on income associated with product sales.

Promote Independent Advisors *We would like to see this healthy trend expand, and believe growers and consumers should seek advice only from independent experts.*

Government can help improve the quality and quantity of advice available to growers and other consumers of pest-management services, in two ways:

Expand Continuing Education Programs *Urban and indoor biointensive IPM certification and continuing education programs should be established, building on progress made by the General Services Administration and National Park Service. The development and application of such programs should be overseen by independent bodies set up at the state level.*

Expand Certification for IPM Practitioners
FIFRA should be amended to require competence in IPM as a qualification for anyone seeking to be certified as a pest control adviser or a pesticide applicator. Public/private partnerships promoting biointensive IPM should develop training modules and offer guidance on certification, continuing education requirements, occupational and environmental safety, and business ethics.

The private sector also can promote increased professional competence in IPM in various ways. For example, exterminators and lawn-care companies should train or re-train their employees in IPM techniques, and have certified IPM practitioners on staff.

Some organizations are studying the feasibility of establishing new categories of licensed professional pest management specialists, focusing on delivery of biointensive IPM services. Such certification would help consumers and public officials locate qualified individuals, and should be strongly encouraged.

3. Redesign Government Policies That Promote Pesticide Reliance

Eradication Programs

Although the mission statement of USDA's Animal Plant Health and Inspection Service expresses a commitment to biological control as the preferred pest management strategy in all agency activities, the federal government has played an important role in sponsoring regional chemical-based pest eradication programs, such as the disastrous Texas cotton boll weevil program profiled in Chapter 6.

Shift the Goal to Management *Pest control programs and government funding that supports them should strive to stabilize pest populations through biological control and biointensive IPM, unless the target pest is recently introduced to the United States and there is solid evidence that subsequent infestations are unlikely and preventable.*

Indemnify Victims *USDA, or others sponsoring regional agricultural pest control programs, should require that a portion of the money spent on pesticides through such programs be held in escrow for up to three years, to provide funds to compensate farmers, landowners or others injured by program spraying or secondary pests triggered by such spraying.*

There is ample evidence that most pesticide-dependent eradication programs are destined to fail. In the cotton case, for example, the complex of lepidopteran pests and secondary pests like mites and aphids has simply outstripped the capacity of broad-spectrum insecticides to control them. The same phenomena are either well advanced or actively under way with other insect pests that have been the targets of eradication campaigns. Eradication is a biologically irrational policy that should long ago have been phased out in favor of approaches based on sounder ecological principles. Federal funding for regional pest management programs targeting major pests like the boll weevil should be redirected to support the discovery and release of biological control agents and to address changes in farming and pest management systems needed to help farmers make progress along the IPM continuum.

Crop Subsidy Programs

For most of four decades, federal programs that subsidize production of selected crops have collectively encouraged farmers to extend cultivation onto marginal soils, wetlands, or land where irrigation is needed to support intensive crop production. Chapter 6 explains how these programs sometimes lead to specialized farming systems with increased crop susceptibility to pest attack and intensified dependence on chemical pesticides. Investments in the equipment and land needed to take advantage of crop subsidies have also created large disincentives to crop rotation and other agricultural practices more inherently compatible with biointensive IPM.

The 1996 farm bill has begun the process of phasing out this era of policy. Its planting flexibility provisions will help lower one barrier to diversification of crop rotations, but the farm bill does little to remove other important hurdles and inequities (see Chapter 6). Billions in subsidies have gone to producers of corn and cotton, helping them finance excessive and often unnecessary pesticide use, while growers trying to develop innovative IPM strategies in high value fruit and vegetable cropping systems have received minimal assistance. To promote more balanced use of tax funds and avoid slippage from the environmental gains made since passage of the 1985 conservation title:

Redirect Payments *Congress should redirect a portion of income support program payments from large farms to research, conservation, food safety and water quality programs benefiting all of agriculture and the general public. Activities supporting IPM adoption should be among those receiving long-overdue funding increases.*

Some of the redirected funds should support intensified water quality monitoring in regions of the country where cropping patterns and pesticide use levels have dramatically changed in recent years or are now rapidly changing.

Build IPM Into Farm Plans *In evaluating requests to remove land ahead of schedule from the 10-year Conservation Reserve Program, to drain a wetland or to plant highly erodible acreage, USDA should give more weight than it currently does to impacts on pests, IPM and pesticide reliance associated with changes in land use.*

Land use changes brought about by expanding production can entail loss in wildlife habitat and intensification in cropping patterns and input levels, with associated threats to water quality. Under those conditions USDA should ensure that growers try to prevent pest problems from reaching levels where use of high risk pesticides becomes hard to avoid. In working with land owners and operators in developing integrated farm plans covering such tracts of land, USDA should seek to

Responding to consumer demand, many companies and commodity organizations are beginning to feature taste, freshness and food safety on packaging and in promotional campaigns. As this trend evolves, consumers will need new information to help evaluate their choices and this need may in turn require USDA and commodity organizations to revisit grading standards and marketing order provisions.
Credit: Wisconsin Potato and Vegetable Growers Association

ensure rotations of sufficient length and diversity to break pest and plant disease cycles, and otherwise encourage use of other proven IPM preventive practices.

Grading Standards and Marketing Orders

USDA and others can lessen pesticide dependency by revising cosmetic and grading standards for fresh market fruit and vegetables. These standards often needlessly increase the frequency and levels of pesticide residues in foods.

End Cosmetically-Motivated Late Season Applications *Cosmetic and grading standards and marketing orders should be revised so they no longer encourage late season pesticide applications, especially on crops destined for processing.*

Create and Broaden New Market Channels *Public institutions, consumer groups and large corporations should work cooperatively with grower-organizations to establish additional market channels for produce with minor cosmetic damage that has little or no impact on food quality.*

Grant Selective Exemptions *Farmers using biointensive IPM and organic farming systems should be exempt from any quantity restrictions under marketing orders as long as their produce is sold as certified organic, or through some other "value-added" market channel.*

Export IPM *USDA and states should feature IPM-grown produce and products in export promotion programs, especially those targeting health conscious markets abroad.*

C. Capturing the Power of Market Forces

A wide variety of investments is needed to create IPM skills, technologies, systems and services. These investments will be financed not by government but primarily by day-to-day expenditures for pest management services and products. If biointensive IPM is to expand, farmers, consumers and others responsible for managing pests will make it happen by consciously choosing how to spend their money.

In a "rational" market where all the costs of reliance on chemical pest control were fairly priced, biointensive IPM should win, hands down. But until a "critical mass" has been reached in product and systems development, in marketing IPM technologies, and in educating people about why they should adopt them and how to use them optimally, IPM advances will emerge slowly and will reach only a small percentage of pest managers. Several key strategies, outlined here, can help bring about that critical mass and promote the market success of biointensive IPM.

1. Broaden the Range of Consumer Choices

Consumer purchasing power can advance biointensive IPM both directly, through choices of pest management products and services, and indirectly, through choices of foods and other products produced with biointensive IPM. In each sector of the marketplace, there are needs for greater choice, more and better information, and simple, credible standards and labels to guide consumer decisions.

IPM-Grown Foods

A small but growing segment of consumers is seeking food grown without pesticides, or under "environmentally friendly" production systems. According to a survey by the Hartman Group, conducted in early 1996, a majority of consumers is interested in purchasing food products grown using "earth sustainable" practices like IPM, but most do not understand the meaning of terms like IPM, sustainable agriculture or even "organically grown." These and other survey findings suggest that there is considerable untapped market potential for IPM-grown food, but also that major consumer education campaigns are needed to take advantage of it (Hartman, 1996).

To help consumers buy and food industries sell more of the environmentally sound foods the public says it wants, innovations in food labeling and point-of-purchase information will need to keep pace with progress in adoption of biointensive IPM. Key elements include:

> "The 'green' consumer is now mainstream ... A majority of American consumers are willing to buy environmentally friendly products and a significant segment—23%— are frustrated that there are not more opportunities for them to buy green."
>
> "In the food industry...foods produced using methods that are 'earth sustainable'...are growing by 20% per year, and yet they represent only 2% of overall sales. The market potential is enormous...at least 52% of consumers want to buy earth-sustainable food products, but most don't [do so] because they can't easily find earth-sustainable products that meet their core purchase criteria."
>
> **The Hartman Report–Food and Environment:**
> **A Consumer's Perspective,** *Phase I Report, Summer, 1996 (Hartman, 1996)*

Many organizations and companies now feature IPM-Grown, organic and "No Detectable Residue" claims in their labeling and promotional material, while others, like Gerber, feature corporate efforts to promote IPM. Many grocery stores offer fresh produce certified under one or a variety of programs. Only a few of the programs are concerned with IPM, per se, and they do not necessarily define "IPM" as we have defined it, i.e., biointensive IPM.

"NutriClean" in Oakland, California certifies fresh produce as "pesticide free" down to 0.01 part per million for a specified list of chemicals. Stemilt Growers in Washington State market fruit through their "Responsible Choice" program, which works on a point system (Reed, 1995). The State of Massachusetts has started an IPM labeling program, also based on a point system. The Rain-Forest Alliance runs an "Eco-O.K." banana certification program. Dozens of private organizations and state departments of agriculture certify crops and processed food products as organic (see logo of Texas Organic Cotton Growers Association).

John Dowdell is a produce buyer for Real Foods in San Francisco, California. A growing percentage of grocery stores, ranging from large chains like Safeway, Giant, Raley's, and Wegman's to Real Foods, Fresh Fields and community coops, compete for market share by offering high quality fresh fruits and vegetables. Many provide point-of-purchase information about where and how food was grown and processed and some feature organic and IPM-grown foods. Easy-to-understand and credible labeling, coupled with point-of-purchase information, will help link consumers looking for "environmentally-friendly" food with farmers working to supply it.
Credit: Richard Steven Street

Expand Certification Programs for "IPM-Grown" Foods *A few programs now certify produce as "IPM-Grown." More, bigger, and better programs of this type are needed.*

Several existing programs certify foods as free of detectable pesticide residues, organically grown or in other ways "environmentally sound" (see box, opposite page). A few of these programs certify foods produced with biointensive IPM, and the number can be expected to grow. We think this is a healthy development that meets an important need. "Free of pesticide residues" is, by itself, no guarantee that food was produced with minimal reliance on chemical pesticides. The market for organically grown foods is expanding but is still small. The potential market share for foods grown with medium or high degrees of IPM seems considerably larger.

Certification programs for IPM-grown foods will require significant effort and investment to develop. Agreeing on what qualifies as "IPM-grown" will not be easy, and the need for definitions to be crop- and region-specific will complicate the task of setting uniform national standards. But the latter are needed so that consumers everywhere can know what they are buying when they choose "IPM-grown" foods. While the challenge is daunting, this effort needs to be made so consumers can reward growers and food marketers who take these extra steps.

Develop Sensible, Effective Approaches to Labeling *Growers, food processors, buyers and retailers, consumer organizations and government officials should cooperate to develop effective, clear, verifiable, and meaningful ways to distinguish food produced using biointensive IPM on product labels and in other point-of-sale information.*

The FDA is unlikely to conclude that it needs to require IPM information to appear on food labels; market pressures will shape whatever communication media eventually come into play. But government—the FDA, the Federal Trade Commission, and perhaps state Attorneys General—will probably need to take part in the process of developing and monitoring information programs. They will also need to help ensure that labels and advertising claims are accurate, fair, and compatible with efforts to harmonize international labeling and promote

"What we did with the new food labels—it's about information. Information created demand. The food label changed the way manufacturers manufacture. What the critics of the new food labeling don't understand is that it's about choice."

Dr. David Kessler, *Commissioner, Food and Drug Administration. Quoted in* The New York Times Magazine, *August 4, 1996*

trade in "value-added" products. The criteria used to define IPM in certification and labeling programs need to be transparent, and the data supporting such labels should be publicly available and verifiable.

> **More Choice in the Supermarket** *Food retailers should experiment with giving more shelf space to, and actively promoting, IPM-grown and organic food.*

Recently Mothers and Others for a Liveable Planet, a consumer group, convinced supermarkets in several cities to increase their offerings of organic and locally grown food, and to promote these products. In each case, the experiment proved financially successful and the change in product mix has continued or expanded. Food retailers are generally well attuned to consumer demand, but encouragement from their customers and consumer groups can help expand choices for foods grown with IPM and reduced pesticide use.

Non-Food IPM-Grown Products and IPM Uses

Comparable certification, labeling and point-of-sale information programs need to be developed for non-food products, such as clothing made with IPM-grown cotton, or ornamental plants produced at nurseries that rely on biointensive IPM. Certification and public notification programs should also be developed for use by golf courses, public buildings and parks, schools, restaurants and other public facilities where pest managers' commitment to using IPM will help reduce public exposure to pesticides.

> **Don't Stop With Foods** *Certification and labeling programs should be developed for non-food products and for a variety of other public facilities and circumstances where pest managers deserve recognition for making progress toward biointensive IPM.*

The same challenges described above in connection with developing certification and labeling programs for foods will arise here. But there are many important non-food pesticide uses, and it is essential to use the experience gained in the food marketplace and to channel the same market forces to promote progress toward biointensive IPM in these other contexts. Awareness of these broader needs should guide participation in efforts to develop certification and labeling programs. Including a range of non-food interests may initially slow the process down, but breadth of participation can perhaps avoid the need to reinvent the process anew for each new application.

Pest Management Products and Services

Consumers seeking do-it-yourself solutions to pest problems buy pest management products at hardware, garden and grocery stores, and at agricultural supply centers. They can also buy pest management services, by hiring an exterminator, a lawn-care company, or a gardener. Access to independent information about pest problems and how to deal with them is essential for consumers to make wise choices. Consumers must assume the responsibility for making informed pest management decisions, but ensuring that good information is available is a very important supporting strategy.

> **Consume Information, Not Products** *Consumers should approach pest problems seeking information first, rather than seeking a product that will solve their problem. Education efforts are needed to change public attitudes in this regard.*

To make effective pest management choices, consumers need to know the identity of the pest, to understand its life cycle and its natural enemies. They need to understand which pesticides could be effective against this pest, and the costs and risks of using chemical controls. They need to know about non-chemical management options, and their benefits and risks. All of this information is not likely to be found in one place. Some may come from product labels and other point-of-sale materials. More may be provided by businesses and individuals who sell pest management products and services.

Unfortunately, much of the information available from these sources is designed to help sell particular products, and is likely to be insufficiently complete or objective. Savvy consumers will seek additional sources, including independent pest management consultants, county extension agents, local and state environmental agencies, books, other library materials, databases on the Internet, and other providers of information and expert advice, which are becoming increasingly available.

But the time and effort a conscientious consumer needs to spend gathering information and weighing complex choices may seem like a luxury when Japanese beetles are munching the begonias. The same information explosion that will support widespread adoption of IPM for home and garden pest problems also seems likely to make the marketplace even more bewildering for the average consumer. Several practical improvements in ways information is delivered can help consumers find their way through this marketing jungle:

Improve Pest Management Product Labels

Labels on pesticides and other mass-marketed pest management products should more clearly state appropriate uses, limitations, safety precautions and environmental risks of the products.

Once EPA registers a pesticide product and approves a product label, "buyer beware" rules in the marketplace. Many people mistakenly assume that registered products must be safe and fail to read or follow the often extensive label safety precautions and limitations on when and how the product should be applied (which are generally in very small print). Improved labels should be used in conjunction with better point-of-purchase information to increase the likelihood of correct use of products. Needed label improvements include:

- *Clear statements of inappropriate or likely ineffective uses of pesticides.*

Common pest species against which a chemical is likely to be ineffective, including any known to have developed resistance to the active ingredient on at least a regional basis, should be indicated.

- *Disclosure of inert ingredient content, and warnings about hazards of toxic inerts.*

Consumers have a right to know this information, so they can better protect themselves. Current pesticide labeling law requires the quantitative disclosure of active ingredient composition, but no such information about inerts, even though some inerts are also quite toxic and they may make up much more of the product than the active ingredients do.

- *Generic warnings about counterproductive effects of over-reliance on pesticides.*

Statements that a product contains a broad-spectrum insecticide that is likely to kill a pest's natural enemies, as well as the target insect, or a general statement that intensive pesticide use can make the pest population resistant to the pesticide, should be on labels, to help discourage the impulse to spray at the first sign of a pest organism, or to spray more often than the label advises.

- *Positive declarations of compatibility with biointensive IPM.*

Statements affirming that a pest management product is appropriate for use in a biointensive IPM system should be permitted and encouraged on labels of products that deserve them. As with certification programs for foods and other IPM-grown products, the criteria for awarding such labels and the details of the labeling approach need to be developed through collaboration among the companies marketing the products, consumer and agricultural organizations and government agencies to ensure that this labeling is clear, effective, accurate and fair.

Improve Point-of-Purchase Information

Materials available at the point of sale should complement information on product labels and provide additional critical facts to help guide consumer choices.

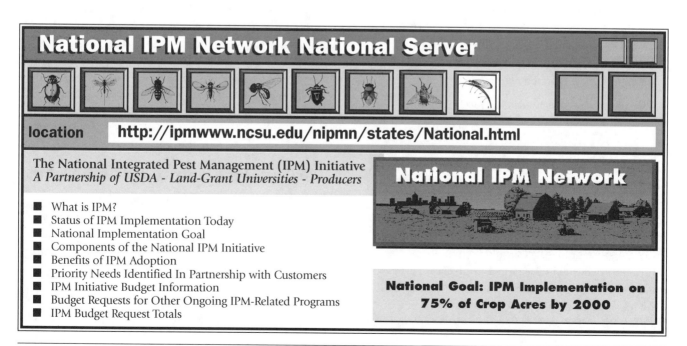

National IPM Network National Server

location http://ipmwww.ncsu.edu/nipmn/states/National.html

The National Integrated Pest Management (IPM) Initiative
A Partnership of USDA - Land-Grant Universities - Producers

National IPM Network

- What is IPM?
- Status of IPM Implementation Today
- National Implementation Goal
- Components of the National IPM Initiative
- Benefits of IPM Adoption
- Priority Needs Identified In Partnership with Customers
- IPM Initiative Budget Information
- Budget Requests for Other Ongoing IPM-Related Programs
- IPM Budget Request Totals

National Goal: IPM Implementation on 75% of Crop Acres by 2000

Extensive information on pest problems is available in some retail outlets now. For instance, in many garden stores consumers can find thick loose-leaf binders packed with full-color publications that identify pest problems. Typically, these materials are provided by pesticide manufacturers and end with a recommendation to apply a proprietary product against the pest. But consumers eager to play a part in the transition to biointensive IPM need better information than that. Among the most central needs are:

■ *Pest species identification guides and information on the pest's biology*

This information is such a fundamental starting point that we believe retailers should offer it routinely, and should make obtaining it for customers an urgent priority. Options for doing so include printed materials, computer terminals for on-line searches, or both. For insect and weed pests, identification should be straightforward; for many plant diseases, providing useful information may be tougher. Where will the information come from? The market is already beginning to supply it. Some state land grant universities are developing accessible, easy to use consumer pest identification systems, like the excellent Internet-based system from the entomology department at Virginia Polytechnic Institute (see boxes on pages 40 and 41).

The information needs to (and the VPI database does) include basic facts about the pest's life-cycle, its habitat needs, its natural enemies, what it eats, the damage it can cause, control alternatives, and where to get more information or help. Once such systems are developed, they should be readily accessible not just in retail stores and pest control business offices, but also in libraries, schools, and other places consumers are likely to go seeking pest management advice.

■ *Basic advice about non-chemical pest-control techniques*

Consumers facing relatively minor pest problems and likely to opt for do-it-yourself pest management need information about non-chemical techniques they can use to keep pest populations below significant damage thresholds. How to determine whether a pest is present at significant levels (trapping, monitoring) and other diagnostic measures should be described. Information about simple steps like physical barriers, removing food or water sources, and planting to create habitats for pests' natural enemies are provided in a number of worthwhile resources (e.g., see *Pest Control for Home*

and Garden [Hansen, 1993] and *Common Sense Pest Control* [Olkowski et al., 1991]).

Provide Comparable Information for Pest-Management Services *Customers of pest control providers should have access to the same kinds of information about the services they buy that purchasers of pest control products can find on the label or in the store.*

The same kinds of information, plus the identity of and labels for any pesticide products that will be used, should be provided by exterminators and other professional pest managers to the consumer and discussed fully before a contract is signed or treatments are applied. And public health agencies and academic institutions should be more candid and assertive in educating the public on pesticide risks, particularly risks associated with widely used (and potentially overused) consumer and professional pesticide products.

Require Notice of Pest Control Measures Used in Public Places *State and local law should require posting or some other form of notification to alert and educate the public when pesticides are applied in public places, and should also encourage posting when low risk IPM measures are used.*

When pests require control in apartment buildings, businesses, recreational facilities, in parks, schools and public places, the general public lives with the consequences of pest management decisions made by others. Consumers have a right to know about pesticide use and risks in public places, as well as about alternatives to routine reliance on pesticides. To alert people to the need for caution, information should be posted when potentially hazardous pesticide applications are made in such settings. Similar postings or notification should also be made when low risk IPM systems and biopesticide products are used, to make people aware of such alternatives and reassure the public when pest managers have chosen lower-risk approaches.

2. Reward Biointensive IPM Innovators

Create and Publicize Awards for IPM Innovations *Government agencies, consumer and environmental organizations should create a variety of awards to recognize and publicize innovative successes in making progress toward biointensive IPM.*

Well-publicized award programs for IPM innovations serve both to reward and encourage IPM innovators and to educate the public about IPM and its benefits. California's Department of Pesticide Regulation created an "IPM Innovator" award program in 1994, which has been enormously popular among IPM practitioners and has generated increasing public interest and media attention each year. There is room for many more such programs.

EPA and USDA should initiate a national IPM innovator award program. The awards should include a significant cash grant to support ongoing work and outreach to others. Cal-EPA should take the same step and begin including meaningful cash awards for its winners. Environmental and consumer groups could collaborate to create an award program for food processing companies, restaurants and food retailers or individuals in the business community that display creativity and commitment in offering consumers safer choices in the marketplace.

Award programs need to be built upon a sound ecological definition of biointensive IPM and rigorous criteria for measuring progress toward that goal. Properly conceived and creatively publicized awards should be effective tools for raising public awareness of IPM innovations and promoting the market success of new ideas.

3. Use Government's Clout to Shape Markets for IPM

Government is a major consumer of pesticides, pest management services and products whose production entails pest management (like food, paper and clothing). Through procurement policies, government can and should build demand for biointensive IPM systems and services, as several federal agencies are doing (see Chapter 5). These efforts need to be coordinated, expanded and guided by clear policy goals. Some important steps government can take include:

Use IPM *When contracting for pest management services, public agencies at all levels—the Department of Defense, a state park, a local school board—should seek out companies and individuals committed to using biointensive IPM and certified as experts in IPM methods. Government agencies should put IPM-certified pest managers in charge of their in-house pest control efforts and buy only IPM-compatible pest control products.*

Lead By Example *Federal, state and local agencies should lead by example, and start by setting clear, measurable IPM adoption goals and openly monitoring progress.*

Governments at all levels should establish policy goals and timetables to ensure that their own use of pest management services is progressively shifted to reliance on biointensive IPM. We believe, for example, that all federal agencies should eliminate the use of high risk pesticides on all of their own lands and facilities by the year 2000, and should have converted essentially 100 percent of their pest control programs and purchases to biointensive IPM by the year 2010. State and local agencies should adopt similar timetables.

Federal agencies that already have successful programs (see Chapter 5) can provide support and leadership for other levels of government. For example, GSA has developed important indoor and urban IPM measurement methodologies useful in setting goals and monitoring progress. It should seek out partners to help with outreach—the PTA for example, in developing IPM for schools.

Buy IPM-Produced Products *Wherever possible, government procurement policy should specify the use of IPM as a criterion for the purchase decision.*

When government buys foods, clothing, ornamental plants, paper, and other products whose production involves pest management choices, promoting progress toward IPM should be one of its criteria in choosing vendors. Imagine the impact on the market for IPM-grown or organic cotton if the Pentagon were to specify such cotton in its procurement of uniforms, or the effect on demand for IPM-grown or organic foods if USDA would accept nothing else for the school lunch and WIC programs.

4. Sharing the Costs of Progress Along the Continuum

Government has another role to play in the market-driven transition to biointensive IPM: boosting or damping market forces produced by government policies that tend to work for or against the national goal of progress along the IPM continuum. This can include eliminating existing policies that distort the market in favor of reliance on pesticides (see Section B of this chapter), and creating additional incentives to speed the switch to IPM, discussed here.

Over the years, USDA conservation cost-sharing programs have covered part of the added expense of certain qualifying conservation practices needed to control erosion. The public's share of the payment has been justified since the 1940s by the public benefits gained—cleaner water, a more productive agricultural sector. In the mid-1980s, the same justification was applied to water quality protection programs. The next logical step is to prevent pesticides from reaching drinking water by supporting adoption of biointensive IPM.

Offer Cost-Share Incentives for Biointensive IPM *Agricultural cost-share assistance and other incentives to improve food safety, water quality or wildlife habitat should be offered to help pay for preventive practices needed to reach biointensive IPM, as long as the practices are formally part of integrated whole farm plans.*

The 1996 farm bill took positive steps toward making room for IPM in traditional and new conservation planning and cost-share programs. We urge Congress and USDA to use these programs aggressively, especially in regions where pesticides have contaminated drinking water. In such circumstances it seems fair for the public to bear up to half the cost of preventive biointensive IPM practices, and for at least half of total USDA payments to farmers to be dedicated to meeting environmental quality and food safety goals.

Extend Crop Insurance to IPM *A provision of the 1996 farm bill directs USDA to experiment with using crop insurance to bolster farmers' willingness to adopt IPM. We urge USDA to make maximum use of this new authority.*

Much of current pesticide use in both agricultural and urban settings is preventive, intended to reduce the chance of losses from pests that may or may not be an actual threat, and to provide "peace of mind." While preventive pesticide applications may make economic sense in the short run, over the longer term they are generally wasteful and counterproductive. There are sounder ways to provide peace of mind. Proven IPM strategies are one alternative. For farmers, insurance that covers plausible but unlikely crop losses can effectively replace pesticide applications made for the same reason.

A new provision in the 1996 farm bill directs USDA's crop insurance program to experiment with ways to extend coverage to farmers using IPM. By covering some of the risks farmers making a transition to unfamiliar and innovative IPM systems face, this policy can make trying IPM more attractive. How well the program will work is yet to be determined. The potential for unjustified claims and high program costs must be confronted. Still, we applaud this step and encourage the USDA to move toward policies that give all farmers an opportunity to purchase crop insurance covering weather and pest-induced crop losses. Premium rates should reflect the relative performance and reliability of biointensive IPM systems, in contrast to other pest management systems.

Some private companies are already experimenting with crop insurance to reduce unnecessary pesticide applications. Campbell Soup Company basically guarantees most of its contract growers a fixed payment per pound of produce harvested per acre (in effect assuming the risk that insects or plant diseases might lower the quality grade in a portion of the produce). It is willing to do so because of its confidence in the IPM program it requires its contract growers to follow. In some cases, government may be able to broaden crop insurance options most cost effectively by supporting private sector efforts

Gallo Winery, California's largest, has invested heavily in organic grape production systems, including this new vineyard near its Dry Creek plant. Close to a third of the grapes crushed annually by Gallo are produced using organic methods and many other California wineries are now comfortably within the biointensive zone of the IPM continuum. By investing in IPM and helping assure farmers a market for IPM-grown produce, large companies like Gallo can hasten the progress of farmers along the IPM continuum.
Credit: Richard Steven Street

Demand for organic ketchup and processed toma-to products is strong and growing, creating new markets for farmers, including the Romingers in Woodland, California. Rich Rominger (right), Deputy Secretary of Agriculture, and sons (left to right, Rick, Charlie and Bruce) grow several hun-dred acres of certified organic processing tomatoes every year, in addition to several hundred acres of conventional tomatoes. Note the excellent weed control and heavy crop in this field of organic processing tomatoes (photo taken August, 1996).
Credit: Evelyne Rominger

rather than by competing with them or offering overlap-ping coverage. We urge USDA to include experiments supportive of private "IPM Grower" crop insurance pro-grams in its efforts to implement this provision of the new farm bill.

5. What Major Corporations Can Do

Large corporations are forces in the marketplace second only to government, and guided by informed corporate policy, they can use their clout to advance progress toward biointensive IPM. Like governments, big companies are consumers of pest management products and services, and of foods, fiber and other goods that can be produced with biointensive IPM. Their purchasing power can give an enormous boost to demand for IPM services. Their ability to communicate with their customers and stockholders, including "corporate image" statements about things they do to make the world a better place, can be an important source of public information about the value of biointen-sive IPM and progress toward its adoption.

> **Buy IPM** *Major corporations should make it company policy to buy IPM-grown products and use IPM-based pest management services. Goals and timetables should pro-mote rapid progress toward buying "100 percent IPM."*

We can envision a very large array of ways corpora-tions can help drive the market toward biointensive IPM. Only a few are listed here, as examples. Some of the pro-posals are feasible today, while others might take several years of work to bring to fruition, once the initial com-mitment was made. To help enliven the illustrations, we have used names of real companies. Most are hypotheti-cal examples; a few refer to existing programs that are models worth emulating. We hope there soon will be a growing list of real cases with well-known companies playing starring roles.

Consider the possibilities:

- *Food processors could adopt programs, as all U.S. baby-food manufacturers and major companies like Campbell Soup and Del Monte already have, that require contract growers to minimize pesticide use and promote rapid progress toward biointensive IPM.*

- *Restaurant chains like McDonald's and Burger King could write progressively stronger requirements for biointensive IPM into their contracts with potato growers and processors.*

- *Heinz and Pizza Hut could buy only IPM-grown tomatoes for their ketchup and pizza sauce, respectively.*

- *Minute Maid and Tropicana could require biointen-sive IPM programs as a condition in their contracts with orange, lemon, grapefruit and lime growers.*

- *Levi-Strauss could purchase only IPM-grown cotton for making blue jeans and other garments. The Patagonia Company now buys organically grown cot-ton for its apparel items; other companies should follow suit.*

■ *IBM, Exxon or Bank of America could choose to use only biointensive IPM for managing pest problems at company-owned facilities, and establish milestones and timetables for progress toward that objective.*

■ *Companies as large as AT&T and as small as Consumers Union could seek out sources of IPM-grown foods and aim to serve only IPM-grown fruits and vegetables in their company cafeterias.*

We have not tried to identify all worthy existing corporate programs that promote IPM, nor to list all the companies that could play high-profile leadership roles in this effort. Our advice to one and all is: Do it, do it well, and tell us (and the rest of the world) how you did it.

As companies already working to advance biointensive IPM have found, there is more involved than simply writing requirements into contracts and expecting growers to comply. Gerber, for example, works closely with its growers, sharing information about successful pesticide-use-reducing strategies and sponsoring educational conferences. When public safety is their primary concern, some companies have even taught their competitors how to imitate their success. Pillsbury, which has been a leader among food processors in adopting HACCP (Hazard Analysis of Critical Control Pathways, a systems approach to ensuring food safety), has sponsored seminars for other companies that urge them to adopt the program and tell them how. Promoting biointensive IPM to reduce the health and environmental risks associated with pesticides deserves no less commitment.

But more than altruistic corporate concern for the environment is at stake. As EPA moves to implement the tolerance-setting provisions of the 1996 food safety bill, public awareness of safety issues related to pesticide residues in foods seems likely to increase. Biointensive IPM programs that help guarantee minimal residues in foods may quickly become what consumers expect of responsible food companies, and hence more valuable, or even essential, as a selling point.

Food processors and retailers can play an additional role by helping to promote more diverse crop rotations, as a key step toward biointensive IPM. As explained in Chapter 7, diversification of rotations is often the single most important change a farmer can make to accelerate progress along the IPM continuum. The food industries should work cooperatively with grower organizations to help ensure that markets exist for rotational crops needed to break pest and disease cycles. Current heavily pesticide-dependent crops that would benefit most from crop rotations include strawberries, cotton, corn, peanuts,

sugar beets, potatoes, and sugar cane.

Even major financial corporations have a role to play in the transition to biointensive IPM, most obviously by eliminating anachronistic policies that promote unnecessary pesticide use. In California, and perhaps other states as well, mortgage lenders commonly require that homes not only be inspected for termites (an almost universal buyer-protecting legal requirement), but that they must also be treated for termites, even when (as is usually the case) there is no sign of active infestation.

Eliminate Bank Policies That Promote Pesticide Use *Banks and other lending institutions should eliminate policies that require termite treatment of a home in order to obtain a mortgage—even when no termites are present.*

Like preventive crop pesticide spraying discussed earlier, such treatments are "insurance" that may seem economically rational to the lender, but whose external costs vastly outweigh their benefits. Banks, like other companies with more central roles in pest management decisions, need to support progress toward biointensive IPM as a corporate goal. Steps they can take to foster that objective include revising policies to require termite treatment only when an active infestation is present, and under those conditions, steering the homeowner to choose a certified IPM practitioner, either by offering economic incentives or by providing a list of IPM-qualified local firms.

Agricultural lending institutions like the Farm Credit System and its affiliated associations have a solid history of assertive management of environmental liability risks. They need to make a concerted effort now to educate themselves and borrowers about the long-term economic and environmental benefits of biointensive IPM, and to factor this criterion into lending decisions.

D. Smarter, More Efficient Regulation

It's time our society stopped expecting regulation to eliminate pesticide problems. It has not done so and cannot realistically do so. For each active ingredient the EPA has removed from the market, the agency has registered about 10 new ones. EPA's pesticide decisions must balance the largely unknown risks of exposure against the essentially unmeasureable benefits of use—an inherently impossible task that opens the process to endless debate and controversy. Science has raised many concerns about health risks of pesticide exposure, such as endocrine disruption, effects on the fetus or on the immune system, and effects of combinations of chemicals, for which it is currently not feasible to determine "safe" exposures. And some of the most important environmental effects of pesticide use—genetic resistance of pest populations, damage to soil microbial communities, impacts on beneficial organisms—are largely outside the cost-benefit calculation.

No wonder, then, that we look primarily to the transition to biointensive IPM, rather than to regulation, to reduce pesticide use, reliance and risks. That is not to say that regulating pesticides is not necessary—it is, and will continue to be, since biointensive IPM will periodically entail some pesticide use. But regulation needs to be used more consciously, intelligently and efficiently as a tool for accelerating progress along the IPM continuum.

There are two basic elements of needed regulatory strategies: More focused and aggressive efforts to reduce reliance on high risk pesticides now in wide use; and expedited approval of low risk biopesticides essential for biointensive IPM systems. EPA can address some of these priorities without new legislation, but for the agency to play a more effective role in promoting progress toward biointensive IPM, Congress may need to craft new authorities.

1. Target High Risk Pesticides

Some pesticides are much riskier to health and the environment than others. In Chapter 3 we showed differences of two and three orders of magnitude between the most toxic tenth and least toxic tenth of active ingredients applied, on some indices of mammalian toxicity. In its efforts to manage the risks of pesticides now in use, EPA has tried to give priority to those that pose the greatest risks, with some success. But much work still remains.

"High risk" pesticides are those that rank higher than most other registered pesticides on one or more of the following criteria: Very high acute toxicity to humans; environmental persistence; capability of leaching into water supplies or other attributes that tend to increase public exposure; significant chronic toxicity, such as carcinogenicity or endocrine disruption; broad-spectrum toxicity to beneficial organisms, including soil microorganisms; established resistance among target pest populations. Widely used pesticides that pose higher risks than alternative products in one or more of these parameters are prime candidates for regulatory priority.

To increase the speed and the certainty of EPA's

efforts to reduce reliance on targeted high risk pesticides, we recommend the following strategies:

Reduce Tolerances for Targeted Pesticides *EPA should use the authority given it by the 1996 food safety bill to progressively lower tolerances for high risk pesticides, focusing on four priority categories: cholinesterase-inhibiting (organophosphate and carbamate) insecticides; known endocrine disruptors; herbicides found frequently in drinking water; and the ten most widely used fungicides.*

The food safety bill passed in July 1996 gives EPA clear and consistent direction for setting new tolerances and adjusting old ones covering pesticide residues in food. The timetable called for in the legislation dovetails reasonably well with the completion of the reregistration process in which EPA has long been engaged. Reasons for targeting the listed categories are detailed in Chapter 3, as well as in the NAS/NRC report *Pesticides in the Diets of Infants and Children* (NRC, 1993a).

In developing regulations and policy guidance documents describing how it will implement the mandates of the 1996 bill, EPA needs to explain how it will decide where tolerances should be set. This information will help pesticide manufacturers and grower groups decide how to change pesticide product formulations, use rates, pre-harvest intervals and other parameters of use. Product labels will then need revision to reflect such changes, to keep residues in foods from exceeding the newly lowered tolerance levels.

Expand Public Residue Testing *Federal agencies should be given ample resources to expand the scope and accuracy of pesticide residue testing programs. Additional steps should be taken to compile, synthesize and disseminate pesticide residue data from multiple sources.*

Implementation of the Food Quality Protection Act will place a premium on accurate data on pesticide residues in food. EPA needs such data to target high risk pesticides and determine where tolerances need to be set. Growers and food processors need the data to determine where pest management systems must change to lessen reliance on high risk chemicals. It is therefore hard to understand the decision by Congress in August, 1996 to stop funding USDA's Pesticide Data Program. Over four years of operation, this program had developed valuable data on 75 pesticides and dozens of crops. Failure to appropriate funds for the program in FY 1997 was called a "colossal blunder" by *Farm Journal*, citing EPA's reliance on the data in setting tolerances under the new law (Klintberg, 1996). More residue data—not less—will be needed for several years as tolerances are adjusted and the reregistration process is completed.

Integrate Tolerance Revisions and Reregistration *EPA should move forward quickly with tolerance revisions on pesticides nearing the completion of reregistration. It should combine tolerance and reregistration decisions and label revisions to the full extent possible, without delaying the tolerance revisions.*

Although registrants may balk at the tolerance reductions required by the 1996 law, EPA must proceed with the process. Registrants, grower groups and states will need to develop the data EPA needs to approve label revisions. In some cases, pesticide manufacturers and users may conclude that cancelling a registered use is more efficient than attempting to show that such a use is consistent with the lower tolerances EPA has promulgated.

Build Incentives for Action Into the Process *EPA should seize this opportunity to create tangible incentives in the tolerance-lowering process that reward registrants who work cooperatively to bring risks within new safety standards.*

Delay is endemic to the reregistration and Special Review processes because products remain on the market while EPA deliberates, and while appeals of EPA decisions work their way through the courts. But the 1996 food safety bill gives EPA an opportunity to turn the tables. The new act requires tolerances to be based on total exposure to an active ingredient, taking into account all exposures to any other active ingredients that pose the same human health risk through the same mode of action. Accordingly, EPA will be calculating some allowable Reference Doses that will apply to more than a dozen active ingredients in hundreds of registered products sold by multiple companies.

EPA could place a premium on swift, decisive cooperation by adopting a "first come, first served" policy in allocating an active ingredient's Reference Dose. Once the allowed exposure is taken up by tolerances EPA has already set, any additional tolerances could be approved only if accompanied by reduction or cancellation of some other tolerance.

To move more effectively on targeted high risk pesticides in reregistration and Special Review actions, EPA will need new authority from Congress on issues not addressed by the 1996 legislation. We believe FIFRA should be revised so that EPA could:

Err on Side of Safety *Substantial scientific evidence that a pesticide poses high risks to health or the environment should lead quickly either to suspension while risk questions are resolved, cancellation or meaningful and enforceable measures that restore ample margins of safety. The burden of proof should shift from EPA to registrants when they wish to contest the basis of EPA risk reduction measures.*

Give Due Weight to Compatibility With Biointensive IPM *EPA should severely restrict, and when necessary cancel, pesticide uses that are incompatible with biointensive IPM because of toxicity to non-target species, environmental fate, or potential to cause or worsen secondary pest outbreaks.*

These criteria are currently seldom if ever major factors in EPA's registration or cancellation decisions. They should be. Regulatory decisions can be more consciously applied to the national goal of accelerating the transition to biointensive IPM, and it is essential that Congress and EPA adopt this perspective on the role of regulation in the process.

Speed Up the Label-Revision Process *Label changes should in general be completed within six months. Old labels should expire shortly after EPA publishes, or otherwise announces, the content of new labels.*

It currently takes far too long for changes in pesticide use required by EPA to meet safety objectives to be implemented. This process (described in Chapter 4) can be speeded up significantly. Provisional labels approved for one to two years should be used in situations where new field studies are needed to fine-tune changes in rates, pre-harvest and field re-entry levels or other safety precautions. EPA should also weigh registrant cooperation in revising labels when deciding whether unused product with old labels may still be used.

Make Some Pesticides "Prescription Use Only" *EPA should create a new "prescription use only" registration category and occasionally use it to provide certified pest managers access to "old label" products or products considered too risky for routine use.*

The prescription would identify the target pest and population levels, confirm that no safer alternative exists, and carefully set forth the timing and the way the high risk pesticide must be applied to insure efficacy and minimize risks. In creating this category EPA would also need to specify who was qualified to issue "prescriptions;" the criteria would be markedly more stringent and focused more on pest management than those now governing the process of certifying applicators of "restricted use" pesticides. The skills and knowledge needed to safely handle, mix, load and apply pesticides are very different from the skills and knowledge needed to determine where—and whether—a pesticide is needed in the first place. The authority to prescribe high risk pesticides should be reserved to people who possess both skills.

2. Don't Register New High Risk Products

EPA has recently registered several new pesticides and transgenic crop varieties that increase risks to health or ecosystems in specific ways. In particular, several biotechnologies approved in the last two years are incompatible with biointensive IPM, for reasons explained in Chapters 6 and 8. The drain on agency resources associated with both the registration process and some required follow-up risk monitoring programs is also a concern, given the priority that must be assigned to reregistration, tolerance revision and registering low risk biopesticides. We urge EPA to:

"Just Say No" *EPA should not register any more category A, B_1 or B_2 carcinogens, nor any pesticides that are potent developmental or reproductive toxicants. It should approve no more Bt-transgenic plants nor plant varieties engineered to resist a herbicide to which there are resistant weeds.*

In recent decisions approving the herbicide acetochlor and *Bt*-transgenic plants, EPA has imposed elaborate safety precautions and resistance management plans. Such requirements are very hard to enforce and are black holes for agency resources. The evidence to date in the case of *Bt*-transgenic plants suggests that the resistance management plans are failing. The water quality protection triggers built into the 1994 acetochlor decision have already been violated, yet rather than act to restrict use of the product EPA has spent many staff-years evaluating the registrants' petition to raise the acetochlor levels allowed in drinking water.

EPA should enforce the terms of recent conditional approvals:

Revoke Certain Transgenic Plant Approvals *EPA should suspend or revoke registrations for previously approved* Bt-*transgenic plants, and those for herbicide tolerant crops when there is credible evidence that the transgenic plant variety is likely to worsen resistance to any currently registered pesticide active ingredient.*

Bt, as we explain in Chapter 8, is uniquely useful and safe for controlling one of the toughest classes of insect pests—the lepidopterans. Widespread introduction of *Bt* toxin into crops threatens to spread resistance and make *Bt* ineffective, a major blow to American agriculture. Resistance to herbicides in weed species is increasing at a stunning rate (see Chapter 2), and many weeds are both cross-resistant and multiple-resistant to herbicides intended for use with herbicide tolerant crop varieties. Approving more such transgenic varieties can only worsen this trend.

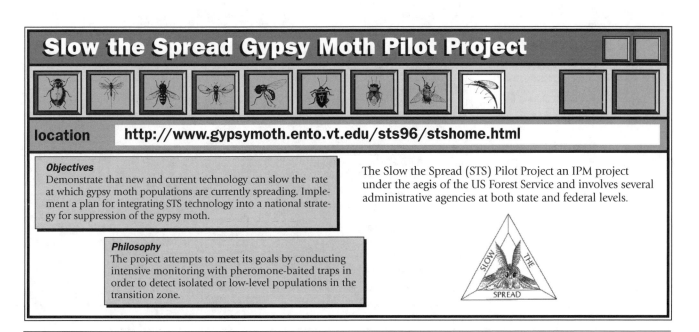

Slow the Spread Gypsy Moth Pilot Project

location http://www.gypsymoth.ento.vt.edu/sts96/stshome.html

Objectives
Demonstrate that new and current technology can slow the rate at which gypsy moth populations are currently spreading. Implement a plan for integrating STS technology into a national strategy for suppression of the gypsy moth.

Philosophy
The project attempts to meet its goals by conducting intensive monitoring with pheromone-baited traps in order to detect isolated or low-level populations in the transition zone.

The Slow the Spread (STS) Pilot Project an IPM project under the aegis of the US Forest Service and involves several administrative agencies at both state and federal levels.

SLOW THE SPREAD

3. *Speed Approval of Low Risk Biopesticides*

Last year EPA set up a new division dedicated to accelerating registration of reduced risk biopesticides, which include biocontrol agents such as microorganisms and viruses, insect pheromones, and natural chemicals derived from plants. The average time required to register biopesticides in 1995 dropped to 11 months, compared to 3 to 4 years for synthetic pesticide active ingredients. The total cost of meeting EPA data requirements for a reduced risk biopesticide is on the order of a few hundred thousand dollars, compared to about $10 million for a moderately or highly toxic synthetic pesticide.

We applaud these steps and urge EPA to continue in this direction by:

Identifying Low Risk Biopesticides *EPA and USDA should develop more rigorous criteria to identify low risk biopesticides, biocontrol organisms and inert ingredients, seeking public input in the process. EPA should then publish lists of biopesticides, organisms and inert ingredients meeting those criteria and update the lists periodically.*

Using Sound Ecological Definitions *The basic criterion used to differentiate low risk biopesticides from other biopesticides should be whether the product reinforces biological and ecological processes and interactions the pest manager is using to prevent pest problems in the* context of biointensive IPM. Biopesticides and biotechnologies that are used much like conventional pesticides, i.e as a treatment for a problem, should generally not be designated "low risk."

Fast-Tracking Approvals *Low risk biopesticides should receive the highest priority and the greatest degree of expedited regulatory process. Other biopesticides and"reduced risk" pesticides should also move through the registration process within 18 months, as EPA has promised. Pesticides that do not meet these criteria should be assigned lower priority for review and approved as resources allow.*

4. *Reconsider the Role of Benefits*

The proper focus of a pesticide benefits assessment is to help determine how fast to restrict or end uses of high risk pesticides. As new and safer pest management alternatives emerge, EPA should become progressively less tolerant of risks, including impacts on beneficial organisms, biodiversity and soil quality.

We concur with a key recommendation in the National Academy of Sciences report *Pesticides in the Diets of Infants and Children*—benefits should *not* play a role in setting tolerances for pesticide residues in food or limits on pesticides in drinking water. These judgments should be based solely on health considerations, and should assure ample margins of safety for all segments of the population.

In high-value strawberry production systems, biointensive IPM has greatly reduced reliance on broad-spectrum insecticides, which has made the picker's job both more pleasant and safer. It has also increased the benefits associated with treatments with biopesticides and the release of beneficial insects, two key elements in biointensive strawberry IPM.
Credit: Merck & Co., Inc.

Assess Benefits Rarely *The number of actions requiring benefits assessment should be markedly reduced. A meaningful benefits assessment is a complex and costly exercise, and should be carried out only when there are compelling reasons to do so.*

Stop Publicly Funded Testimonials *USDA and experiment station resources should not be wasted on submissions to EPA about the efficacy of and need for pesticides.*

Such arguments should be left to registrants. Submissions from government agencies should be based on and limited to original research results and findings in review articles on the pesticide in question, on registered alternatives or on alternative pest management tactics or systems.

Consider Safer Alternatives *When benefits assessments are carried out, they should include examination of low risk biopesticides and other safer alternatives to the pesticide in question, which could achieve the same benefits with substantially lower risk.*

As a matter of policy, when EPA reevaluates high risk pesticides it should take into account the registration of reduced risk pesticides and biopesticides for the affected crops and pest problems. When the efficacy of safer options is well established, EPA should be free to impose more aggressive restrictions on high risk alternatives through simplified procedures that require no new risk analysis.

Evaluate Biopesticide Benefits Realistically
When evaluating new product applications or carrying out a comparative benefits assessment, biopesticides should be judged by standards of efficacy reflecting what biological control agents and mechanisms accomplish in nature, not standards applicable to synthetic pesticides designed to kill 100 percent of target pest populations.

The efficacy of most biopesticides will depend on proper use and many variables inherent in the biology of farming systems. Most biopesticides are designed to support multitactic pest management systems, perhaps providing a boost for the plant's natural defenses during a particularly vulnerable time. But often it will be difficult or impossible to isolate the contribution of biopesticides from other factors, and those contributions will vary from year to year.

5. *Reduce and Share the Costs of Regulation*

In Chapter 4 we estimate that pesticide regulation has cost $17 billion in public and private expenditures since 1971, and project that costs for the next 25 years will approach $40 billion. The public share of these costs, about 31 percent in 1995, will rise to nearly 40 percent by 2020, with states bearing more of the burden as EPA delegates more tasks to them. New sources of funding will likely be needed to develop training and certification programs, build the information infrastructure, promote public/private partnerships to advance biointensive IPM, and achieve other worthy goals.

Use the Tax Code to Encourage Constructive Investment *Congress should amend the tax laws to remove incentives that promote increased pesticide use.*

At the federal level, a search is under way for new revenue sources that could help support biointensive IPM and related regulatory activities. Congress is also seeking to eliminate several categories of "corporate welfare," in the interests of balancing the budget and more equitably sharing the tax burden. Research and development expenditures and safety assessments serve the public good and should remain legitimate tax deductions. But prime targets of the Congressional ax should include the following activities by pesticide companies that are currently fully tax-deductible:

- *the costs of cleaning up polluted sites, Superfund settlements, or related legal judgments in which the company was found negligent;*

- *rebates, bonuses for sales people, herbicide respray program costs and other expenditures designed to boost pesticide sales.*

Impose Equitable User Fees *Congress should empower EPA to charge registration fees sufficient to cover most costs of pesticide risk and benefit assessment and regulatory decision-making. Fees might be adjusted in accord with pesticide toxicity per treated area to better tap market forces. Low risk biopesticides should be exempt from such fees.*

User fees embody the theory that the price of a product should reflect its true costs. In an era of shrinking budgets and aversion to tax increases, such fees are a sensible way to pay for essential regulation. Registration fees might also be tapped to finance IPM research and education.

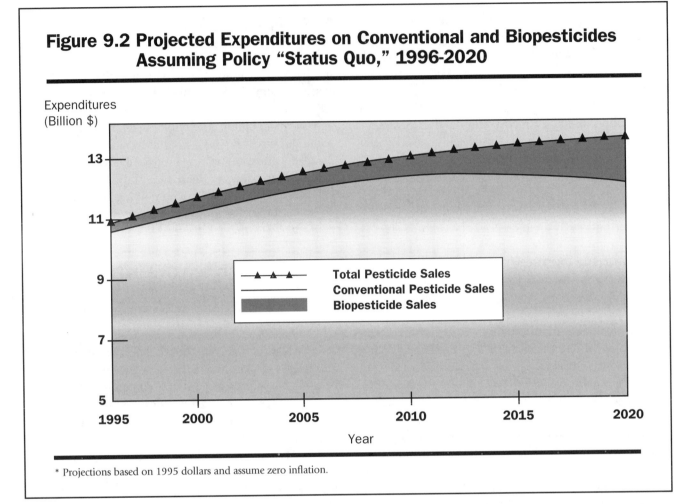

Figure 9.2 Projected Expenditures on Conventional and Biopesticides Assuming Policy "Status Quo," 1996-2020

Expenditures (Billion $)

Legend:
- Total Pesticide Sales
- Conventional Pesticide Sales
- Biopesticide Sales

Year

* Projections based on 1995 dollars and assume zero inflation.

Use Pesticide Sales Taxes to Remediate Pesticide Problems *Taxes on pesticide sales should cover the cost of community drinking water testing programs for pesticides, as well as costs entailed in efforts to filter pesticides out of water and, when needed, secure uncontaminated sources of drinking water.*

States now raise about half the cost of state pesticide regulatory programs from registration fees, and another portion of expenditures from a variety of taxes. As states are called upon to do more, most are likely to use taxes and fees to finance program efforts. Such steps are better than a diminished, ineffective and slow regulatory presence. Sensibly structured tax incentives can reduce use of high risk compounds and promote use of safer alternatives.

E. Moving Forward

Our recommendations have laid out a roadmap for the transition to biointensive IPM, a transformation in approaches to managing pest problems that we believe

is absolutely essential. With the creative commitment of good people in all sectors to this goal, it will happen more rapidly and spare us much of the costs of protracted reliance on failing chemical-intensive approaches.

Where will the money come from to finance the major expansion in infrastructure needed to support universal adoption of biointensive IPM? The answer lies in the marketplace. Biointensive IPM will become the pest management *status quo* only when pest managers view biointensive IPM systems as more effective and profitable than their currently underpriced chemical competition. As biointensive IPM gains acceptance and demand grows, expanding income will support new research and development and sustainable growth in the IPM infrastructure.

Figures 9.2 and 9.3 present scenarios for revenue streams from sales of conventional pesticides and low risk biopesticides, under two sets of assumptions. Figure 9.2 assumes no concerted national effort to promote biointensive IPM, and extension of current policies without much change to the year 2020. Figure 9.3 assumes

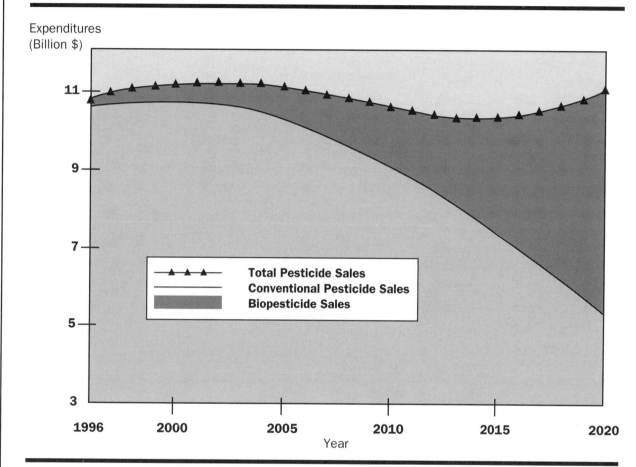

Figure 9.3 Projected Expenditures on Conventional and Biopesticides Assuming "Policy Change," 1996-2020

Expenditures
(Billion $)

Total Pesticide Sales
Conventional Pesticide Sales
Biopesticide Sales

1996   2000   2005   2010   2015   2020
Year

* Projections based on 1995 dollars and assume zero inflation.

that our basic recommendations are followed and that a transition to biointensive IPM of the magnitude shown in Figure 9.1 (page 228) takes place. (The assumptions and data sources we used to make these projections are discussed in Appendix 1.)

The figure shows that under the "policy change" scenario, total pesticide expenditures by the year 2020 would be about 20 percent lower than they would with no national commitment to IPM, and conventional pesticides would account for about half the total. The reduction in market share for conventional pesticides would bring about at least a 75 percent reduction in overall risks, we estimate. The share of total pesticide expenditures accounted for by low risk biopesticides would expand from about 2 percent in 1996 to about 50 percent of the market in 2020—growing from about

$200 million a year now to around $5 billion a year in 2020. Further revenue will be earned by those combining the sale of biopesticides, diagnostic services and IPM tools with the delivery of biointensive IPM services, and some of this service-oriented income will in turn finance further refinement of IPM strategies, products and services.

The area between the two curves in each graph represents biopesticide and related biologically based sales. This is the income stream most likely to support expansion of the IPM infrastructure. While the transition has started slowly, it is picking up steam, and success will build on itself. This analysis also suggests how important it is to promote progress along the IPM continuum at every opportunity, as the benefits of even small steps today will be magnified many times over, a few years down the road.

Appendix 1: Data Sources and Assumptions in Projecting the Costs of Managing Pesticide Risks and Regulating Pesticide Use

Two tables appear in Chapter 4 reporting estimates over the last 25 years (1971-1995) and next 25 years (1996-2020) of public and private sector expenditures associated with pesticide risks and regulation. The major sources of data and assumptions made in extrapolating from limited data sources are described herein.

All estimates in Tables 4.3 and 4.4 are reported in 1995 dollars for ease of comparison. Hence, the expenditure levels in the early years in Table 4.3 appear higher than typically reported in other tables based on nominal dollars. In adjusting the data for inflation, we used standard Consumer Price Index adjustment factors. EPA's estimates of regulatory program expenditures were all reported in constant 1986 dollars (see Appendix J, Carlin, 1990); a factor of 1.39 was used to convert 1986 dollars to 1995 dollars.

Our estimates strive to cover public and private sector costs of assessing, monitoring, reducing, and regulating pesticide risks and benefits. These costs are all a function, in one way or another, of pesticide use and toxicity. The estimates do not include pest management research expenditures, the cost of discovering new pesticides, or costs associated with testing for and filtering pesticides out of drinking water. We were unable to develop estimates of water quality monitoring, filtration, and related costs.

1. Pesticide Sales Data

Data on pesticide sales by sector (agriculture, consumer and industry) for the years 1979-1993 are from (Aspelin, 1994, 1996, Tables 15 and 16).

An estimate of 1971 agricultural sector sales of conventional pesticides in nominal dollars was obtained from "Farmers Use of Pesticides in 1971: Expenditures" (USDA, 1975). Pesticide sales figures for the agricultural sector from 1972 through 1978 were extrapolated from the level in the 1971 USDA report to the level reported by EPA for 1979.

Pesticide sales for the consumer and industry sectors for 1971-1978 were extrapolated at the same percentage relative to the agriculture sector as in 1979 in EPA's dataset. Total sales for 1971 through 1978 are the sum of expenditures in the three sectors. Total pesticide sales for 1994 and 1995 are from EPA data (Aspelin, 1996).

Total pesticide sales, conventional pesticide sales and sales of biopesticides and associated biologically based pest management products (see Chapters 7 and 8 for more discussion) were estimated under two scenarios. Under the

"No Change" Scenario discussed in Chapter 9, data values for 1996-2020 conventional pesticide sales were extrapolated from recent trends and industry market projections. Starting from the 1995 baseline, the rate of sales growth was assumed to decline one-tenth of one percent each year, dropping from 1.8 percent in 1996 to 1.7 percent in 1997, and so on. In the year 2015, the rate of growth becomes negative and by 2020 we project a 0.6 percent decline in conventional pesticides sales in that year.

Under the "Policy Change" Scenario, data values for 1996-2020 conventional pesticide sales were extrapolated to decline more rapidly as follows (year: rate of growth or decline): 1996: 1.5%, 1997: 1.35%, 1998: 1.2%, 1999: 1.0%, 2000: 0.75%, 2001: 0.40%, 2002: 0.1%, 2003: -0.2%, 2004: -0.35%, 2005: -0.5%, 2006: -0.6%, 2007: -0.7%, 2008: -0.8%, 2009: -0.9%, 2010: -1.0%, 2011: -1.1%, 2012: -1.2%, 2013: -1.3%, 2014: -1.4%, 2015: -1.5%, 2016: -1.6%, 2017: -1.7%, 2018: -1.8%, 2019: -1.9%, 2020: -2.0%.

Biopesticide Sales

Baseline sales of biopesticides in 1995 were obtained from the National Center for Food and Agricultural Policy (Gianessi, 1995) and data in various reports by USDA pest management experts (Ridgway et al., 1994; Ridgway and Inscoe, 1996). Projected expenditures and growth rates from 1995 to the year 2000 were estimated from several government and private sector sources (see Office of Technology Assessment Background Paper, Ridgway et al., 1994; Little, 1996; Freedonia Group forecast reported in *Chemical and Engineering News*, 1996).

Biopesticide sales from 2001-2020 under the "No Change" Scenario are based on 4.0% to 8.4% annual growth. The "Policy Change" Scenario assumes a broad-based national commitment to progress along the IPM continuum, reinforced by public and private sector initiatives of the nature and scope as recommended in Chapter 9. Under these assumptions we would expect major progress toward our stated 100 percent biointensive IPM goal by the year 2020, and significant increases in the sales of biopesticides, which we project to grow 10.5% to 12.4% annually during the period.

The emergence of new pests, growing demand for food and other factors will affect progress along the continuum in different regions and periods of time. The actual percent of agricultural production under biointensive IPM will fluctuate somewhat from year to year as a result of the emergence of new pests, changes in technology, resistance and other factors. Hence, actual total pesticide, conventional pesticide and biopesticide sales will vary from year to year, as will the percent of national acreage managed under biointensive IPM.

2. Residue Testing Costs

We developed estimates of both public and private sector pesticide residue testing costs based on information from a variety of government and private sector sources. The number of samples of foods and drinks tested and average cost per sample were estimated from "Enhancement of the Pesticide Residue Information System" (Nies, 1993).

Food and Drug Administration data on number of samples from 1978 through 1995 were provided by Dr. John H. Jones (Jones, 1996). The average total cost per sample was estimated by Dr. Jones as $900. This cost includes sample collection, analytical chemistry, confirmations, data entry and record keeping.

U.S. Department of Agriculture Pesticide Data Program information was obtained from Martha Lamont, Chief, Residue Branch, Science and Technology Division, Agricultural Marketing Service, USDA, fax transmittal, May 5, 1996. Data on Food Safety Inspection Service residue testing expenditures are from USDA budget documents.

Private sector residue testing costs are based on estimates of the number of samples, cost per sample, and cost per acre of managing pesticide residue and record keeping requirements, as provided by several food industry sources including Dr. Ed Elkins, National Food Processors Association and Dr. Steven Balling, Del Monte Foods.

3. Regulatory Compliance Data

Several categories of expenditures were estimated encompassing most but not all steps by the pesticide industry, pesticide retailers and applicators, farmers and the food industry to: comply with EPA regulations; adhere to safety precautions on pesticide product labels; meet record keeping requirements; apply pesticides safely; cover liability and insurance costs; and, dispose of pesticide containers. Data for the areas shown below for the years 1972-2000 were taken from Appendix J, Cost of Clean, "Environmental Investments," (Carlin, 1990).

The Cost of Clean estimates of industry costs in 1989-2000 were based on the assumption that the

reregistration process would move forward on schedule, leading to several major cancellation and suspension actions, which has not happened. Working with EPA experts we therefor adjusted the Cost of Clean estimates to more closely reflect actual EPA program levels and actions in recent years and the foreseeable future.

All data from Appendix J are reported in 1986 constant dollars and were converted to 1995 dollars using the Consumer Price Index. Projections were made in 1995 dollars and were extrapolated as follows for the years 2001-2020:

Area	Annual Change
Private Regulatory Compliance	-5% to 4%
Other Private Regulatory Costs	-5% to 6%
Farm worker Safety	-5% to 6%
Application & Training	-5% to 6%
EPA Expenditures	0.5% to 1.5%
USDA Expenditures	4% to 5%
State/Local Regulatory Compliance	N/A

Data for 1971 for all of these areas was estimated to be 95% of 1972 values.

4. Regulatory Costs

EPA program expenditures for 1972 through the year 2000 are from Appendix J, Cost of Clean. Estimates for 1972 through 1989 reflect EPA's best estimates of actual expenditures. State regulatory program expenditures are also from Cost of Clean and Mr. Ed Brandt, U.S. EPA Biological and Economic Analysis Branch (facsimile dated April 19, 1996), who provided estimates of state regulatory program costs and revenue sources for 1994 and 1995. Costs from 1995 through the year 2020 were projected based on recent trends and available estimates of the costs of meeting current state regulatory program expenditures.

The Food Quality Protection Act of 1996 was passed after the projections in Table 4.4 had been completed. It is likely this major legislation will impact several categories of expenditures including industry compliance costs, residue testing program levels, and EPA and state program costs, but it is too soon to project how. Near-term costs are likely to rise somewhat above the projections now in Table 4.4 but longer-term costs might then decline more than anticipated, especially if EPA is able to implement the new health-based tolerance standard set forth in the bill within the 10 year time frame required in the legislation.

Bibliography

Abelson, P.H. 1995. "Plant Pathogens in Soils," Editorial. *Science*, Volume 269 (August 25): 1027.

Abernathy, J.R. and D.C. Bridges. 1994. "Research Priority Dynamics in Weed Science." *Weed Technology*, Volume 8, Number 2: 396-399.

Ahrens, W.H. and E.P. Fuerst. 1990. "Carryover Injury of Clomazone Applied in Soybeans (*Glycine max*) and Fallow," *Weed Technology*, Volume 4: 855-861.

Alderson, C. and A. Greene. 1995. "Bird-Deterrence Technology for Historic Buildings," *APT Bulletin*, Volume 26, Numbers 2-3, Association for Preservation Technology International, Williamsburg, Virginia, pages 18-30.

Alford, A.R., Drummond, F.A., Gallandt, E.R., Groden, E., Lambert, D.A., Liebman, M., Marra, M.C., McBurnie, J.C., Porter, G.A. and B. Salas. 1996. "The Ecology, Economics, and Management of Potato Cropping Systems: A Report of the First Four Years of the Maine Potato Ecosystem Project," Bulletin 843, Maine Agricultural and Forest Experiment Station, University of Maine, April 1996. 204 pages.

American Council on Science and Health. 1990. "ALAR: One Year Later, A Media Analysis of a Hypothetical Health Risk," K. Smith, *Special Report*, American Council on Science and Health, New York, New York.

American Council on Science and Health. 1992. "Alar Three Years Later: Science Unmasks a Hypothetical Health Scare," K. Smith, *Special Report*, American Council on Science and Health, New York, New York.

American Council on Science and Health. 1994. "Alar Five Years Later: Science Triumphs over Fear," K. Smith, *Special Report*, American Council on Science and Health, New York, New York.

American Crop Protection Association. 1994. "From Lab to Label: The Research, Testing and Registration of Agricultural Chemicals," Washington, D.C.

American Crop Protection Association. 1996. "Industry Profile: 1995," Compiled by Association Services Group, LLC, American Crop Protection Association, Washington, D.C.

Ames, B.N. and L.S. Gold. 1991. "Risk Assessment of Pesticides, News Forum," *Chemical and Engineering News* (January 7): 27-32.

Amir, H. and C. Alabouvette. 1993. "Involvement of Soil Abiotic Factors in the Mechanisms of Soil Suppressiveness to Fusarium Wilts," *Soil Biology and Biochemistry*, Volume 25, Number 2, pages 157-164.

Anderson, M. (Editor). 1994. *Agricultural Resources and Environmental Indicators*. Agricultural Handbook Number 705. Economic Research Service, U. S. Department of Agriculture, Washington, D.C.

Angers, D. A., N'dayegamiye, A. and D. Cote. 1993. "Tillage-Induced Differences in Organic Matter of Particle-Size Fractions and Microbial Biomass," *Soil Science Society of America Journal*, Volume 57 (March-April): 512-516.

Arnold, S.F., Klotz, D.M., Collins, B.M., Vonier, P.M., Guillette, L.J. Jr. and J.A. McLachlan. 1996. "Synergistic Activation of Estrogen Receptor with Combinations of Environmental Chemicals," *Science*, Volume 272 (June 7): 1489-1492.

Aspelin, A.L. 1994 (June). *Pesticides Industry Sales and Usage: 1992 and 1993 Market Estimates*. U. S. Environmental Protection Agency, Washington, D.C.

Aspelin, A.L. 1996 (March). *Pesticides Industry Sales and Usage: 1994 and 1995 Market Estimates — Preliminary*. U. S. Environmental Protection Agency, Washington, D.C. (In press)

Associated Press. 1996. "Genetically altered cotton...," Little Rock, Arkansas, Associated Press Wire Service.

Baby, U.I. and K. Manibhushanrao. 1993. "Control of Rice Sheath Blight through the Integration of Fungal Antagonists and Organic Amendments," *Tropical Agriculture*. (Trinidad) Volume 70, Number 3: 240-244.

Bagdon, J.K, Plotkin, S. and E.S. Hesketh. 1994. *NAPRA Technology Transfer Overview: An Introduction*. USDA Soil Conservation Service, Washington, D.C.

Balling, S. 1994. "The IPM Continuum," In A.A. Sorensen [ed.] *Constraints to the Adoption of Integrated Pest Management: Regional Producer Workshops*, National Foundation for IPM Education.

Barnes, M.M., Millar, J.G., Kirsch, P.A. and D.C. Hawks. 1992. "Codling Moth (Lepidoptera: Torticidae) Control by Dissemination of Synthetic Female Sex Pheromone," *Journal of Economic Entomology*, Volume 85, Number 4: 1274-1277.

Barrier, G.E. 1988. "Final Report on the Response of Vegetation Near the Cernay Plant to Sulfonylureas" (February 19, 1988), E.I. Du Pont Nemours & Co. (Inc.), Agricultural Products Department, Stine-Haskell Laboratory, Newark, Delaware.

Becker, H. 1996. "New American Elms Restore Stately Trees," *Agricultural Research*, Agricultural Research Service, U. S. Department of Agriculture, pages 4-8.

Becker, H., Corliss, J., De Quattro, J., Gerrietts, M., Senft, D., Stanley, D. and M. Wood. 1992 (November). "Get the Whitefly Swatters Fast," *Agricultural Research*, Agricultural Research Service, USDA, pages 4-13.

Becker, R. 1995. "Integrating Weed Management and Environmental Concerns," Presentation: Weed Biology, Soil Management and New Approaches to Weeds Workshop, Sponsored by the USDA-ARS National Soil Tilth Laboratory, June 26-28, 1995, Ames, Iowa.

Benbrook, C.M. 1995. *Healthy Food, Healthy Farms: Pest Management in the Public Interest.* National Campaign for Pesticide Policy Reform, Washington, D. C.

Benbrook, C.M. 1996. "Adoption of Integrated Weed Management Systems by Corn and Soybean Farmers in 1994: Application of a New Methodology to Measure Adoption of IPM and Pesticide Use and Reliance." Paper presented at the Weed Science Society of America Annual Meeting, February 1996, Norfolk, Virginia.

Benbrook, C.M. and D.J. Marquart. 1993. *Challenge and Change: A Progressive Approach to Pesticide Regulation in California.* California Environmental Protection Agency, Department of Pesticide Regulation, Sacramento, California.

Best, L.B. and D.L. Fischer. 1992. "Granular Insecticides and Birds: Factors to be Considered in Understanding Exposure and Reducing Risk," *Environmental Toxicology and Chemistry*, Volume 11:1495-1508.

Bezark, L.G. 1989. "Suppliers of Beneficial Insects," California Department of Pesticide Regulation, Sacramento, California.

Bezark, L.G., and E.J. Rey. 1982. "Suppliers of Beneficial Organisms in North America," California Department of Pesticide Regulation, Sacramento, California.

Bezdicek, D.F. and D. Granatstein. 1989. "Crop Rotation Efficiencies and Biological Diversity in Farming Systems," *American Journal of Alternative Agriculture*, Volume 4(3-4): 111-119.

Bio-Integral Resource Center. 1996a. "Products," *Common Sense Pest Control*, Volume 12, Number 1, Winter 1996, page 17.

Bio-Integral Resource Center. 1996b. "Termite Good News," *Common Sense Pest Control*, Volume 12, Number 3, Summer 1996, page 3.

Blondell, J. 1992. "Pesticide Poisoning Summary," Health Effects Division, Office of Pesticide Programs, U.S. Environmental Protection Agency, Washington, D.C.

Bohlen, P.J. and C.A. Edwards. 1995. "Earthworm Effects on N Dynamics and Soil Respiration in Microcosms Receiving Organic and Inorganic Nutrients," *Soil Biology and Biochemistry*, Volume 27:341-348.

Bolkan, H.A. and W.R. Reinert. 1994. "Developing and Implementing IPM Strategies to Assist Farmers: An Industry Approach," *Plant Disease*, American Phytopathological Society, Volume 78, Number 6, pages 545-550.

Bosso, C.J. 1987. *Pesticides and Politics: The Life Cycle of a Public Issue.* University of Pittsburgh Press.

Bottrell, D. G. 1979. *Integrated Pest Management.* Council on Environmental Quality, Washington, D.C.

Bottrell, D.G. , and G.B. Lim. 1994. *Neem Pesticides in Rice: Potential and Limitations.* International Rice Research Institute, Los Banos, Philippines.

Bottrell, D.G., and R.R. Weil. 1995. "Protecting Crops and the Environment: Striving for Durability," *Agriculture and the Environment: Bridging Food Production and Environmental Protection in Developing Countries*, A. S. R. Juo and R. D. Freed, [eds.], pages 55-73, American Society of Agronomy, Inc., Crop Science Society of America, Inc. and Soil Science Society of America, Inc., Madison, Wisconsin.

Briggs, S.A. 1992. *Basic Guide to Pesticides: Their Characteristics and Hazards.* Taylor and Francis, Washington, D.C.

Brown, G.C. 1991. "Research and Extension Roles in Development of Computer-Based Technologies in Integrated Pest Management," *Environmental Entomology* Volume 20, Number 5: 1236-1240.

Brunetti, K.M. 1981. "Suppliers of Beneficial Organisms in North America," California Department of Food and Agriculture, Sacramento, California.

Brust, G.E. and G.J. House. 1988. "Weed Seed Destruction by Arthropods and Rodents in Low-Input Soybean Agroecosystems," *American Journal of Alternative Agriculture*, Volume 3, Number 1.

Buffer, P.A. and A.D. Kyle. 1996. *Regulatory Reform Proposals and the Public Health.* School of Public Health, University of California — Berkeley, Berkeley, California.

Buhler, D.D. 1992. "Population Dynamics and Control of Annual Weeds in Corn (*Zea mays*) as Influenced by Tillage Systems," *Weed Science* Volume 40, Number 2: 241-248.

Buhler, D.D., Gunsolus, J.L. and D.F. Ralston. 1992. "Integrated Weed Management Techniques to Reduce Herbicide Inputs in Soybean," *Agronomy Journal*, Volume 84: 973-978.

Bultena, G., Hoiberg, E., Jarnagin, S. and R. Exner. 1993. "Transition to a More Sustainable Agriculture in Iowa," Sociological Report Number 166, Iowa State University, Ames, Iowa.

Burnet, M.W.M., Hart, Q., Holtum, J.A.M. and S.B. Powles. 1994. "Resistance to Nine Herbicide Classes in a Population of Rigid Ryegrass (*Lolium rigidum*)," *Weed Science*, Volume 42, Number 3: 369-377.

Burnham, T.J. 1996. "Researchers Use Computer to Help Forecast Blackmold," *Ag Alert*, May 1, 1996.

Burpee, L.L. 1990. "The Influence of Abiotic Factors on Biological Control of Soilborne Plant Pathogenic Fungi," *Canadian Journal of Plant Pathology*, Volume 12: 308-317.

Buske, M.C., Guge, G.G., Root, T.A. and G.E. Gage. 1991 (November 25). *Integrated Pest Management Demonstration and Education Project at DeSoto National Wildlife Refuge: A Final Report Prepared for the Leopold Center for Sustainable Agriculture.* Iowa State University Extension,

California Department of Pesticide Regulation. 1996. "Pesticide Use Reporting System," Cal-EPA, Sacramento, California.

Carlin, A. 1990. "Environmental Investments: The Cost of a Clean Environment – A Summary." Science, Economics and Statistics Division; Office of Regulatory Management and Evaluation; Office of Policy, Planning and Evaluation; U. S. Environmental Protection Agency. EPA-230-12-90-084. Available over the Internet at (requires Adobe Acrobat Reader): [http://www.epa.gov/docs/oppe/eaed/eedfull.htm#cost]. Click on appropriate file: a summary document, the full document and appendices are available in separate files. Appendix J contains detailed information on the data sources used in estimating the costs of pesticide regulation. Questions regarding access to these documents can be sent to Alan Carlin, e-mail address: carlin.alan@epamail.epa.gov.

Carson, R. 1962. *Silent Spring*. Houghton Mifflin Co., Boston, Massachusetts.

Cate, J. and M. Hinkle. 1993. *Integrated Pest Management: The Path of a Paradigm*. National Audubon Society, Washington, D.C.

Chemical and Engineering News. 1996. "Product Sophistication Drives U. S. Pesticide Market Growth Despite Decreased Volume Use," American Chemical Society, Washington, D.C., April 29, 1996, page 36.

Chemical and Pharmaceutical Press. 1994 [reissued annually]. *Crop Protection Chemicals Reference*. John Wiley and Sons, New York, New York.

Coble, H.D. and D.A. Mortensen. 1992. "The Threshold Concept and Its Application to Weed Science," *Weed Technology* Volume 61, Number 1: 191-195.

Cohen, B., Campbell, C. and R. Wiles. 1995a. *In the Drink*. Environmental Working Group, Washington, D.C.

Cohen, B., Wiles, R. and E. Bondoc. 1995b. *Weed Killers by the Glass: A Citizen's Tap Water Monitoring Project in 29 Cities*. Environmental Working Group, Washington, D.C.

Colborn, T., vom Saal, F.S. and A.M. Soto. 1993. "Developmental Effects of Endocrine-Disrupting Chemicals in Wildlife and Humans," *Environmental Health Perspectives*, Volume 101, Number 5: 378-384.

Colborn, T., Dumanoski, D. and J.P. Myers. 1996. *Our Stolen Future: How We are Threatening Our Fertility, Intelligence, and Survival - A Scientific Detective Story*. Dutton Book, New York, New York.

Colby, S.R., Hill, E.R., Humburg, N.E., Kitchen, L.M., Lym, R.G., McAvoy, W.J. and R. Prasad. 1994. *Herbicide Handbook*, 7th edition. Weed Science Society of America, Champaign, Ill.

Congressional Record. 1971 (November 8). Page 39976.

Conservation Foundation. 1989. *Pesticides and Birds: Improving Impact Assessment*. Report of the Avian Effects Dialogue Group, Washington, D.C., 67 pages.

Cook, R.J. 1991. "Challenges and Rewards of Sustainable Agriculture Research and Education," in *Sustainable Agriculture Research and Education in the Field: A Proceedings*, National Research Council, National Academy Press, 1991.

Cook, R.J. 1994. "The Place for IPM in the Next Decade," speech presented April 1994, Second National IPM Forum, Las Vegas, Nevada.

Cook, R.J. and R.J. Veseth. 1991. *Wheat Health Management*. American Phytopathological Society, St. Paul, Minnesota.

Council on Environmental Quality. 1972. "Integrated Pest Management," Executive Office of the President, Washington, D.C.

Croft, B. 1990. "Pesticide Effects on Arthropod Natural Enemies: A Database Summary," Chapter 2, *Arthropod Biological Control Agents and Pesticides*. Wiley Press, 1990.

Crookston, R.K., Kurle, J.E., Copeland, P.J., Ford, J.H. and | W.E. Lueschen. 1991. "Rotational Cropping Sequence Affects Yield of Corn and Soybean," *Agronomy Journal* Volume 83:108-113.

de la Cruz, A.R., Poplawsky, A.R. and M.V. Wiese. 1992. "Biological Suppression of Potato Ring Rot by Fluorescent Pseudomonads," *Applied and Environment Microbiology*, Volume 58, Number 6, pages 1986-1991.

Curl, E.A. 1982. "The Rhizosphere: Relation to Pathogen Behavior and Root Disease," *Plant Disease*, Volume 66, Number 7: 624-630.

Curtis, J., Mott, L., and T. Profeta. 1993. *After Silent Spring: The Unsolved Problems of Pesticide Use in the United States.* Natural Resources Defense Council, New York, New York.

Daane, K.M. et al. 1995. "Excess Nitrogen Raises Nectarine Susceptibility to Disease and Insects," *California Agriculture*, July-August 1995.

Dealer Progress. 1995. "High Tech Seed Products," Volume 26, Number 6: 19.

Delaney, T.P., Uknes, S., Vernooij, B., Friedrich, L., Weymann, K., Negrotto, D., Gaffney, T., Gut-Rella, M., Kessmann, H., Ward, E. and J. Ryals. 1994. "A Central Role of Salicylic Acid in Plant Disease Resistance," *Science*, Volume 266, November 18, 1994.

Delp, C.J. [ed.]. 1988. *Fungicide Resistance in North America.* The American Phytopathological Society, St. Paul, Minnesota.

De Quattro, J. 1992. "A pest is a pest...Or is it?" *Agricultural Research*, Volume 40, Number 11.

Donegan, K.K., Palm, C.J., Fieland, V.J., Porteous, L.A., Ganio, L.M., Schaller, D.L., Bucao, L.Q. and R.J. Seidler. 1995. "Changes in Levels, Species and DNA Fingerprints of Soil Microorganisms Associated with Cotton Expressing the *Bacillus Thuringiensis* Var. *Kurstaki* Endotoxin," *Applied Soil Ecology*, Volume 2, Number 2: 111-124.

Drinkwater, L.E., Letourneau, D.K., Workneh, F., van Bruggen, A.H.C. and C. Shennan. 1995. "Fundamental Differences Between Conventional and Organic Tomato Agroecosystems in California," *Ecological Applications*, Volume 5, Number 4: 1098-1112.

Dunier, M. and A.J. Siwicki. 1993. "Effects of Pesticides and Organic Pollutants in the Aquatic Environment on Immunity of Fish: A Review," *Fish and Shellfish Immunology*, Volume 3 [1993], pages 423-438.

Dunlap, T. 1981. *DDT: Scientists, Citizens, and Public Policy.* Princeton University Press, Princeton, New Jersey.

Dushoff, J., Caldwell, B., and C.L. Mohler. 1994. "Evaluating the Environmental Effect of Pesticides: A Critique of the Environmental Impact Quotient," *American Entomologist* (Fall) Volume 40, Number 3: 180-184.

Earthington, S.R., Lim, S.M., Nickell, C.D., Pataky, J.K. and R.W. Esgar. 1993. "Disease Pressure on Soybean in Illinois," *Plant Disease*, Volume 77, Number 11: 1136-1139.

Edwards, C.A. 1993. "The Impact of Pesticides on the Environment," Chapter 2 in, D. Pimentel, H. Lehman [eds.], *The Pesticide Question: Environment, Economics, and Ethics*, Chapman and Hall, London and New York, pages 13-46.

Ehler, L.E. 1990. "Revitalizing Biological Control," *Issues in Science and Technology* (Fall): 91-96.

Elderkin, S., Wiles, R. and C. Campbell. 1995. *Forbidden Fruit: Illegal Pesticides in the U. S. Food Supply.* Environmental Working Group, Washington, D.C.

Environmental Working Group, Physicians for Social Responsibility and National Campaign for Pesticide Policy Reform. 1995. *Pesticide Industry Propaganda: The Real Story.* Washington, D.C.

Fahnestock, A.L. 1996. "Revitalizing Roundup," *Farm Chemicals Magazine*, July 1996, pages 16-17.

Farm Chemicals Magazine. 1996. "Turn, Turn, Turn," May 1996, page 11.

Fawcett, R. 1995a. "It's Time for Practical Respray Standards," *Farm Journal* (Mid-January): 17.

Fawcett, R. 1995b. "Protect Yourself from Injury Disputes," *Farm Journal* (Mid-February): E-1.

Ferguson, W. and A. Padula. 1994. "Economic Effects of Banning Methyl Bromide for Soil Fumigation," *Agricultural Economic Report* No. 677, Economic Research Service, U. S. Department of Agriculture, Washington, D.C.

Fisher, L.J. 1992. Letter to Committee on Labor and Human Resources, Chairman Edward M. Kennedy, March 30, 1992.

Fletcher, J.S., Pfleeger, T.G. and H.C. Ratsch. 1993. "Potential Environmental Risks Associated with the New Sulfonylurea Herbicides," *Environmental Science and Technology*, Volume 27, Number 10: 2250 - 2252

Forlani, G., Mantelli, M., Branzoni, M., Nielsen, E. and F. Favilli. 1995. "Differential Sensitivity of Plant-Associated Bacteria to Sulfonylurea and Imidazolinone Herbicides," *Plant and Soil*, Volume 176: 243-253. The Netherlands.

Foster, R.C., Rovira, A.D. and T.W. Cock. 1983. *Ultrastructure of the Root-Soil Interface*. American Phytopathological Society, St. Paul, Minnesota.

Frisbie, R.E., and J.W. Smith. 1989. "Biologically Intensive IPM: The Future," in *Progress and Perspectives for the 21st Century*, J.J., Menn and A.L. Steinhauer, [eds.], Entomological Society of America, pages 151-164.

Gallep, G. 1994. "The Hunt for the Wunderburg," *Science Report* University of Wisconsin-Madison, College of Agricultural and Life Sciences, 1994: pages 25-31.

Garry, V.F., Schreinemachers, D., Harkins, M.E. and J. Griffith. 1996. "Pesticide Appliers, Biocides, and Birth Defects in Rural Minnesota," *Environmental Health Perspectives*, Volume 104, pages 394-399.

Gay, Lt. Cmdr. R. 1996. "Controlled Atmospheres for Stored Products," *The IPM Practitioner*, Volume 28, Number 5/6, May/June 1996, Bio-Integral Resource Center, Berkeley, California.

Geiger, C.R. 1993. "The Health Safety Concerns of Common Insecticides," *Journal of Environmental Health*, Volume 55, Number 8: 11-15.

Ghersa, C.M., Roush, M.L., Radosevich, S.R. and S.M. Cordray. 1994. "Coevolution of Agroecosystems and Weed Management," *BioScience*, Volume 44, Number 2: 85-94.

Gianessi, L.P. 1992. *U. S. Pesticide Use Trends: 1966-1989*. Resources for the Future, Washington, D.C.

Gianessi, L.P. 1995. *An Economic Profile of the U. S. Crop Protection Pesticide Industry*. National Center for Food and Agricultural Policy, Washington, D.C.

Gianessi, L.P. and J.E. Anderson. 1993. *Pesticide Use Trends in U. S. Agriculture, 1979-1992*. National Center for Food and Agricultural Policy, Washington, D. C.

Gianessi, L.P. and J.E. Anderson. 1995. *Pesticide Use in U. S. Crop Production: National Data Report*. National Center for Food and Agricultural Policy, Washington, D.C.

Gianessi, L.P. and C. Puffer. 1991. *Herbicide Use in the United States: National Summary Report*. Quality of the Environment Division, Resources for the Future, Washington, D.C., 127 pages.

Gilbert, G.S., Handelsman, J. and J.L. Parke. 1994. "Root Camouflage and Disease Control," *Phytopathology*, Volume 84, Number 3: 222-225.

Gilbert, G.S., Parke, J.L., Clayton, M.K. and J. Handelsman. 1993. "Effects of an Introduced Bacterium on Bacterial Communities on Roots," *Ecology*, Volume 74, Number 3: 840-854.

Gill, G.S. 1995. "Development of Herbicide Resistance in Annual Ryegrass Populations (Lolium rigidum Gaud.) in the Cropping Belt of Western Australia," *American Journal of Experimental Agriculture*, Volume 35: 67-72.

Glenister, C.S. and M.P. Hoffman. 1996. "Mass-Reared Natural Enemies: Science, Technology, and Information Needs," Chapter 11, Conference Proceedings, Thomas Say Publications in Entomology, Entomological Society of America, Lanham, Maryland.

Goldburg, R., Rissler, J., Shand, H. and C. Hassebrook. 1990. *Biotechnology's Bitter Harvest: Herbicide-Tolerant Crops and the Threat to Sustainable Agriculture*. Biotechnology Working Group, Washington, D. C.

Goldman, P. and R. Wiles. 1994. *Trading Away U. S. Food Safety*. Environmental Working Group and Public Citizen, Washington, D.C.

Goodwin, P. and A.H. Purcell. 1992. "Pierce's Disease," pages 76-84 in *Grape Pest Management*, Second Edition, Flaherty, Christensen, Lanini, Marois, Phillips and Wilson, [eds.], Univ. of California Div. of Agriculture and Natural Resources.

Goolsby, D.A., Coupe, R.C. and D.J. Markovchick. 1991. "Distribution of Selected Herbicides and Nitrate in the Mississippi River and its Major Tributaries, April through June, 1991," *Water-Resources Investigations Report No. 91-4163*. U. S. Geological Survey, Denver, Colorado.

Goolsby, D.A., Battaglin, W.A. and E.M. Thurman. "Occurrence and Transport of Agricultural Chemicals in the Mississippi River Basin, July through August, 1993," Circular No. 1120-C, U. S. Geological Survey, Denver, Colorado.

Goss, D.W. 1992. "Screening Procedure for Soils and Pesticides for Potential Water Quality Impacts," *Weed Technology*, Volume 6: 701-708.

Gould, F. 1991. "The Evolutionary Potential of Crop Pests," *American Scientist*, Volume 79: 496-507.

Gould, S.J. 1996. *Dinosaur in a Haystack: Reflections in Natural History*. Harmony Books/Crown.

Graham, F., Jr. 1970. *Since Silent Spring*. Houghton Mifflin Co., Boston, Massachusetts.

Gray, M.E. 1995. "Status of CES-IPM Programs: Results of a National IPM Coordinators Survey," *American Entomologist*, Fall 1995.

Greene, A.E., and R. F. Allison 1994. "Recombination Between Viral RNA and Transgenic Plant Transcripts," *Science*, volume 263: 1423-25.

Grier, N., Clough, E. and A. Clewell. 1994. *Toxic Water:*

A Report on the Adverse Effects of Pesticides on the Pacific Coho Salmon and the Prevalence of Pesticides in Coho Habitat. Northwest Coalition for Alternatives to Pesticides, Eugene, Oregon.

Grieshop, J.I., MacMullan, E., Brush, S., Pickel, C. and F.G. Zalom. 1990. "Extending Integrated Pest Management by Public Mandate: A Case Study from California," *Society and Natural Resources*, Volume 3: 33-51.

Grossman, J. 1995. "What's Hiding Under the Sink: Dangers of Household Pesticides," *Environmental Health Perspectives*, Volume 103, Number 6: 550-554.

Grossman, J. 1996. "Entomological Society of America's 1995 Meeting — Part 2," *IPM Practitioner*, Volume XVIII, Number 3, March 1996.

Guerrero, P.F. 1993. "Pesticides: Reregistration Delays Jeopardize Success of Proposed Policy Reforms," Statement of P.F. Guerrero; Associate Director; Environmental Protection Issues, Resources, Community and Economic Development Division; U. S. General Accounting Office, Washington, D.C.

Gunsolus, J.L. 1990. "Mechanical and Cultural Weed Control in Corn and Soybeans," *American Journal of Alternative Agriculture*, Volume 5, Number 3: 114-119.

Hager, A.G. 1996. "Weed Resistance to Herbicides: Understanding How Resistance Develops in Weeds is the First Line of Defense," *Weed Control Manual: Volume 30*. Meister Publishing Company, Willoughby, Ohio.

Hall, R. 1966. "Utility Player," *California Farmer*, July 1996.

Halverson, L.F., Clayton, M.K. and J. Handelsman. 1993. "Population Biology of *Bacillus cereus* UW85 in the Rhizosphere of Field-Grown Soybeans," *Soil Biology and Biochemistry*, Volume 25, Number 4: 485-493.

Handelsman, J. 1996. Personal communication, Dr. Jo Handelsman, Department of Plant Pathology, University of Wisconsin-Madison, March 25, 1996.

Handelsman, J., Raffel, S., Mester, E.H., Wunderlich, L. and C.R. Grau. 1990. "Biological Control of Damping-off of Alfalfa Seedlings with *Bacillus cereus* UW85," *Applied and Environmental Microbiology*, Volume 56, Number 3: 713-718.

Hanna, R., Zalom, F.G. and C.L. Elmore. 1995. "Integrating Cover Crops into Grapevine Pest and Nutrition Management: The Transition Phase," *Sustainable Agriculture/Technical Reviews*, Volume 7, Number 3: 11-15.

Hansen, M. 1987. *Escape from the Pesticide Treadmill: Alternatives to Pesticides in Developing Countries.* The Institute for Consumer Policy Research, Mount Vernon, New York.

Hansen, M. 1993. *Pest Control for Home and Garden.* Consumer Reports Books, Yonkers, New York.

Harris, M.K. 1991. "*Bacillus thuringiensis* and Pest Control," Letter to the Editor, *Science*, Volume 253 (September 6): 1075.

Harris, P.A. and P.W. Stahlman. 1996. "Soil Bacteria as Selective Biological Control Agents of Winter Annual Grass Weeds in Winter Wheat," *Applied Soil Ecology*, Volume 33, Number 3: 275-281.

Hartman, H. 1996. "The Hartman Report, Food and the Environment: A Consumers' Perspective," Phase 1, Summer 1996, Preliminary Draft. The Hartman Group, Seattle, Washington.

Hattingh, V. 1996. "The Use of Insect Growth Regulators in IPM of Citrus in South Africa," *Citrus Journal*, Outspan International, Ltd., pages 14-16.

Hayes, W.J., Jr. and E.R. Laws, Jr., [eds.] 1991. *Handbook of Pesticide Toxicology: Volume 1 - General Principles.* Academic Press, Inc., New York, New York.

Heap, I.M. and R. Knight. 1990. "Variation in Herbicide Cross-Resistance Among Populations of Annual Ryegrass (*Lolium rigidum*) Resistant to Diclofop-methyl," *Australian Journal of Agricultural Research*, Volume 41: 121-128.

Hemingway, J., Small, G.J. and A.G. Monro. 1993. "Possible Mechanisms of Organophosphorus and Carbamate Insecticide Resistance in German Cockroaches (*Dictyoptera: Blattelidae*) from Different Geographical Areas," *Journal of Economic Entomology*, Volume 86, Number 6: 1623-1630.

Hewitt, T.I. and K.R. Smith. 1995. *Intensive Agriculture and Environmental Quality: Examining the Newest Agricultural Myth.* Henry A. Wallace Institute for Alternative Agriculture, Greenbelt, Maryland.

Higley, L.G. and W.K. Wintersteen. 1992. "A Novel Approach to Environmental Risk Assessment of Pesticides as a Basis for Incorporating Environmental Costs into Economic Injury Levels," *American Entomologist* (Spring): 34-39.

Hileman, B. 1994. "Environmental Estrogens Linked to Reproductive Abnormalities, Cancer," *Chemical and Engineering News* (January 31): 19-23.

Hoag, D.L. and A.G. Hornsby. 1992. "Coupling Groundwater Contamination with Economic Returns When Applying Farm Pesticides," *Journal of Environmental Quality*, Volume 21: 579-586.

Hoffman, M.P., Ridgway, R.L., Petitt, F.L., Show, E.D. and J. Matteoni. 1996. "Practical Applications of Natural Enemies," In *Mass-Reared Natural Enemies: Application,*

Regulation, and Needs. R.L. Ridgway, M.P. Hoffman, M.N. Inscoe and S.C. Glenister [eds.], Thomas Say Publications in Entomology, Entomological Society of America, Lanham, Maryland.

Hoffman, W.L. 1993. *Stemming the Flow: Agrichemical Dealers and Pollution Prevention: Case Studies from the Great Lake Basin.* Environmental Working Group, Washington, D.C.

Holden, C. [ed.]. 1995. "Biocontrol for Kiwi Mold, Random Samples," *Science*, Volume 270 (December 1): 1443.

Holmes, C. 1995. "Farmer's Perspective on Food Technology," *Bangor Daily News*, Bangor, Maine, May 10, 1995.

Holt, J.S. 1992. "History of Identification of Herbicide-Resistant Weeds," *Weed Technology*, Volume 6, Number 3: 615-620.

Holt, J.S. and H.M. LeBaron. 1990. "Significance and Distribution of Herbicide Resistance," *Weed Technology*, Volume 4, Number 1: 141-149.

Hoppin, P. 1996. Presentation to Third National IPM Forum. Proceedings Document, U. S. Department of Agriculture, Washington, D.C. (In Press).

Hoppin, P.J., Liroff, R.A. and M.M. Miller. 1996. *Reducing Reliance on Pesticides in Great Lakes Basin Agriculture*, International Policy Program, World Wildlife Fund, Washington, D.C. (June 1996 Pre-Publication Version).

Hornsby, A.G. 1992. "Site-Specific Pesticide Recommendations: The Final Step in Environmental Impact Prevention," *Weed Technology*, Volume 6: 736-742.

Horstmeier, G.D. 1995. "The Next Plateau: As the First Seeds of Biotech Hit the Market, Company Execs Plot Phase Two," *Top Producer* (November): 10-12.

Howell, J.F., Knight, A.L., Unruh, T.R., Brown, D.F., Krysan, J.L., Sell, C.R. and P.A. Kirsch. 1992. "Control of Codling Moth in Apple and Pear with Sex Pheromone-Mediated Mating Disruption" *Journal of Economic Entomology*, Volume 85, Number 3: 918-925.

Huber, D.M. and R.D. Watson. 1974. "Nitrogen Form and Plant Disease," *Annual Rev. Phytopathology*, Volume 12: 139-165.

Huber, D.M. and T.S. McCay-Buis. 1993. "A Multiple Component Analysis of the Take-all Disease of Cereals," *Plant Disease*, Volume 77, Number 5: 437-447.

Hudson, B.D. 1994. "Soil Organic Matter and Available Water Capacity," *Journal of Soil and Water Conservation*, Volume 49, Number 2: 189-94.

Hughes, J.M., Griffiths, M.W. and D.A. Harrison. 1992. "The Effects of an Organophosphate Insecticide on Two Enzyme Loci in the Shrimp *Caradina*, sp.," *Biochemical Systematics and Ecology*, Volume 20, Number 2: 89-97.

Hunter, C. 1979, 1992, 1994. "Suppliers of Beneficial Organisms in North America," Department of Pesticide Regulation, Sacramento, California. Available over the Internet at: [http://www.cdpr.ca.gov/docs/dprdocs/goodbug/organism.htm].

Ingels, C. 1995. " Lodi-Woodbridge Winegrape Commission," *Sustainable Agriculture*, Volume 7, Number 3: 5-6.

International Joint Commission. 1994. *Seventh Biennial Report on Great Lakes Water Quality*. Washington, D.C.

International Programme on Chemical Safety. 1994. *The WHO Recommended Classification of Pesticides by Hazard and Guidelines to Classification, 1994-1995*. World Health Organization.

International School of Ethology. 1995. "Statement from the Work Session on Environmental Endocrine-Disrupting Chemicals: Neural, Endocrine, and Behavioral Effects," Ettore Majorana Centre for Scientific Culture, Erice, Sicily, November 10, 1995. [For copy, contact office of Dr. Theo Colborn, World Wildlife Fund, Washington, D.C., 202-778-9643]

IPM Practitioner. 1994. "Alternatives to Methyl Bromide," Bio-Integral Resource Center, July 1994.

IPM Practitioner. 1996. "1996 Directory of Least Toxic Pest Control Products," Bio-Integral Resource Center, Volume 17, Numbers 11-12: 1-37.

Irene, S.R. 1995. "Office of Pesticide Programs List of Chemicals Evaluated for Carcinogenic Potential," Memorandum, August 7, 1995.

Jawson, M.D., Franzluebbers, A.J., Galusha, D.K. and R.M. Aiken. 1993. "Soil Fumigation Within Monoculture and Rotations: Response of Corn and Mycorrhizae," *Agronomy Journal*, Volume 85: 1174-1180.

Johnson, N. 1993. "Clean Water and Clear Profits," *Science Report*, College of Agricultural and Life Sciences, University of Wisconsin-Madison, 1993.

Jones, J. 1996. "FDA Pesticide Residue Analyses Data," Provided via facsimile dated May 7, 1996 to Charles Benbrook from Dr. John Jones, Pesticides and Chemical Contaminants, Center for Food Safety and Applied Nutrition, U. S. Food and Drug Administration.

Jorgensen, R.B., and B. Andersen. 1994. "Spontaneous

Hybridization Between Oilseed Rape (*Brassica napus*) and Weedy B. *campestris* (Brassicaceae): A Risk of Growing Genetically Modified Oilseed Rape," *American Journal of Botany*, Volume 81: 1620-1626.

Kaiser, J. 1996. "Pests Overwhelm *Bt* Cotton Crop," *Science*, Volume 273, July 1996, page 423.

Kelce, W.R., Monosson, E., Gamcsik, M.P., Laws, S.C. and L.E. Gray Jr. 1994. "Environmental Hormone Disruptors: Evidence That Vinclozolin Developmental Toxicity is Mediated by Antiandrogenic Metabolites," *Toxicology and Applied Pharmacology*, Volume 126, pages 276-285.

Kennedy, A.C., Elliot, L.F., Young, F.L. and C.L. Douglas. 1991. "Rhizobacteria Suppressive to the Weed Downy Brome," *Soil Science Society of America Journal*, Volume 55: 722-727.

Kennedy, G.C. and M.E. Whalon. 1995. "Managing Pest Resistance to *Bacillus thuringiensis* Endotoxins: Constrains and Incentives to Implementation," *Journal of Economic Entomology*, Volume 88, Number 3: 453-460.

Kinzel, B. 1989. "Cockroaches in the Attic: It Takes a Lot of Technology to Sound Out the Secretive Critters," *Agricultural Research Magazine*, Agricultural Research Service, U. S. Department of Agriculture, Washington, D.C., September 1989.

Kirchner, M.J., Wollum II, A.G. and L.D. King. 1993. "Soil Microbial Populations and Activities in Reduced Chemical Input Agroecosystems," *Soil Science Society of America Journal*, Volume 57: 1289-1295.

Kirsch, P. 1988. "Pheromones: Their Potential Role in Control of Agricultural Insect Pests," *American Journal of Alternative Agriculture*, Volume 3, Numbers 2-3: 83-97.

Klintberg, P.P. 1996. "New Food Safety Law Approved," *Farm Journal*, September 1996, page 20

Knutson, R.D., Hall, C.R., Smith, E.G., Cotner, S.D. and J.W. Miller. 1993. *Economic Impacts of Reduced Pesticide Use on Fruits and Vegetables*. American Farm Bureau Research Foundation,

Kolpin, D.W., Thurman, E.M. and D.A. Goolsby. 1996. "Occurrence of Selected Pesticides and Their Metabolites in Near-Surface Acquifers of the Midwestern United States," *Environmental Science and Technology*, Volume 30, Number 1: 335-340.

Kovach, J., Petzoldt, C., Degnil, J. and J. Tette. 1992. "A Method to Measure the Environmental Impacts of Pesticides," *New York's Food and Life Sciences Bulletin*, Volume 139: 1-4.

Kremer, R.J. 1996. "Biologically Active Metabolites of

Rhizobacteria with Potential Application in Weed Management," Poster and Abstract Number 237, *Weed Science Society of America Abstracts*, Volume 36, 1996. Annual Meeting, Norfolk, Virginia.

Kruess, A. and T. Tscharntke. 1994. "Habitat Fragmentation, Species Loss, and Biological Control," *Science*, Volume 264 (June 10): 1581-1584.

Kuc, J. 1995. "Induced Systemic Resistance - An Overview," R. Hammerschmidt and J. Kuc [eds.], *Induced Resistance to Disease in Plants*, Kluwer Academic Publishers, Netherlands, 169-175.

Landy, D. 1995. "Multiattribute Ranking Systems for Pesticides," Masters of Science Thesis. Energy and Resources Department, University of California-Berkeley.

LeBaron, H.M. and J. McFarland. 1990. "Herbicide Resistance in Weeds and Crops: An Overview and Prognosis," In *Managing Resistance to Agrochemicals*, M.B. Green, H.M. LeBaron, and W.K. Moberg, [eds.] From *Fundamental Research to Practical Strategies*. ACS Symposium Series No. 421, ACS Books, Washington, D. C., pages 336-352.

Lee, G. 1995. "As Eagles Soar, A Battle Looms," *The Washington Post*, October, 13: A3.

Leng, M.L., Leovey, E.M.K. and P.L. Zubkoff, [eds.] 1995. *Agrochemical Environmental Fate: State of the Art*. Lewis Publishers, New York, New York.

Levine, T. 1988. "Pesticide Findings in Lanolin," Memorandum, October 17, 1988, U.S. Environmental Protection Agency, Washington, D.C.

Liebman, J. and S. Daar. 1995. "Alternatives to Methyl Bromide in California Grape Production," *The IPM Practitioner*, Volume 17, Number 2: 1-12.

Liebman, J. and W.S. Pease. 1995. *Pesticide in California: Use Patterns and Strategies for Reducing Environmental Health Impacts*, Review Draft. Environmental Health Policy Program Report, Berkeley, California.

Liebman, J.A. and L. Epstein. 1992. "Activity of Fungistatic Compounds from Soil," *Phytopathology*, Volume 82, Number 2: 147-153.

Liebman, J.A. and L. Epstein. 1994. "Partial Characterization of Volatile Fungistatic Compound(s) from Soil," *Phytopathology*, Volume 84, Number 5: 442-446.

Liebman, M. and E. Dyck. 1992. "Crop Rotation and Intercropping Strategies for Weed Management," *Ecological Applications*, Volume 3, Number 1: 92-122.

Liebman, M. and E. Dyck. 1993. "Weed Management: A Need to Develop Ecological Approaches," *Ecological Applications,* Volume 3, Number 1: 39-41.

Liebman, M. and E.R. Gallandt. 1996. "Many Little Hammers: Ecological Approaches for Management of Crop-Weed Interactions," in *Agricultural Ecology,* L.E. Jackson, [ed.], Academic Press, San Diego, California (in press).

Liebman, M. and R.R. Janke. 1990. "Sustainable Weed Management Practices," in *Sustainable Agriculture in Temperate Zones,* C.A. Francis, C. B. Flora and L.D. King, [eds.], pages 111-197, John Wiley, New York, New York.

Liebman, M., Mohler, C.L. and C.P. Staver. 1996. *Ecological Management of Agricultural Weeds.* Cambridge University Press (Forthcoming, 1996).

Lin, B.H., Padgitt, M., Bull, L., Delvo, H., Shank, D. and H. Taylor. 1995. *Pesticide and Fertilizer Use and Trends in U. S. Agriculture.* Agricultural Economic Report No. 717, Economic Research Service, U. S. Department of Agriculture, Washington, D.C.

Little, D. 1996. "Grappling for Growth: It's a Brave New World for Basic Manufacturers as They Jockey for Market Position and Profitability," *Farm Chemicals Magazine,* Meister Publishing Company, Willoughby, Ohio, March 1996.

Lodi/Woodbridge Winegrape Commission. 1996. "Nation's Largest Premium Winegrowing Region Pledges 100% Adoption of Environmentally-Friendly Farming Practices," Press Release (Contact: Mark Chandler or Michael Miller).

Lodovici, M., Aiolli, S., Monserrat, C., Dolara, P., Medica, A., P. Di Simplicio. 1994. "Effect of a Mixture of 15 Commonly Used Pesticides on DNA Levels of 8-Hydroxy-2-Deoxyguanosine and Xenobiotic Metabolizing Enzymes in Rat Liver," *Journal of Environmental Pathology, Toxicology and Oncology,* Volume 13 [1994], Number 3, pages 163-168.

Loux, M.M., Liebl, R.A. and F.W. Slife. 1989. "Availability and Persistence of Imazaquin, Imazethapyr, and Clomazone in Soil," *Weed Science,* Volume 37: 259-267.

Madden, J.P. [ed.]. 1992. *Beyond Pesticides: Biological Approaches to Pest Management in California.* Division of Agriculture and Natural Resources, University of California, Oakland, California. 183 pages.

Malamy, J., Carr, J.P., Klessig, D.F. and I. Raskin. 1990. "Salicylic Acid: A Likely Endogenous Signal in the Resistance Response of Tobacco to Viral Infection," *Science,* Volume 250: 1002-1004.

Matteson, P.C. 1995. "The '50% Pesticide Cuts' in Europe: A Glimpse of Our Future?," *American Entomologist,*

Entomological Society of America, Volume 41, Number 4, Winter 1995.

Maxwell, B.D., Roush, M.L. and S.R. Radosevich. 1990. "Predicting Evolution and Dynamics of Herbicide Resistance in Weed Populations," *Weed Technology,* Volume 4, Number 1: 2-13.

Mayer, F.L., Jr. 1986. *Acute Toxicity Handbook of Chemicals to Estuarine Organisms.* Report EPA/600/X-86-231, Environmental Research Laboratory, U. S. Environmental Protection Agency, Gulf Breeze, Florida.

Mayer, F.L., Jr. and M.R. Ellersieck. 1986. *Manual of Acute Toxicity: Interpretation and Data Base for 410 Chemicals and 66 Species of Freshwater Animals.* Resource Publication No. 160, U. S. Fish and Wildlife Service, Washington, D.C.

Mayerfeld, D.B., Hallberg, G.R., Miller, G.A., Wintersteen, W.K., Hartzler, R.G., Brown, S.S., Duffy, M.D. and J.R. DeWitt. 1996. *Pest Management in Iowa: Planning for the Future.* Integrated Farm Management Report Number 17, Iowa State University Cooperative Extension, June 1996.

McMullin, E. 1996. "Weather Watchers," *California Farmer,* April 1996.

Meister Publishing Co. 1996. *Ag Consultant Magazine,* March, 1996

Mellinger, C. 1995. "Sustainable Agriculture Research and Extension Grant Report," Ted Winsberg Farm Project, Glades Crop Care, Jupiter, Florida.

Mellinger, C. 1996. Personal communication, Dr. Charles Mellinger, Technical Director, Glades Crop Care, Jupiter, Florida.

Merlo, C. 1996. "Expensive Lessons: A System that Relies Too Heavily on Broad-Spectrum Pesticides May Have Contributed to Last Season's Insect Problems in San Joaquin Valley Cotton Fields," *California Farmer,* May 1996.

Metcalf, R.L. 1980. "Changing Role of Insecticides in Crop Protection," *Annual Review of Entomology,* Volume 25: 219-56.

Metcalf, R.L. 1993. "An Increasing Public Concern," Chapter in *The Pesticide Question: Environment, Economics, and Ethics."* Chapman and Hall, New York, New York.

Mikkelsen, T.R., Andersen, B., and R.B. Jorgensen. 1996. "The Risk of Crop Transgene Spread," *Nature,* Volume 380: 31.

Mines, R. and M. Kearney. 1982. "The Health of Tulare County Farmworkers: A Report of the 1981 Survey and Ethnographic Research for the Tulare County Health Department," Program in U.S.-Mexican Studies, Univ. of California Riverside College of Humanities, Riverside, California.

Ministry of Environment, Lands and Parks. 1994. *Green/Yellow/Red Pesticide Classification Feasibility Study.* Victoria, British Columbia.

Moffat, A.S. 1996. "Biodiversity is a Boon to Ecosystems, Not Species," *Science*, Volume 271, March 15, 1996.

Morell, V. 1995. "Zeroing in on How Hormones Affect the Immune System," *Science*, Volume 269 (August 11): 773-775.

Morgan, D.P. 1989. *Recognition and Management of Pesticide Poisonings.* EPA-540/9-88-001, U. S. Environmental Protection Agency, Washington, D.C.

Morrison, H., Savitz, D., Semenciw, R., Hulka, B., Mao, Y., Morison, D. and D. Wigle. 1993. "Farming and Prostrate Cancer Mortality," *American Journal of Epidemiology*, Volume 137, Number 3, pages 270-280.

Moses, M. 1996. Telephone interview with Dr. Michael Hansen, July 31, 1996.

Moses, M., Johnson, E., Anger, W.K., Burse, V.W., Horstman, S.H., Jackson, R.J., Lewis, R.G., Maddy, K.T., McDonnell, B., Meggs, W.J., and S. Hoar Zahm. 1993. "Environmental Equity and Pesticide Exposure," *Toxicology and Industrial Health*, Volume 9, Number 5 pages 913-959.

Murty, A.S. 1986. *Toxicity of Pesticides to Fish - Vol. I.* CRC Press, Boca Raton, Florida.

Murty, A.S. 1986. *Toxicity of Pesticides to Fish - Vol. II.* CRC Press, Boca Raton, Florida.

National Coalition Against the Misuse of Pesticides. 1995. *A Failure to Protect: The Unnecessary Use of Hazardous Pesticides at Federal Facilities Threatens Human Health and the Environment*, National Coalition Against the Misuse of Pesticides and Government Purchasing Project, Washington, D.C.

National Research Council. 1961. *The Use of Chemicals in Food Production, Processing, Storage, and Distribution.* Publication No. 887, Washington, D.C.

National Research Council. 1966. *Scientific Aspects of Pest Control.* Publication 1402, National Academy of Sciences/National Research Council, Washington, D.C.

National Research Council. 1972. *Pest Control: Strategies for the Future.* National Academy of Sciences/National Research Council, Washington, D.C.

National Research Council. 1974. *Productive Agriculture and a Quality Environment.* Committee on Agriculture and the Environment, National Academy of Sciences/National Research Council, Washington, D.C.

National Research Council. 1975. *Pest Control: An Assessment of Present and Alternative Technologies, Volume 1: Contemporary Pest Control Practices and Prospects: The Report of the Executive Committee*, Chaired by Dr. Donald Kennedy, National Academy of Sciences, Washington, D.C.

National Research Council. 1978. *Pesticide Decision Making.* Commission on Natural Resources, National Academy of Sciences/National Research Council, Washington, D.C.

National Research Council. 1980a. *Regulating Pesticides.* Committee on Prototype Explicit Analyses for Pesticides, National Academy Press, Washington, D.C.

National Research Council. 1980b. *Urban Pest Management.* National Academy Press, Washington, D.C.

National Research Council. 1986. *Pesticide Resistance: Strategies and Tactics for Management.* National Academy Press, Washington, D.C.

National Research Council. 1987. *Regulating Pesticides in Food: The Delaney Paradox.* National Academy Press, Washington, D.C.

National Research Council. 1989a. *Alternative Agriculture.* National Academy Press, Washington, D.C.

National Research Council. 1989b. *Investing in Research: A Proposal to Strengthen the Agricultural, Food, and Environmental System.* National Academy Press, Washington, D.C.

National Research Council. 1993a. *Pesticides in the Diets of Infants and Children.* National Academy Press, Washington, D.C.

National Research Council. 1993b. *Soil and Water Quality: An Agenda for Agriculture.* National Academy Press, Washington, D.C.

National Research Council. 1996. *Ecologically Based Pest Management: New Solutions for a New Century.* National Academy Press, Washington, D.C.

Natural Resources Defense Council. 1989. *Intolerable Risk: Pesticides in our Children's Food*, B. Sewell, R. Whyatt, J. Hathaway, and L. Mott, Natural Resources Defense Council Publications Department, New York, New York.

Nelson, H. and R.D. Jones. 1994. "Potential Regulatory Problems Associated with Atrazine, Cyanazine, and Alachlor in Surface Water Source Drinking Water," *Weed Technology*, Volume 8, pages 852-861.

Nies, J.D. 1993. *Enhancement of the Pesticide Residues Information System (PRIS).* U.S. Environmental Protection Agency, Washington, D.C.

Norton, G.W. and J. Mullen. 1994. *Economic Evaluation of Integrated Pest Management Programs: A Literature Review.* Virginia Cooperative Extension, Blacksburg, Va.

Oedjijono, Line, M.A. and C. Dragar. 1993. "Isolation of Bacteria Antagonistic to a Range of Plant Pathogenic Fungi," *Soil Biology and Biochemistry*, Volume 25, Number 2, pages 247-250.

Olkowski, W., Daar, S. and H. Olkowski. 1991. *Common Sense Pest Control.* Taunton Press, Newton, Connecticut.

Olkowski, W. and H. Olkowski. 1996. "IPM for California Processing Tomatoes," *The IPM Practitioner,* Bio-Integral Resource Center, Volume 28, Number 4: 1-13.

Ollinger, M., and L. Pope. 1995. "Plant Biotechnology: Out of the Laboratory and into the Field," Agricultural Economic Report Number 697, Economic Research Service, U.S. Department of Agriculture, April, 1995, 13 pages.

Oltman, D. 1995. "Disruptive Behavior: New Technology Shows Promise in Interfering with the Communication Process Necessary for Certain Species of Insects to Reproduce," *California Farmer,* October 1995: F1-F7.

Oltman, D. 1996. "Staying Alive: A Strategy Has Been Developed to Keep Some Central Coast Vineyards Producing Despite an Infestation of the Deadly *Phylloxera* Root Louse," *California Farmer,* July 1996.

Organization for Economic Cooperation and Development. 1996. "Report of the OECD/FAO Workshop on Pesticide Risk Reduction: Uppsala, Sweden, October 16-18, 1995," Directorate of the Environment, Health and Safety Division, Paris, France, 66 pages.

Osburn, R.M., Milner, J.L., Oplinger, E.S., Smith, R.S. and J. Handelsman. 1995. "Effect of *Bacillus cereus* UW85 on the Yield of Soybean at Two Field Sites in Wisconsin," *Plant Disease,* June 1995: 551-556.

Osteen, C.D. and P.I. Szmedra. 1989. *Agricultural Pesticide Use Trends and Policy Issues.* Agricultural Economic Report No. 622, Economic Research Service, U. S. Department of Agriculture, Washington, D. C.

Pease, W.S., Morello-Frosch, R.A., Albright, D.S., Kyle, A.D. and J.C. Robinson. 1993. "Preventing Pesticide-Related Illness in California Agriculture: Strategies and Priorities," California Policy Seminar, Berkeley, California.

Pease, W.S., Albright, D.S., DeRoos, C.. Gottsman, L., Kyle, A.D,. Morello-Frosch, R.A. and J.C. Robinson. 1993. "Pesticide Contamination of Groundwater in California," California Policy Seminar, Berkeley, California.

Pedigo, L.P. and L.G. Higley. 1992. "The Economic Injury Level Concept and Environmental Quality: A New Perspective," *American Entomologist* (September).

Penrose, L.J., Thwaite, W.G. and C.C. Bower. 1994. "Rating Index as a Basis for Decision Making on Pesticide Use Reduction and for Accreditation of Fruit Produced under Integrated Pest Management," *Crop Protection,* Volume 13, Number 2: 146-152.

Pesticide Action Network. 1995. "Alternatives to Methyl Bromide: Excerpts from the U. N. Methyl Bromide Technical Options Committee 1995 Assessment," San Francisco, California.

Pesticide Action Network North America Update Service. 1994. "U.S. Farmworker Protection Standard Delayed," May 12, 1994, San Francisco, California.

Pesticide Action Network North America Update Service. 1996. "Australian Ryegrass Resists Glyphosate," July 8, 1996, San Francisco, California.

Pesticide and Toxic Chemical News. 1995a. "Goldman Denies EPA was Slow to Issue Beet Army Worm Exemptions," (November 15): 10-11.

Pesticide and Toxic Chemical News. 1995b. "EPA Safe Food 2005 Milestones Detailed in Goals Report," (September): 24-26.

Pesticide and Toxic Chemical News. 1995c. "Consumer Group Names Commodities with Highest Residue Levels," (November 22): 18-19.

Pesticide and Toxic Chemical News. 1995g. "Risks Outweigh Benefits of Azinphos-Methyl on Sugarcane: Barolo," (December 6): 12-13.

Pesticide Farm Safety Center Advisory Panel. 1992. *Final Report to the U.S. EPA from the Pesticide Farm Safety Center Advisory Panel,* Univ. of California Agricultural Health and Safety Center, Davis and Western Consortium for Public Health, Berkeley, California.

Pimentel, D., Acquay, H., Biltonen, M., Rice, P., Silva, M., Nelson, J., Lipner, V., Giordano, S., Horowitz, A. and M. D'Amore. 1992. "Environmental and Economic Costs of Pesticide Use," *BioScience,* Volume 42, Number 10: 750-760.

Pistorius, A. 1996. "Nature's Cycles and Systems," *Harvard Magazine,* March-April 1996.

Poe, G. L., Klemme, R.M., McComb, S.J. and J. E. Ambrosious 1991. "Commodity Programs and the Internalization of Erosion Costs: Do They Affect Crop Rotation Decisions?" *Review of Agricultural Economics,* Volume 13, Number 2: 223-235.

Porter, W.P., Green, S.M., Debbink, N.L. and I. Carlson. 1993. "Groundwater Pesticides: Interactive Effects of Low Concentrations of Carbamates Aldicarb and Methomyl and the Triazine Metribuzin on Thyroxine and Somatoropin Levels in White Rats," *Journal of Toxicology and Environmental Health,* Volume 40 Number 1: 15-34. Taylor & Francis.

Potts, G.R. 1986. *The Partridge: Pesticides, Predation and Conservation.* Collins and Sons, London.

Powles, S.B. and P.D. Howat. 1990. "Herbicide-Resistant Weeds in Australia," *Weed Technology*, Volume 4, Number 1: 178-185.

Purcell, A.H. 1981. "Vector Preference and Inoculation Efficiency as Components of Resistance to Pierce's Disease in European Grape Cultivators," *Phytopathology*, Volume 71, Number 4: 429-435.

Purcell, A.H. 1993. "Pierce's Disease: Part I," *Practical Winery and Vineyard*, Volume 8 (March-April): 13-16.

Purcell, A.H. 1993. "Pierce's Disease: Part II," *Practical Winery and Vineyard*, Volume 8 (May-June): 50-51, 73-76.

Purcell, A.H. 1994. "Pierce's Disease: Part III," *Practical Winery and Vineyard*, Volume 9 (March-April).

Purcell, A.H. and S. Saunders. "Harvested Grape Clusters an Inoculum for Pierce's Disease," *Plant Disease*, Volume 79, Number 2: 190-192.

Pylypiw, H.M. and L. Hankin. 1991. "Herbicides in Pooled Raw Milk in Connecticut," *Journal of Food Protection*, Volume 54 (February): 136-137.

Quarles, W. 1996a. "Electro-Gun 98% Effective Against Termites," *IPM Practitioner*, Bio-Integral Resource Center, Volume XVIII, Number 2, February 1996.

Quarles, W. 1996b. "Alternative Treatments Effective Against Drywood Termites," *Common Sense Pest Control Quarterly*, Bio-Integral Resource Center, Volume 23, Summer 1996.

Racke, K.D., Laskowski, D.A. and M R. Schultz. 1990. "Resistance of Chlorpyrifos to Enhanced Biodegradation in Soil," *Journal of American Food Chemicals*, Volume 28, Number 6: 1430-1435.

Ragsdale, N.N. and H.D. Sisler. 1994. "Social and Political Implications of Managing Plant Diseases with Decreased Availability of Fungicides in the United States," *Annual Review of Phytopathology*, Volume 32, pages 545-547.

Rajotte, E.G. 1993. "From Profitability to Food Safety and the Environment: Shifting the Objectives of IPM," *Plant Disease*, Volume 77, Number 3: 296-299.

Ramel, G.J.L. 1996. "Gordon's Entomological Home Page." Accessible on the World Wide Web at http://www.ex.ac.uk/~gjlramel/welcome.html

Rayner, H. 1995. "A Unified Approach: Arizona Growers are Finding that Working Together to Combat Pests is an Effective Strategy, Especially in a Heavy Infestation Year Such as 1995," *California Farmer*, (November): 14-19.

Reed, N. 1995. "Responsible Choice: A Systems Approach to Growing, Packing and Marketing Fruit," Available by request to: Dr. A. Nathan Reed, Stemilt Growers, Inc., Box 2779, Wenatchee, Washington 98807.

Reganold, J.P. 1995. "Soil Quality and Profitability of Biodynamic and Conventional Farming Systems: A Review," *American Journal of Alternative Agriculture*, Volume 10, Number 1: 36-45.

Rehrman, F. 1996. "Evolving Strategy: Tank Mixing Insecticides Can Help Prevent or At Least Delay Insect Resistance," *California Farmer*, (June 1996): 41-42.

Repetto, R. and S.S. Baliga. 1996. *Pesticides and the Immune System: The Public Health Risks.* World Resources Institute, Washington, D.C. (March, 1996).

Reus, J.A.W.A, Weckseler H.J. and G.A. Pak. 1994. *Towards a Future EC Pesticide Policy.* Centre for Agriculture & Environment.

Reuveni, R., [ed.]. 1995. *Novel Approaches to Integrated Pest Management.* Lewis Publishers, Ann Arbor, Michigan.

Ribaudo, M.O. and A. Bouzaher. 1994. *Atrazine: Environmental Characteristics and Economics of Management.* Agricultural Economic Report No. 699, Economic Research Service, U. S. Department of Agriculture, Washington, D. C.

Ridgway, R.L. and M.N. Inscoe. 1996. "Mass-Produced Natural Enemies, with Special Reference to Arthropods," presented at the Symposium on Commercialization of Biopesticides: Applied Products and Transgenic Plants, sponsored by International Business Communications, Washington, D.C. January 22-24, 1996.

Ridgway, R.L., Inscoe, M.N. and K.W. Thorpe. 1994. "Biologically Based Pest Controls: Markets, Industries, and Products," Agricultural Research Service, U. S. Department of Agriculture, Washington, D.C.

Ridgway, R.L. and S.B. Vinson, [eds.]. 1977. *Biological Control by Augmentation of Natural Enemies: Insect and Mite Control with Parasites and Predators.* Plenum Press, New York, New York.

Riley, B. 1996. "Monthly Dursban Spraying in Helena Schools Halted," *Journal of Pesticide Reform*, Volume 16, Number 2, Summer 1996, pages 11-12.

Rissler, J. and M. Mellon. 1993. *Perils Amidst the Promise: Ecological Risks of Transgenic Crops in a Global Market.* Union of Concerned Scientists, Washington, D.C.

Roberts, P. 1994. "Who Killed the Red Delicious? How Fallout from the Alar Scare has Reshaped the Apple Industry," *Seattle Weekly*, February 23, 1994, Seattle, Washington.

Robinson, A.Y. 1990. *Sustainable Agriculture: A Brighter Outlook for Fish and Wildlife.* Izaak Walton League of America.

Robinson, J.C., Pease, W.S., Albright, D.S. and R.A. Morello-Frosch. 1994. "Pesticides in the Home and Community: Health Risks and Policy Alternatives," California Policy Seminar, Berkeley, California

Robinson, J.C., Tuden, D. and W.S. Pease. *Taxing Pesticides to Fund Environmental Protection and Integrated Pest Management,* Environmental Health Policy Program, University of California, Berkeley, California.

Robinson, R.A. 1996. *Return to Resistance: Breeding Crops to Reduce Pesticide Dependence.* agAccess, Davis, California.

Rodier, P.M. 1995. "Developing Brain as a Target of Toxicity," *Environmental Health Perspectives,* Volume 103, Supplement 6, September 1995, pages 73-75.

Rothrock, C.S., Kirkpatrick, T.L., Frans, R.E. and H.D. Scott. 1995. "The Influence of Winter Legume Cover Crops on Soilborne Plant Pathogens and Cotton Seedling Diseases," *Plant Disease,* Volume 79, Number 2: 167-171.

Russell, D.W. 1996. "Green Light for Steroid Hormones," *Science,* Volume 272, April 19, 1996.

Schmidt, K. 1994. "Genetic Engineering Yields First Pest-Resistant Seeds," *Science,* Volume 265, August 5, 1994.

Schreiber, M.M. 1992. "Influence of Tillage, Crop Rotation, and Weed Management on Giant Foxtail (Setaria faberi) Population Dynamics and Corn Yield," *Weed Science,* Volume 40, Number 4: 645-653.

Sciumbato, G.L. 1993. "Soybean Disease Loss Estimates for the Southern United States During 1988-1991," *Plant Disease,* Volume 77, Number 9: 954-956.

Senus, M.P., Esser, A.J. and F.B. Gaffney. 1995. "National Agricultural Pesticide Risk Analysis Implementation Trial," U. S. Department of Agriculture, Washington, D.C.

Sharpe, C.R., Franco, E.L., de Camargo, B., Lopes, L.F., Barreto, J.H., Johnsson, R.R. and M.A. Mauad. 1995. "Parental Exposures to Pesticides and Risk of Wilms' Tumor in Brazil," *American Journal of Epidemiology,* Volume 141, Number 3, pages 210-217.

Sherald, J.L. 1982. "Dutch Elm Disease and Its Management," *Ecological Services Bulletin,* Number 6, U. S. Department of Interior, National Park Service, Washington, D.C.

Shitienberg, D., Raposo, D.R., Bergeron, S.N., Legard, D.E., Dyer, A.T. and W.E. Fry. 1994. "Incorporation of Cultivar Resistance in a Reduced-Sprays Strategy to Suppress Early and Late Blights on Potato," *Plant Disease,* Volume 78, Number 1: 23-26.

Silo-Suh, L.A., Lethbridge, B.J., Raffel, S.J., He, H., Clardy, J. and J. Handelsman. 1994. "Biological Activities of Two Fungistatic Antibiotics Produced by *Bacillus cereus* UW85," *Applied and Environmental Microbiology,* Volume 60, Number 6: 2023-2030.

Simonich, S.L. and R.A. Hites. 1995. "Global Distribution of Persistent Organochlorine Compounds," *Science,* Volume 269 (September 29): 1851-1854.

Sine, C., [ed.]. 1996 (Updated annually). *Farm Chemicals Handbook.* Meister, Willoughby, Ohio.

Singer, J. 1982. *Pesticide Safety: Guidelines for Personnel Protection.* Forest Pest Management 83-1, U. S. Forest Service.

Smith, G.J. 1987. *Pesticide Use and Toxicology in Relation to Wildlife: Organophosphorus and Carbamate Compounds.* Resource Publication No. 170, U. S. Fish and Wildlife Service, Washington, D.C.

Smolik, J.D., Dobbs, T.L. and D.H. Rickerl. 1995. "The Relative Sustainability of Alternative, Conventional, and Reduced-Till Farming Systems," *American Journal of Alternative Agriculture,* Volume 10, Number 1: 25-35.

Sorensen, A.A. 1992. *Proceedings of the National Integrated Pest Management Forum.* Published by American Farmland Trust, Washington, D.C.

Sorensen, A.A. 1993. "IPM and Growers: An Evolution in Thinking," in A.R. Leslie and G.W. Cuperus' [eds.] *Successful Implementation of IPM for Agricultural Crops.* Lewis Publishers,

Sorensen, A.A. 1994. *Regional Producer Workshops: Constraints to the Adoption of Integrated Pest Management.* National Foundation for Integrated Pest Management Education, Austin, Texas.

Spollen, K.M., Johnson, M.W. and B.E. Tabashnik. 1995. "Stability of Fenvalerate Resistance in the Leafminer Parasitoid Diglphus begini (Hymenoptera: Eulophidae)," *Journal of Economic Entomology,* Volume 88, Number 2: 192-197.

Stabb, E.V., Jacobson, L.M. and J. Handelsman. 1994. "Zwittermicin A-Producing Strains of *Bacillus cereus* from Diverse Soils," *Applied and Environmental Microbiology,* Volume 60, Number 12: 4404-4412.

State FIFRA Issues Research and Evaluation Group. 1995. July 11, 1995 statement.

Stelljes, K.B. and B. Hardin. 1995. "Tackling Wheat Take-All," *Agricultural Research*, Agricultural Research Service, U. S. Department of Agriculture, August 1995.

Sterling, S. Acting Chief, Registration Branch, Special Review and Reregistration Division, Correspondence with Sandra Marquardt, March 19, 1996.

Stinson, E.R. and P.T. Bromley. 1991. *Pesticides and Wildlife: A Guide to Reducing Impacts on Animals and Their Habitat.* Virginia Cooperative Extension Communications, Blacksburg, Virginia.

Stone, R. 1994. "Large Plots are Next Test for Transgenic Crop Safety," *Science*, Volume 266, December 2, 1994, pages 1472-1473.

Stonehouse, D.P. 1991. "Economics of Weed Control in Alternative Farming Systems," pages 3-10 in *Proceedings of the Fifth Annual REAP Conference*, Macdonald College, Ste-Anne-de-Bellevue, Quebec.

Stout, C.B. 1996. "Time to Rethink Resprays?" *Prairie Farmer*, April 1996.

Sugimura, T. 1992. "Multistep Carcinogenesis: A 1992 Perspective," *Science*, Volume 258 (October 23): 603-607.

Swinton, S.M. and R.P. King. 1994. "A Bioeconomic Model for Weed Management in Corn and Soybean," *Agricultural Systems*, Volume 44: 313-335.

Taylor, C.R. 1995. *Economic Impacts and Environmental and Food Safety Tradeoffs of Pesticide Use Reduction on Fruit and Vegetables.* Auburn University, Auburn, Alabama.

Theiling, K.M. and Croft, B. 1988. "Pesticide Side-Effects on Arthropod Natural Enemies: A Database Summary." Unpublished manuscript, Oregon State University Department of Entomology. For a copy contact Dr. Brian Croft, Department of Entomology, Oregon State University, Corvalis, Oregon 97330.

Thompson, R., Thompson, S. and Thompson, R. Jr. 1995 (and other years). *Alternatives in Agriculture: Thompson On-Farm Research and Wallace Institute 1995 Report.* Available from Thompson On-Farm Research, 2035 190th Street, Boone, Iowa 50036-7432.

Thrupp, L.A. 1990. "Pesticide Action Network Dirty Dozen Campaigner," Pesticide Action Network, May, 1989.

Thurman, E.M., Goolsby, D.A., Meyer, M.T. and D.W. Kolpin. 1991. "Herbicides in Surface Waters of the Midwestern United States: The Effect of Spring Flush," *Environmental Science Technology*, Volume 25, Number 10: 1794-1796.

Timmons, F.L. 1970. "A History of Weed Control in the United States and Canada," *Weed Science*, (March): 294-307.

Tolin, S. 1996. "Facing the Issues: A New Role for APS?" *Phytopathology*, Volume 86, Number 6: 556-560.

Tonneson, L. 1996. "Pesticide Battle Brews," *The Farmer/Dakota Farmer*, Mid-January 1996.

Top Producer, Early March, 1996.

Tweedy, B.G., Dishburger, H.J., Ballantine, L.G. and J. McCarthy, [eds.] 1991. *Pesticide Residues and Food Safety: A Harvest of View Points.* Symposium Series No. 446, American Chemical Society, Washington, D. C.

Twombly, R. 1990. "Firms Foresee High Stakes in Emerging Biopesticide Market," *The Scientist*, July 9: 1-5.

Union of Concerned Scientists. 1996. "Guess Who's coming to Market?," *The Gene Exchange*, Washington, D.C. [June, 1996].

U. S. Code of Federal Regulations, Title 40, Parts 150-189. Reissued each year on July 1 [Pesticide regulations].

U. S. Department of Agriculture. 1968. *Quantities of Pesticides Used by Farmers in 1964.* Agricultural Economic Report No. 131, Economic Research Service, Washington, D.C.

U. S. Department of Agriculture. 1970a. *Quantities of Pesticides Used by Farmers in 1966.* Agricultural Economic Report No. 179, Economic Research Service, Washington, D.C.

U. S. Department of Agriculture. 1970b. *Farmers' Pesticide Expenditures in 1966.* Agricultural Economic Report No. 192, Economic Research Service, Washington, D. C.

U. S. Department of Agriculture. 1974. *Farmers' Use of Pesticides in 1971: Quantities.* Agricultural Economic Report No. 252, Economic Research Service, Washington, D.C.

U. S. Department of Agriculture. 1975. *Farmer's Use of Pesticides in 1971…Expenditures.* Agricultural Economic Report No. 296, Economic Research Service, Washington, D. C.

U. S. Department of Agriculture. 1983. *Chemical Use Survey*, computer disk data product. Economic Research Service, Washington, D. C.

U. S. Department of Agriculture. 1991. *Cropping Practices Survey*, National Agricultural Statistics Service/Economic Research Service, Washington, D.C.

U. S. Department of Agriculture. 1992. "Get the Whitefly Swatters - Fast!" *Agricultural Research*, Volume 40, Number 11: 4-5.

U. S. Department of Agriculture. 1993a. Three Agency Release, Presidential Announcement Regarding IPM Adoption. Office of Communications, June 23, 1993.

U. S. Department of Agriculture. 1993b. *Agricultural Chemical Usage Vegetables: 1992 Summary*, National Agricultural

Statistical Service, Ag Ch 1(93), Washington, D.C. 270 pages.

U. S. Department of Agriculture. 1993c. *Biological Control of the Russian Wheat Aphid*. Animal and Plant Health Inspection Service, Program Aid Number 1507, Washington, D. C.

U. S. Department of Agriculture. 1994a. *Inventory of Agricultural Research Fiscal Year 1993: Current Research Information System*. Cooperative State Research Service /USDA, Washington, D.C.

U. S. Department of Agriculture. 1994b. *Cropping Practices Survey 1993*, Tables in Data Product. Economic Research Service, Washington, D.C.

U. S. Department of Agriculture. 1994c. "Evicting the Boll Weevil," *Agricultural Research*, Volume 42, Number 3: 4-10.

U. S. Department of Agriculture. 1994d. "Agricultural Chemical Usage 1993 Fruits Summary," National Agricultural Statistics Service, Ag Ch 1 (94), Washington, D.C. 146 pages.

U. S. Department of Agriculture. 1994e. "USDA Announces National Plan to Increase Use of Integrated Pest Management," Release Number 0943.94; and "Backgrounder: USDA's IPM Initiative," Release Number 0942.94, Office of Communications, , USDA, Washington, D.C.

U. S. Department of Agriculture. 1995a. "IPM Goes Areawide: Fruit Growers Back New Approach to Codling Moth Control," *Agricultural Research*, Volume 43, Number 7: 4-8.

U. S. Department of Agriculture. 1995b. *Cropping Practices Survey*, National Agricultural Statistics Service/Economic Research Service, Washington, D.C.

U. S. Department of Agriculture. 1995c. *1994 Cropping Practices Survey: Data File Specifications and Documentation*. Economic Research Service, Washington, D. C.

U. S. Department of Agriculture. 1995d. *Agricultural Chemical Usage Vegetables: 1994 Summary*. National Agricultural Statistics Survey, USDA, Washington, D.C. 289 pages.

U. S. Department of Agriculture. 1995e. *An Analysis of the Beet Armyworm Outbreak on Cotton in the Lower Rio Grande Valley of Texas During the 1995 Production Season*. Agricultural Research Service, Washington, D. C.

U. S. Department of Agriculture. 1995f. "Pesticide Data Program: Annual Summary Calendar Year 1993," Agricultural Marketing Service, June 1995.

U. S. Department of Agriculture. 1995g. *Agricultural Chemical Usage: 1994 Field Crops Summary*, National Agricultural Statistics Service, USDA, Washington, D.C. 106 pages.

U. S. Department of Agriculture. 1996a. "1996 Budget Summary." Washington, D.C.

U. S. Department of Agriculture. 1996b. "Pesticide Data Program: Annual Summary Calendar Year 1994," Agricultural Marketing Service.

U. S. Department of Agriculture. 1996c. *Agricultural Chemical Use Report*. National Agricultural Statistics Service, March 1996.

U. S. Department of Agriculture. 1996d. *Agricultural Chemical Usage: 1995 Fruits Summary*, National Agricultural Statistics Service, USDA, Washington, D.C. 151 pages.

U. S. Department of Commerce. 1985. *A Competitive Assessment of the U. S. Herbicide Industry*. Office of Chemical and Allied Products, Washington, D. C.

U. S. Department of Defense. Issued quarterly. *Technical Information Bulletin (TIB)*. Defense Pest Management Information Analysis Center (DPMIAC), Armed Forces Pest Management Board, Forest Glen Section, Walter Reed Army Medical Center, Washington, D.C.

U. S. Department of Defense. Issued periodically. *Pest Management Bulletin*. ATTN: HSHB-MR-EMO, Army Environmental Hygiene Agency, Aberdeen Proving Ground, Maryland.

U. S. Department of Defense. 1983. "Directive No. 4150.7," Washington, D.C., October 24, 1983.

U. S. Department of Defense. 1994. "Comprehensive Pollution Prevention Strategy," Department of Defense, Washington, D.C.

U. S. Department of Defense. 1995. "Proceedings of the DoD Pest Management Workshop on Sustainable Integrated Pest Management for the Department of Defense: Vision for the 21st Century," Armed Services Pest Management Board, Washington, D.C.

U. S. Department of Defense. 1996a. "Department of Defense Pest Management Program, Instruction No. 4150.7," April 22, 1996, Washington, D.C.

U. S. Department of Defense. 1996b. "Memorandum of Understanding Between the U.S. EPA and the U.S. DOD with Respect to Integrated Pest Management," Department of Defense, Washington, D.C.

U. S. Department of Health, Education, and Welfare. 1969. [Mrak Commission] *Report of the Secretary's Commission on Pesticides and Their Relationship to Environmental Health. Parts I and II*. Washington, D. C.

U. S. Department of the Interior. 1984. National Park Service Integrated Pest Management Information Packages. National Park Service.

U. S. Environmental Protection Agency. 1978. *Economic Trends and Outlook of Pesticide Industry: Need for "Exclusive Use" Amendments to FIFRA.* Office of Pesticide Programs, Washington, D.C.

U. S. Environmental Protection Agency. 1987. *Research Development: Inter-Taxa Correlations for Toxicity to Aquatic Organisms.* EPA/600/x-87/332, Environmental Research Laboratory, Gulf Breeze, Florida.

U. S. Environmental Protection Agency. 1989. "The Problem of Undetectable Residues of Drifted Herbicide Causing Non-Target Crop Damage," Memorandum from Gary O'Neal, Air and Toxics Division, Region 10 to Anne Lindsay, Registration Division, Office of Pesticide Program, April 28, 1989.

U. S. Environmental Protection Agency. 1990a. *Citizen's Guide to Pesticides.* Pesticides and Toxic Substances, 2OT-1003, Washington, D. C.

U. S. Environmental Protection Agency. 1990b. *National Survey of Pesticides in Drinking Water Wells, Phase I Report.* Office of Water and Office of Pesticides and Toxic Substances.

U. S. Environmental Protection Agency. 1993. "Testimony of Carol M. Browner, Administrator EPA; Richard Rominger, Deputy Secretary of Agriculture; and David A. Kessler, Commissioner of FDA Before Committee on Labor and Human Resources, United States Senate and Subcommittee on Health and the Environment, Committee on Energy and Commerce, U.S. House of Representatives," September 21, 1993.

U. S. Environmental Protection Agency. 1994a. *Status of Pesticides in Reregistration and Special Review.* 738-R-94-008, Prevention, Pesticides and Toxic Substances, Washington, D.C.

U. S. Environmental Protection Agency. 1994b. "Pesticide Monitoring and Risk Assessment in the Northwest," Pesticides Section, Region 10, December 20, 1994.

U. S. Environmental Protection Agency. 1994c. "Chemicals Registered for the First Time as Pesticidal Active Ingredients Under FIFRA," Jihad A. Alsadek, Economic Analysis Branch, Biological and Economic Analysis Division, Office of Pesticide Programs, July 1994.

U. S. Environmental Protection Agency. 1995a. *Citizen's Guide to Pest Control and Pesticide Safety.* Washington, D. C.

U. S. Environmental Protection Agency. 1995b. *Office of Pesticide Programs 1994 Annual Report.* Washington, D.C.

U. S. Environmental Protection Agency. 1995c. *Office of Pesticide Programs Reference Dose Tracking Report.* Washington, D. C.

U. S. Environmental Protection Agency. 1995d. *Office of Pesticide Programs Annual Report for 1995.* Office of Prevention, Pesticides and Toxic Substances, EPA 730-R-95-002, December 1995. 69 pages.

U. S. Environmental Protection Agency. 1996a. *EPA Activities on Endocrine Disruptors Background Paper*, U.S. EPA, Washington, D.C.

U. S. Environmental Protection Agency. 1996b. *Pesticide Status Report*, Office of Pesticide Programs, U.S. EPA, Washington, D.C.

U. S. Environmental Protection Agency. 1996c. "Potential of Chemicals to Affect the Endocrine System," Office of Pesticide Programs, U.S. EPA, Washington, D.C.

U. S. Environmental Protection Agency. 1996d. "Responding to President's Call for Reducing Regulatory Burdens, EPA Exempts Certain Low Risk Substances From Federal Pesticide Regulation," Press Release, March 4, 1996. Accompanying *Federal Register* Notice, "Exemption of Certain Pesticide Substances from FIFRA Requirements," Final Rule, *Federal Register*, Volume 61, Number 45: 8876-8879, March 6, 1996.

U. S. Environmental Protection Agency. 1996e. "Microbial Pesticide Active Ingredients and Biochemical Active Ingredients," Poster Number 52 presented at Third Annual National IPM Forum, Washington, D.C. February 1996.

U. S. Environmental Protection Agency. 1996f. "Pesticide Monitoring and Risk Assessment in the Northwest," Pesticides Section, Region 10, January 15, 1996.

U. S. Environmental Protection Agency. 1996g. "Pesticide Resistance Management: Issue Paper for Pesticide Dialogue Committee Meeting," Office of Pesticide Programs, June 25, 1996.

U. S. Environmental Protection Agency, U. S. Department of Agriculture and U. S. Food and Drug Administration. 1995. "Partners for Pesticide Environmental Stewardship," Washington, D. C.

U. S. Fish and Wildlife Service. 1993. "Carbofuran Briefing Statement," *Guide to Pesticides Notebook*, Special Agent Basic Training, Federal Law Enforcement Training Center, Glynco, Georgia, August 1993.

U. S. General Accounting Office. 1992. *Sustainable Agriculture: Program Management, Accomplishments, and Opportunities.* No. 233, Resources, Community, and Economic Development Division, Washington, D. C.

U. S. General Services Administration. 1992a. "Terminating Exterminating," *Federal Managers Quarterly*, Issue 4. General Services Administration, Washington, D.C.

U. S. General Services Administration. 1992b. "Desk Guide for

Facilities Managers," General Services Administration, Washington, D.C.

U. S. General Services Administration. 1993. "Integrated Pest Management: The Contract Specification Guidelines," Building Services Group, General Services Administration, Washington, D.C.

U. S. General Services Administration. 1995. "Pest Control Turns Green," General Services Administration, Washington, D.C.

U. S. House of Representatives. 1992. "Agriculture, Rural Development, Food and Drug Administration, and Related Agencies Appropriations for Fiscal Year 1993." Hearings, 102nd Congress, 2nd Session, Part 4, Agricultural Programs, U. S. Government Printing Office, Washington, D.C.

U. S. House of Representatives. 1996. Committee Report: H.R. 1627, the Food Quality Protection Act of 1996, Committee on Commerce, U. S. Government Printing Office, Washington, D.C.

U. S. National Park Service. 1977. "Pest Control: Environmental Assessment: Guidelines and Program," Department of the Interior, National Park Service, Washington, D.C.

U. S. National Park Service. 1988. "Management Policies; Native Species ," Department of the Interior, National Park Service, Washington, D.C.

U. S. National Park Service. 1990. *Park Landscape Manual: National Capital Region*. Department of Interior, National Park Service, Washington, D.C.

U. S. National Park Service. 1991. *Policy Guidelines: Integrated Pest Management*. NPS-77, Department of the Interior, National Park Service, Washington, D.C.

U. S. National Park Service. 1996. "Memorandum on Procedures for Integrated Pest Management Pesticide Use Approvals in Calendar Year," May 6, 1996, Department of the Interior, National Park Service, Washington, D.C.

van Acker, R. C., Swanton, C.J. and S.F. Weise. 1993. "The Critical Period of Weed Control in Soybean [*Glycine max* (L.) Merr.]," *Weed Science*, Volume 41, Number 2: 194-200.

van den Bosch, R. 1978. *The Pesticide Conspiracy*. Doubleday & Co., Garden City, New York.

van Lenteren, J.C. 1988. "Implementation of Biological Control," *American Journal of Alternative Agriculture*, Volume 3, Numbers 2-3: 102-109.

Vandeman, A., Fernandez-Cornejo, J., Jans, S. and B.H. Lin. 1994. *Adoption of Integrated Pest Management in U. S.*

Agriculture. Agricultural Information Bulletin No. 707, Economic Research Service, Washington, D.C.

Vasquez, B.L. 1996. "Resistant to the Most Insecticides," Chapter 15 in *University of Florida Book of Insect Records*, Published on the World Wide Web at http://gnv.ifas.ufl.edu/~tjw/recbk.htm.

Walker, G.P., Richards, C.B. Jones W.G. and D.C.G. Aitken. 1991. "Toxicity of Five Insecticides Used to Control California Red Scale (*Homoptera: Diaspididae*) Against Susceptible Red Scale Strains," *Journal of Economic Entomology*, Volume 84, Number 1: 17-23.

Walker, K., Liebman, J. and W. Pease. 1995. *Pesticide-Induced Disruptions of Agricultural Ecosystems*. California Policy Seminar, Berkeley, California.

Ware, G.W. 1982. *Fundamentals of Pesticides: A Self-Instruction Guide*. Thomson Publications, Fresno, California.

Wargo, J. 1996. *Our Children's Toxic Legacy*. Yale University Press, New Haven, Connecticut.

Warwick, S.I. 1991. "Herbicide Resistance in Weedy Plants: Physiology and Population Biology," *Annual Review of Ecological Systems*, Volume 22: 95-114.

Wauchope, R.D., Butler, T.M., Hornsby, A.G., Augustijn-Beckers, P.W.M. and J. P. Burt. 1992. "The SCS/ARD/CES Pesticides Properties Database for Environmental Decision-making," *Review of Environmental Contamination and Toxicology*, Volume 123: 1-164.

Weddle, P.W. 1994. *Management of Codling Moth in Bartlett Pears in California: A Preliminary Analysis of the Relative Costs of Insecticide- and Pesticide-Based IPM Strategies*. Weddle, Hansen and Associates, Inc., Placerville, California.

Werner, M.R. and D.L. Dindal. 1990. "Effects of Conversion to Organic Agricultural Practices on Soil Biota," *American Journal of Alternative Agriculture*, Volume 5, Number 1:24-32.

Westerdahl, H.E. and K.D. Getsinger, [eds.]. 1988. *Aquatic Plant Identification and Herbicide Use Guide*. Technical Report A-88-9, Army Corps of Engineers, U. S. Department of the Army, Vicksburg, Mississippi.

Whipps, J.M., McQuilken, M.P. and S.P. Budge. 1993. "Use of Fungal Antagonists for Biocontrol of Damping-off and Sclerotinia Diseases," in *Pesticide Science*, Volume 37, Papers from the Meeting "Biological Control: Use of Living Organisms in the Management of Invertebrate Pests, Pathogens and Weeds," Elsevier Applied Science, Great Britain, pages 309-313.

White, F.M.M., Cohen, F.G., Sherman, G. and R. McCurdy. 1988. "Chemicals, Birth Defects and Stillbirths in New

Brunswick: Associations with Agricultural Activity," *Canadian Medical Association Journal*, Volume 138, January 15, 1988, pages 117-124.

White, J.M., Allen, P.G., Moffitt, L.J. and Kingsley, P.P. 1995. "Economic Analysis of an Areawide Program for Biological Control of the Alfalfa Weevil,"*American Journal of Alternative Agriculture*, Volume 10, Number 4: 173-180.

White, R., Jobling, S., Hoare, S.A., Sumpter, J.P. and Parker, M.G. 1994. "Environmentally Persistent Alkylphenolic Compounds Are Estrogenic," *Endocrinology*, Volume 135: 175-182.

White House. 1994. "Memorandum for the Heads of Executive Departments and Agencies: Environmentally and Economically Beneficial Practices on Federal Landscaped Grounds," April 24, 1994.

White House. 1996a. "Remarks By the President at the Food Quality Protection Act Bill Signing," Office of the Press Secretary, August 3, 1996.

White House. 1996b. "Memorandum for the Heads of Executive Departments and Agencies: Environmentally and Economically Beneficial Practices on Federal Landscaped Grounds," April 24, 1994.

Whitmore, R.W., Kelly, J.E. and P.L. Reading. 1992. *National Home and Garden Pesticide Use Survey Final Report Volume One: Results and Recommendations*. Research Triangle Institute Report Number 5100/17-01F.

Wiles, R. and C. Campbell. 1993a. *Pesticides in Children's Foods*. Environmental Working Group, Washington, D.C.

Wiles, R. and C. Campbell. 1993b. *Washed, Peeled - Contaminated*. Environmental Working Group, Washington, D.C.

Wiles, R., Cohen, B., Campbell, C. and S. Elderkin. 1994. *Tap Water Blues: Herbicides in Drinking Water*. Environmental Working Group and Physicians for Social Responsibility, Washington, D.C.

Wiles, R., Davies, K. and S. Elderkin. 1995. *A Shopper's Guide to Pesticides in Produce*. Environmental Working Group, Washington, D.C.

Wilkinson, C. 1990. "Introduction and Overview," In *Effects of Pesticides on Human Health*, Baker and Wilkinson [eds.], Princeton Scientific Publishing Co., Princeton, New Jersey, pages 5-33.

Williams, C.M. 1967. "Third-Generation Pesticides," *Scientific American*, Volume 217, Number 1.

Williams, T. 1993. "Hard News on 'Soft' Pesticides," *Audubon*, (March-April): 30-40.

World Bank. 1996. *Integrated Pest Management: Strategy and Policy Options for Promoting Effective Implementation*. Environmentally Sustainable Development.

Wrubel, R.P. and J. Gressel. 1994. "Are Herbicide Mixtures Useful for Delaying the Rapid Evolution of Resistance? A Case Study," *Weed Technology*, Volume 8, Number 3: 635-648.

Wyse, D.L. 1992. "Future of Weed Science Research," *Weed Technology*, Volume 6, Number 1: 162-165.

Wyse, D.L. 1994. "New Technologies and Approaches for Weed Management in Sustainable Agriculture Systems," *Weed Technology*, Volume 8, Number 2: 403-407.

Yenish, J.P., Doll, J.D. and D.D. Buhler. 1992. "Effects of Tillage on Vertical Distribution and Viability of Weed Seed in Soil," *Weed Science*, Volume 40, Number 3: 429-433.

Zeakes, S.J., Hansen, M.F. and R.J. Robel. 1981. "Increased Susceptibility of Bobwhites (*Colinus virginianus*) to *Histomonas meleagridis* after Exposure to Sevin Insecticide," *Avian Diseases*, Volume 25, Number 4, pages 981-987.

Zimdahl, R.L. 1991. *Weed Science: A Plea for Thought*. U. S. Department of Agriculture and Cooperative State Research Service, Washington, D. C.

Zins, A.B., Wyse, D.L. and W.C. Koskinen. 1991. "Effect of Alfalfa (*Medicago sativa*) Roots on Movement of Atrazine and Alachlor Through Soil," *Weed Science*, Volume 39, Number 2: 262-269.

Zoschke, A. 1994. "Toward Reduced Herbicide Rates and Adapted Weed Management," *Weed Technology*, Volume 8, Number 2: 376-386.

Understanding Stages of Moral Development is indeed a workbook to help in the understanding of Kohlberg's stage theory of moral development. Since there has yet to appear an intensive guide to moral development stage theory via analysis of moral judgment interviews, this workbook is a welcome introduction to Kohlberg's stage theory through a programmed analysis of each of the six stages of moral development. The workbook is a guide to understanding, as the title indicates, and it should take the reader who uses the workbook into a more intensive understanding of the stage theory proper. Because of its step wise nature it is a helpful introduction to anyone interested in Kohlberg's work beyond a superficial analysis. Since the outcome of this process is the ability to discern a stage of someone, a word of caution is in order. I think it is important to keep in mind that this work is designed to help in an understanding of the theory and not as an easy method for staging students or teachers etc. We are just becoming aware of some of the negative consequences of labelling and labelling with moral development stages is no exception in this light. If the reader uses the guide as a working programme for a clearer understanding of Kohlberg's theory and research he will benefit greatly from this short but excellent piece of work. As a scoring guide it is an excellent introduction to potential researchers in this field. Lay readers such as teachers, school administrators will find it helpful in gaining a fuller understanding of the stage properties of moral judgments.

Edmund V. Sullivan
Toronto
February, 1976

CONTENTS

INTRODUCTION 3

MORAL JUDGMENT INTERVIEW (FORM A) 6

LEVELS OF MORAL DEVELOPMENT 16   Items
    ☐ Conventional Level of Moral Development 17   1-15
    △ Preconventional Level of Moral Development 21   16-27
    ○ Postconventional Level of Moral Development 25   28-43

STAGES OF MORAL DEVELOPMENT 33

    Some Basic Principles and Age Norms 34   44-52

    How We Will Proceed 37   53-61

    Stage △1: Punishment & Obedience 41   62-92

    Stage △2: Instrumentality 50   93-129

    Stage ☐3: Conformity 63   130-173

    Stage ☐4: Social Systems 78   174-209

    Transition 92   210-212

    Stage ○5: Social Contract/Individual Rights 93   213-251

    Stage ○6: Universal Principles 111   252

LOOKING AT A WHOLE MORAL JUDGMENT INTERVIEW 113   253-260

APPENDICES 120

    A. Moral Judgment Interview (Form B) 122

    B. Sample Interviews 124
        1. Summary Sheet
        2. Stories With Questions 125
        3. 15 Sample Interviews 131

    C. Assessment of Sample Interviews 150

    D. References 151

INTRODUCTION

This is a workbook for people who want to become acquainted with the "Kohlberg Scoring System" of moral development. Lawrence Kohlberg (Harvard) conceptualized a system to describe the moral development of children and adults. It is a social-moral perspective based around the idea of conventional thinking. He describes PRECONVENTIONAL, CONVENTIONAL and POSTCONVENTIONAL thinking as a basic orientation to life. He then divided these 3 levels into 6 stages. The work at Harvard has gone on to further differentiate and expand these 6 stages as can be seen in Diagram A. This workbook will not go into these further differentiations – these can be learned from the literature after the basic stages are fully understood.

The approach we will take is from general to specific. We will go over the distinctions between stages so that a questionnaire can be scored as to which stages it contains and a general description of a person's level of development can be obtained. You may think initially that the discriminations are simple but you may find that the distinctions blur when you are confronted with 30 questionnaires to score. Hence, it is necessary to continually define what one stage or another means and review often.

We have arranged the workbook in a programmed learning style. This should enable you to learn the system in a step-by-step, clear way. When reading through the workbook use a clear piece of paper to cover the page and move down item by item writing your responses when indicated.

If you have not taken the moral judgment interview, you should do it before you begin working on the scoring system. This will enable you to get an idea of what it feels like to take it and also satisfy your curiosity as to your own stage of moral development. It would be a good

idea not to score your answers until you have studied all the stages.
The following questionnaire contains three stories. Many other stories
have been written which are included in the appendices. Different dilemmas
pull upon different areas of life, e.g. family relationships, law, mercy
killing, etc. However, for initial conceptualization of the basic stages,
we will use the enclosed stories as examples; this is sufficient.

After you have answered these stories, begin to read about the
THREE LEVELS OF MORAL DEVELOPMENT.

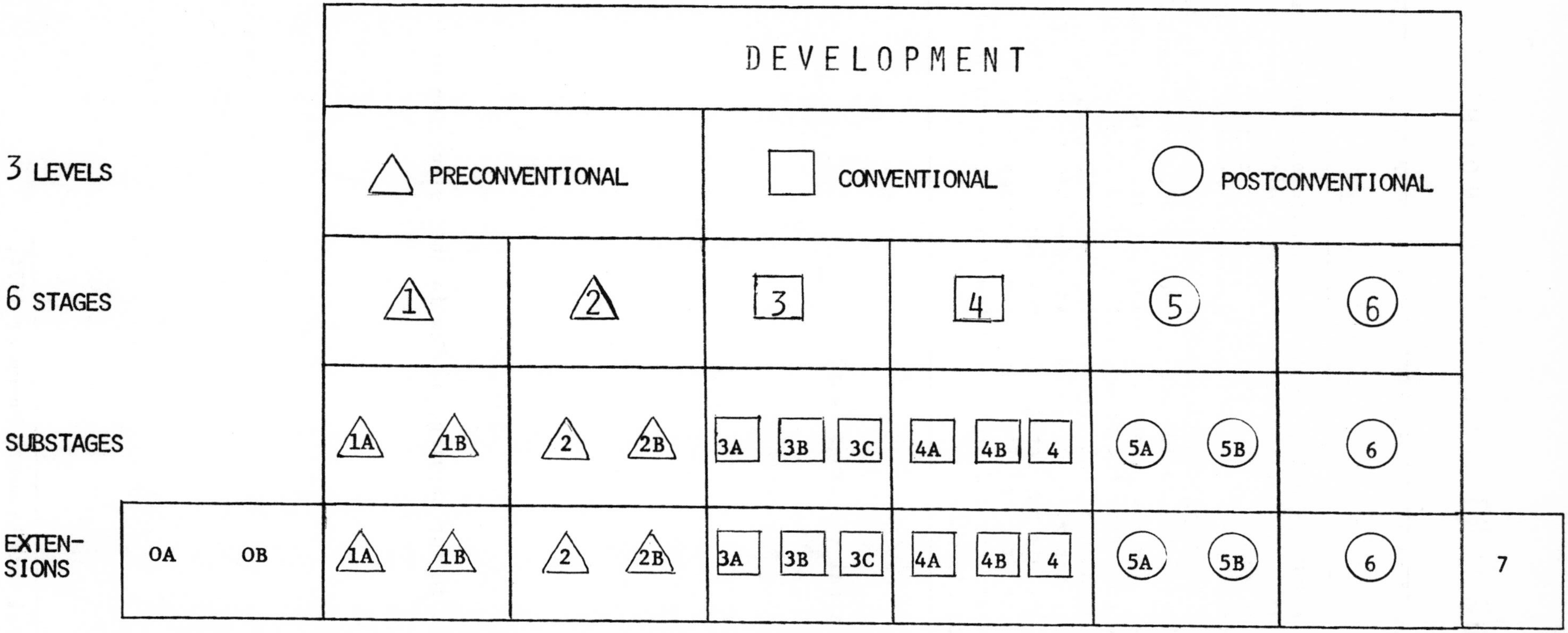

DEVELOPMENT

3 LEVELS	△ PRECONVENTIONAL		□ CONVENTIONAL		◯ POSTCONVENTIONAL		
6 STAGES	△1	△2	□3	□4	◯5		◯6
SUBSTAGES	△1A △1B	△2 △2B	□3A □3B □3C	□4A □4B □4	◯5A ◯5B		◯6
EXTEN-SIONS	△1A △1B	△2 △2B	□3A □3B □3C	□4A □4B □4	◯5A ◯5B		◯6

OA			7
OB			

DIAGRAM A: CONTINUING DIFFERENTIATION BETWEEN STAGES OF MORAL DEVELOPMENT

5

> **HEINZ**
>
> In Europe, a woman was near death from a special kind of cancer.
> There was one drug that the doctors thought might save her. It
> was a form of radium that a druggist in the same town had
> recently discovered. The drug was expensive to make, but the
> druggist was charging ten times what the drug cost him to make.
> He paid $200 for the radium and charged $2,000 for a small dose
> of the drug. The sick woman's husband, Heinz, went to every-
> one he knew to borrow the money, but he could only get together
> about $1,000 which is half of what it cost. He told the
> druggist that his wife was dying, and asked him to sell it
> cheaper or let him pay later. But the druggist said, "No, I
> discovered the drug and I'm going to make money from it." So
> Heinz got desperate and broke into the man's store to steal
> the drug for his wife.

1. Should Heinz steal the drug? Why?

2. What's to be said for obeying the law in this situation or in general?

Harvard Centre for Moral Development, November 1974.

6

HEINZ (cont'd)

3. In this situation law and life come into conflict. How can you resolve the conflict taking the best arguments for both into account?

4. If the husband doesn't love his wife is he obligated to steal the drug for her? Why or why not?

5. Why is it so important to save the woman's life? Would it be as right to steal it for a stranger as for his wife? Why?

HEINZ (cont'd)

6. Heinz steals the drug and is caught. Should the judge sentence him or should he let him go free? Why?

7. Thinking in terms of society, what would be the best reasons for the judge to give him some sentence?

8. Thinking in terms of society, what would be the best reasons for the judge to _not_ give him some sentence?

```
 JOE
┌─────────────────────────────────────────────────────────────┐
│ Joe is a fourteen-year-old boy who wanted to go to camp very │
│ much.  His father promised him he could go if he saved up the│
│ money for it himself.  So Joe worked hard at his paper route │
│ and saved up the $40 it cost to go to camp and a little more │
│ besides.  But just before camp was going to start, his father│
│ changed his mind.  Some of his friends decided to go on a    │
│ special fishing trip, and Joe's father was short of the money│
│ it would cost.  So he told Joe to give him the money he had  │
│ saved from the paper route.  Joe didn't want to give up going│
│ to camp, so he thought of refusing to give his father the    │
│ money.                                                       │
└─────────────────────────────────────────────────────────────┘
```

1. Should Joe refuse to give his father the money? Why?

2. Can you give me the best reasons to support the other point of view?

JOE (cont'd)

3. Is the fact that Joe earned the money himself an important consideration here? Why or why not?

4. Why should a promise be kept?

5. What makes a person feel bad when a promise is broken?

JOE (cont'd)

6. Why is it important to keep a promise to someone you don't know well or are not close to?

7. Trust is one important thing in a good father-son relationship. What are some other important considerations that a good father should recognize in his relations with his son? Why are they important?

8. How is a good parent-child relationship similar to any good human relationship? Why is that?

```
┌─ BOB & KARL ─┐
```
Two young men, brothers, had gotten into serious trouble.
They were secretly leaving town in a hurry and needed money.
Karl, the older one, broke into a store and stole $1,000.
Bob, the younger one, went to a retired old man who was
known to help people in town. Bob told the man that he was
very sick and he needed $500 to pay for the operation. Really
he wasn't sick at all, and he had no intention of paying the
man back. Although the man didn't know Bob very well, he
loaned him the money. So they skipped town, Bob with $500 and
Karl with $1,000.

1. Which would be worse, stealing like Karl or cheating like Bob? Why?

2. What is so bad about lying to people, in general?

BOB & KARL   (cont'd)

3.   Why shouldn't someone steal from a store?

4.   What is the basic value or importance of property rights?

5.   Which would be worse in terms of society's welfare, cheating like Bob
     or stealing like Karl?   Why?

13

6. Would your conscience feel worse if you cheated like Bob or stole like Karl? Why?

7. What do you mean by conscience? What do you think of as your conscience and what does it do?

8. What do the words morality or ethics mean to you?

BOB & KARL   (cont'd)

9. Do you believe there is an objective right or wrong in morality or is it
   a matter of personal opinion? For instance, in the first story some
   people say that Heinz should steal the drug, some say he shouldn't.
   Do you think there is an objective right answer to that kind of question?
   Explain.

10. It was common practice in some ancient societies to kill many of their
    female babies. Can you say whether something like this is really right
    or wrong? That is, can one make valid moral judgments about a practice
    in another society? Explain.

LEVELS of MORAL DEVELOPMENT

☐ CONVENTIONAL LEVEL

1. There are three levels of moral development:
      PRE CONVENTIONAL
      C O N V E N T I O N A L
      POST CONVENTIONAL	

2. The names of these three levels indicate that the central concept is _____.	
3. What is the basic meaning of a "CONVENTION"? _____	2. ☐ conventionality

4. Give three examples of generally agreed upon conventions:
    a._____
    b._____
    c._____
	3. <u>agreement</u> of a group upon action, thought, etc.

5. Most people in our culture know about the convention of the handshake; it is taught to children.	4a. handshake
	  b. dinner toast
	  c. ways of dressing

6. Some conventions are more formalized than others. For example, children are told to "Wash your hands before eating," "Don't interrupt another who is talking." These more formalized conventions are called R_ _ _ _.	
7. Rules which are applicable in a broader context and are formally accepted are _ _ _ _.	6. RULES
8. Both rules and laws prescribe a way of behaving and reflect common, shared ways of behaving, which may be called N _ _ _ _.	7. LAWS

☐ CONVENTIONAL LEVEL

9. The ☐ CONVENTIONAL LEVEL OF MORAL DEVELOPMENT indicates that a person is thinking from within a <u>system</u> which has been agreed upon formally or informally by a group of people. The system includes rules, laws, norms, expectations, etc.	8. NORMS
10. People may agree upon one set of rules, norms, laws, etc. or another and hence may be members of different G_ _ _ _.	
11. Name <u>ALL</u> the groups of which you are a member simultaneously. _____ _____ _____	10. GROUPS
12. Your membership in each group may have a greater or lesser effect on your life. In any case the membership which you have in different groups will influence the point of view which you take, your <u>SOCIAL PERSPECTIVE</u>. If you take <u>the point of view of the group</u> (whichever one it is) your thinking is at the CONVENTIONAL LEVEL. (A person's SOCIAL PERSPECTIVE is a very useful indication of stage and level of moral development.)	11. e.g. family, class in school, community, church, country.
13. Since CONVENTIONAL THINKING reflects the point of view of agroup, it follows that there would be much concern about friendship motivation, communication, ways of behaving, in general, "human concerns". TRUE or FALSE?	
	13. TRUE

18

14. ☐ TEST   Circle T or F

CONVENTIONAL thinking is indicated by;

a. T   F   accepting the importance of having rules
              for the good of the group.

b. T   F   putting one's own interests <u>before</u> the
              goals of the group when there is a
              conflict.

c. T   F   keeping rules so as not to be punished.

d. T   F   doing your own thing without concern about
              what the group is doing.

e. T   F   following laws which have been made in
              order to keep things in order.

14a. T Rules help
         maintain the group.

  b. F The group is
         felt to be very
         important

  c. F The motivation
         is not self-centered
         as in avoiding
         punishment.

  d. F There is much
         concern about
         approval by the
         group.

  e. T The structure
         of the group should
         be protected.

15. Putting what you have learned in your own words.

Write your description of ☐ CONVENTIONAL THINKING

Here is mine:

CONVENTIONAL THINKING stems from group membership. Because the group is so important, it has a profound influence on the way people think and act. The group has a <u>structure</u> within which people live. It is important to define and maintain this structure; rules and laws help to do this. There is much concern about the interaction between people within the CONTEXT of the group (be it large or small).

Here is Kohlberg's:

CONVENTIONAL LEVEL. At this level, maintaining the expect-ations of the individual's family, group, or nation is perceived as valuable in its own right, regardless of immediate and obvious consequences. The attitude is not only one of <u>conformity</u> to personal expectations and social order but of loyalty to it, of actively <u>maintaining</u>, supporting, and justifying the order, and of identifying with the persons or group involved in it.

16. There are three levels of moral development. It is important to learn to distinguish between them when learning to score. We have presented the CONVENTIONAL LEVEL first because it contains the central concept of the stages of moral development ... CONVENTIONALITY.

    We now will look at the level which PRECEDES the conventional level ... the △ PRECONVENTIONAL LEVEL.

---

17. At the conventional level conventions are accepted because they allow the group to continue; the group is important and desirable, there is identification with the group.

    At the △ PRECONVENTIONAL LEVEL do you think that conventions are accepted in order to maintain and promote the group? YES or NO?

---

18. The idea of group ways has not yet developed at the PRECONVENTIONAL LEVEL. Distinguish between these 2 examples:

    a. △ or ☐ "I will be on time for school because our class is working on a project which we decided to finish in a week."

    b. △ or ☐ "I will be on time for school because you have to go to the office if you are late."

17. NO. Rules may be accepted but for personal gain, laws may be upheld to be FAIR rather than to keep peace in society.

---

19. Notice that the ACTION taken in these 2 examples is the same, however the REASONS are different.

    The ☐ CONVENTIONAL reason reflects agreement with group goals and functioning.

    The △ PRECONVENTIONAL reason does not consider the group but rather the good of the _____.

18a. ☐ CONVENTIONAL identification with the group.

b. △ PRECONVENTIONAL avoidance of (personal) punishment.

---

20. PRECONVENTIONAL thinking reflects an individual orientation; there is much interest in fulfilling one's own needs and avoiding harm to the self. This in itself is not bad except that at the preconventional level the satisfaction of the self is so paramount, so overriding of others and other considerations. This is the basic SOCIAL PERSPECTIVE of the PRECONVENTIONAL LEVEL. Is this a normal stage of development?

19. individual.

---

21. _____ = PRE-GROUP WAYS

    = INDIVIDUAL ORIENTATION.

20. Yes, this is a stage which naturally precedes group identification.

---

22. There are other aspects which point to △ PRE-CONVENTIONAL THINKING. In terms of relationships between people there is an attitude which could be described as if a person is like a bucket of a certain size. If it is not filled, then resources are sought to fill it up. If, on the other hand, something is given out, it is only done if it is possible to get back the same in return; this maintains the "full bucket". This kind of interaction is very R _ _ _ _ _ _ _ _ _.

21. △ PRECONVENTIONAL

---

23. Another way of saying it is that in △ PRECONVENTIONAL thinking a balance of exchange is maintained. For example, "I'll lend you my skates if you lend me your wagon." Nothing is lost in the transaction. There is a strict, tit-for-tat basis. The exchange between people must be, above all, _ _ _ _.

22. RECIPROCAL.

---

24. Since the group ways are not recognized as important in △ PRECONVENTIONAL THINKING, something else is needed to train and educate. In △ PRECONVENTIONAL thinking, POWER serves this function. Power comes in many forms for the young child: the "biggest", _____, _____, _____, (name more).

23. fair

---

25. This is the REASON why rules, laws, etc. are followed in △ PRECONVENTIONAL THINKING, and not because conventions are _____ or _____.

24. strongest, oldest, loudest, etc.

TEST

26. Let us take some examples of both △PRECONVENTIONAL
and ☐CONVENTIONAL remarks.   From what you have
learned indicate whether each of these reflects
△PRECONVENTIONAL or ☐CONVENTIONAL thinking.

(Why should a promise be kept?)

a. _____ "A promise should be kept because it shows
the person's sense of responsibility and
it keeps a link between people."

(Should the tailor report Heinz to the police?)

b. _____ "The Tailor would not want to tell on his
friend because you wouldn't want your
friend to get in trouble because maybe he
did a favour for the tailor before."

(Should the judge sentence him or let him
go free?)

c. _____ "Heinz should be sent to jail because if he
breaks a law, society has agreed that there
must be sanctions."

(Should Heinz steal the drug?)

d. _____ "Heinz shouldn't have stolen the drug because
he could be put in jail for it."

26a.☐ person is talking
as a group member.

b.△ a reciprocal
arrangement, one
favour deserves
another.

c.☐ society has
agreed that stealing
will be punished by
jail.

d.△ punishment comes
automatically with
wrongdoing.

PRECONVENTIONAL LEVEL

27. Putting what you have learned into words.

 PRECONVENTIONAL THINKING is (give your description)

Here is mine:

 PRECONVENTIONAL THINKING reflects an individual perspective, before group ways are accepted. The needs of the individual are most important and must be maintained. Any exchange must carry a guarantee of getting as much as is given. Power is a ruling factor in any dispute. At this level, there is a restricted sense of time and space.

Here is Kohlberg's:

 PRECONVENTIONAL LEVEL: The child is responsive to cultural rules and labels of good and bad, right and wrong, but interprets these labels in terms of either the physical or the hedonistic consequences of action (punishment, reward, exchange of favors) or in terms of the physical power of those who enunciate the rules and labels.

28. A person's thinking develops through the _____ level to the _____ level. Many people find this level of development sufficient in order to lead normal lives. Other people develop <u>beyond</u> the ☐ CONVENTIONAL level to the ◯ POSTCONVENTIONAL level.

---

29. Indicate whether the following are △ PRECONVENTIONAL, ☐ CONVENTIONAL, or ◯ POSTCONVENTIONAL attitudes:

a._____ identifies with the group.

b._____ an individual perspective beyond the group.

c._____ an egocentric, self-maintaining perspective.

28. △ preconventional
☐ conventional

---

30. Note there are 2 levels with a more <u>individual</u> perspective. Name them:

_____   _____

29. ☐
b. ◯
c. △

---

31. There is a difference of course between the individual perspective of the △ PRECONVENTIONAL level and that of the ◯ POSTCONVENTIONAL level.

30. △ PRECONVENTIONAL
◯ POSTCONVENTIONAL

32.

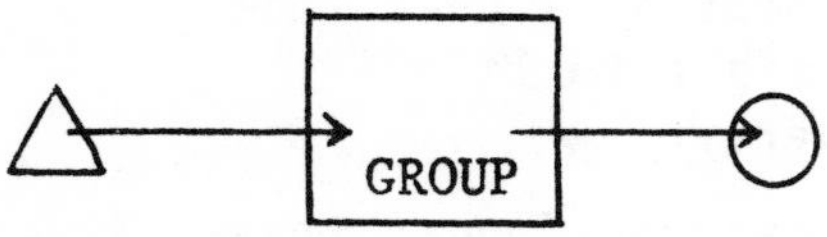

△ → [GROUP] → ◯

A person begins as individual, becomes incorporated into the group and it's thinking, then may develop the ability to think in terms much <u>larger</u> than the group. This is the SOCIAL PERSPECTIVE of POSTCONVENTIONAL THINKING.

---

33. This progression from △ to ☐ to ◯ illustrates the idea of D _ _ _ _ _ _ _ _ _ .

Normal development proceeds in this manner, without skipping any levels and in one direction.

POSTCONVENTIONAL LEVEL

34. Let us take as an example, following rules (laws) at each level. See if you can identify the response.

   a._____ I think it's wrong to steal because we have agreed that stealing will disrupt our society.

   b._____ I think it's wrong to steal because I would get punished if I did.

   c._____ I think it's wrong to steal because it would be a violation of the right of every person to possess property.

33. DEVELOPMENT.

---

35. Notice that in the ◯POSTCONVENTIONAL response, thinking develops on the basis of a more general and abstract notion of the order necessary to live in society. A common misunderstanding of the ◯POSTCONVENTIONAL level leads people to think that rules and laws are thrown out. What is thrown out is acceptance of group concensus alone as defining the right and as sufficient reason for acting (or not).

34a. ☐ group maintenance.

   b. △ avoid harm to the self.

   c. ◯ maintain human rights.

---

36. Let us take 3 other examples of NOT following rules. Indicate which level (△ ☐ ◯) each of these follow:

   a._____ I think it's right to steal because I want this and there is no chance I'd get caught.

   b._____ I think it's right to steal because I need this to live (e.g. food) and the right to life supercedes the right to property.

   c._____ I think it's right to steal because I need this to help our family but I know the law must be upheld and I'm prepared to take the consequences.

---

37. From the six examples just given, we can see that the most important consideration in determining the level of development is:

   a._____ what action is advocated.

   b._____ the reasons given for any action.

36a. △ OK if doesn't get caught.

   b. ◯ rights are prior to rules and there is a hierarchy of rights.

   c. ☐ must still operate within the system.

38. Here are 2 responses to dilemmas. Which response indicates ◯POSTCONVENTIONAL thinking?

(Should the judge sentence him or let him go free?)

SB: "The law is the law. It may not be perfect but it is what we have to live by until it changes. We must try and uphold the law. When we break the law we should be prepared to be punished if we are caught regardless of motives."

(Should the judge sentence him or let him go free?)

PK: "I think a compassionate judge should allow Heinz to go free for his motives were not menacing or threatening to society. Laws, judges and juries have a responsibility to the humanity of man not just to set a code of laws. It is the judge's responsibility to do what he thinks is best for the society and in this case jailing Heinz would do the society no good at all while reprimanding the druggist instead would do society a definite good turn."

---

39. a. What does SB consider as a very basic factor in thiniing about what to do?

_____

b. What factors does PK consider as basic when thinking about what to do?

_____

---

40. What is the difference between these two approaches? (and what is the same)? Mark X in symbol for level where it applies.

a. ☐ ◯ may uphold the law.

b. ☐ ◯ the result may be good order in society.

c. ☐ ◯ will consider the basic rights of individuals as most fundamental.

d. ☐ ◯ will consider the group agreement (i.e. law) as most fundamental.

---

37. b. The REASONS given.
All 3 levels can do the same thing.

38. SB is ☐ CONVENTIONAL THINKING.

PK is ◯ POST-CONVENTIONAL THINKING.

39. SB: upholding the law. The law is the first, prior consideration.

PK: the well-being of society. The humanity of man is prior to the "set code of law."

41. [TEST]

Put △ ☐ or ◯ to indicate whether the follo following statements reflect a △ PRECONVENTIONAL, ☐ CONVENTIONAL, or ◯ POSTCONVENTIONAL attitude.

a._____ A good citizen feels that he must obey law because it has been agreed upon.

b._____ A good citizen obeys the law so as not to get punished.

c._____ A good citizen is responsible for insuring the welfare of each individual whether this agrees with the law or not.

d._____ It is most important to act in such a way as to promote life & ensure individual human rights.

e._____ It is most important to maintain one's society. One's personal goals may have to be sacrificed.

f._____ One's own specific needs come first.

g._____ In a conflict, strength determines who wins.

h._____ In a conflict, the most basic right must be upheld.

i._____ In a conflict, the law determines what is right.

j._____ Each person is responsible for creating laws which promote and insure the rights of each individual.

k._____ The law cannot be changed because an individual is powerless.

l._____ The law can be changed by majority agreement.

41a. ☐
b. △
c. ◯
d. ◯
e. ☐
f. △
g. △
h. ◯
i. ☐
j. ◯
k. △
l. ☐

42. Putting what you have learned into your own words.

◯ POSTCONVENTIONAL THINKING is (give your own description)

Here is mine:

◯ POSTCONVENTIONAL THINKING reflects an individual rather than a group orientation. Through a broader and deeper conceptual development, consideration is given to much more abstract principles and rights. The rights of each individual are considered as well as the well being of society as a whole.

Here is Kohlberg's:

At this level there is a clear effort to define moral values and principles which have validity and application apart from the authority of the groups or persons holding these principles and apart from the individual's own identification with these groups.

43. Here are some responses which are likely to be given to the dilemmas. Indicate with △ , ☐ or ◯ the highest level of each response.

Level:

a. (Should the judge sentence him or let him go free?)
"Sentence him. He broke the law of the state. If we all thought like Heinz there would be no need of judges. But we do have judges to protect us from people like the druggist. We made the rules, we must abide by them. If our morals prevail, we must be prepared to face the consequences."

_____

b. (Why shouldn't someone steal from a store?)
"Because you're not stealing from 1 person, you're stealing from many people. The storeowner probably needs money to support a family, to pay bills, etc."

_____

c. (Should Heinz steal the drug?)
"It was definitely wrong to steal this drug. Heinz knew this deep down inside, but at this point he was desperate. There seemed no other way. Heinz's wife had to have this drug. There was nothing to do but steal it. It was wrong but desperate men do many bad things in times of stress. I feel Heinz had no other choice."

_____

d. (Should the judge sentence him or let him go free?)
"I think he should be (sent to jail) because he is an ex-con and he has to serve his term."

_____

e. (Why shouldn't someone steal from a store?)
"One of the rules of society is that you respect other people's property. Without respect for and observance of such rules society would soon become a nightmare where no one would be safe."

_____

f. (Should Heinz steal the drug?)
"Yes, it was right. The druggist was wrong in his demands. Though technically Heinz was in the wrong my conscience demands that I draw the line somewhere to confine the rights of the druggist. The materials used in the drugs are natural materials owned by all. The druggist does deserve a profit for his labours. The druggist was demanding an unfair profit which under the circumstances amounted to life or death for the woman. In terms of Justice Heinz was right."

_____

g. (Should the judge sentence him or let him go free?)
"The law is the law. It may not be perfect but it is what we have to live by. Until it changes we must try and uphold the law. When we break the law we should be prepared to be punished if we are caught, regardless of motives."

_____

30

h. (Should Joe refuse to give his father the money?
    Why?)
    "I think Joe should refuse giving the money because
    he really wants to go to camp and have some fun and
    learn things."   _____

i. (Should the judge sentence him or let him go free?)
    "He should send him to jail. You shouldn't really
    steal unless you have a very, very good reason."   _____

43a. ☐ Clearly a con-
     ventional response;
we made the rules &
must abide by them.

    b. △ You may have
mislead here by the ref-
erence to "many people,"
and scored this conven-
tional. However, a
concern about the number
of people wronged is a
preconventional concern.
Also, the importance of
meeting the storeowner's
own personal needs is
preconventional. This
response indicates a
rather late preconven-
tional response and one
would expect more con-
ventional thinking from
the person very soon.
The awareness of the
group and family respon-
sibilities is present
but responded to in a
preconventional way.

    c. ☐ It is very
important to keep the
rules, but under extreme
circumstances they can
be broken - a common
conventional response

d. △ Here we see an attempt to deal with the problem of helping the woman. There is a focus on the wrong done and the punishment which follows automatically. The emphasis is more on the punishment than on keeping the rules – hence preconventional.

e. □ Recognizes what is necessary for people to live together in society.

f. ○ A postconventional concern about rights and principles involved in a situation. Note that this response is more abstract than response e.

g. □ A firm conventional acceptance of the law.

h. △ A definite priority is given to one's own personal need and pleasure. A conventional response could say this but would also include response to their relationship, or the roles, of father and son and the like.

i. □ Again, we see that rules are very important and apply to everyone.

STAGES OF MORAL DEVELOPMENT

Some basic principles & observations:

44. Each level of moral development is divided into two stages:

PRE-CONVENTIONAL △	△1	Punishment & Obedience
	△2	Instrumentality
CONVENTIONAL ☐	3	Conformity
	4	Social Systems
POST-CONVENTIONAL ○	5	Social Contract/Individual Rights
	6	Universal Principles

45. "Average" development proceeds from Stage 1 thinking to Stage 2 thinking, to Stage 3 thinking, then Stage 4 thinking, Stage 5 and Stage 6 thinking.

AVERAGE DEVELOPMENT:

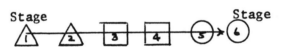

46. In other words we are discussing a <u>continuous</u> development which may be represented more adequately like this:

The task of scoring is to determine where the response lies along this continuum. Is it, for example, a beginning Stage 3 response? or a firmly held Stage 3 response? or on the fence between 2 and 3? Experience and study help to clarify these finer distinctions. For now we will concentrate on the <u>main</u> distinctions between stages.

45. AVERAGE DEVELOPMENT

△1 △2 3 4 5 6

47. In developing through the Stages, it is possible that a person's thinking may span two or three Stages at one time. For example:

Indicate Stages
of Thinking Shown

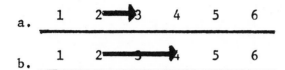

a.   1   2 → 3   4   5   6   _____

b.   1   2 → 3 → 4   5   6   _____

c.   1 → 2   3   4   5   6   _____

---

48. The preceding combinations of stages are frequently found when assessing level of moral development. Here are some possible patterns of development and others which are unlikely (if not impossible) to find. Mark these with an "X".

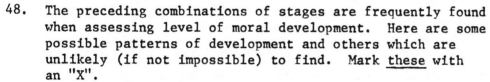

a.   1 → 2 → 3   4   5   6   _____

b.   1 → 2   3   4 → 5   6   _____

c.   1   2   3   4 → 5   6   _____

d.   1   2   3 → 4   5 → 6   _____

e.   1   2   3   4 → 5   6   _____

(Answer column, right:)

47a. 2 & 3

   b. 2, 3 & 4

   c. 1 & 2

---

49. Recalling what you have learned about the 3 levels of development and your own experience with development, make a rough estimate of the correspondence between age and stage of moral development.

    ①   ages_____

    ②   ages_____

    ③   ages_____

    ④   ages_____

    ⑤   ages_____

    ⑥   ages_____

(Answer column, right:)

48. b. & d.
Development is a process of building —you can't build the 5th floor on top of the 2nd. Stages are not skipped.

50. Based on our research (with 10-25 year olds) we have found that:

Stage /1\ thinking is strong at ages 10-11.

Stage /2\ thinking is strong at ages 10-13.

Stage |3| thinking is strong at ages 11-25.

Stage |4| thinking begins to appear at age 15 and increases to 25.

Stage (5) thinking appears in young adults 21-25.

Stage (6) thinking is non-existent at any of these ages.

---

51. In other words, in school age children,

△ PRECONVENTIONAL thinking is often/seldom seen....

□ CONVENTIONAL thinking is often/seldom seen....

○ POSTCONVENTIONAL thinking is often/seldom seen....

---

52. Here is the data on stages of moral development obtained through our research at OISE in the Moral Education Project:

AGE	PERCENT OF STAGE USAGE						
	1	2	3	4	5	6	N
10	41%	33%	16%				78
11	27%	31%	32%				58
12	2%	29%	66%				198
13	1%	34%	65%				154
15	1%	18%	75%	6%			99
16		12%	71%	11%			90
17		6%	70%	12%	1%		87
21-25+		3.5%	62%	29%	5.5%		92

Per cent of Students at Major Stage. For example: 41% of 10 year olds tested showed over half of their responses reflected a Stage 1 orientation. Note that the per cents for each do not necessarily equal 100% because some people span 3 stages (and hence often do not have 50% for one stage) or span two stages equally (50-50).

51. △ often seen
□ often seen
○ seldom seen

53. Now that you have a rough idea of what stages to expect and when to expect them (i.e. not to expect postconventional thinking in elementary school), let us see how we will procede to study the 6 stages of development.

54. We have said that there are 6 stages of thinking which develop in an orderly way. We can look at the kind of thinking at each stage in more detail. <u>For each stage we will examine 9 areas:</u>

   | SP | SOCIAL PERSPECTIVE: the point of view from which judgment is made.

   | RT | ROTE-TAKING: the ability to understand different points of view.

   | Ex | EXCHANGE: the way that physical or emotional exchange between people is seen.

   | IR | INTERPERSONAL RELATIONSHIPS: the basic form the relationships take.

   | G | GOVERNANCE: whoever is responsible for setting up structures between people.

   | R | RULES: the means through which the structure is made known.

   | S | SANCTIONS: the means through which the structure is maintained.

   | P | PROPERTY: how property is viewed and valued.

   | L | LIFE: how life is valued.

55. Name the areas which we will discuss:

SP _____

RT _____

Ex _____

IR _____

G _____

R _____

S _____

P _____

L _____

56. These areas are points of focus from which we can describe the STRUCTURE of a person's thinking. Just as we can describe a person's physical structure by describing hair, eyes, height, foot size, skin, build,etc. so we can describe the STRUCTURE of one's thinking by describing SOCIAL PERSPECTIVE, ROLE TAKING,   EXCHANGE, INTERPERSONAL RELATIONSHIPS, GOVERNANCE, RULES, SANCTIONS, PROPERTY and LIFE

57. Moral judgment includes all these areas (and more). But note that thinking may not develop at the same rate in every area (just as adolescents sometimes have long legs and short trunks), for example:

    [SP]   1————•————6 (social perspective at stage 3)

    [RT]   1————•————6 (role taking ability at stage 3)

    [G]   1——•————6 (governance at stage 2)

    [L]   1——•————6 (life at stage 2)

    [P]   1——•————6 (property at stage 2)

58. Here are a number of phrases. Each describes one of
the areas from one stage or another. Let us not
consider what <u>stage</u> the phrases are from, but rather
indicate which <u>area</u> the phrase describes.

SP   RT   Ex   IR   G   R   S   P   L

<u>Areas</u>

a._____ laws let us know what is required.

b._____ each person has absolute ownership of his property.

c._____ being with people simply means getting our own needs
met.

d._____ fines, prison, death.

e._____ has the ability to see that somebody else may have
different ideas.

f._____ it is most important to preserve one's own life.

g._____ give and take on a fair, equal, reciprocal basis.

h._____ point of view of a dependent child.

i._____ society makes the laws.

---

59. We can talk about these areas in 2 different ways:

A. <u>All</u> of them used to understand one stage at a time;

B. <u>One</u> of them followed over 6 stages in order to
understand how one specific area develops.

Stage ←————————— A —————————→

1 ↑ SP   RT   Ex   IR   G   R   S   P   L

2   SP

3   SP

  B

4   SP

5   SP

6 ↓ SP

We will proceed to study all the areas for one stage, and
then all the areas for the next stage and so on, in order
to clarify the kind of thinking to expect at each
stage (as in A).

58a.	R
b.	P
c.	IR
d.	S
e.	RT
f.	L
g.	Ex
h.	SP
i.	G

60. However, you may wish to proceed to study a particular area over the stages (as in B) to see how development occurs. You can do this by matching up all of the same area over all stages. The area and the stage will be indicated just below the item number, for example: 1 / RT , i.e. stage 1, Role Taking.

61. So let us begin to study stage 1 thinking as seen in the areas we have listed. Name them again.

1. _____

2. _____

3. _____

4. _____

5. _____

6. _____

7. _____

8. _____

9. _____

62. Recall what we said about the △PRECONVENTIONAL level.

a. What does △"PRECONVENTIONAL" mean?

b. There are 2 △PRECONVENTIONAL stages. Name them:

_____   _____

c. At what ages is there an emphasis on △PRE-CONVENTIONAL thinking?

Let us now consider the SOCIAL PERSPECTIVE, the point of view, out of which thinking at the lowest △PRE-CONVENTIONAL stage - the Punishment and Obedience Stage - arises.

61.1. Social Perspective

2. Role Taking

3. Exchange

4. Interpersonal Relationships

5. Governance

6. Rules

7. Sanction

8. Property

9. Life

63. **1/SP** The earliest △preconventional PERSPECTIVE must be:

    a._____ an individual perspective

    b._____ a group member perspective

since it is a PRECONVENTIONAL perspective.

62a. before GROUP WAYS have been incorporated.

  b. ①punishment & obedience.

    ②instrumentality.

c. ages 9-14.

---

64. **1/SP** What is unique about the Stage 1 - Punishment and Obedience SOCIAL PERSPECTIVE - is that one's own perspective is the only perspective which is recognized - a very _ _ _CENTRIC point of view.

63. a. an individual perspective.

---

65. **1/SP** However, it is true that people in fact do have different points of view. This conflicting state of affairs is handled in at least 2 different ways so that one's egocentric position is maintained:

a. The Authority's point of view is incorporated into the person's thinking, and not recognized as somebody else's. The Authority's point of view equals one's point of view.

    For example: (Why should a promise be kept?)
           "A promise is a promise and don't you
              ever forget it."
This sounds very much like some authority has said this so often that now the person says it himself.

b. Other people's point of view (other than the Authority's) is considered the same as one's own point of view. Differing points of view are simply not recognized.

    For example: (Should the judge send him to jail?)
           "I should let him go free because if the
           judge's wife was dying he would do the
           same thing so he had a reason for not
           going to jail."

64. EGOCENTRIC (from Just Community paper)

---

66. **1/RT** The social perspective which is taken is made possible by one's _____ _____ability, one's ability to place oneself in others' shoes.

67. What ROLE TAKING ability underlies the Stage 1 egocentric
1/RT social perspective?

What level of Role Taking skill is indicated by such a
perspective?

What can you conclude from what we have already said?

66. Role Taking

---

68. Since the ability to look at another's point of view
1/RT is slight, MOTIVES (a) would or (b) would not be
considered when talking about an act?

67. There is very little
ability, if any,
to put oneself in
the other's shoes.

---

69. Considering the lack of ability to take another's point
1/Ex of view, the kind of EXCHANGE - what passes between
people (physically or emotionally) - can easily be
described.

Would you expect a one-way or a reciprocal exchange to
happen? Why?

a. ONE WAY, because_____

b. RECIRPOCAL, because_____

68.b. would NOT.
In order to be able
to say, e.g. "He
really meant to..."
there has to be the
ability to consider
what somebody else
thought.

---

70. This one way relationship results from a vewpoint which
1/Ex considers the Authority as having much _ _ _ _ _. The
Authority is seen as owner, boss, parent, guardian,
protector, provider, etc.

69.a. ONE WAY because
the person feels
powerless, small;
simply one who
receives - be it
reward or punishment

---

71. How would you describe the exchange between the
1/Ex Authority and the person under the Authority in light of
what we have just said? (Describe it from the point of
view of the person not in authority):

70. POWER

72.
1/IR What is the shape of INTERPERSONAL RELATIONSHIPS which develop within an egocentric, one-sided context such as this? Interpersonal relationships are best described in terms of OBEDIENCE to the Authority (or if not obedience then punishment).

71. The person under the Authority takes the attitude of a passive RECEIVER.

73.
1/IR From this we draw the name of this stage:
△ _____ & _____.

74.
1/IR Stage 1 Interpersonal Relationships are unbalanced relationships. There is on the one hand the _____ who has greater age, size and power and, on the other hand, those wo must _____ the authority.

73. PUNISHMENT & OBEDIENCE

75. So far we have described Stage 1 thinking in terms of SOCIAL PERSPECTIVE, ROLE TAKING ABILITY, EXCHANGE and INTERPERSONAL RELATIONSHIPS. Here are some responses given to dilemmas which reflect Stage 1 thinking. From such responses to dilemmas we are able to deduce a person's thinking in the different areas. Of course every response to a question will not contain enough information to judge thinking in every area. To obtain a total picture requires many responses to different dilemmas. Indicate on the responses below the areas in which you can begin to draw a picture of this person's thinking. (We will discuss other areas shortly):

AREAS: SP   RT   Ex   IR

a.____ (Should Heinz steal the drug? Why?)
"No. You are not supposed to steal."

b.____ (Should Joe refuse to give his father the money?)
"No, because you should obey your father. Because they are your parents.)

c.____ (Should Joe refuse to give his father the money?)
"No. I think Joe should offer it to his father or give it up."

d.____ (If the husband doesn't love his wife is he obligated to steal the drug for her?)
"I don't know, I'm not married."

e.____ (Should the judge sentence him or let him go free?)
"He should sentence him because Heinz should get shot for breaking out of jail and also for other things."

74. Authority
obey

76. So you should be forming an idea of how one infers from a response to a question within a dilemma the kind of thinking out of which the response arose. Notice that we are concerned with THINKING, not action.

(If you wish to consider the whole question of the relation between THOUGHT and ACTION consult Kohlberg, L. "Stage and Sequence: The Cognitive-Developmental Approach to Socialization," Chapter 6 in D. Goslin (Ed.), Handbook of Socialization Theory and Research. New York: Rand McNally, 1969.)

75a. [SP]
He has incorporated the point of view of an Authority as his own. You can imagine in the back of this statement an Authority saying the exact same thing: "You're not supposed to steal."

b. [IR]
The kind of relationship is described: the father has the rights, age and authority.

c. [Ex]
Joe doesn't have much choice in light of his father's power. One way or another he is compelled to give it up.

d. [RT]
Most limited RT abilit
The person responding can't even stay within the story.

e. [RT]
This response does not consider the motive but just the physical act. Again a low level of RT ability.

77. Another aspect of the Interpersonal Relationships which
[1/G] develops between people is the development of some kind of "structure" between people.

Here are some examples of how structure is set up:

- by choosing a leader;

- by setting out rules (of behavior, a game, etc.);

- by making laws;

- by the relationship: parent/child, teacher/student

Another word for this kind of structure is: (a) feelings or (b) order between people or (c) governance.

78.
1/G In Stage 1 thinking the structure between people is set up by the Authority, who is viewed as the person with <u>the</u> power, biggest size, oldest, etc. What are some obvious examples of such an Authority setting out a structure?

77. (b) order
(c) governance

79.
1/G <u>Who</u> is responsible for the structuring which develops between people according to Stage 1 thinking?

_____

78. e.g. a parent setting down rules of conduct for two brothers.

A teacher establishing him/herself as leader of the classroom.

80.
1/G The Authority governs (i.e. determines the structure) hence we call this area: _____.

79. The Authority

81.
1/R Once it has been determined, how is this "structure" communicated, how is it passed on to those who are part of it? Would you expect communication to occur verbally or non-verbally?

80. Governance.

82.
1/R Rules are one way in which the structure is set out. Such rules, as Stage 1 thinking sees it, are made by the authority (as we just said) and tell you what to do or not to do. Rules are quite definite and very important.

81. Both what is said and what is done get the message across.

83.
1/R We have talked about rules previously – in relation to □CONVENTIONAL THINKING. What is the distinction between perception of rules at the □CONVENTIONAL level and the perception of rules at the Stage 1 – Punishment and Obedience Stage?

a. Who makes the rules?   □ : _____

△ : _____

b. For what reason are rules made (as the person sees it?)

□ : _____

△ : _____

84.
1/R

There is an even earlier Stage 1 perspective (before rules). Very young children can't remember rules. Instead each time they have to be told. So the earliest attempt to communicate some sort of structure is through _____.

83a. [ ] the group

△ Authority (individual)

b. [ ] to maintain th[ ] group.

△ so you know wh[ ] to do.

85.
1/S

If there is someone generating a structure within the situation and it is made known, what will determine whether this structure actually becomes established? At Stage 1 thinking how is any sort of structure MAINTAINED? What do you feel the Stage 1 method of enforcement is?

84. direct command.

86.
1/S

State 1 is described as the _____ and obedience stage. Avoiding _____ (or seeking _____) is the reason behind actions, the WHY for actions.

This is so strongly held that what is rewarded becomes the same as what is a good act. (Conversely, punishment indicates a bad act.)

85. Through the use o[ ] punishment and reward.

87.
1/P

One area which we will use as an example of how the structure between people is revealed is that of PROPERTY.

From all that has been said, answer the following, True or False:

In Stage 1 thinking:

a._____ There is a very strong feeling of having the right to own property oneself.

b._____ You respect other people's property because, if you don't you'll get punished (or rewarded if you do respect it).

c._____ It is worse to break 2 glasses accidentally than one glass on purpose.

86. punishment,
    punishment,
    reward.

88.
1/L Finally, we can look at the last area which we will consider for each stage, the VALUE OF LIFE ITSELF.

As you may guess, at this level of thinking LIFE has to do with one's own life. The life of others is considered only insofar as it has an effect on one's own life. This follows from the basic _____ perspective with which we began our discussion of Stage 1 thinking.

89.
1/L Life is valued in terms of physical external criteria. A famous person's life is more valuable than the lady's down the street, just because he's famous.

90. This completes our description of the more structural relationship which develops between people plus the value which is placed on life itself. Let us look at some more responses to these areas. Indicate below the AREAS which the responses describe:

AREAS: ☐G ☐R ☐S ☐P ☐L

a._____ (Why shouldn't someone steal from a store anyhow?) "Because if you get caught you have to go to jail."

b._____ (Should Heinz have done that?) "You are not supposed to steal."

c._____ (Why shouldn't someone steal from a store anyhow?) "If the police found out they would put him in reform school for being bad."

d._____ (Should Heinz steal the drug? Why?) "No, I don't think he should steal it, no matter what. He could go to jail. He just shouldn't steal."

e._____ (Should Joe refuse to give his father the money?) "No, because his father has the right to do this. Because he is his father and he owns everything."

87a. F. Only the Authority has such rights.

b. T. It is an education - to learn respect for other's property.

c. T. The greater the damage, the worse the crime, regardless of intentions.

88. egocentric

47

91. At this point it may be difficult for you to draw this kind of information from a few words. In addition, responses of short length may reveal many things or nothing. Only experience with scoring will clarify many of these distinctions. Here are a few more practice responses - not all Stage 1.

1. Find the Stage 1 responses and circle the letters.
2. A response may reveal thinking in different areas. Indicate the areas revealed by the response (SP/RT/Ex/IR/G/R/S/P/L) for the Stage 1 responses which you have found.

Areas (Circle Stage 1 responses first):

a.____ (Should Joe refuse to give his father the money?) "Yes, because more than likely something else special will come along later on and his father will likely treat him in thanks for helping him out."

b.____ (Should Joe refuse to give the father the money?) "No, because you should respect elders."

c.____ (Should Heinz be sent back to jail by the judge?) "Heinz shouldn't be sent back by the judge because it was twenty years after."

d.____ (Should Joe refuse to give his father the money?) "Yes, because his father wouldn't give him the money for camp, so why should Joe give him the money for fishing."

e.____ (Should Heinz have done that?) "It was wrong because he stole it from the store. It was necessary because he needed it or his wife would die."

f.____ (Should Heinz be sent back to jail by the judge?) "Yes, Heinz should be sent back to jail because he broke out."

g.____ (Why shouldn't someone steal from a store anyhow?) "Because it is a very bad thing to do and one of God's commandments said 'Thou shalt not steal!' "

h.____ (Should Heinz have done that?) "Heinz shouldn't have because he could be put in jail for breaking in."

90a. S. This answer shows that punishment is the reason not to steal.

b. R. A rule which has been learned. Such a rule is intended to communicate what to do to allow property to be owned.

c. G. The authority which is given to "them" is clear.

d. L. It is more important not to go to jail than to save a life.

e. P. The authority (parents) has the right to property.

91a. △2

b. △1 SP, IR.

c. △2

d. △2

e. △2

f. △1 R, S.

g. △1 G, R, S.

h. △1 L.

A response or set of responses may give you clues about one or several areas.

92.

- An EGOCENTRIC SOCIAL PERSPECTIVE.

- Very limited ROLE TAKING ability.

- One way EXCHANGE between person and Authority person receives.

- Unbalanced INTERPERSONAL RELATIONSHIPS: obey the Authority.

- The Authority is responsible for setting up the structure between people.

- RULES are set up by the Authority; the purpose of rules is to tell people what to do.

- Punishment and reward are used as SANCTIONS.

- Very poor sense of owning PROPERTY.

- LIFE is valued because of external, physical criteria.

93. Thinking develops from the Stage 1 attitude into the Stage 2 focus on Instrumentality attitude. Look back at Item 91 parts a,c,d, & e. These are some examples of responses from a Stage 2 perspective. Let us look at the SOCIAL PERSPECTIVE from which such responses come.

94.
2/SP

The person thinking in a Stage 2 way now sees his own interests as distinct from the Authority's (or other's) interests. Stage 2 Instrumental thinking stems from a CONCRETE INDIVIDUALISTIC SOCIAL PERSPECTIVE.

95.
2/SP

Compare the following 2 responses. Which one shows this separate individual perspective?

a. (Why shouldn't someone steal from a store?)
   "Because it is a very bad thing to do and one of God's commandments said 'Thou shalt not steal.'"

b. (Should Joe refuse to give his father the money?)
   "Yes because his father did not carry papers for the route."

96.
2/RT

In Stage 2 thinking the ability to consider anothers point of view is beginning to develop. It is now known that another person may have an idea or attitude which is separate from ones own.

95. b. Father has no claim to the money on the basis of being the father, the authority, the power (which Stage 1 thinking accepts.) Both father and son are separate INDIVIDUALS. Father must work for money same as son. Everyone must pursue their own interests.

97.

`2/RT`

But ---- this does not include the ability to understand WHAT the other's idea or attitude <u>may be</u>.

In Stage 2 thinking a person has an idea, desire. He knows that others have ideas too. He imputes <u>his</u> idea to others, but calls it <u>their</u> idea.

We see an example of this here:
"Well if you were the judge and you got a case of a man stealing a drug for his wife so that she wouldn't die would you send him to jail for stealing? If you would, your a little nuts because if your wife was dieing of cancer and he shouldn't sell the drug to you for a 1,000$ you would break in the store."

Now change all the personal pronouns to the first person. This seems to be what he is actually saying:

"Well if ___ were the judge and ___ got a case of a man stealing a drug for his wife so that she wouldn't die would ___ send him to jail for stealing? If ___ would, ___ am a little nuts because if ___ wife was dieing of cancer and he wouldn't sell the drug to ___ for a 1,000$, ___ would break in the store."

98.

`2/RT`

Stage 2 ROLE TAKING ABILITY: the ability to recognize the ideas or attitudes of another as _____ but not _____.

99.

`2/RT`

If it is now recognized that other people do have ideas (although not being clear as to what they are) it is now possible to have consideration for the MOTIVES behind action. What is the motive for stealing the drug given in #97? _____

_____

---

98. separate
different

---

99. The man stole the drug <u>so his wife wouldn't die.</u> Recall that Stage 1 thinking most often condemns stealing no matter what the reason.

51

100.
2/EX

This _____ view of people as being separate and distinct from oneself sets the stage for a new kind of EXCHANGE between people. Recall that in situations of exchange Stage 1 thinking sees the Powerful person and the one under it who just _____ and doesn't give very much.

101.
2/EX

As Stage 2 - Instrumental thinking develops individuals are viewed as being able to GIVE TO ONE ANOTHER (not just get). It is no longer a lop-sided, one-way EXCHANGE but a _____ - _____ EXCHANGE between people.

| 100. | receives |

102.
2/EX

Since a give and take situation is so new in Stage 2 thinking certain conditions go with any exchange between people.

1) If I give something to you, you must give something to me (either now or later).

2) If I give something to you, you must give something just as big, beautiful, numerous, expensive, etc., etc. as the thing I gave you.

In other words EXCHANGE between people is seen as being   R _____

   F _____.

| 101. | two-way |

103.
2/EX

Such "scale-balancing" is seen in many areas e.g., to commit a crime automatically means a certain punishment; a favour is given if one is expected in return; if you've been wronged you are justified in retaliating the same (or 2 wrongs make a right). This is a very simple _ _ _ _ _ _ _ _ notion.

| 102. | reciprocal fair |

104.
2/EX

But as well the early notion of FAIRNESS results in the notion that all should get the same. This is the beginning of a very important consideration in terms of later thinking about J _ _ _ _ _ _. This is a very simple notion of E _ _ _ _ _ _ _.

| 103. | exchange |

---

105. 2/IR	In Stage 1 Interpersonal Relationships are based on _____ to Authority. The heavy dominance of Authority declines in Stage 2 thinking.	**104.** justice equality
106. 2/IR	The strength, rights, abilities, desires, etc. of <u>each</u> person are becoming recognized in Stage 2 thinking. The person is seen now as much more I _____ of Authority.	**105.** obedience
107. 2/IR	An _____ person, concerned with simple _____ and _____. One more dimension is necessary to get the notion of Stage △2. Interpersonal Relationships – and this is the most basic notion.	**106.** independent
108. 2/IR	<u>Ones own welfare plus the welfare of others (if we care about them)</u> is the most BASIC consideration in any situation. Situations are <u>used</u> for ones own welfare first. From this we take the name of this stage: _____.	**107.** independent exchange, equality

109.
2/IR
	Considering oneself as <u>first</u> in terms of need results in thinking which sees as right
	    ● seeking your own pleasure
	    ● helping others if you get something out of it
	    ● saving your own self in dangerous situations
	    ● having friends and relations in order to get what you need etc.
		108. Instrumentality

110. 2/IR	While Stage △2 development doesn't look very sociable and altruistic it is quite an advancement over the passive, rather powerless yet egocentric perspective of Stage 1. Now the person relates to many more people on a much more equal basis. The world of peers develops at this time	

111. Let us look at some responses to dilemmas and see how stage 2 characteristics are revealed. Indicate in which area(s) each response gives information.

AREAS: SP RT EX IR

a. _____ (Should Joe refuse to give his father the money?)
"Yes, because the father had no right to take away the boy's money he earned himself."

b. _____ (Should Heinz steal the drug?)
"Yes because man whose store he broke into wasn't honest. Well because the guy was cheating."

c. _____ (Should the judge sentence him?)
"No, the judge should understand in the first place that his wife was dying of sickness and the doctor would not make a deal with him, so that is why he is trying to help people."

d. _____ (Why should a promise be kept?)
"Because when you make a promise to somebody you get the other person to believe or make sure that you are going to do it and then you say no and his hopes go down and you might lose him as a friend."

e. _____ (Should the judge send him to jail?)
"I think that he shouldn't go to jail because the judge and the druggist would have done that to save his wife's life (at least I would have).

111.
a. SP, IR. Joe has rights which are not superceded by by father's authority.

b. EX. If someone does wrong to you, do the same in return.

c. RT. Judge should understand what he is saying.

d. IR, EX. Basically people should not be stopped from getting what they want and if you lose what you want you can retaliate against the culprit
e. RT

112.
2/G
Recall what we mean when we speak of GOVERNANCE. Give some examples. _____

_____

_____

_____

112. GOVERNANCE. Whoever is responsible for setting up structure between people. For example a group chooses a leader, a country makes laws, a parent/child relationship.

113.
2/G
In Stage 1 thinking the _____ was quite responsible for a great deal of structure.

In Stage 2 thinking the _____ has little authority now. He is in the same position as anyone else.

114.
2/G

What is left when the authority is diminished and the group identification is not yet made? Any structure or form between people is made on a very _____ basis. Each person is his own authority in some sense.

113. Authority, authority

115.
2/R

However people still do live in a society with rules and laws already made. How are the rules seen at Stage 2?

Rules are viewed as means to an end

- They may be obeyed (even staunchly defended) if that is advantageous.

- They may be disobeyed if <u>that</u> is advantageous.

114. individual

116.
2/R

Think of some Stage 2 reasons which could be given about the stealing rule.

It is wrong to steal because ...

a _____

b _____

It is OK to steal because ...

c _____

d _____

117.
2/S

There is a much greater awareness of SANCTIONS in Stage 2 thinking than in Stage 1 thinking. Recall that in Stage 1 thinking the sanction was simply _____ (defined and administered by the Authority)

116.a. "... who wants to get a bad reputation." (Stealing is not seen as wrong because of peoples rights but because the person speaking has to keep up HIS name.)

b. ."its not fair. You have to work for what you get. Why should I have to work and somebody else take without working?"

c. "... you really need it." (The need is defined by the self here. It could be simply personal pleasure which is called need or life and death matters. The person's personal needs always come first.)

d. "... no one can find out." or "Take what you want if you can get away with it." - self gratification.

118.
2/S

The notion of PUNISHMENT has now deepened in Stage 2 thinking.
Punishment is still quite physical, but the purpose of Punishment is seen as
- preventing repetition of the wrong act again.
- repayment for a wrong act.
- or no purpose at all.

117. punishment

119.
2/S

What is the purpose of punishment in these responses?

a. _____ "Put him in jail because he might do it again if he thought he could get away with it."

b. _____ "Why should the judge give him a sentence, cuz in the first place the druggist should have let him have it."

c. _____ "The druggist should get really mad and demand they throw Heinz in jail for breaking into his store."

120.
2/S

There are also <u>social sanctions</u> which are recognized as operating: One does not want to do anything through which you might loose your friends, or become unpopular or disliked. But remember that this is within the context (which we have discussed already) of

- a very _____ social perspective
- most basic concern for _____ _____
_____

119. a. prevent re-
petition

b. none

c. revenge

121.
2/S

Recall that the _____ of the _____ has diminished by this time. A CONSCIENCE therefore can begin to develop - the self telling the self what is right rather than the Authority telling the person what to do.

120. individualistic
ones own welfare

122. [2/P]	Since the _____ of the _____ is diminished the person now is seen as having <u>absolute rights</u> over himself and his PROPERTY. This is quite an important development.	**121.** authority Authority
123. [2/P]	The way he sees himself as obtaining his property has also changed quite radically. He now sees that PROPERTY is obtained through WORK. ● One has a _____ to _____ ● Which is obtained through _____.	**122.** authority Authority
124. [2/P]	And further it follows from all this that you can do what you want with your own property. (including your <u>life</u>)	**123.** right property work
125. [2/L]	So LIFE is valued according to the needs of the self. (As in all Stage 2 thinking: _____ _____ _____ is first and foremost). If you don't like someone or don't want to, you don't have to save a life.	
126. [2/L]	It is recognized _____ that each person wants to live above all else.	**125.** ones own welfare

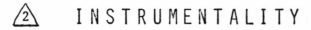

127. Let us look at some responses to dilemma questions which show a Stage 2 orientation. Indicate the area(s) which the response sheds some light on.

| G | R | S | P | L |

Area(s)

a. _____ (Should Joe refuse to give his father the money?)
"Yes because Joe earned it. It is his to have and not his father and he can do whatever he wants to do with it."

b. _____ (Should the judge sentence him?)
"He should let him go free. Because it wasn't really his fault that he had to steal the drug to save his wife's life, it was the druggist's fault."

c. _____ (Should Heinz steal the drug?)
"Yes if he wants to do it.

d. _____ (Should the doctor give her the drug?)
"If the women wants to die, yes, it's her life."

e. _____ (If the husband doesn't love his wife is he obligated to steal the drug for her?)
"If the husband did love his wife he would steal the drugs but if he did not love his wife he might not steal the drugs."

128. Here are some more examples of responses to dilemmas. Indicate the area(s) revealed by the response.

SP   G
RT   R
Ex   S
IR   P
            L

Area(s)

a. _____ (Should Joe refuse to give his father the money?)
"Yes, because Joe earned it, it was his money."

b. _____ (Why shouldn't someone steal from a store?)
"Because it's not their money to have and they could get into serious trouble."

c. _____ (Should the tailor report Valjean to the police?)
"Well you should look at it two different ways. I would have kept it quiet because if you were in that state you would not like to go back to jail."

d. _____ (Should the tailor report Valjean to the police?)
"It would be right to keep it quiet because Heinz shouldn't be in jail for saving a person's life."

e. _____ (Should Joe refuse to give his father the money?)
"Yes because his father wouldn't give him the money for camp so why should Joe give him the money for fishing?"

f. _____ (If the husband does not love the wife very much is he obligated to steal for her?)
"No because if he did not like her very much he would want her to die."

g. _____ (Should Joe refuse to give his father the money?)
"Yes. Because his father told him to save up the money so he (father) should save up the money for his trip."

h. _____ (Should the judge sentence him?)
"Yes because he might do it again if he thought he could get away with it."

i. _____ (Should the judge sentence him?)
"No, he shouldn't let him go free but I would not give him a stiff sentence, I would give him about 6 months in jail and about 2 years probation."

127. a. P Right to own property which you have earned.

b. S Punishment simply doesn't apply here.

c. G He sets his own rules.

d. L Can decide about own life.

e. R Obey or disobey the rule depending on what you want out of the situation.

128.

a.	P	f.	IR
b.	P,R	g.	SP
c.	RT	h.	S
d.	L,R	i.	G
e.	Ex		

129.

- SOCIAL PERSPECTIVE of individual distinct from Authority.

- ROLE-TAKING ABILITY needed to recognize that others have ideas or attitudes of their own but tends to think others ideas are just like his.

- EXCHANGES between people on a fair and reciprocal basis.

- INTERPERSONAL RELATIONSHIPS are based on maintaining ones own welfare first and foremost; hence stage name "Instrumentality".

- GOVERANCE is accomplished through each individual, the Authority has lost much power.

- RULES are viewed as a means to ones end.

- SANCTIONS may be physical punishment, or psychological discomfort, or none at all.

- PROPERTY is obtained through work and everyone has a right to property.

- LIFE is valued highly; each individual decides about his own life.

130. We have talked about the △PRECONVENTIONAL development which occurs in childhood. Do you remember the ages of children during which Preconventional thinking is expected?	

131. Recall the characteristics of the ☐CONVENTIONAL level of moral development.
 	
    a. thinking is done from within a _____
 	
    b. there is formal or informal _____ between people
 	
    c. agreement may be about
    _____, _____, _____, _____
 	
    d. ones SOCIAL PERSPECTIVE is from the point of view of the _____
 	
Keeping these points in mind we will discuss the simplest conventional level - stage 3
 	
       ☐3☐   CONFORMITY.
	130. 10-13

132. In Stage ☐3☐ thinking there is <u>agreement</u> about rules, norms, laws, expectations, etc. Now individuals see the necessity of sharing: SHARED INTERESTS TAKE PRECEDENCE OVER INDIVIDUAL INTERESTS. Is this a very radical change from Stage △2△ Instrumental thinking?
 	
☐3/SP☐
	131. a. system
	     b. agreement
	     c. rules, norms, laws, expect-ations
	     d. group

133. A person now is seen as part of a relationship which includes _____ expectations. Relationships now <u>are defined</u>, come to be through _____, rather than through trying to satisfy ones <u>own</u> need. ☐3/SP☐	132. a very dramatic difference
134. And further, Stage ☐3☐ SOCIAL PERSPECTIVE is a ROLE PERSPECTIVE. What is acceptable is that which any "good" or "average" member of the role class would accept. (not that which a specific individual in a specific situation would accept). ☐3/SP☐	133. shared sharing

135. A shared role perspective may be based on different
3/SP things. For example,

- shared empathy, affection mutuality between people

- shared respect for rules, authority, objective consequences of action for the group.

What is the basis of the perspective in these responses:
shared affection or shared respect for rules and
authority?)

a. (Should the judge sentence him?)
"Well, he should be sent to jail in a way he should
and in a way he shouldn't. He was only trying to
save his wife's life and he should be put into jail
for breaking the law."

b. (Should Heinz steal the drug?)
"Yes. The man was desperate to save his wife and
his love for his wife couldn't be broken." _____

_____

c. (Should the judge sentence him?)
"He should put him in jail for about a year for
stealing. Because it is not very right to steal
and this time he wanted to save his wife but that
is another matter but still he shouldn't have
stolen the drug."_____

---

136. The preceding responses are, of course, all Stage 3
3/SP Conformity responses. Some agree with stealing, some
don't. Underline whether the responses above indicate
stealing or not stealing and the reason for it.

a. steal don't steal _____

b. steal don't steal _____

c. steal don't steal _____

Note that we must always try to determine how the person
is thinking. Action will not tell us that, as we see
here. Stage 3 thinking results in stealing, not
stealing and both at the same time (unresolved).

135. a. both
b. shared affection
c. shared respect
for rules and
authority

137. `3/RT` Stage 2 ROLE TAKING ability did not allow very accurate knowledge of what the other might be thinking. This ability has now developed so that it is possible to put oneself in the other person's shoes and recognize that others have ideas <u>different</u> from ones own.	**136.** a. both. Sees love of wife and importance of keeping law. b. steal. love of wife c. don't steal not <u>right to steal</u>
138. `3/RT` The Stage `3` Social Perspective – a _____ perspective – requires even further development of role taking ability. It requires an understanding of a <u>group's</u> idea of things. Through this ability is developed the idea of "good" "nice" "mean" etc. behavior.	
139. `3/RT` Here are some responses to dilemmas. Underline the parts which especially reflect a picture of things which is produced by the group. a. (Should Heinz steal the drug?) "Yes because she was dying and if he was a druggist he should care about people instead of making money on it." b. (Should the judge sentence him?) "No because he has proven himself a strong and loyal citizen trying to help humanity. This alone is prove (sic) of his good intentions." c. (Should the judge sentence him?) "No because Heinz had proved that he can lead a good life and has changed his ways." d. (Should the tailor report Valjean to the police?) "He would be right to keep it quiet. He did a good deed. He helped the society, he cleared up the problems of medicine."	**138.** ROLE

140. 3/RT What do you think the Stage 3 attitude toward motives would be: understood and accepted as modifying the situation or not accepted?

_____

_____

139. group idea of
   a. he should care about people

   b. strong and loyal citizen trying to help humanity

   c. a good life

   d. a good deed

141. 3/Ex Stage △2 Exchange situations were described as _____- way, _____, _____ transactions.

Stage 3 Exchange situations are seen as a further development of these.

140. definitely understood as part of a situation because the others point of view is more easily understood.

142. 3/Ex Of course a two-way interaction is possible in Stage 3 Conformity thinking. But whose side is taken? How is a conflict decided? One way is in terms of helping the needier.

Notice that helping the needier is not the same as concentrating on fulfilling ones own needs FIRST and foremost.

141. two-way
fair
reciprocated

143. 3/Ex The attitude of "You _____" so often seen in Stage 2 thinking develops into a back and forth interplay of feelings and things WITHIN A RELATIONSHIP. So that exchanges are made between people but not in such a strict, balanced, tit-for-tat way.

144. 3/Ex Some of these responses stem from a Stage △2 notion of EXCHANGE and some from a Stage [3] notion of EXCHANGE: Indicate which attitude is shown:

a. △2 [3] (Why should a promise be kept?)
"Sometimes you really want what someone has promised you. If you keep a promise to someone else they are more likely to keep a promise to you."

b. △2 [3] (Why should a promise be kept?)
"A promise is a sacred agreement between 2 people that represents trust, understanding and loyalty."

c. △2 [3] (Should the judge sentence him?)
"No because what he did was out of kindness and love and not just for the heck of it or to sell it to get the money for himself."

d. △2 [3] (Should Heinz steal the drug?)
"The druggist was not fair to sell the medication 10 times higher so it isn't wrong too much for Heinz to break in but he should repay the druggist a bit."

143. "You scratch my back and I'll scratch yours."

---

145. 3/IR Now read over the preceding examples considering the kind of Interpersonal Relationships they reflect: 135 a.b.c., 139 a.b.c.d., 144 b.c. Write down the new kinds of words which are now being used (and not found in Preconventional thinking): _____

_____

_____

144. a. △2 c. [3]
b. [3] d. △2

---

146. 3/IR These kinds of responses indicate the type of inter-personal relationships which develop from a Stage [3] perspective. Relationships are often based on mutual concern and sympathy. Recall the Stage △2 type of relationship: _____
and observe the change.

145. love, desperate, care, loyal, good, helped, sacred, trust, understanding, kindesss, right

147. **3/IR** Interpersonal Relationships may also develop around shared respect for rules and authority. Note that the new development in Interpersonal Relationships (either around mutual concern or rules) is the aspect of _____.

146. ones own welfare comes first

148. **3/IR** Let us look at Stage 1, 2 and 3 Interpersonal Relationships. These circles represent people; indicate the kind of relationship (and Stage) each represents:

a.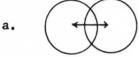

b.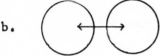

c.

147. sharing

149. **3/IR** An added dimension to the ability to form shared relationships is that of sharing some things with several people at the same time - this is the capacity to relate as a _____ member.

148.
a. mutual sharing Stage 3. Much interaction between people plus their desire result in the building of a relationship.

b. simple exchange, Stage 2. Things are given back and forth but no common ground is held and built upon.

c. one way, Stage 1. The Authority gives or punishes etc. and the other person simply receives.

150. 3/IR	Groups are built from the shared ideas and viewpoints of individuals. After a while <u>a GROUP develops a life of</u> <u>its own not quite equal to the sum of the individuals in it.</u>	**149.** group
151. 3/IR	There is a tendnecy for the GROUP to try to keep itself going. People may voluntarily or through group pressure conform to the group. From this desire to maintain the group (by the individual or the group) we obtain the name of this stage: ☐3 _____.	
152. 3/IR	In this sense we mean CONFORMITY: keeping the GROUP together. Here are some sample responses. Some reflect this GROUP maintaining attitude. Mark these. a. (Should the tailor report Valjean to the police?) "The tailor should report Valjean. It would be wrong to keep it quiet. Every citizen has a duty to the community. If Valjean was wanted by the authorities, the tailor should turn him in." b. (Should the judge have him finish his sentence or let him go free?) "Valjean should be sent back to jail because he broke out." c. (Which would be worse, stealing like Karl or cheating like Bob?) "I think Karl did worse because when you break into a store you can get into trouble. But if you lend it you can pay it back." d. (Should the judge have him finish his sentence or let him go free?) "Finish his sentence because he has to finish the term of the sentence just as everyone else has to."	**151.** ☐3 CONFORMITY
153. 3/G	Any sort of structure between people or GOVERANCE is set on an _____ basis at the PRECONVENTIONAL LEVEL.	**152.** a. a duty to the community d. rules apply equally to all

154.

3/G

We are dealing with a GROUP at Stage ☐3 . This requires something much more in terms of setting up structure. No ONE person is responsible - the group is ultimately where GOVERNANCE arises. Of course one person may have an idea but it may not happen without group acceptance.

153. individual

155.

3/G

Especially early Stage ☐3 thinking sees certain ROLES as being especially responsible for maintaining the structure. Such roles are judge, father, police, etc. How is this a development of Stage △2 thinking about GOVERANCE? _____

_____

_____

156.

3/R

The Stage ☐3 attitude toward RULES is quite different than the Stage △2 attitude toward RULES.

In Stage △2 thinking RULES were seen as a _____ ; they were things <u>outside</u> oneself which were used for oneself.

In Stage ☐3 thinking RULES are <u>believed</u>, <u>taken in</u> as part of the self, <u>incorporated</u>.

156. A structure at Stage 2:

a. was set up between individuals

b. set up individuals as individuals: John's father, Judge Brown, etc.

157. **3/R** Dintinguish between : △2 rules outside oneself used for ones own ends and ☐3 rules which are part of oneself, believed.

a. △2 ☐3 (Should the tailor report Valjean to the police?)
"Yes. Valjean had committed a crime and should take his punishment."

b. △2 ☐3 (Should Valjean steal the drug?)
"No because stealing is bad and you can get into a lot of trouble."

c. △2 ☐3 (Should Valjean steal the drug?)
"I think Heinz should have done it if his wife was dying. Well it was wrong and right because he shouldn't steal but if it meant saving his wife's life it's alright."

d. △2 ☐3 (Why shouldn't someone steal from a store?)
"Because the money or whatever doesn't belong to you and you have no right taking it."

e. △2 ☐3 (Which would be worse, stealing like Karl or cheating like Bob?)
"Stealing like Al because police would be after you and you could be sent to prison."

156. means to an end

158. **3/R** You will notice that Stage 3 thinking (as with Stage 2 thinking) may result in a decision to steal or not to steal. Rules are very important but <u>may be broken for a good reason</u>. Reread the sample responses in this chapter and observe the exceptions to rules which are made.

157. a. ☐3 d. ☐3
b. △2 e. △2
c. ☐3

159. **3/R** Rule keeping takes another very common form at Stage 3. The need in the situation is seen as legitimate, but the rule is stronger. This results in suggestions of alternate behavior:

● borrow the money from a bank

● go to the authorities about it

● get another job and save the money etc.

160.
3/R
In Stage [3] thinking a RULE is <u>a guide to being good</u>. What forms may rules take? _____

_____

161.
3/S
Rules may be enforced through physical punishment. In Stage [3] thinking physical punishment indicates _____ disapproval of an act. Physical punishment may be used to reform and strengthen the desire to be good.

160. laws, expecta-
tions, duty, etc

162.
3/S
We discussed [social] sanctions at Stage /2\ . In Stage [3] thinking <u>disapproval from others</u> is a very strong force in determining what to do. What do you perceive as the difference between the Stage /2\ and Stage [3] kind of social sanction?

161. shared

163.
3/S
The <u>inner knowledge</u> of what is right, acceptable behavior, is growing through interaction with others in the group. So group membership broadens the basis for ones _____.

162. /2\ social sanc-
tion in terms of
not wanting to
lose what you
want (friend,
reputation, etc.

[3] social sanc-
tion in terms of
not wanting to
depart from
acceptable socia
behavior.

164.
3/S
The need for physical or social sanctions depends upon the act and the INTENTIONS beneath the act. Good intentions are given much weight in Stage [3] thinking. Recall the development in _____ ability which allows this attitude.

163. conscience

165.
3/S
Which examples given thus far in this chapter reveal an awareness of intentionality? _____

164. role-taking

---

166. 3/P The concept of ownership of property is developing within the context of the group. A good role-occupant - "good father," "good son," "good doctor" - has certain rights because of his position. For example,

(Should Joe refuse to give his father the money?)
"No. The father has done a lot of things for his son probably and I think he should be able to get something back from him."

165. 135 a.c.
139 b.
144 c.
157 c.

167. 3/P Note that this attitude is not the same as that very reciprocal. "You scratch my back, I'll scratch yours" attitude in Stage 2 thinking. Identify these responses to the question. "Should Joe refuse to give his father the money?" as /2\ or [3].

a. /2\ [3] "I think Joe should give his father the money because more than likely something else special will come along later on and his father will likely treat him in thanks for helping him out."

b. /2\ [3] "No because he is his father and should be able to ask favours from you."

c. /2\ [3] "Yes, because if I was Joe I would do the same thing. Because I made the money ... he (father) has his own."

d. /2\ [3] "The father should have more brains than that. The concern for the child should be first. The fishing could be done later."

168. 3/P At this stage a violation of property rights disrupts good relationships between people. This is an important development from the Stage 2 attitude about loosing property:

167. a. /2\   c. /2\
b. [3]   d. [3]

169. 3/L Good relationships between people also have a great impact on how life is valued. In Stage [3] thinking if you care about someone, their life is more valuable and worth saving.

168. a personal disappointment, a loss to the self (relationships are not involved)

170. **3/L** Stemming from the _____ PERSPECTIVE of the group, we see the attitude that people should care for others and their lives. This is "good" and "human" behavior.

---

171. **3/L** People should care and have more feeling for life than for material things. How would you answer the question "Should Heinz steal the drug?" using this attitude?

_____

_____

170. role

---

172. Here are some more sample responses to dilemmas.

1) Judge whether the response contains enough information from which to determine the stage.

2) Indicate the Stage 3 responses and note why you think they reflect Stage 3 thinking

3) Note the areas about which you get clues from the response.

a. (Should Heinz steal the drug?)
"It was wrong to steal the drug ecause he was breaking the law and could go to jail and then he wouldn't be helping his wife."

STAGE _____ AREAS _____

WHY _____

b. (Should the judge sentence him or let him go free?)
"If Heinz was reported, the judge should consider his case and see the contributions he is making to the community. Perhaps he could fine Heinz for having broken the law by escaping from prison."

STAGE _____ AREAS _____

WHY _____

_____

c. (Which would be worse, stealing like Karl or cheating like Bob?)
"I would feel worse cheating like Bob because it would bother my conscience and I would always feel obligated to do for others."

STAGE _____ AREAS _____

WHY _____

_____

171. "Yes. The life of his wife was at stake. Her life is more important than the druggists' property rights."

172. a. STAGE: 3   AREAS: SP, RT, R,S

   WHY: His most important concern is being there
        to help his wife (RT, a good husband). In
        terms of breaking the law and going to jail
        we can't really tell if he is part of the law
        or if he is subject to it in a preconventional
        way. (R,S)

   b. STAGE: 3   AREAS: RT, SP, S

   WHY: Judge can take Heinz's point of view (RT)
        One should contribute to the community (SP)
        Keep law with a fine (S)

   c. STAGE   3   AREAS: IR, S,

   WHY: Recognizes certain good behavior between
        people (IR)
        Conscience developing (S)

   d. STAGE   3   AREAS: IR

   WHY: Bonds are important between people.

   e. STAGE   3   AREAS: SP,   R

   WHY: Following rules and role expectations (SP, R)

   f. STAGE   3   AREAS: L

   WHY: Life is important and people help each other
        in it (L)

   g. STAGE   3   AREAS: RT,

   WHY: Heinz had good intentions.

   h. STAGE   3   AREAS: R,IR

   WHY: Usual conflict between following the law and
        affection for wife (R, IR)

172. d. (Why should a promise be kept?)
"A promise should be kept because you gave your word
of honour to give a promise to anybody."

STAGE _____ AREAS _____

WHY _____

_____

e. (If the husband doesn't love his wife is he
obligated to steal the drug for her?)
"Yes. When you get married it says you must love
and care for them. What else could he do?"

STAGE _____ AREAS _____

WHY _____

_____

f. (If the husband does not love his wife is he
obligated ...?)
"Yes, every human being deserves to live and it is
up to others to let each other live."

STAGE _____ AREAS _____

WHY _____

_____

g. (Should the tailor report Valjean to the police?)
"It would be right for the tailor to keep quite as
Valjean had not committed his crime in evil, but to
help his wife and he has proved it by building the
hospital for cancer research."

STAGE _____ AREAS _____

WHY _____

_____

h. (Should Heinz steal the drug?)
"When a person is desperate like that he would do
that. I can think of another way to go about it and
that's by going to the law or trying harder to
bargain with the druggist."

STAGE _____ AREAS _____

WHY _____

_____

173.

- SOCIAL PERSPECTIVE is a "role perspective", of <u>shared</u> empathy or respect for rules.

- ROLE-TAKING ABILITY allows putting oneself in others shoes and understanding of group ideas.

- EXCHANGE takes place within the context of relationships; a give and take exchange occurs.

- INTERPERSONAL RELATIONSHIPS are more important; group memberships is held and results in some pressure to maintain the group and hence Stage 3 thinking is named CONFORMITY.

- GOVERANCE (structure) stems from the group (roles, etc.)

- RULES are shared guides for being good which can be broken for a good reason.

- SANCTIONS represent shared disapproval of an act; physical and social sanctions are used.

- PROPERTY rights are understood in light of good role occupants, e.g., good father, good doctor.

- LIFE is more valuable than property; people should care for others and their life.

174.
4/SP Recall that the Stage 3 SOCIAL PERSPECTIVE was described as a _____ perspective, based on _____ empathy or respect for rules. Development may take place from this perspective to the Stage 4 perspective of SOCIAL SYSTEMS.

174. role, shared.

175.
4/SP The Stage 4 social perspective is still based on shared empathy and/or respect. The difference is in the <u>size of the context</u>:

    Stage 3 : group context

    Stage 4 : society context (all groups considered <u>together</u>)

176.
4/SP All these groups and people <u>together</u> hold some things in common: there is agreement (we are talking about the _____ level) about certain rules and roles. From this agreement we can talk about the <u>average member</u> of society.

176.   CONVENTIONAL

177.
4/SP This agreement of so many people results in the formation of society with some <u>order</u>; hence we obtain the name of this stage:

    Stage ☐ : _____

177. Stage 4 : Social Systems.

178.
4/RT We are now talking about a SYSTEM orientation – a much broader orientation than simply an interpersonal one. A corresponding development in ROLE-TAKING ABILITY is necessary in order to be able to take this perspective.

179.
4/RT In Stage 4 thinking it is necessary to be able to take the point of view of a generalized member of society. Which one of these examples shows this ability?

(Why shouldn't someone steal from a store anyhow?)
a. "It is wrong to steal no matter how you go about doing it. A store is run by people and they live by the money they receive as a salary. Stealing from a store might affect these people."

b. "Because a store is someone's livelihood. And if everyone stole from stores the system couldn't operate for others (the majority)."

c. "You are taking from someone something which does not belong to you."

78

180.
4/RT

Role taking ability at Stage 4 allows for quite a variety of points of view:

- any member of society;

- member of a particular role class in society;

- the individual.

In the dilemmas, the role of the <u>judge</u> is quite definite at this time. Which perspective would you expect a judge must hold?

179a. does not generalize beyond the specific situation of stealing.

c. does not consider what effect this has on the whole, this is just a statement of the rule.

b. considers the more abstract, general case

181.
4/Ex

The EXCHANGE which happens between people is seen within the context of the SYSTEM. So that if John steals from Bob,

- at Stages 1, 2 & 3 it <u>stays</u> between John and Bob for the most part;

- at Stage 4 John must account for his behavior to society, the law, the system.

180. that of society.

182.
4/Ex

So we find in Stage 4 thinking the notion of a "debt to society." Note that this is similar but not the same as the strict exchange of Stage 2. Distinguish between Stage 2 and 4 thinking in these examples:

(Should the tailor report Valjean?)

a. △2 □4 "Yes, he should. It would be wrong to allow an escaped criminal live a life without first repaying to society what is owed. In this system there are rules to follow and these rules apply to everyone."

b. △2 □4 "It would be right now to report him because he broke out of prison and is on the loose."

183.
4/Ex

The notion of JUSTICE in situations of exchange is becoming important.

- At Stage 2 <u>individuals</u> should treat each other _____.

- At Stage 4 the <u>system</u> should treat individuals _____ (a full consideration of the situation).

182a. 4 one is accountable to society.

b. 2 if one breaks out of prison one should be reported.

184.
4/Ex
Justice is the most important consideration in situations where exchange occurs. Considerations of justice are set out by the people in the system and apply to the people in the system. What do these responses say about justice? Which example shows the weakest understanding of justice?

a. (Should the judge sentence him?)
"I think the judge should punish Heinz because everyone steals for a reason, unless it's an illness. Whether you steal for food, or for a life it is still a crime. And as bad as it may seem, if you let one person off, then you have to let everyone off."

JUSTICE: _____

_____

b. (Should Heinz steal the drug?)
"Heinz should not have done that. It was morally wrong to steal anything from anyone. Although I may tend to feel pity for him and his wife, there is a code by which we are all set to live and there cannot be exceptions if we wish to maintain a just society. He should have appealed to someone for the money."

JUSTICE: _____

_____

Most understanding: _____ ; Weak understanding: _____ .

185.
4/IR
Exchange is viewed as taking place within the context of a _____ - the individual in relation to society. Interpersonal relationships also take place within this context. This is a further development of the Stage 3 context of the _____.

186.
4/IR
There is now not only concern for individuals who are known personally, but also concern for the society as a whole. People are seen within a relationship to society.

---

183. fairly
justly

184a. Justice is applying the law equally to all.

b. Justice involves maintaining the code.

The lower Stage 4 response is a.

185. social system;
group.

187.
4/IR
The Stage 3 qualities of mutual concern and sympathy for the other guy deepen into Stage 4 qualities of honesty, integrity and consistency which are frequently discussed in terms of character development. Here are some examples: (distinguish Stage 3 from Stage 4 responses)

(Why should a promise be kept?)

a. 3 4 "It should be kept so that a person can form a good opinion and have faith in the person who keeps it. If you keep a promise it raises your self-worth."

b. 3 4 "I think a promise is one of the most sacred agreements between two people that represents loyalty, trust, understanding and a feeling of intimacy."

c. 3 4 "It teaches honesty, trust, respect and responsibility to the one who makes the promise.

d. 3 4 "A promise should be kept because it is something between two different people or a group of people and it is a way of trusting or learning to trust a person."

188.
4/IR
Notice that responses 187b. and c. both mention TRUST. Stage 3 trust is very much a matter between two people, it is quite personal. The Stage 4 notion of TRUST is held within the context of _____ _____. Society is not possible without trust:

"A promise should be kept because you have committed yourself to another person. The person is leaning on you and expecting you to come through. If promises were not kept there would be no trust in other human beings and no code to live by."

187a. 4 raised self-worth is a result of promise keeping.

b. 3 "sacred agreement" etc. looks higher than it is. The action here is still only between two people.

c. 4 promise keeping can be used as character development.

d. 3 development of trust among people, but not yet within context of society.

189.
4/IR

Interpersonal Relationships in Stage 4 thinking also include the rights and responsibilities given to individuals by society. Conflict is not just between two people; society has something to say about matters. E.g.

(Should Joe refuse to give his father the money?)

"Yes. His father should go to the bank for a loan. He should not take money from a minor."

How is this a development of the Stage 3 attitude?

_____

_____

_____

---

188. social system.

190.
4/IR

Implicit in our discussion of Stage 4 Interpersonal Relationships is an underlying force to <u>maintain</u> the social system (just as Stage 3 thinking strove to maintain the _____).

---

189. Stage 3 attitude was based on decent and good behavior between people, more or less informally agreed upon by people. Stage 4 attitude is based on a firmer and more formal definition of acceptable behavior and corresponding benefits.

191.
4/G
"The Social System" - <u>who is responsible</u> for the order of society? What do these Stage 4 responses indicate?

a. (Should the tailor report Valjean to the police?)
"Yes. The tailor would be making a decision for the whole public and I don't think he is qualified to do this. He should report it to the police and let them make the decision."

b. (Should the judge have him finish his sentence?)
"No because Heinz has showed himself to fit into society very well. Jail should be a correction not a punishment. Nobody can say what's right or wrong, but society can say what is antisocial behavior, so prison can't be a punishment but must be a place where they reform the person back to society's mold and Heinz already fitted fine."

c. (Should the judge sentence him?)
"I think that it is time to honestly bring the entire story into public and have a law passed to limit the price, then have Heinz pay for the drug and any damages and be set free, but with a suspended sentence because of circumstances."

ORDER OF SOCIETY SET UP BY:_____

_____

190. group.

192.
4/G
Note in the above examples how much the individual feels part of the "public" or "society" - whether he feels able to be part of the process of shaping society or not. Rank the above responses on this continuum:

Subject to
results of ————————————— shaping
process   process

In general Stage 4 thinking should develop toward a full-fledged membership of society which is part of the process which shapes society.

191a. whole public/
     police

   b. society

   c. public

193.
4/G
There are people specifically charged with the responsibility of keeping the order, maintaining the law. Judges are seen to fulfill this function.

192. a. b. c.

194.
4/R
Rules (considered broadley) are the vehicle through which order is set out. The purpose of rules in Stage 4 thinking is to protect society as a cooperative scheme. Rules are produced out of the general will.

195.
4/R
Different kinds of rules may be recognized: legal - religious - moral. As long as the orientation is to the rule, code, agreement, etc., as long as we are WITHIN A CONVENTIONAL SYSTEM we are still within Stage 4 thinking (don't be fooled by talk of "moral law").

Note the kind of rule to which these responses attend:

a._____ (Why shouldn't some steal from a store anyhow?)
"A society must function within acceptable rules. Stealing does not provide for a good society. It produces stress in the form of loss for someone, anger, revenge, punishment and mistrust of fellow man."

b._____ (Should Heinz steal the drug?)
"Yes. There exists in society two types of laws. There is legal laws, concerned and administered by agents in society. There also exists in society moral laws which override any legal law. Moral laws would require that each individual in society has the right to rebel against society if by so doing it will save his own life or the life of others. Heinz was only exercising the moral unwritten laws of society."

c._____ (Should the tailor report Valjean?)
"By law the tailor should report Heinz to the police. I feel that it would be morally wrong but it would be right according to law."

196.
4/R
We see some kind of hierarchy in these kinds of laws. _____ law seems to override _____ law. Reference to religious law is not a very common response.

195a. legal
b. legal & mor
c. legal & mor

197.
4/R
This hiearchy explains in some sense how it is possible to make exceptions to rules (that is you are following a rule which overrides a lesser rule, e.g. in moral over legal rules). An earlier, more simple perception of the nature and scope of rules does NOT allow for exceptions to rules out of fear that the social system would break down. Note that there is rather a wide range of reactions in Stage 4 thinking.

198. Note whether exceptions are allowed or not. Determine
4/R   whether the response reflects an earlier or a later
      Stage 4 orientation:

      Exception to Rule: YES/NO
      Place in Stage: Early/Late

    Y/N E/L

a. ___ ___ (Should the judge sentence Heinz?)
           "The law is the law. It may not be perfect
           but it is what we have to live by until it
           changes; we must try and uphold the law.
           When we break the law we should be prepared
           to be punished if we are caught regardless
           of motives."

b. ___ ___ (Should Heinz steal the drug?)
           "Yes. There must be exceptions to every law.
           Heinz was acting on behalf of a life so he
           was justified."

c. ___ ___ (Should the judge sentence him?)
           "The judge should send Heinz to jail for
           stealing because he has a duty to defend
           people's right to hold property under normal
           circumstances, and this cannot be done if
           exceptions are continually being made."

d. ___ ___ (Should the judge sentence him?)
           "No, the judge should not send Heinz to jail
           for stealing. In society men committing
           crimes in self-defense are not punished. Did
           not Heinz steal so that the life of his wife
           may be saved? Heinz was in fact acting in a
           form of defense, if not exactly self-defense."

---

199. We said that at Stage 3 rules were enforced primarily
4/S   through group _____. At Stage 4 this pressure
      may be either _____ formalized and/or _____ internalized.

198a. N, E.

  b. Y, ?.

  c. N, L.

  d. Y, L.

200. 4/S The group, i.e. society, may agree to certain (formal) physical punishment for the purpose of maintaining social order. How is this different from the Stage 3 concept of punishment? _____

_____

_____.

199. disapproval.

---

201. 4/S The rules of society may be internalized so as to form a <u>conscience</u>. Right and wrong become judged by the conscience. Moral character and integrity are developed with the help of the conscience. This is a kind of sanction, i.e., a force which influences thought and action.

200. Stage 3 punishment indicates shared disapproval of an act.

Stage 4 punishment says this also but in addition includes a direction to keep the social order intact.

---

202. 4/S Let us see how sanctions are talked about. What sanctions are operating in these examples: (a) legal punishment or (b) conscience.

a._____ (Should Heinz steal the drug?)
"No, it was neither wrong nor right, it was against the law. I believe that in following his conscience Heinz was right but in breaking the law Heinz was wrong, meaning that something is lacking in the system of law."

b._____ (Should the tailor report Heinz to the police?)
"Yes. I believe Heinz broke the law and should be punished accordingly. It would be wrong to keep it quiet because we are obliged to society to keep criminals off the streets, if they have been designated as criminals."

c._____ (Should Heinz steal the drug?)
"No. I think conscienciously he thought it was right. He did everything in his power to save his wife and failed. He now had to resort to theft to save the woman he loved. I feel he was right due to the druggist's ignorance."

203.
4/P

Looking at the Stage 4 notion of Property rights we see it is regarded as very basic to the continuance of the _____ _____. This is an expansion of the Stage 3 notion that property is a matter between _____.

202a. legal and con-
science sanctions
are in conflict.

b. legal sanctions.

c. conscience allows
him to steal.

204.
4/P

Property is not only a right earned through _____, but now becomes a social responsibility which affects the lives of many people.

202. social system.
individuals.

205.
4/P

Let us see the development from Stage 3 to Stage 4 thinking about Property. Determine whether the following responses are Stage 3 or Stage 4:

a. ☐3 ☐4 (Should Heinz steal the drug?)
"One of the rules of society is that you respect other people's property. Without a respect for and observance of such rules society would soon become a nightmare where no one would be safe."

b. ☐3 ☐4 (Why shouldn't someone steal from a store?)
"They shouldn't steal from a store because the people who own the store have to make a living too."

c. ☐3 ☐4 (Should Joe refuse to give his father the money?)

"Yes, because the father had no right to take away the boy's money he earned himself."

d. ☐3 ☐4 (Should the judge sentence him?)
"He should send him to jail for stealing because theft is not morally acceptable, although sometimes necessary. Sometimes self-sacrifices must be made that others may benefit."

204. work

206.
4/L

The idea of property and property rights is strongly associated with maintenance of the social system. Here are some Stage 4 responses. What attitude toward LIFE do they reveal?

a. (Should Heinz steal the drug?)
"If there was a chance, as there was in this case, the man is right in breaking in to get the drug for his wife. Should he not have he would have been as unjust as the druggist for in a way what the druggist was doing is passing judgement on what is more, i.e. life or material wealth and this is immoral in our society."

b. (Should Heinz steal the drug?)
"I have definite moral values. Yes, Heinz should have stolen the drug. I would have done the same myself. In my view it was not only right to steal the drug but necessary and the only humane action possible. Why? Because human life is of a value beyond man's conceivability."

c. (If Heinz does not love his wife is he obligated to steal the drug for her?)
"Yes, he is still her husband and responsible for the life and livelihood of his spouse."

205a. [4]
  b. [3]
  c. [3]
  d. [4]

207.
4/L

So life has the highest value and must be preserved. It is seen as having value,

- because God created it

- because life is basic to society

- because life is a basic right.

How does this show a further development of the Stage 3 attitude? _____

_____

_____

206a. life is valued more than property by society.

  b. life has greatest value.

  c. life must be saved no matter what personal feelings or relationships hold.

208.   Below are some responses to dilemmas. Which stage
        thinking does each represent:

        △1   △2   3   or   4 ?

a.____ (Should the tailor report Valjean to the police?)
        "Yes, he should because he cared for his town and what
        kind of people roamed around in it."

b.____ (Should Joe refuse to give his father the money?)
        "Joe should not refuse giving his father the money. We
        look at what our parents have done for us from the day
        we are born till time we get married and sometimes past
        that, they always are doing things for us. So when we
        can pay them back we should be willing to do so."

c.____ (Should the judge have him finish his sentence or let
        him go free?)
        "Well, he probably set him free because he was stealing
        because his wife was going to die. He wouldn't put him
        in prison because he was trying to do his best to save
        his wife by stealing from the drug store."

d.____ (Should Heinz steal the drug?)
        "There is not enough information here to make a
        decision. Was the drug proven, tested and government
        certified? Did that drug have to be? Is the druggist
        in any legal hassle if the drug is bad? It seems to be
        a simple case of the druggist ripping off Heinz or is
        it? Heinz was desperate, his wife was dying. He was
        probably right to do this and the consequences of his
        act are probably not as great as the possible benefits
        if the drug is successful. Any gambler would take
        this chance."

e.____ (Should the tailor report Valjean to the police?)
        "No, he shouldn't. He should keep it quiet because
        Valj.is in business and is not making any trouble."

f.____ (Should Heinz steal the drug?)
        "No, it was not the correct reaction. I believe that
        other outlets should have been investigated and that
        regardless of the outcome of that search the immoral
        act of theft should not have been used. I believe
        strongly that religion and moral standards are a very
        personal thing and that those standards should not
        change with variations in environmental factors. In
        this case the only justification given for his immoral
        act was his perception of immoral conduct on the part
        of the druggist."

207. Stage 3 value
      of life is often
      dependent on person-
      al relationships.
      One "should" care
      for life; the value
      of life is not as
      much a basic tenet
      for Stage 3 as
      for Stage 4 .

208. (cont'd)

g. _____ (Should Joe refuse to give his father the money?)
"Joe should refuse to give his father the money
because it was saved for a specific goal and if he
starts to disregard his goals at such an early age he
may end up doing some kind of work which has no meaning
to him for the rest of his life and receive no
satisfaction from it."

h. _____ (Should Heinz steal the drug?)
"Well, it's not right to steal. If you did steal a
policeman would get after him and lock him up."

208a. 3
   b. 3
   c. 3
   d. 4
   e. ⟨2⟩
   f. 4
   g. 4
   h. ⟨1⟩

209.

- SOCIAL PERSPECTIVE is taken from within a <u>social system</u> with agreed upon rules and roles.

- ROLE-TAKING ABILITY develops so that perspective of any member of society, a member of a role class or an individual can be taken.

- EXCHANGE takes place between the individual and the system (as well as on an interpersonal basis).

- INTERPERSONAL RELATIONSHIPS occur within a societal context so that rights and responsibilities are recognized: development of honesty, integrity and commitment between people.

- GOVERNANCE (structure) is produced by society/public.

- RULES are made to protect society as a cooperative scheme.

- SANCTIONS may be legal punishment or one's own conscience.

- PROPERTY rights must be upheld in order to maintain the social system.

- LIFE has the highest value because God created it, it is basic to society or it is a basic right.

210. The transition out of ☐CONVENTIONAL thinking into
4-5/T ◯POSTCONVENTIONAL thinking may reveal itself in (at
least) two attitudes:

a. A gradually expanding view of laws and society
    into an understanding of more basic principles.

b. A rejection of conventional moral reasoning without
    a direction into more basic principles. More like
    negative Stage 4 thinking than actual postconven-
    tional thinking.

211. What sort of transition do these responses reflect?
4-5/T a. (Should Heinz steal the drug?)
    "Due to personal bias I feel negatively toward any
    capitalist. I would support Heinz in taking the
    drug."

b. (Should the tailor report Valjean to the police?)
    "A citizen's duty is to help secure and promote the
    good order and well being of society. The law is
    only a means to that end and the citizen should help
    enforce the law only insofar as it serves as a means
    to that end. Reporting Valj. is no longer necessary
    to promote that end."

c. (Should Heinz steal the drug?)
    "There's a million ways to look at it. Heinz had a
    moral decision to make. Was it worse to steal or
    let his wife die? In my mind I can either condemn
    him or condone him. In this case I think it was fine.
    But possibly the druggist was working on a capitalist
    morality of supply and demand."*

212. The type of more difficult transition can be recognized
4-5/T from an attitude which views morality as RELATIVE - not
relative as we saw in Stage 2 thinking, but relative
in a much more abstract sense.

△2 "You scratch my back and I'll scratch
    yours."

☐4-◯5 "Do your own thing (because there is no
    way of determining what is right)."

211a. difficult and
       negative

b. smoother

c. more difficult

---

*Kohlberg, L. & Gilligan, C. "The Adolescent as Philosopher: The Discovery
of the Self in a Postconventional World," Deadalus, 100, 4, Fall 1971,
pp. 1051-1086.

213.
5/SP

Let us step (whether easily or with great difficulty) into POSTCONVENTIONAL thinking. If this development does occur, it begins to be significant during the middle twenties. Take a moment now to review at which ages various stage thinkings are strongest (cf. No. 50):

Stage (1) _____

Stage (2) _____

Stage [3] _____

Stage [4] _____

Stage (5) _____

214.
5/SP

So young adults may develop a much broader PERSPECTIVE - a perspective which is prior to society; this is no longer a group perspective as found in conventional thinking but an _____ perspective.

213. (1) 10-11 years
(2) 10-13 years
[3] 11-25 years
[4] 15-25 years
(5) 21-25+ years

215.
5/SP

So we have seen that development begins with an individual perspective:

Stage (1) _____social perspective

Stage (2) _____social perspective

develops into a group perspective:

Stage [3] _____social perspective

Stage [4] _____social perspective

and develops further into an individual perspective:

Stage (5) _____social perspective.

214. individual

216.
5/SP

What is the difference between the individual perspectives of the (△) PRECONVENTIONAL and the (◯) POST-CONVENTIONAL levels?

_____

_____

_____

215. (1) egocentric
(2) concrete individual
[3] role, shared
[4] social system
(5) prior to society

217. | 5/SP | This rational, moral point of view is <u>before</u>, <u>prior to</u>, society's point of view – this is the development from the social system perspective of Stage 4. Can you tell which of the following responses show a Stage 5 social perspective?

(Should the tailor report Valjean to the police?)

a._____ "It would be right to keep it quiet, Valjean was unfairly treated in the first place. Valjean was doing excellent good work now, helping others obviously. Men must be dedicated to other men, not   to the system of government or law they have created."

b._____ "If the tailor does not know the circumstances which led to Valjean's arrest he would be right in reporting him. Valjean is a thief according to society's standards. If the tailor knew why Valjean stole the drug then he should not report him. Also, Valjean, as a businessman is a good man, he harms no one, therefore he should not be reported to the authorities.

c._____ "The tailor should not report Valjean as he was the subject of unfair justice. The tailor would be in the right because he wouldn't be letting 'the establishment stop him from caring about his fellow man.'"

d._____ "From my philosophy on life he should not report Valjean. Valjean has done more good to the community than most individuals and is working to better the people more so than himself."

e._____ "No, the tailor should not report Valjean. Each human being has a right to judge another in some cases. In this case it is questionable whether or not the law would be just so the best solution would be for the tailor to be silent."

216. △ a <u>concrete</u> individual.

○ any rational individual (a more abstract concept)

218. | 5/RT | Role-taking ability has expanded to allow a person to take the rational or moral point of view as well as society's point of view and the individual's immediate point of view.

217a. ⑤   d. |3|

b. |4| e. ⑤

c. ⑤

219. | **5/RT** In the responses above (No. 217) which point of view is taken: rational/moral, society or individual (immediate)?

a. _____ c. _____

b. _____ d. _____

e. _____

---

220. | **5/Ex** A rational/moral point of view on how EXCHANGE ought to happen between people sees exchange as happening:

- between individuals
- within a system
- all subject to more BASIC PRINCIPLES

219a. rational/moral

b. society

c. rational/moral

d. individual, group (though group standards)

e. rational/moral

---

221. | **5/Ex** Recall that the Stage 4 notion of exchange was between the individual and the _____, which was the ultimate reference. Now, in POSTCONVENTIONAL thought the ultimate reference is no longer the _____ but more basic principles.

---

222. | **5/Ex** Within CONVENTIONAL thinking there is no application to persons outside the social order. POSTCONVENTIONAL thought expands on the basis of _____ so that the RIGHTS OF <u>ALL</u> INDIVIDUALS are considered.

221. system
     system

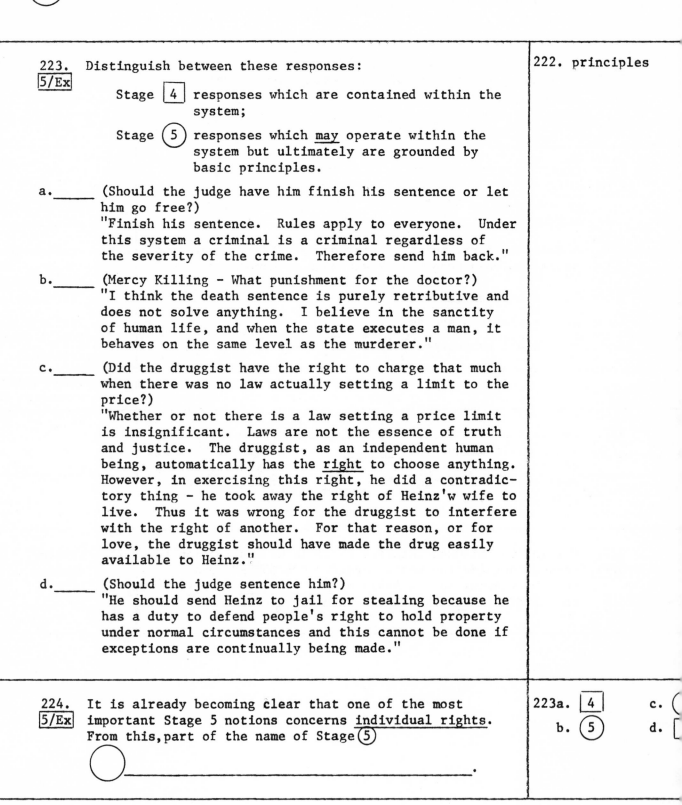

223. Distinguish between these responses:
5/Ex

Stage [4] responses which are contained within the system;

Stage (5) responses which <u>may</u> operate within the system but ultimately are grounded by basic principles.

a._____ (Should the judge have him finish his sentence or let him go free?)
"Finish his sentence. Rules apply to everyone. Under this system a criminal is a criminal regardless of the severity of the crime. Therefore send him back."

b._____ (Mercy Killing - What punishment for the doctor?)
"I think the death sentence is purely retributive and does not solve anything. I believe in the sanctity of human life, and when the state executes a man, it behaves on the same level as the murderer."

c._____ (Did the druggist have the right to charge that much when there was no law actually setting a limit to the price?)
"Whether or not there is a law setting a price limit is insignificant. Laws are not the essence of truth and justice. The druggist, as an independent human being, automatically has the <u>right</u> to choose anything. However, in exercising this right, he did a contradictory thing - he took away the right of Heinz'w wife to live. Thus it was wrong for the druggist to interfere with the right of another. For that reason, or for love, the druggist should have made the drug easily available to Heinz."

d._____ (Should the judge sentence him?)
"He should send Heinz to jail for stealing because he has a duty to defend people's right to hold property under normal circumstances and this cannot be done if exceptions are continually being made."

222. principles

223a. [4]   c. (
b. (5)   d. [

224. It is already becoming clear that one of the most
5/Ex important Stage 5 notions concerns <u>individual rights</u>.
From this, part of the name of Stage (5)

( )_____.

225. 5/IR	An orientation to individual rights sets the context within which Interpersonal Relationships are seen to occur. The context is that of ALL HUMAN BEINGS – (whether within the social system or not).	224. (5) SOCIAL CONTRACT /INDIVIDUAL RIGHTS
226. 5/IR	There is, as well, a view of people as being <u>free</u> and <u>equal individuals</u>. Se we see that the Stage 5 orientation to Interpersonal Relationships is both an orientation to the _____ <u>and</u> to the whole.	
227. 5/IR	At Stage 4 trust was seen as _____ _____. Now we are saying that this notion has deepened so that <u>all human relationships</u> must be based on trust.	226. individual
228. 5/IR	In addition that which we owe to one another – duties and responsibilities – are no longer given to us by the _____ _____. Duties and responsibilities are personal moral choices.	227. necessary for society to exist.

229.
5/IR
Here are some sample responses which show this kind of orientation to Interpersonal Relationships. Do you see the change in orientation from the Stage 4 perspective?

a. (Why should a promise be kept?)
"A promise should be kept since a promise indicates a moral responsibility toward another human being. It is a spiritual bond which is part of a relationship, if the bond is broken then part of that communication is gone or destroyed."

b. (Should Joe refuse to give his father the money?)
"A person has certain inalienable rights which have more importance than even obedience to parents. A good son does not give in even to his father when he thinks his father is wrong."

c. (If the husband doesn't love his wife, is he obliged to steal the drug for her?)
"The idea that just because he is her husband he should save her is wrong. Being someone's husband is not a moral obligation, at least it shouldn't be. On the highest level of life, we are not sons, daughters, mothers, fathers and husbands and wives - we are all brothers - fellow human beings."

d. (If the husband doesn't love his wife is he obligated to steal the drug for her?)
"In a civilization as advanced as ours it should be the duty of everyone, whether they are married or not, to see to it that any person's needs are filled, if it is possible for them to do it."

e. (Why should a promise be kept?)
"Because it involves the feelings and susceptibility of another person. It involves the occurence of the denial of trust and without trust a relationship is not comfortable - it becomes rather a nightmare where two isolated individuals depend on each other for reasons other than a warm mutual growing bond."

f. (Why should a promise be kept?)
"Under true friendship what is spoken between friends should not be spread around. Also if the society is built on truth and honesty and not material gains then this would not be a question to worry about."

228. social system.

230.
5/G
From the Stage 5 examples we have cited so far can you tell (a) who is responsible for setting up structures between people (governance)? and (b) on what basis is this set up?

a. _____

b. _____

231.
5/G
It must be clear by now that such an individual basis is a very different story from the △PRECONVENTIONAL individual basis. An "individual" orientation toward governance at the ◯POSTCONVENTIONAL level reflects the _____, not the _____ individual.

230a. individuals

b. principles.

232.
5/G
What do the Stage 5 responses say about the degree of participation possible in one's own governance?

_____

_____

231. abstract
concrete

233.
5/G
The judge, our guardian, is now seen as responsible not only for _____ (as in Stage 4), but also for ensuring as best he can the rights of ALL individuals.

232. 223c., for example, says INDEPENDENT HUMAN BEINGS HAVE THE RIGHT TO CHOOSE and that says it.

234.
5/R
Rules (law) are seen as a mechanism to <u>preserve individual rights</u>—should a conflict occur between the property rights of one group (or individual) and another rules(law) can be applied to settle the dispute. What is the function of law in Stage 4 thought?

_____

_____

233. society

235.
5/R
There is also quite a change from Stage 4 thinking in how rules(law) are produced.

Stage ☐4☐ rules are produced out of _____

_____ .

Stage ◯5◯ rules are produced on the basis of principles such as liberty, justice and equality.

234. Law serves to keep <u>society</u> functioning as a cooperative scheme. The individual is part of society.

---

236. 5/R	There <u>is</u> agreement between people in Stage 5 thinking as in Stage 4 thinking. However, this is a more <u>fundamental</u> agreement than in Stage 4 thinking. Rational PROCEDURES which all men <u>can</u> agree on are chosen. These procedures make it possible to generate the rules needed to preserve individual rights.	**235.** out of the general will, group agreement, etc.
237. 5/R	This kind of prior agreement is not the same as a democratic vote. It is called a _____ _____ and hence we state the stage name fully: ⑤ _____ / _____	
238. 5/R	This SOCIAL CONTRACT is the basis of the socio-moral order. This social contract is more like a <u>procedure</u> than a <u>content</u> (as Stage 4 thinking sees it).	**237.** social contract social contract/ individual rights
239. 5/R	Exceptions to rules can be made to preserve human welfare and rights. An individual may choose <u>not</u> to follow a rule but must take responsibility for this as a personal choice for which he may have to answer to the law.	

240.
5/R
Here are some Social System and Social Contract/Individual Rights responses. Identify which are Stage 4 and which are Stage 5:

a. _____ (Should the judge sentence him?)
"According to the law, Heinz should go to jail. Morally, Heinz knew he was doing wrong and he made the choice - the judge is there (I gather) to uphold the law and order. Yes, the judge should send him to jail."

b. _____ (Should the judge have him finish his sentence or let him go free?)
"Heinz should not be sent to jail because he was fighting an injustice. He was trying to save a life. He had tried all the other means. When it comes to a question of a life or money there is only one choice to be made."

c. _____ (Should the judge sentence him?)
"The judge has no power over the actions of Heinz, therefore he cannot impose punishments. However, if a judgment is to be made, Heinz should not be sent to jail anyway, for his cause was justified. Thus his actions were natural and right. Why should he be punished?"

d. _____ (Should Heinz steal the drug?)
"No, Heinz should not have done it. It was wrong because not only was Heinz breaking the law but he was disrupting society. He was breaking rules already set, and this was bound to come back on him."

241.
5/S
When it comes to SANCTIONS at the ◯POSTCONVENTIONAL level there is a question which is often raised: if conventional attitudes have been rejectdd, how can any order be kept; won't chaos result? Can you reply to this question based on what you have learned so far?

_____

_____

_____

240a. ☐4
  b. Ⓢ
  c. Ⓢ
  d. ☐4

242. [5/S] The SOCIAL CONTRACT, which we have spoken about, brings with it an obligation to keep rules. So the sanction stems from the agreement, the commitment to protect the rights of all.

241. There is a very strong sense of order, not chaos. The agreement on order in society is not conventional but much more basic & personally binding.

243. [5/S] Conscience has developed into an intuitive and rational response, reason holding the most important place. How is this a development from the Stage 4 notion of conscience? _____

_____

Is this an individual or group perspective? _____

_____

244. [5/S] Physical punishment still has a place in Stage 5 thinking, but only as either a means of rehabilitation or as a means of maintaining consistency of the law (with exceptions, of course). Here are a couple of examples:

(Should the tailor report Valjean to the police?)
"I think a compassionate judge should allow Valjean to go free for his motives were not menacing or threatening to society. Laws, judges, and jurys have a responsibility to humanity of man not just to a set code of laws. It is the judge's responsibility to do what he thinks is best for society and in this case jailing Valjean would do society no good at all while reprimanding the druggist instead would do society a definite good turn."

(Should the tailor report Valjean to the police?)
"The purpose of jail is not punishment but rather rehabilitation. Obviously Valjean was rehabilitated from any crime society accused him of. The tailor, however, should report Valjean, hoping that justice has a compassionate side to it and Valjean will remain unpunished."

243. Stage 4's notion of CONSCIENCE was to internalize the rules of society and go by them. Stage 5 is determining for one-self OUT OF PRINCI-PLES what is right. So although it is more "individual", it is definitely more general and less individual as in the Stage 2 notion of "concrete individual"

245.
5/P
The understanding of property is deepening at Stage 5. Property rights are seen as a <u>precondition</u> to society. The structure of society is highly involved with how property is handled. How is this a development of Stage 4 thinking? _____

_____

_____

246.
5/P
Of course Stage 5 thinking is all about rights and principles. The right to property is more basic than the right to life: TRUE?

Where does the right to property come from? _____

_____

247.
5/P
Here are some responses which show thinking about Property. Indicate whether they are CONVENTIONAL or Stage 5:

a._____ (Should Heinz steal the drug?)
"Yes, it was right. The druggist was wrong in his demands. Though technically Heinz was in the wrong my conscience demands that I draw the line somewhere to confine the rights of the druggist. The materials used in the drugs are natural materials owned by all. The druggist does deserve a profit for his labours. The druggist was demanding an unfair profit which, under the circumstances, amounted to life or death for the woman. In terms of justice Heinz was right."

b._____ (Should Heinz steal the drug?)
"One of the rules of society is that you respect other people's property. Without a respect for, and observance of such rules society would soon become a nightmare where no one would be safe."

c._____(Why shouldn't someone steal from a store?)
"It was not Joe's property. By mutual agreement each man respects the other's belongings. If you break this agreement, you have no right to ask others to respect your rights."

---

245. Stage 4 thinking maintains property rights so that the <u>social system</u> may continue. Now we are talking about a more general notion of society, not a particular structure.

---

246. NOT TRUE.
The right to property is derived from the right to life.

103

247. (cont'd)

d._____ (Why shouldn't someone steal from a store?)
"The answer depends on your concept of personal
property and how much of an imbalance of it there can
be in society. If the store was small and the owner
made a bare living on it, it is wrong. If it was a
big store where more than a living is made by the
owner, where profits are used by individuals to make
more money or where profits are put back to create an
unnecessary luxury type store, e.g. the advertising in
Dominion, or to create merchandise that does not last,
a false need - the needs of personal property have been
surpassed and advantage is being taken of others then
they would not miss $500 which would be covered by
insurance anyway.

e._____ (Should Heinz have done that?)
"No. He was right in wanting to preserve life.
Although he did infringe on the rights of others and
it is ok because the right to life is more fundamental
than the right to property. The druggist illustrated
a weakness but not a wrong by placing monetary values
ahead of life."

f._____ (Why shouldn't someone steal from a store?)
"They shouldn't because a store is someone's livelihood and if everyone stole from stores the system
couldn't operate for others (the majority).

---

248. | There is one most basic point about Stage 5 thinking
5/L | about life and we have already said it, really. The
RIGHT TO LIFE is the most basic right - it is the
foundation upon which all rights are built.

247a. ⑤	d. ⑤
b. ☐	e. ⑤
c. ⑤	f. ☐

249.
|5/L| Here are several different responses to the question:

> If the husband doesn't love his wife, is he
> obligated to steal the drug for her?

Check the responses which indicate Stage 5 thinking.

a. "Depends on the degree of his affection. When all
   the pros are weighed against all the cons, the
   decision could go either way."

b. "Heinz, as a husband is not required to steal anything. As a human being, that his actions were
   appealed to by the situation. It is desirable for
   his wife that Heinz steal the drug, but in no way is
   he responsible to. Thus it is not a question of
   "should". The only time he "should" do it, is if he
   feels very strongly it is right for him to."

c. "He must weigh the pros and cons and decide for himself what the overall consequences of the theft will
   be, how the theft will benefit and/or harm himself
   and others, and then steal or refrain from doing so.

d. "Each human being has a responsibility for the welfare
   of other human beings. The husband is no less
   responsible for his wife than the druggist. Both
   should be morally committed to saving the wife's life."

e. "Yes, he should because a human's life is at stake
   and any possible way of saving it should be tried.
   Unless Heinz overlooked this fact and decided through
   his emotions and feelings I think that since he stole
   the drug once he would steal it (considering
   situation) again."

250. Here are a sampling of responses. Each set is one
person's responses to these 3 questions:

- (Should Heinz steal the drug?)

- (If the husband doesn't love his wife, is he obligated
  to steal the drug for her?)

- (Should the judge sentence him or should he let him
  go free?)

You can begin to get a feel for how several responses
from one story fit together. Thus far we have only
used single responses which we made as clear as possible.
Now you will see that more often than not a response to
one question in itself may be quite ambiguous and
difficult to assign to a stage; several responses may
span a couple of stages.

249. d. only. Note
that the other
responses talk of
"human beings,"
"human life," etc.
- not Stage 5 but
common Stage 3 talk.

250. (cont'd)

Your task is to decide whether the set of responses is

Stage △1 Punishment and Obedience

Stage △2 Instrumentality

Stage [3] Conformity

Stage [4] Social Systems

Stage (5) Social Contract/Individual Rights

or a combination of stages.

a. _____ "Yes, he should have, although in today's society it would be called wrong and he would be punished for doing something out of necessity for another human being."

"Yes, every human being has the right to live and it is up to others to let each other live."

"No, Heinz has not really committed a crime. The crime is in the sense of law and not human nature. His contribution to humanity is greater than what his crime was. He was trying to help, not hinder or destroy."

b. _____ "Heinz shouldn't have because he could be put in jail for breaking in."

"Well, still should because if he didn't love his wife he should care."

"He should send him to jail for stealing. But he saved his wife's life."

c. _____ "Heinz should not have done it because stealing is bad and you can get into a lot of trouble and yet it is good for his wife's sake."

"Even if he is not very close or affectionate, I think he should steal them to save a person's life."

"I think he should let Heinz go free because all he wanted to do was to save someone's life."

d. _____ "Heinz is perfectly justified in his actions. He had exhausted all means of raising the required money. The price asked for the drug was grossly inflated. When we talk about it being right or wrong we have two views: 1) the moralist who says it is wrong to steal, it is a sin. 2) the realist who says it is wrong to steal but in this case it is justified in order to save a life. In other words there are exceptions."

250d. (cont'd)

"Yes, he is still dealing with a human life. We, as humans should strive to save life if at all possible."

"After viewing the case the judge should let Heinz go free. If there is anything called justice and mercy this would be a good time for the judge to prove it. Heinz is not a common criminal but a man who tried to save a life at the risk of imprisonment."

e._____   "Heinz did what he thought was right! The attempt at saving his wife - through only possible means, break and enter. In terms of law this is wrong, in terms of human rights - he should have been given the drug, but if he had wanted to, he could have sold out almost everything to get that drug legitimately. Since he didn't go that way, I feel Heinz is trying to play on sympathy and steals it, hoping everyone will see it his way - but I feel he took easy way out - should not have taken it."

"If there was no other choice - after begging and pleading, etc. after every possible means of obtaining it had failed, and I LOVED HER VERY MUCH <u>THEN</u> I would have someone else do any violence and get it for me!"

"Heinz should go to jail as he broke the law - it would make a good case in court as you'd have human values vs. inhuman laws. Should serve <u>some time</u> in jail for breaking basic law. If someone else did job for him he wouldn't be in this predicament."

f._____   "Yes, Heinz should have broken into the druggist's store for the simple purpose of saving his wife's life. There exists in society two types of laws. There is legal laws, conceived and administered by agents in society. There also exists in society moral laws which override any legal law. Moral laws would require that each individual in society has the right to rebel against society if by so doing it will save his own life or the life of others. Heinz was only exercising the moral unwritten laws of society."

"Yes, he is still her husband and responsible for the life and livelihood of his spouse."

"No, the judge should not send Heinz to jail for stealing. In society men committing crimes in self-defense are not punished. Did not Heinz steal so that the life of his wife may be saved? Heinz was in fact acting in a form of unit defense, if not exactly self-defense."

250. (cont'd)

g._____   "No. He was right in wanting to preserve life but
was wrong to break the law thereby infringing on the
rights of others. At the same time the druggist
illustrated a weakness but not a wrong by placing
monetary values ahead of life. Neither men were
actually wrong, the system was wrong. This system
which places more values on monetary, material things
can only breed contempt."
     "He should do so only if he values life and its
preservation."
     "He should be charged and face the consequences. He
had no right to infringe upon the rights, in this case
property, of others."

h._____   "No. He would be stealing. Wrong. It would be a
sin. It is the wrong thing.
     "No. I would feel it would be wrong and I would be
running. Because your parents could get in trouble and
have to pay a big fine or be put in jail."
     "Put him in jail because he might do it again if he
thought he could get away with it."

250a. ⊡3⊡ Don't be mislead by words such as SOCIETY, HUMAN BEING, RIGHT TO LIVE, LAW, HUMAN NATURE, HUMANITY. What he is saying is do something for another, let each other live, try to help ... ⊡3⊡ .

b. △2△ & ⊡3⊡ First he tries to save his own skin 2 then he talks of socially acceptable behavior (should care) 3 , then the motivation for the act, 3 .

c. △1△ or △2△ & ⊡3⊡ "Stealing is bad" and "you can get in a lot of trouble" could be either 1 or 2 . The rest are common 3 responses.

d. ⊡3⊡ Again this all boils down to there are exceptions, we should save lives and you shouldn't be punished for trying to save a life.

e. △2△ 3 A strange mixture of 3 "try to do what is right" and 2 using someone in the situation to your own ends.

f. ⊡4⊡ Stays within legal or moral SYSTEM.

g. ⊡4⊡ (5) Some Stage 5 concepts emerging – wanting to preserve life, rights of others, money is not ahead of life, and a criticism (negative view) of social system – ⊡4⊡

h. △1△ △2△ Very early responses – very little role taking ability.

251.

- SOCIAL PERSPECTIVE is a perspective <u>prior to society</u>.

- ROLE-TAKING ABILITY has developed so that a rational or moral perspective is possible.

- EXCHANGE happens between people so that the <u>individual rights</u> of people are preserved.

- INTERPERSONAL RELATIONSHIPS are between free and equal human beings who recognize certain duties and responsibilities.

- GOVERNANCE (structure) is produced on the basis of principles.

- RULES are a mechanism to preserve individual rights.

- SANCTIONS are primarily the agreement of the social contract and one's conscience.

- PROPERTY rights are derived from the right to life and are a precondition to society.

- LIFE is the most fundamental right from which all others are derived.

252. For a beginning idea of Stage 6 thinking, we quote here
from Kohlberg"s The Just Community Approach to
Correction: A Manual II:

> Stage 6: The stage of Universal Ethical Principles
>
> Stage 6 is guided by self-chosen ethical principles.
> Particular laws or social agreements are usually
> valid because they rest on such principles. When
> laws violate these principles, one acts in accordance
> with the principle. Principles are universal
> principles of justice: the equality of human rights
> and respect for the dignity of human being as
> individual persons. These are not merely values
> which are recognized, they are principles used to
> generate particular decisions.
>
> The reason for doing right is that, as a rational
> person, the Stage 6 individual has seen the
> validity of principles and has become committed to
> them.
>
> The social perspective of the Stage 6 is a perspective
> of a "moral point of view" from which social arrange-
> ments derive or on which they are grounded. The
> perspective is that of any rational individual
> recognizing the nature of morality or the basic moral
> premise of respect for other persons as ends, not
> means.

Stage 6 thinking, although crucial to the whole theory,
is hardly ever encountered. We will not go into it in
detail here but suggest further reading be done if you
are interested. See the References section for further
reading.

LOOKING AT A WHOLE MORAL JUDGMENT INTERVIEW

253. A whole moral judgment consists of at least 3 stories. Form A
has Heinz, Joe, Bob and Karl. Form B has Mercy-killing, Judy
and Louise, tailor. There are other stories which have been used
as well, which are available from the Harvard Moral Education
Research Foundation. The interview can be given orally or written.
The object is to obtain as much indication of a person's thinking
as possible.

254. There are at least two ways to approach judging the level of
thinking of an interview:

BY AREAS   Read the entire interview and judge the stage
of each area. For example:

SP	- 3	G	- 2(3)
RT	- 3	R	- 2(3)
Ex	- 2(3)	S	- 2(3)
IR	- 3	P	- 3(2)
		L	- 3

BY STORIES Read each story and judge that story (on the basis of
whatever information about various areas is there). For example:

Heinz	3	Joe	3(2)
Tailor	3(2)	Bob and Karl	3(2)

The examples which we will give are scored by story rather than by
area since our intention is to teach a general understanding of the
stages.

255. Let us go through an interview to see how it is all put together.
At the left we have the interview and the responses given; at the
right we have reflections on scoring it. (Note that the questions
are slightly different than those you have in Form A and B. These
are an earlier form of the interview) Parentheses are used to delineate a phrase which adds information in judging stage of development.

HEINZ

1. Should Heinz have done that? Was it
actually wrong or right? Why?
"I think that Heinz should not have
done it because, even though he got
the drug, and it worked, (he would
a probably half to go to jail) and
b (he would not be able to see his
wife)."

a) 2? save his own neck
b) 2? he would be deprived or 3?
he cares about his wife

2. Is it a husband's duty to steal the
    drug for his wife if he can get it
    no other way? Would a good husband
    do it? "It is not the husbands
  a duty to steal the drug, (a good hus-
    band would try to get a lawyer that
    could help him out), but then (it
  b might be too late and his wife might
    die)."

a) __3__ don't break rules, find alternative
b) ____   doesn't say much

3. Did the druggist have the right to
    charge that much when there was no
    law actually setting a limit to the
    price?
    Why?
    "I think the druggist had no right
    to charge that much money. (The
  a druggist made the drug to help
    people and save people, life), and
  b (he knows that all people aren't
    rich and can't pay that much money.
    He should lower the price)."

a) __3__ steroetyped view of druggist -
    helping people.

5a. Would you steal the drug to save
    your wife's life?
    "I'm not sure if I would steal the
    drug, but (if you love your husband
  a its hard not to do something like
    that to save his life)."

a) __3__ affection

5b. If you were dying of cancer but
    were strong enough, would you steal
    the drug to save your own life?
    "I would steal the drug to save my
  a life because (you have to care about
    others, and everyone cares about their
    self and most everyone wants to
    life)."

a) __3__ stage 3 caring - a hedonistic
    stage 2 self caring sounds very different

6. Should the judge send Heinz to jail
    for stealing, or should he let him
    go free? Why? "I think that Heinz
    should not have stolen the drug and
  a (I don't think the judge should let
    him go free because he did steal the
    drug and that was wrong), but (the
  b druggist had no right to make him
    pay so much)."

a) __3__ finally settles on 3 role keeping
b) __3__ with the druggist as a bad guy

We have read through this story and put
down any stages we could find. We did
not take each sentence and score it.
It is much more like being a detective
and looking for clues and then at the
end putting them together in a intuitive
rather than mechanical way. So far this
first story we definitely found Stage 3
thinking. Look at 1, now. In light of all
he later said this could well be Stage 3 1a)
he would have to go to jail as that is the
rule and 1b) more in terms of affection. So
you could fairly definitely say this is a pure
stage 3 response.

TAILOR

16. Should the tailor report Heinz to the police? Would it be right or wrong to keep it quiet?
"I think that the tailor should report him because he did do wrong, it would be wrong to keep it quiet,
a because (if Heinz was ever in a position like that before with his wife he might just try stealing something again.)"

a) __2__ - physical prevention from repeating
act

17. Is it a citizen's duty to report Heinz? Would a good citizen?
"Yes it is a citizen's duty to report Heinz and a good citizen would because (he cared for his
a own and what kind of people roamed around in it.) The (good citizen
b would want to stop of bad.)"

a) __3__ - caring
b) __?__

18. If Heinz was a good friend of the tailor would that make a difference? Why?
"I think it would make a difference if they were good friends because (the tailor would not want to hurt his friend or send him back to jail because they liked each other and wanted to help each other.)"

a) __3__ - friendship

19. Should Heinz be sent back to jail by the judge? Why?
"Yes he should because (if every person who stole something and broke out of jail was about to roam around and not be punished, it would be a pretty sad world and in bad shape.)"

a) __3__ have to keep things in order. Since the answer to 16 is such a clear stage 2 response, I would give it some say in the overall score for this story. Mostly stage 3 - I would finally say this is major 3, minor 2 or 3(2). We'll talk about "major" and "minor" scores shortly.

JOE

20. Should Joe refuse to give his father the money? Why?
   "Yes Joe should refuse because (his
   a dad made a promise that he could go to camp if he saved the money for it) and the (father has no right to take his money.)"

   a) ___ just a restatement of the story
   b) ___ it's hard to tell what this is

21. Does his father have the right to tell Joe to give him the money?
   a "No because (it is Joe's money).
   b (It would be a different case if his dad needed the money to buy food or something and he would pay him back) but Joe was just going to to on his trip that very day and the father wanted his money."

   a) ___ again can't tell if it's 2 or 3
   b) _3_ helping out for a good reason

22. Does giving the money have anything to do with being a good son?
   a "Yes it does because (you should do what your parents tell you) to
   b do but (you just can't disappoint someone like that when he had his heart set on going.)"

   a) 1 or _3_ - but from all thats said obeying parents here is not out of fear (as in 1)
   b) 2 or _3_ - sounds more like concern for others than self

23. Which is worse, a father breaking a promise to his son or a son breaking a promise to his father?
   "A father breaking a promise to his son because (the father is suppose
   a to set a good example for his son) and the father is going around breaking promises to his son."

   a) _3_ - family relationships

24. Why should a promise be kept?
   "A promise should be kept because (it is something between 2 different people or a group of people, and it's a way of trusting or learning to trust a person.)"

   a) _3_ - trust

   So we can easily give full 3 for this story.

BOB AND KARL

25. If you had to say who did worse, would you say Al did worse to break in the store and steal the $500 or Joe did worse to borrow the $500 with no intention of paying it back? Why?

   a "I think Joe did worse because (he lied to a old man and the old man took pity on him and gave him the money, and Joe was not even going to pay the man back.) (He took
   b advantage of the oldman.)"

   a) ___ doesn't say much but repeats the story
   b) _3_ shouldn't take advantage of people

26. Would you feel like a worse person stealing like Al or cheating like Joe? "I would feel worse cheating like Joe did because (you tricked
   a the old man and the man trusted you). (There is not too many people that would lend a boy $500.)"

   a) _3_ how to treat people
   b) ?

27. Why shouldn't someone steal from a store anyhow?
   "-You should not steal from the store
   a because (its only going to get you into bad trouble. If you get caught stealing money you won't even be able to enjoy the money and it was all for nothing.)"

   a). _2_ pretty much looking out for the self

28. Who would feel worse, the store-owner, who was robbed or the man who was cheated out of the loan? Why?
   "The oldman would feel worse because
   a (he trusted the boy and really believed he would pay him back.)"

   a). _3_ trust is broken

29. Which should the law be more harsh or strong against, stealing like Al or cheating like Joe? Why?
   "I think that the law would probably be more harsh on the boy that stold
   a some money because (they would really only think of breaking into the store not how the old man felt, the boy that cheated should get a worse punishment for being so cruel and mean to the old man.)"

   a). _3_ don't be cruel and mean

   Very strong 3 orientation but also there really is some stage 2 thinking. Therefore we give it a major 3 and a minor 2, 3(2).

256. Now we have made the following judgments:

Heinz: 3
Tailor: 3(2)
Joe: 3
Bob and Karl: 3(2)

There is a way of combining these to get one score for an inter-vier. It is simply a mathematical average. Here is how to do it.

1. Weights   PURE STAGE   as Heinz and Joe = 3 points
                MAJOR STAGE   as Tailor, Bob   = 2 points
                  In 3(2), 3 is major
                MINOR STAGE   = 1 point

2. Set up table and assign weights (that is how much WEIGHT is given to each stage)

Stage   1   -   0

Stage   2   -   2   (1 point each for 2 minors)

Stage   3   -   10 (3 points on Heinz - pure
                     2 points on Tailor - major
                     3 points on Joe   - pure
                     2 points on Bob   - major

Stage 4-6   -   0

3. Add all the weights together

Stage 2 - 2
Stage 3 - 10
            ――
            12

4. Convert to percents

Stage 2 -   2 = 17%
Stage 3 - 10 = 83%
             ――
             12

5. _Multiply_ the Stage by this percent

Stage 2   x   17% = 34
Stage 3   x   83% =249

6. Add these together and you have what is called a MORAL MATURITY SCORE.

34 + 249 = 283

257.

SUMMARY:

HEINZ: 3 JOE: 3

TAILOR: 3(2) BOB & KARL: 3(2)

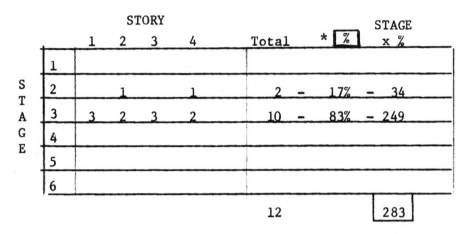

STAGE	Story 1	Story 2	Story 3	Story 4	Total	* %	STAGE x %
1							
2		1		1	2	17%	34
3	3	2	3	2	10	83%	249
4							
5							
6							
					12		283

258. So from this Moral Maturity Score we can get a fairly good idea of what stage is represented. Note that a pure

stage 1 interview is scored 100
2 " " " 200
3 " " " 300
4 " " " 400
5 " " " 500
6 " " " 600

259. Enclosed in the Appendix B are 5 interviews from elementary school students, 5 interviews from secondary school students, and 5 interviews from adults. Try your hand at scoring these. Appendix C contains the author's assessment of these interviews.

260. When you have practiced a bit on these, score your own interview!

APPENDICES

APPENDICES

A Moral Judgment Interview, Form B

B Sample Interviews

  1. Summary Sheet

  2. Stories with Questions

  3. 15 Sample Interviews

C Assessment of Sample Interviews

D References

MORAL JUDGMENT INTERVIEW (FORM B)

MERCY KILLING

There was a woman who had very bad cancer, and there was no treatment known to medicine that could save her. Her doctor knew that she had only about six months to live. She was in terrible pain, but she was so weak that a good dose of a pain-killer like ether or morphine would make her die sooner. She was delirious and almost crazy with pain, and in her calm periods, she would ask the doctor to give her enough ether to kill her. She said she couldn't stand the pain and she was going to die in a few months anyway.

1. Should the doctor give her the drug that would make her die? Why?
2. How does the fact that mercy-killing is against the law affect your decision as to whether it's right or wrong? Why?
3. What does the husband have to do with the decision?
4. Thinking in terms of society, should the woman have the right to make the final decision? Why or why not?
5. What should the doctor do if she wants to respect the woman's rights? Why?
6. In what sense do people have a duty or obligation to live when they don't want to, when they want to commit suicide?
7. Why is mercy-killing humans so different from mercy-killing animals? Why is there a difference between animal and human life?
8. The doctor kills the woman and is brought to court. He is found guilty of murder. The usual sentence is life imprisonment. What should the judge do? Why?
9. Thinking in terms of society, what is the best reason for the judge to give the doctor a sentence?
10. Thinking in terms of society, what is the best reason for the judge to let the doctor go free?

JUDY & LOUISE

Judy was a twelve-year-old girl. She had saved up from babysitting and lunch money for a long time so she would have enough money to buy a ticket to a special out-of-town rock concert that was coming to her town. She had managed to save up the $5 the ticket cost plus another $3. Her mother had promised her that she could go to the rock concert if she saved the money herself. Later her mother changed her mind and told Judy that she had to spend the money on new clothes for school. Judy was disappointed, and decided to go to the concert anyway. She bought a ticket and told her mother that she had only been able to save $3. That Saturday she went to the performance and told her mother that she was spending the day with a friend. A week passed without her mother finding out. Judy then told her older sister, Louise, that she had gone to the performance and had lied to her mother about it.

Harvard Centre for Moral Development, November 1974.

JUDY & LOUISE (cont'd)

1. Should Louise, the older sister, tell their mother that Judy had lied about the money or should she keep quiet? Why?
2. Can you give me the best reasons to support the other point of view?
3. Why should a promise be kept?
4. What makes a person feel bad if a promise is broken?
5. Why is it important to keep a promise to someone you don't know well or are not close to?
6. Trust is one important thing in a good mother-daughter relationship. What are some other important considerations that a good mother should recognize in her relation with her daughter? Why are these important?
7. How is a good parent-childrrelationship similar to any good human relationship? Why is that?

TAILOR

In a country in Europe, a poor man named Valjean could find no work, nor could his sister and brother. Without money, he stole food and medicine that they needed. He was captured and sentenced to prison for six years. After a couple of years, he escaped from the prison and went to live in another part of the country under a new name. He saved money and slowly built up a big factory. He gave his workers the highest wages and used most of his profits to build a hospital for people who couldn't affordggood medical care. Twenty years had passed when a tailor recognized the factory owner as being Valjean, the escaped convict whom the police had been looking for back in his home town.

1. Should the tailor report Valjean to the police? Why?
2. Suppose Valjean were reported and brought before the judge. Should the judge have him finish his sentence or let him go free? Why?
3. What is the best reason(s) for generally punishing people who break the law? Explain.
4. Is Valjean's case an exception to the reasons you discussed in question 3? Why or why not?
5. Would your conscience bother you if you turned Valjean in? Why or why not?
6. What do you mean by conscience? What do you think of as your conscience and what does it do?
7. What do the words ethics or morality mean to you?
8. Do you believe there is an objective right or wrong in morality or is it a matter of personal opinion? For example, some people say that the tailor should turn Valjean in to the police, some say he should not. Do you believe the answer you chose is objectively right or could someone come to the opposite conclusion and be just as right?
9. It was a common practice in some ancient societies to kill many of their female babies. Can you say whether something like this is really right or wrong? That is, can one make valid moral judgments about a practice in another society? Explain.

		Percent of Response at Stage*						
		1	2	3	4	5	6	MMS
ELEMENTARY SCHOOL STUDENTS	1							
	2							
	3							
	4							
	5							
SECONDARY SCHOOL STUDENTS	6							
	7							
	8							
	9							
	10							
ADULTS	11							
	12							
	13							
	14							
	15							

*Percent of response at various stages gives a good picture of an interview. Cf. item 255 on how it is obtained.

NOTE: Many different forms of the interview have been used besides Form A and Form B which we have included already. The fifteen sample interviews include many different stories. We enclose these stories with their questions. Instead of repeating the story and questions for each interview, we give the story name and question numbers with the respondent's reply.

HEINZ

In Europe, a woman was near death from a special kind of cancer. There was one drug that the doctors thought might save her. It was a form radium that a druggist in the same town had recently discovered. The drug was expensive to make, but the druggist was charging ten times what the drug cost him to make. He paid $200 for the radium and charged $2,000 for a small dose of the drug. The sick woman's husband, Heinz, went to everyone he knew to borrow the money, but he could only get together about $1,000 which is half of what it cost. He told the druggist that his wife was dying, and asked him to sell it cheaper or let him pay later. But the druggist said, "No, I discovered the drug and I'm going to make money from it." So Heinz got desperate and broke into the man's store to steal the drug for his wife.

1. Should Heinz have done that? Was it actually wrong or right? Why?
2. Is it a husband's duty to steal the drug for his wife if he can get it no other way? Would a good husband do it?
3. Did the druggist have the right to charge that much when there was no law actually setting a limit to the price? Why?

Answer the next two questions only if you think he should steal the drug.

4a. If the husband does not feel very close or affectionate to his wife, should he still steal the drug?
4b. Suppose it wasn't Heinz's wife who was dying of cancer but it was Heinz's best friend. His friend didn't have any money and there was no one in his family willing to steal the drug. Should Heinz steal the drug for his friend in that case? Why?

Answer the next two questions only if you think Heinz should not steal the drug.

5a. Would you steal the drug to save your wife's life?
5b. If you were dying of cancer but were strong enough, would you steal the drug to save your own life?
6. Heinz broke in the store and stole the drug and gave it to his wife. He was caught and brought before the judge. Should the judge send Heinz to jail for stealing, or should he let him go free? Why?

TAILOR

While all this was happening, Heinz was in jail for breaking in and trying to steal the medicine. He had been sentenced for 10 years. But after a couple of years, he escaped from the prison and went to live in another part of the country under a new name. He saved money and slowly built up a big factory. He gave his workers the highest wages and used most of his profits to build a hospital for work in curing cancer. Twenty years had passed when a tailor recognized the factory owner as being Heinz, the escaped convict whom the police had been looking for back in his home town.

TAILOR (cont'd)

1. Should the tailor report Heinz to the police? Would it be right or wrong to keep it quiet? Why?
2. Is it a citizen's duty to report Heinz? Would a good citizen?
3. If Heinz was a good friend of the tailor, would that make a difference? Why?
4. Should Heinz be sent back to jail by the judge? Why?

JOE

Joe is a 14 year-old boy who wanted to go to camp very much. His father promised him he could go if he saved up the money for it himself. So Joe worked hard at his paper route and saved up the $40 it cost to go to camp and a little more besides. But just before camp was going to start, his father changed his mind. Some of his friends decided to go on a special fishing trip, and Joe's father was short of the money it would cost. So he told Joe to give him the money he had saved from the paper route. Joe didn't want to give up going to camp, so he thought of refusing to give his father the money.

1. Should Joe refuse to give his father the money? Why?
2. Does his father have the right to tell Joe to give him the money?
3. Does giving the money have anything to do with being a good son?
4. Which is worse, a father breaking a promise to his son or a son breaking a promise to his father?
5. Why should a promise be kept?

JOE & ALEX

Joe had an older brother called Alex. Several years later, the grown up brothers had gotten into serious trouble. They were secretly leaving town in a hurry and needed money. Alex, the older one, broke into a store and stole $500. Joe, the younger one, went to a retired old man who was known to help people in town. Joe told the man that he was very sick and he needed $500 to pay for the operation. Really he wasn't sick at all, and he had no intention of paying the man back. Although the man didn't know Joe very well, he loaned him the money. So Joe and Alex skipped town, each with $500.

1. If you had to say who did worse, would you say Al did worse to break in the store and steal the $500 or Joe did worse to borrow the $500 with no intention of paying it back? Why?
2. Would you feel like a worse person stealing like Al or cheating like Joe?
3. Why shouldn't someone steal from a store anyhow?
4. Who would feel worse, the storeowner who was robbed or the man who was cheated out of the loan? Why?
5. Which should the law be more harsh or strong against, stealing like Al or cheating like Joe? Why?

126

MERCY KILLING

The drug didn't work, and there was no other treatment known to medicine which could save Heinz's wife, so the doctor knew that she had only about 6 months to live. She was in terrible pain, but she was so weak that a good dose of a pain-killer like ether or morphine would make her die sooner. She was delirious and almost crazy with pain, and in her calm periods, she would ask the doctor to give her enough ether to kill her. She said she couldn't stand the pain and she was going to die in a few months anyway.

1. Should the doctor do what she asks and give her the drug that will make her die? Why?
2. When a pet animal is badly wounded and will die, it is killed to put it out of its pain. Does the same thing apply here? Why?
   Answer the following questions only if you think the doctor should not give her the drug:
3. Would you blame the doctor for giving her the drug?
4. What would have been the best for the woman herself, to have had live for six months more in great pain or have died sooner? Why?
5. Some countries have a law that doctors could put away a suffering person who will die anyway. Should the doctor do it in that case?
   Everyone should answer the remaining questions.
6. The doctor finally decided to kill the woman to put her out of her pain, so he did it without consulting the law. The police found out and the doctor was brought up on a charge of murder. The jury decided he had done it, so they found him guilty of murder even though they knew the woman had asked him. What punishment should the judge give the doctor? Why?
7. Would it be right to give the doctor the death sentence?
8. Do you believe that the death sentence should be given in some cases? Why?
9. The law prescribes the death penalty for treason against the country. Do you think the death sentence should be given for treason? Why?

SLAVERY

Before the civil war, America had laws that allowed slavery. According to the law if a slave escaped, he had to be returned to his owner like a runaway horse. Some people who didn't believe in slavery disobeyed the law and hid the runaway slaves and helped them to escape.

1. Were they doing right or wrong? Why?
2. Is it alright to disobey a law like that if you really think it's a bad law? Why?
3. At the time before the Civil War when America had slavery, was it wrong to have slavery? Why?
4. Is it wrong now for the South in America to have segregated schools? Why?
5. If you were living in the South in America what would you think about desegregating the schools? Why?

JOE & ALEX: LIEING

Joe wanted to go to camp but he was afraid to refuse go give his father
the money. So he gave his father $10 and told him that was all he
made. He took the other $40 and paid for camp with it. He told his
father the head of the camp said he could pay later. So he went off
to camp, and the father didn't go on the fishing trip.
Before Joe went to camp, he told his older brother, Alexander, that
he really made $50 and that he lied to his father and said he'd made
$10. Alexander wonders whether he should tell his father or not.

1. Should Alexander, the older brother, tell their father that Joe had
   lied about the money or should he keep quiet about what Joe had done? Why?
2. Why would a teenager think he shouldn't tell on a friend or a brother?
3. Which is more important, being a loyal son or a loyal brother? Why?
4. If the father finds out, should he punish Joe for lying and going
   off with the money? Why?

VIETNAM: CAPTAIN

In Vietnam, a company of Marines was way outnumbered and was retreating
before the enemy. The company had crossed a bridge over a river, but
the enemy were mostly still on the other side. If someone went back
to the bridge and blew it up as the enemy were coming over it, it
would weaken the enemy. With the head start the rest of the men in
the company would have, they could probably then escape. But the
man who stayed back to blow up the bridge would probably not be able
to escape alive; there would be about a 4 to 1 chance he would be
killed. The captain of the company has to decide who should go back
and do the job. The captain himself is the man who knows best how
to lead the retreat. He asks for volunteers, but no one will volunteer.
If he goes himself, the man will probably not get back safely and he
is the only one who knows how to lead the retreat.

1. Should the captain order a man to go on this very dangerous mission
   or should he go himself? Why?
2. Does the captain have the right to order a man if he thinks it best
   to? Why?
3. Which would be best for the survival of all the men, ordering a man
   or the captain going himself?
4. If it were absolutely certain that many more lives would be lost if
   he went himself and were killed, should he order another man to go
   against his will?
5. Would a man have the right to refuse such an order? Why?

VIETNAM: WHICH MAN

The captain finally decided to order one of the men to stay behind. One of the men he thought of was one who had a lot of strength and courage but he was a bad trouble maker. He was always stealing things from the other men, beating them up and wouldn't do his work. The second man he thought of had gotten a bad disease in VietNam and was likely to die in a short time anyway, though he was strong enough to do the job.

1. Should the captain send the trouble maker or the sick man? Why?
2. Who would it be fairer to send?
3. Would it be fair to send the trouble maker as a punishment?
4. Whose life would be worth more to the company?

BOMBING INCIDENT

During the war in Europe, a city was often bombed by the enemy. So each man in the city was given a post he was to go to right after the bombing to help put out the fires the bombs started and to rescue people in the burning buildings. A man named Diesing was made the chief in charge of one fire engine post. The post was near where he worked so he could get there quickly during the day, but it was a long way from his home. One day there was a very heavy bombing and Diesing left the shelter in the place he worked and went toward his fire station. But when he saw how much of the city was burning he got worried about his family. So he decided he had to go home first to see if his family was safe, even though his home was a long way off and the station was nearby and there was somebody assigned to protect his family's area.

1. Was it right or wrong for Diesing to leave his station to protect his family? Why?
2. Suppose Diesing were just a volunteer and wasn't paid, would that make a difference? Why?
3. Suppose other men were leaving for their families. Would that make a difference?
4. Suppose it were against the law to leave one's post and only a few men besides Diesing did it. Should Diesing be punished? Why?

BOMB SHELTER

One day the air raid sirens began to sound. Everyone realized that a hydrogen bomb was going to be dropped on the city by the enemy, and that the only way to survive was to be in a bomb shelter. Not everyone had bomb shelters, but those who did ran quickly to them. Since Mr. and Mrs. Jones had built a shelter, they immediately went to it where they had enough air space inside to last them exactly five days. They knew that after five days the fall-out would have diminished to the point where they could safely leave the shelter. If they left before that, they would die. There was enough air for the Joneses only. Their next door neighbors had not built a shelter and were trying to get in. The Joneses knew that they would not have enough air if they let the neighbors in, and that they would all die if they came inside. So they refused to let them in.

So now the neighbors were trying to break the door down in order to get in. Mr. Jones took out his rifle and told them to go away or else he would shoot. They would not go away. So now he either had to shoot them or let them come into the shelter.

1. What should Mr. Jones do not? Why?
2. Does he have the right to shoot his neighbors if he feels that they would all die if he let them in since there would not be enough air to last them very long? Why?
3. Does he have the right to keep his neighbors out of his shelter even though he knews they will die if he keeps them out? Why?
4. Does he have the right to let them in if he knows they will all die? Why?

SAMPLE INTERVIEW 1

HEINZ

1. Heinz should not have done it because stealing is bad and you can get in a lot of trouble and yet it is good for his wife's sake.

2. No, it is not the husband's duty to steal for his wife. I think he should make some kind of deal. I think he should steal it if he won't make a deal, if his wife was dying. No, a good husband would not do it.

3. No, the druggist had no right whatsoever to make him pay more, knowing his wife was dying.

4a. Even if he is not very close or affectionate I think he should steal them to save a person's life.

4b. Even if it is not his wife I think he should still steal them if he knew how much trouble he was getting into.

6. I think he should let Heinz go free because all he wanted to do was to save someone's life.

TAILOR

1. No, the tailor should not report Heinz because he is trying to save people's lives, not like the other, being mean.

2. Even a good citizen would understand that he is trying to help people just like him or her.

3. It should make no difference whether friend or not, he should see that he is trying to help people.

4. No, the judge should understand in the first place that his wife was dying of a sickness and the doctor would not make a deal with him, so that is why he is trying to help people.

JOE

1. No, Joe should be glad to give the money to his father because not many boys get to go fishing.

2. No, I think Joe should offer it to his father or give it up.

3. Yes, because his father might share some left over and send him to camp next year.

4. I think father breaking his promise to his son because the father is older and should understand more.

5. A promise should be kept all the time or it will be a habit of breaking them all the time.

JOE & ALEX

1. I think Joe did worse from taking from an old man who needs it.

2. I think I would feel very bad if I had $500 from an old man who needs it more than I.

3. You should not steal from a store unless you want to be in jail.

4. I think the old man would because he could not get it back and the store owner could get a loan.

5. The law should be harsh on both. They both did bad things.

SAMPLE INTERVIEW 2

HEINZ

1. I think Heinz should have done it if his wife was dying. Well it was wrong and right because he shouldn't steal but if it meant saving his wife's life, it's alright.
2. I think it is a husband's duty. I don't know but I think a good husband would if he loved his wife.
3. He had the right if there is no set limit because he made it so he should be allowed to sell at his own price. But I don't think he should charge so much.
4a. I think it depends on what the husband felt, but still his wife is a human being so he should try to save her.
4b. Yes, I think he should because after all it was a person's life that was at stake.
6. I think he should let him go free because he was only trying to save his wife's life.

TAILOR

1. I think he should report it to the police because Heinz broke out of jail, but he was getting up a hospital for cancer so his work would be wasted if he was put in jail. It would be wrong because he was aiding a convict.
2. Yes, it is a citizen's duty to report him because he was a criminal. I think a good citizen should report him because if he didn't he might get in trouble from the police.
3. I don't think it should have made a difference because Heinz still was a criminal under the judge's eyes.
4. I don't think he should because he was getting up a hospital to cure cancer in and all of his work would go down the drain.

JOE

1. I think Joe should refuse to give him the money because he had worked hard for it so that he could go to camp.
2. No, he doesn't because Joe earned it all by himself so it was his money.
3. No, I don't think it does because if Joe was a good son money wouldn't make him bad.
4. I think they are both bad but I suppose a father breaking a promise to his son is worse because the son would probably look forward to the promise more than the father.
5. A promise should be kept because you would be letting a person or people down if you break it.

JOE & ALEX

1. I would say Al did worse because he is older and should know better.
2. I would feel worse cheating like Joe because he would be lying to the old man.
3. They shouldn't steal from a store because the people who own the store have to make a living too.
4. The man who was cheated out of the loan because he had confidence in Joe that he would get his money back.
5. I think they should be harder on Joe because there are lots of robberies these days and they can be solved but there isn't really that much cheating done.

SAMPLE INTERVIEW 3

HEINZ

1. I think it is right because his wife was dying and it was too expensive.
2. Yes, it is a husband's duty to save his wife if he loved her and a good husband loves his wife.
3. No, because some people can't afford it and he would be killing people instead of helping people.
4a. Yes, if he wanted to help her. I think no if he didn't care if she lived or died.
4b. Yes, I think he should steal the drug to help his best friend and maybe when Heinz needed help his friend will remember what Heinz did for him and he would help Heinz.
6. I think the judge should let him go free and put the man who invented the drug in jail because the price was too high and the man would be killing people not helping people.

TAILOR

1. It would be right to keep it quiet because Heinz shouldn't be in jail for saving a person's life.
2. It's not a citizen's duty, and a good citizen wouldn't do it because a citizen is not supposed to hurt someone, they're supposed to help someone.
3. No, because if the tailor understood what Heinz had to say he wouldn't tell the police.
4. No, because the judge should go to jail for not listening to Heinz and why he stole the drug.

JOE

1. Yes, because the father had no right to take away the boy's money he earned himself.
2. No, because they boy earned it himself and it is not the father's money.
3. No, because the boy saved it up to go camping with his friends.
4. A father breaking a promise to his son because the son can take it more seriously and might hate his father.
5. A promise should be kept because then someone won't trust you anymore.

JOE & ALEX

1. Al did worse because he gave a bad example to Joe who is younger.
2. I would feel bad doing both because they're both not good things to do.
3. If they steal they could go to jail and it would be their fault.
4. The storeowner because he has a family to feed and he won't have any money to buy food.
5. Stealing like Al because it's not right to steal.

SAMPLE INTERVIEW 4

HEINZ

1. It was wrong because he stole it from the store. It was necessary because he needed it or his wife would die.
2. It is a husband's duty because his wife is near death. If I was married and I had to I would.
3. No the druggist didn't have the right because it is not fair to someone who is dying. The price should stay at a limitable price.
4a. He still should because he is saving someone's life.
4b. Yes, because he is still saving someone's life.
6. He should let him go free because he only wanted to help his wife and let her live.

TAILOR

1. It would be right now to report him because he broke out of prison and is on the lose.
2. Yes, because if Heinz had killed someone while on the lose then he would be killing a citizen for nothing.
3. Yes, because Heinz would give him money or something so he would not tell.
4. Yes, he should because Heinz could get shot for breaking out of jail and also for other things.

JOE

1. Yes, because if I was Joe I would do the same thing. Because I made the money..he has his own.
2. No, because his father did not carry papers for the route, so I say no.
3. No because giving money to someone else that is not fair to his son so he shouldn't give him money.
4. A father breaking a promise to his son. Because it means more to a son than to a man.
5. Because if a promise is not kept you can hurt someone's feelings.

JOE & ALEX

1. Al breaking into a store because you can get put in jail for something like that because that is stealing.
2. Cheating like Joe because you had intentions of paying it back at least.
3. They shouldn't because that owner made the money fair and someone steals it.
4. The old man because that money could have gone to the town.
5. Al because stealing is against the law.

SAMPLE INTERVIEW 5

HEINZ

1. Yes, I think he should have. It was right because he didn't want to have his wife die.
2. Yes, I think it is his duty to steal the drug if he loved his wife.
3. No, I don't think so because 10 times that amount was too expensive for Heinz.
4a. If he really wants to , but I don't think so if he's not very close to his wife.
4b. He could if he really wanted to and didn't want his best friend to die so he would steal the drug for better chance of his friend to live.
6. I think he should let him go free because he was in the right to save his wife's life and the druggist was in the wrong to charge so much money for Heinz.

TAILOR

1. I think the tailor shouldn't report Heinz to the police because really Heinz was in the right to steal the drug.
2. It's a good duty to report Heinz and a good citizen would.
3. Yes, it would because he wouldn't be much of a friend if he reported Heinz.
4. Yes, Heinz should be sent back to jail because he broke out.

JOE

1. Yes, I think so because Joe earned it. It is his to have, not his father and he can do whatever he wants to do with it.
2. No he doesn't because it's Joe's money so his father can't do anything about it.
3. Yes, it does because only a really good respectable son would give it away and only a really good respectable father wouldn't ask for it.
4. A father breaking a promise to his son because it would set a bad example for the father.
5. A promise should be kept because you gave your word of honour to give a promise to anybody so that's why you should keep a promise.

JOE & ALEX

1. I think Joe did the worse because he lied to the man and the man was an old guy and needed the money a lot.
2. I would feel worse cheating like Joe.
3. Because it is a very bad thing to do and one of God's commandments said "Thou shalt not steal."
4. I think the man who was cheated because he couldn't get it back but the storeowner could make it in one day.
5. The law should be more harsh against Joe because the old man didn't have insurance for his money for as the store probably would have insurance.

SAMPLE INTERVIEW 6

HEINZ

1. No, he shouldn't have done it but it wasn't necessarily wrong because he was doing the only thing that he thought could cure his wife.
2. No, it's not his duty but if a husband loved his wife enough he wouldn't hesitate to do anything in his power to save her.
3. He had the right but it wasn't a very humane thing to do since the man's wife was dying and he couldn't afford it.
5a. Yes, if I knew there was no other way and I was desperate.
5b. Yes, I would, because I would have nothing to lose.
6. Due to circumstances the judge should let him go because it is only the instinct of man to protect what he loves the best way he knows how.

MERCY KILLING

1. It is against the law but it is hard to judge which would be right or wrong morally.
2. No, unless it's a "mercy killing" which I think in special cases should be legal.
3. No, unless it wasn't absolutely sure she was going to die.
4. For the woman herself, I think it would have been best to die because she couldn't stand it any more and this way it would be less painful and quicker.
5. Yes, I think the doctor has the right to do it with the permission of the suffering patient.
6. I don't think he should give him any punishment because he was only trying to help a fellow human being.
7. I think it would be wrong.
8. Yes, if the patient's consent is not given, he may be taking a life not willing to die.
9. It all depends what the treason may lead to. It if could result in the killing of innocent people then yes.

TAILOR

1. No, I don't think he should because obviously he learned his lesson and is now donating money for the benefit of others who might die.
2. Yes, it is his duty and I think a good citizen would.
3. No, it would still be his duty as a citizen but as a person and friend I don't think he could do it.
4. Yes, because he has to finish the term of the sentence just as everyone else has to.

SLAVERY

1. According to the law they were wrong, but as a truly human person they were doing the right thing.
2. The laws are made by the majority of the people and until they are changed it is wrong to go against a majority.
3. No, it wasn't because the majority thought it was right until other ideas about slavery from the North influenced a change.
4. Morally it is wrong but if the people want it, both black and white, then it is acceptable.
5. I think it would tend to cause trouble in the schools unless everyone wanted it like this.

1. No, because his father does have authority over him and, legally, the right to do it.
2. No, I don't think his father has any right at all to ask him for the money, if he wants his son to grow up to be any kind of a person.
3. Not necessarily a good son but just obedient.
4. I think a father breaking a promise to his son because he is supposed to set the example and teach his son who can be expected to make a few mistakes.
5. I think a promise is one of the most sacred agreements between two people. It represents loyalty, trust, understanding and a feeling of intimacy.

SAMPLE INTERVIEW 7

HEINZ

1. Yes, Heinz should have done that. It was right for we live in a world of "the survival of the fittest." Heinz because he could not get ahold of the money was justified in stealing the drug so that he could bring his wife to health.
2. Yes, I would consider it the husband's duty. A good husband would do it because I feel that the husband or wife should be prepared to do any-thing for each other for the other's benefit. (of course, action within reason.)
3. The druggist had the right, but to me the druggist was an example of the lowest of human beings. He had the right to charge any price he wanted because he discovered it, however he should not have been so selfish and head-strong.
4a. A good husband would because of his morals as a human being and because of the marriage law.
4b. Yes, because saving a person's life is the greatest accomplishment in this world.
6. He should let him go free on the grounds that Heinz was only thinking for the welfare of his wife and that he had no other means of obtaining the drug and that if he hadn't stolen the drug his wife would have died.

MERCY KILLING

1. YEs, if the fact that she would die in a few months is 100% correct. It is her life and she should be able to decide for herself if she wants to be left in this world or not. ANother matter is that she is in deep pain and it would be for her benefit.she died and did not have to suffer any longer.
2. Yes, because if the person is going to die and is in deep pain you might as well kill the person so as to eliminate his or her sufferings.
6. The only punishment he should give the doctor was to accuse him of failing to consult and inform the law. However, if he knew the law would refuse him the right to kill her, I feel that he was justified in going on without the law.

7. Definitely wrong. He did not kill her he just killed her sufferings under her wish. However, if the lady did not give her permission he is guilty of murder.

8. Yes, because without it the criminal negligence and the number of murders will rise extremely, as is now. There will be less people who will want to be policemen or have anything to do with justice. I feel there is no reason why someone should live when he has taken another person's life except in special circumstances.

9. Yes, because in cases of treason, the person could be indirectly responsible for the death of many people. That would be the only reason.

TAILOR

1. The tailor should not report Heinz to the police and it would not be wrong to keep it quiet for Heinz is being a great help to society and is leading a great life.

2. No it is not and a good itizen would not unless the convict is still a nuisance to society.

3. No, because every human being should feel that Heinz should be left alone for he had changed his ways and is of benefit to society.

4. No, because Heinz had proved that he can lead a good life and has changed his ways.

SLAVERY

1. They were right because they felt that the slaves were as human as they were and they were. No human has the right to have another human his slave.

2. Yes, because it is my own personal view as a human being and it is within my beliefs of the rights of human beings.

3. Yes, because you were forcing a human to work for you.

JOE

1. Yes, because he earned that money and intended to use it himself. It is his money, so why should he let his father enjoy it?

2. No, he does not for it is Joe's money.

3. No, it doesn't.

4. Depends what comes first.

5. It should be kept because of the trust and understanding it should represent between one human and another.

SAMPLE INTERVIEW 8

HEINZ

1. NO, Heinz should not have broken into a person's privacy. The doctor has his right as to whether to sell the drug or not. Heinz does not have the right. Everyone is out for themselves. Heinz should have faced the problem in a different manner.

2. No one can steal. I think the doctor would have given in eventually. Only a very ignorant husband would steal.

HEINZ - cont.
3. The druggist had a right for he invented the drug. It was his to do
as he pleases. I think he wasn't fair.
5a. I would get the drug if it was the only drug but not by stealing it.
5b. I would have the money but if I didn't I probably would
6. The judge should send him to jail because if he lets him go free it
will be setting a bad example for soceity.

MERCY KILLING
1. This is mercy killing and I think only relates with animals. But if
the husband agrees which he won't, I say put her out of her misery.
2. Yes, because the person would have his or her last request and if she
really wants to go just give her the ether and let her do it herself.
6. He should be charged with murder for taking someone else's life. That's
how it is usually done. The judge can't go on what the lady said because
she could have been delirious.
7. Sure because it will set a good example.
9. Yes, very much so. Because everyone wants to keep a country together.

TAILOR
1. He should fulfill his duty to society and shouldn't keep it to himself.
2. Yes, it is his responsibility. WE can't have convicts running around
lose.
3. Probably because Heinz would most likely bribe his friend.
4. Yes, because there can't be exceptions in the law.

SLAVERY
1. They were doing right because man is equal no matter what colour.
2. Because it is a profitable law and besides slaves became slave for
no reason whatsoever.
4. I think it is because like I said before man is equal. This will only
cause more trouble anyway.

JOE
1. He has no right to refuse his father after all his father spent much
on him through the 14 years.
2. Sure, he is his father, he has every right.
3. No, it is not a question of good but of being brought up good.
4. They are both bad but the father breaking a promise is the worse because father is like big brother and should guide the boy.

SAMPLE INTERVIEW 9

HEINZ
1. When a person is desperate like that he would do that. I can think of
another way to go about it and that's by going to the law or trying harder to
bargain with the druggist.
It was wrong in the eyes of the law but right in human nature to do everything possible to save someone who you care for.

- cont.
2. I think it is if he cared for her at all. Of course a good husband
would do it probably the other kind would too.
3. No, but he knew how much that man needed it so he figured he'd make a
lot of money out of it. He (the druggist) shouldn't have done that
because he is a murderer in a roundabout way.
4a. I feel he would be close or affectionate in the first place to be
her husband. Even if he hadn't been lately he would still feel affection.
Love is something that you don't lose or pick up again whenever you feel
like it. It's lasting.
4b. Heinz's friend should steal his own drug for his own wife, I don't agree
with someone else doing your own work or stealing.
5a. I would, I couldn't just stand by.
5b. If I was dying of cancer I wouldn't be strong enough to do too much.
So if no one else cared to steal it for me why should I go on living.
6. He should help Heinz and get to the bottom of the whole thing. It's not
Heinz that is guilty, it's the druggist.

MERCY KILLING
1. No, he shouldn't. A doctor is supposed to be a healer, not God. Life
should die naturally not the other way.
2. A pet animal and a human life is a lot different. Humans should mean
more to other humans.
3. Yes. My reason is No. 1.
4. To have pain, to be alive is better than being dead.
5. It's up to the doctor, patient and family.
6. The doctor should lose his practice of medicine and let free. He shouldn't
be a doctor if he wants to play God.
7. Wrong.
8. Yes, because if there was capital punishment then more people would think
more about committing crime.
9. Yes, because you're supposed to be doing good for your country and
if you don't then you should leave and live where you like it better or
else face the consequences.

TAILOR
1. He shouldn't be reported and it wouldn't be wrong to keep it quiet because
if you know the circumstances then you would understand that Heinz is a good
man and shouldn't be punished.
2. An ordinary "Joe" with no information about the history of the case would.
3. Yes, it would because then the tailor would know what was going on. What
kind of friend would turn his friend in anyway?
4. No, it should have been cleared up a long time ago. That's the whole
problem with society and this test.

SLAVERY
1. Again wrong in eyes of government and society but this people had
feelings for their fellow man even though difference in race.
2. Yes, because whose to say what's right and what's wrong. Just as long
as you don't harm anyone's property or life it's alright. These people
were helping.
3. Yes, people should never be owned by other people. Everyone should be free.

- cont.

4. That's a long hot issue. The States will always have some funny feelings between blacks and whites because whites feel they are more superior. They shouldn't have segregated schools because that makes the feeling more recognizable.
5. It would be a good idea because of my reason above.

JOE

1. Yes, his father is unreal and not the ideal kind to have.
2. No, It's Joe's money that he earned by himself. You have Joe needing money from father but no way is he going to give money to son. Now shoe is on opposite foot.
4. Father breaking promise to son. Son never made a promise.
5. It is a special thing and is made as person will trust each other.

SAMPLE INTERVIEW 10

HEINZ

1. In the sense of the law it was wrong but morally I feel it is right. The druggist seems like a selfish person so if you are up against a person like that in a matter of life and death you should be able to take from them what is morally right.
2. Yes, to both because a good husband loves his wife and part of the marriage ceremony can be interpreted to help each other any way it is possible.
3. No, because it was morally wrong and selfish. It would destroy his relationships with others.
4a. No, because he just might be wishing her dead soon.
4b. No, the friend might just be using Heinz to get the drug.

MERCY KILLING

1. No because there is always a chance that a drug may be found to cure her.
2. NO, because humans feel and experience more than an animal and are able to help themselves and others more than an animal.
3. Yes. It would show he had a weak character and not regard to his professional promise.
4. There should always be hope even if it causes suffering.
5. No, unless the person is willing to sign a contract so the doctor will feel no guilt or blame if a drug is discovered that can help.
6. If this was his first mistake and he regrets it he should be placed as a doctor in a jail. He should not be allowed to resume his private practice ever.
7. Not because he was doing what the patient wanted and doctors are scarce to just go and kill one when he might save hundreds of lives.
8. Yes, if the offense has been done so often it is habit, the person should be removed from society.
9. No, because maybe the country is wrong in charging you for treason.

TAILOR

1. No, in this case right to keep quiet. Heinz had done so much good and no wrong. His past should be forgotten.
2. No. Unless it would bother the person too much. If he was a civic minded citizen he wouldn't report Heinz because of all the good Heinz has done.
3. No, it should because if Heinz was doing bad instead of good he should be reported.
4. No, because Heinz is more use for the general good running his factory making money, paying high wages and donating to the cancer hospital.

SLAVERY

1. They were right. A person should be allowed to choose if they want to be free or a slave. The way some of them were treated, it was totally right.

JOE

1. Yes, because it is Joe's hard earned money. If his father needs extra money he should save for special occasions.
2. No he doesn't. It shows the father to be selfish and nasty if he tells him to give him the money.
3. No, because the son will teach his father to be thrifty.
4. A father should never break a promise to a son because he is trying to mold his son's character and actions speak louder than telling them something.
5. People rely on one's word most of the time and you get a bad reputation and your word won't be good enough if you keep breaking promises.

SAMPLE INTERVIEW 11

HEINZ

1. Yes, I agree with Heinz. I feel he made the right decision because a life was involved and in my opinion a human life should have priority over material interests, no matter what the law states.
2. If he can get it no other way, then a husband has a <u>choise</u> (sic) of stealing the drug depending on how much he values his wife. A husband doesn't have to be "good" to do it.
3. No the druggist had no right to charge that much. Since when are the elements around us (especially the life giving or preserving elements) the property of just one person? I think he was greedy beyond all reason and if the wife had died without the husband getting the medicine, then I believe he could be classified as helping to kill her.
4a. The decision and the responsibility lies with him. If he had no feelings for her and for the values of a life - he would hardly be motivated to help her.
4b. Again the decision lies with Heinz. If he values a life ahead of money or law, then he should steal the drug because he might be more mentally pre-pared to handle the task rather than the family of the friend who may have been too influenced by the dictates of authority.

6. He should be set free, because he was not <u>just</u> stealing, he was attempting to save a life that he loved. The emotional aspect is understandable.

TAILOR

1. No. In my opinion it would be right to keep quiet for the sake of the value he is contributing to society.
2. A "citizen" is also a person with judgement and feeling. He is not a robot who must uphold the law constantly <u>because</u> if the law were inflexible it might destroy us all - because of the fact that we are human.
3. Yes it probably would make a difference, because then Heinz would be a person with emotions - and the tailor would probably understand how he thought and felt, rather than if he was just a stranger.
4. No, because he shouldn't have been sent in the first place and because he is being of value to many people and their lives and well-being.

JOE

1. Yes. Because his father is being a creep! But he can also give the money to his father as long as he does it willingly and without complaint in the hope that the father will realize his own fault and realize the meaning of generosity - but the latter is much harder to do sincerely. But is much more effective!
2. No. We don't <u>own</u> people - even if the "people" is a son or daughter. Therefore what <u>right</u> have we to manipulate them and possible worth while experiences?
3. <u>No.</u>
4. The father breaking a promise to the son because that type of relationship is probably the factor that starts the son breaking promises to the father and probably to others.
5. Because it involves the feelings and susceptibility of another person. It involves the occurence or the denial of trust and without trust a relationship is not comfortable - it becomes rather a nightmare where two isolated individuals depend on each other for reasons other than a warm mutual growing bond.

JOE & ALEX

1. I would say that Joe did worse, because money doesn't grow on trees for old retired people. And also he presented a situation that was deceiving by manipulating the old mans emotions.
2. Cheating like Joe.
3. They shouldn't because a store is someone's livlihood. And if everyone stole from stores the system couldn't operate for others, (the majority).
4. It depends on how much the store-owner values money. But I would say that emotions recieve more damage than cold hard cash. <u>But</u> probably both the old man <u>and</u> the store-owner would be affected in their trust of people in the future.
5. I'm not sure. If the law has anything to do with emotions, then it would be clear cut (I think). But I'm not sure about the operation of the law. I couldn't really judge from the eyes of the law.

SAMPLE INTERVIEW 12

HEINZ
1. No. I think conscienciously he thought it was right. He did everything in his power to save his wife and failed. He now had to resort to
theft to save the woman he loved. I feel he was right due to the druggists
ignorance.
2. It is not his duty but a husband who truly loved his wife would do
what Heinz. Save her life at the cost of a few years of his own if convicted.
3. Legally he did. Morally he was wrong. Just because he holds the power
of life and death in his hands is no cause to charge such an exhorbatent price.
4a. It's not a question of should its a question of will he do it.
4b. No. I feel it is not right to steal unless in very, very severe
circumstances. The end does justify the means. The husband is the one
who owes his love to his wife, not his best friend.
6. With the law like it is today Heinz should be punished. Theft is a
crime but he was forced by circumstances to go beyond the law. Since no
one is beyond the law Heinz I feel should get a suspended sentence to be
with his wife now that she is recovering and needs him.

TAILOR
1. Yes. It would not be wrong due to the statute of limitations which I
believe would allow Heinz to remain free. If it is wrong the police will
allow him to be free or arrest him. Doing this would cut off many jobs
and charitable money. It would hurt society but within the law.
2. Yes it is if he is a good member of society. Yes he would. He would
feel it his duty.
3. No. Friendship is not beyond the law.
4. No. He is doing much good for the society in which he lives and has
become a model citizen. A fine maybe but no more jail.

JOE
1. Yes. He worked like hell to save that money on the condition he could
go. I feel his father knew of the fishing and in a way plotted to get
extra money from Joe.
2. No. It is the kid's money from his job.
3. No. He can still be a good son but if he is hurt enough by the broken
promise he would resent giving up his money.
4. The father breaking the promise. Youth looks up to age. and if youth is
hurt it will carry over into the following years.
5. Just for the principal of it. People look forward to promises and
disappointment is not a happy thing. Your word should be looked on as your
bond.

JOE & ALEX
1. They both stole but in different forms. They are both wrong.
2. Cheating. It is rotten to dupe a trusting old man who believes in you.
3. It is against the law and morally wrong.
4. It depends on the character of the men. The store owner could be very
materialistic and be angry about the loss of the money. The old man could
be kindly and understand the position of the man and be sympathetic. It
is possible they both could be the reverse.
5. It should be equally harsh but sympathy toward the aged may sway the
punishment against Joe.

SAMPLE INTERVIEW 13

HEINZ

1. Yes. It was right. 1st there was a love at stake - a human life which is infinitely more important than one's security (monetary profits) 2nd Heinz had tried all avenues desparately - legally 3rd The theft of radium was not the theft of the idea and there was no guarantee of cure so actually Heinz is doing the man a favour.

2. No. A good husband would do it but must use discretion and consideration (ie don't take other lives for the sake of his own.)

3. Yes. The druggist sets the standard for the system he is in. He has every right to ask $2000 as well as every right to incure a loss if he asked $20.

4a. Definitely. Whatever the psychological triumphs - they are really secondary - death is so final?

4b. Yes. It doesn't matter is nobody else wants him - you do - so you do something about it.

6. I'm doing the splits over two extremes and want to fall in the middle. Yes he should be - the laws have to be like grass (strong but able to bend) not made for two but for a society - a permanent structure to "rely" on. The judgement is weighed to circumstances and these changed.

TAILOR

1. No. Right to stay quiet for Heinz is doing more for society out of rather than in prison.

2. Yes. No a good citizen wouldn't just as a good husband would save his wife.

3. Yes. There would be an obvious bias. If they were good friends they could agree with each others judgements and respect them. Therefore, the very first judgement (to steal cure) is respected and all precipitations from that equally so. Just as if he met a "bad" friend - would it make a difference.

4. No. He has done more good out. The judge must weigh the actions in the light of what occured (ie - good wages, building a hospital, mans personal judgement overcoming societies bad judgement) There is no need for punishment - what good will or can it do (maybe escape again, and use factory profits for MS)

JOE

1. Yes. Its his money and only he has the perogative to decide its destination.

2. No. It is like saying you own the son therefore you own everything he owns.

3. No. It may be given in fear (of instant or future punishment, loss of love etc.). It means you have a severely obedient dog son.

4. Father breaking promises - since the father is the symbol. He's the one who sets the stage, the law, the standard and if that's mixed-up who can you trust.

5. A promise is a personal thing. To take one's word is abstract and if that can't be relied on then everytime you say "I'll do it" you have to make out 3 forms get it signed by both parties and two witnesses who don't want to have anything to do with it.

145

1. Joe did worse. He stoled under false pretenses and took advantage of one who did much good to the society. At least in the store the money was gone for good. The old man still depended on the money for aiding others.
2. I would feel worse as Joe. You have really stolen the money but masked it to delude yourself.
3. The store serves the needs of the people and is a livelihood of a few. By stealing from it you may bankrupt a few and lose an honourable system to be replaced by one more despotic.
4. The loaner would feel worse because you are lending money on trust and word and that was broken down (a higher level of understanding).
5. It should be more harsh on Joe because you are using words and breaking down the mutual understanding of them. Society is founded on communication and that is how it will be destroyed.

SAMPLE INTERVIEW 14

HEINZ
1. I have definite moral values. Yes Heinz should have stolen the drug, I would have done the same myself. In my view, it was not only right to steal the drug but necessary and the only humane action possible. Why? Because human life is of a value beyond mans conceivablity.
2. It is not a husbands duty to steal the drug for his wife but rather the husbands conviction to humanity to do anything possible to preserve the life of another.
3. The druggist could charge what he wanted, but when someones life depends on the drug he should be lawfully bound to hand over the drug in respect to all that is sacred - ie -"human life".
4a. As I already mentioned as a man his conviction to life itself makes it necessary for him to steal the drug. No other solution.
4b. Yes because a man is bound to serve his fellow man within the syndrum of humanity. Life is sacred and one must do everything within ones power to preserve it.
6. Should let him go home free because he was morally justified in stealing the drug for his dying wife.

TAILOR
1. He should not report Heinz because Heinz was wrongly condemned in the first place. The tailor would have to decide upon his personal moral convictions.
2. Depending whether or not the citizen knew the history of the case. If the citizen just knows Heinz as a convict then yes his duty to society is to report him but if citizen knows the case then his action would depend again on his moral conviction.
3. Yes it would because then the tailor would probably know the case and understand the implications, but again it would strictly depend on the tailor's moral attitudes.

146

TAILOR - cont.
4. No. because he has proven himself a strong and loyal citizen trying to help humanity. This alone is prove of his good intentions.

JOE
1. Yes because his father's motives are selfish and he gave his son his word that he could go camping if he saved the money.
2. No his father definitely does not have the right to ask for Joes money. His father must respect his sons feelings as a person.
3. No it does not. Joe, by refusing, is simply practicing his rights as a human being and his father lacks pride to even ask his son for that money.
4. Both are of equal wrong. A promise is one word and if ones word turns out to be worthless it say little for the person himself.
5. A promise should be kept for reasons mentioned above. There are special cases when to keep a promise would do the person more harm than good.

JOE & ALEX
1. Both are wrong but Joe involved a person a deliberatly deceived the old man. Joes method seems more dishonourable.
2. Cheating like Joe because Joe involved a person in his wrong doing.
3. Because it is inflicting troubles on another and no one should have the right to do this. But of course this depends on the situation.
4. The man because he was deceived and made a fool of. The storekeeper would also feel a loss but not in the same way.
5. The law should be harder on Joe because of his deceiving methods.

SAMPLE INTERVIEW 15

HEINZ
1. In my opinion Hienz was right in doing what he did because his wife was in great need of the drug. Hienz offered to pay for it in part but the druggist refused him. It would be more of a crime for Hienz to not try and help his wife. Society may judge Hienz as a criminal but from a moral standpoint Hienz was not the guilty party but the druggist was.
2. Hienz is a good man he did offer to pay the full price for the drug but the druggist wanted the full price. When this happened Hienz had no ulternative but to steal the drug or else watch his wife die.
3. The druggist had no right in selling the drug at a high price. Even at $1000 he would have made a good profit. Morally the druggist is guilty because he has no right in determining who should get the drug (at a high price few would be able to get it). The Druggist is playing God when he allows only those people who can afford the drug to get it. All people regardless of their social status should be able to have access to the drug.
4a. Yes because to let someone die without giving them some help or trying to prevent death is the worst crime possible. Life is a precious thing which everyone has a right to and to deny them life makes that person a murderer. If Hienz did not get the drug for his wife he would be as guilty as the druggist.

HEINZ - cont.
4b. Yes, for the same reasons as stated in 4a. Those people who would not sacrifice themselves for someone else in this case are guilty of apathy to the sick person.
6. No the judge should not send Hienz to jail because he did try to buy the drug but the greedy druggist would not sell. Hienz had to take the drug so that his wife would live. It would have been a worse crime to not steal the drug and let the women die. Justice did not protect Hienz's wife by forcing the druggist to sell the drug to Hienz for $1000 so Hienz had to do something and the only way he could was to steal the drug.

TAILOR
1. If the tailor does not know the circumstances which led to Hienz's arrest he would be right in reporting him. Hienz is a thief according to societies standards. If the tailor knew why Hienz stole the drug, then he should not report him. Also, Hienz as a business man is a good man he harms no one therefore he should not be reported to the authorities.
2. It is a citizen's duty to report a criminal but if the criminal is morally right in what he had done there is no need to report him. If Hienz had continued to steal then he should be reported but Hienz remained a good man and should not go back to jail.
3. If Hienz is a good friend of the tailor's and is still a good man then the tailor should not report him but if Hienz continued to break the law then regardless if he was his his friend or not then he should not be reported.
4. I do not agree that Hienz should have been sent to jail in the first place but his few years in jail is punishment enough. Therefore he should not be sent back.
Hienz was not a bad man and circumstances forced him to do what he did. Even though he is guilty of stealing (by societies standards) his life after he escaped from prison shows that he is not a harden criminal but a good man with only one flaw in his record which was not really his fault therefore he should not go back to jail.

JOE
1. No. It is not his father's money, he did not earn it so he has no right to it.
2. No. For the same reasons in question 1.
3. No. Joe is a good boy who worked hard for what he wants but his father is not right in trying to get the money from Joe.
4. To break a promise either way is wrong. Once you have given your word you should stick by it.
5. If you do not keep your promises you cannot be depended upon or trusted. Also it shows a lack of responsibility and a weak character on your part if you do not keep your promise

JOE & ALEX
1. They are both equally to blame because they had no right to the money how they got it is immaterial. The fact that they took it by stealing or lying shows that they are guilty (the amount of money is not the important thing).
2. Cheating an old man out of money would make me feel worse because the store may suffer the loss easier than the old man.
3. Because the money does not belong to you and it is wrong to steal just for the sake of getting some money.

JOE & ALEX - cont.
4. The old man would feel worse because he probably needs the money more than the store owner does. Being retired he does not have as much money to spend on necessities as the store owner does.
5. The law should be harder on Joe for taking the money from a retired old man who probably needs the money more than the storeowner.

APPENDIX C: Assessment of Sample Interviews

| | Percent of Response at Stage | | | | | | |
	1	2	3	4	5	6	MMS
ELEMENTARY SCHOOL STUDENTS 1	17	50	33				216
2		17	83				283
3		50	50				250
4		83	17				217
5		17	83				283
SECONDARY SCHOOL STUDENTS 6			87	13			313
7			53	40	7		354
8			100				300
9		7	93				293
10		8	75	17			309
ADULTS 11			8	42	50		442
12			33	67			367
13			17	83			383
14			92	8			292
15			42	50	8		366

APPENDIX D: REFERENCES

	TOPIC
Kohlberg:	
STAGE & SEQUENCE: THE COGNITIVE-DEVELOPMENTAL APPROACH TO SOCIALIZATION, Chapter 6 in D. Goslin, (ed.), <u>Handbook of Socialization Theory & Research</u>, New York; Rand McNally. 1969	Stages 1 - 6
EDUCATION FOR JUSTICE, A MODERN STATEMENT OF THE PLATONIC VIEW. In Sizer, (ed.), <u>Moral Education</u>, Cambridge, Mass.: Harvard University Press. 1970	Stage 6
FROM IS TO OUGHT: HOW TO COMMIT THE NATURALISTIC FALLACY AND GET AWAY WITH IT. In T. Mischel, (ed.), <u>Cognitive Development & Epistemology,</u> New York: Academic Press. 1971	Stages 1 - 6
THE ADOLESCENT AS PHILOSOPHER: THE DISCOVERY OF THE SELF IN A POSTCONVENTIONAL WORLD. In <u>Deadalus</u>, Journal of American Academy of Arts & Science, Vol. 100, No. 4, Fall 1971, 1051-1086.	TRANSITION (4 1/2) conventional to postconventional
BEYOND PSYCHOLOGY & BEYOND ETHICS: SPINOZA'S VIEW. Unpublished. 1971	Stage 7
STAGE TRANSITION IN MORAL DEVELOPMENT. In R. Travers, (ed.), <u>Second Handbook of Research on Teaching,</u> Chicago: Rand McNally & Co. 1972	
THE HIERARCHICAL NATURE OF MORAL JUDGMENT: A STUDY OF PATTERNS OF COMPREHENSION & PREFERENCE OF MORAL STAGES. In Rest, Kohlberg & Turiel (eds.), <u>Recent Research in Moral Development.</u>	
THE CLAIM TO MORAL ADEQUACY OF A HIGHEST STAGE OF MORAL JUDGMENT. In <u>Journal of Philosophy</u>, <u>LXX</u>, 18, October 25, 1973. 1973	Stage 6
CONTINUITIES & DISCONTINUITIES IN CHILDHOOD & ADULT MORAL DEVELOPMENT REVISITED. In Baltes & Schaie, (eds.), <u>Life-Span Developmental Psychology</u>, New York: Academic Press. 1973	
THE JUST COMMUNITY APPROACH TO CORRECTIONS: A MANUAL PART II, with Kauffman, Scharf, & Hickey, Harvard: Moral Education Research Foundation. 1974	Stages 1-3, 4A, 4B, 4 1/2, 5B, 6 & 7
Damon, W. "Assessment of Children's Conception of Fairness (Ages 4-10)". Paper, Dept. of Psychology, Clark University, Worcester, Mass.	Fairness, ages 4-10
Porter, N. & Taylor, N. <u>How to Assess the Moral Reasoning</u> of Students, Toronto: OISE. 1972	Stages 1 - 6
Selman, Robert L. "Stages of Role-Taking and Moral Judgment as Guides to Social Intervention." Paper, Harvard Graduate School of Education, Cambridge, Mass.	Role Taking, ages 3-12
Sullivan, E.V., Beck, C., Joy, M., & Pagliuso, S. <u>Moral Learning: Some Findings, Issues & Questions</u>, Toronto: Paulist, 1975.	Moral Education Projects in Elementary & Secondary School, Normative Data.